D1279719

An Introduction to Radiation Chemistry

An Introduction to Radiation Chemistry

J. W. T. SPINKS

President
University of Saskatchewan
Saskatoon, Saskatchewan, Canada

Formerly, Head of the Chemistry Department
and Dean of Graduate Studies
University of Saskatchewan

R. J. WOODS

Assistant Professor of Chemistry
University of Saskatchewan
Saskatoon, Saskatchewan, Canada

John Wiley & Sons, Inc., New York • London • Sydney

Library of Congress Catalog Card Number: 64-13224

Printed in the United States of America

PREFACE

This book arose from a course of lectures on radiation chemistry given to graduate students at the University of Saskatchewan over a number of years, initially by the senior author, Dr. Spinks, and then by Dr. Woods. At first the number of books and review articles bearing on the subject was extremely limited, and it is only within the last year or so that the log-jam has broken and a number of books, on specific aspects of the subject, have appeared, such as Allen's *Radiation Chemistry of Water and Aqueous Solutions,* and Charlesby's *Atomic Radiation and Polymers.* There is also the excellent series of publications, *Actions Chimiques et Biologiques des Radiations,* edited by Haissinsky. However, there is as yet no unified textbook on the subject, and the time seemed ripe to produce such a book, if only to spur others to write a better one.

A more serious reason is that the interest in the field and the number of publications related to it have increased enormously during the last decade. This is due in part to the intrinsic interest of the subject and in part to the imperative necessity of our understanding the fundamental principles underlying the action of radiation on matter in this atomic age. It is also due to the relative ease with which large sources of radiation can now be obtained and to an awakening interest of industry in the possibilities of launching a radiation-chemical industry.

Important, too, is the fact that one can now see the broad outlines of a definite "philosophy" of radiation chemical research. With the help of the physicist we can measure the amount of radiation energy absorbed by a given system. Thanks also to the physicist, we now have a good general idea of the series of physical events following the absorption of radiation. We can measure the final products of the reaction, and we can also detect with certainty and measure many of the reactive species involved as intermediates in the "chemical" part of the process, thus making it possible to give a reasonably accurate explanation of the courses of a given radiation chemical reaction.

Radiation chemistry has benefited enormously from a number of powerful new experimental techniques, such as e.p.r., mass spectrometry, gas chromatography, and isotope dilution, and has benefited from theoretical developments in chemical kinetics, such as the theory of chain reactions. In a sense radiation chemistry stands on the shoulders of a number of earlier disciplines such as chemical kinetics, photochemistry, spectroscopy, radiochemistry, and radiology, and even an initial publication in radiation chemistry can be expected to adopt a more definitive and unified approach than was possible for the early textbooks on chemical kinetics and photochemistry. The authors are strengthened in this view by a rather broad personal experience, extending over thirty-five years, in the field of photochemistry, spectroscopy, chemical kinetics, radiochemistry, and radiation chemistry, *as they were developing.*

It may be argued that such a broad experience must inevitably result in thinness of coverage, but it did, by good chance, happen to cover those subjects helpful to a thorough understanding of radiation chemistry.

The approach to the subject is, of necessity, academic since both authors are academics. However, the approach is at the same time practical, and reasonably down to earth in that the authors have had first-hand experience of most of the matters dealt with. The methodology of the subject is also clearly stated, and the industrial possibilities are clearly indicated. Indeed, the greatest possible gratification to the authors would be that this book should contribute, even in a modest way, to the widespread use of radiation in industry.

We wish to acknowledge our special indebtedness to C. J. Mackenzie, past President of the National Research Council of Canada, and to Sir John Cockcroft, one-time Director of the joint Canadian-United Kingdom Atomic Energy Project, who were responsible for our early entrance into atomic energy work, and to the late Dr. E. W. R. Steacie who, while President of the National Research Council, gave strong financial support to university radiation research programs. We are indebted in a personal way to a number of our colleagues at the University of Saskatchewan, in particular to Drs. Johns and Cormack of the Department of Physics, who introduced us to the mysteries of radiation energy absorption and measurement, and to Dr. K. J. McCallum, Head of the Department of Chemistry, who kindly read the greater part of the manuscript. The senior author (J.W.T.S.) is particularly grateful to his co-author for cheerfully accepting a much greater part of the writing of this book than had been initially agreed upon.

Finally we must record our particular appreciation to our wives, who showed great understanding and forbearance while the book was in the course of preparation.

J. W. T. Spinks
R. J. Woods

December, 1963
Saskatoon, Saskatchewan,
Canada

CONTENTS

CHAPTER 1

Introduction

Radiation chemistry may be defined as the study of the chemical effects produced in a system by the absorption of ionizing radiation. Included in this definition are the chemical effects produced by radiation from radioactive nuclei (α-, β-, and γ-rays),[1] by high-energy charged particles (electrons, protons, deuterons, etc.), and by electromagnetic radiation of short wavelength (x-rays with a wavelength less than about 250 Å, i.e., with an energy greater than about 50 electron volts).

Electromagnetic radiation of rather longer wavelength, in the ultraviolet and visible regions of the spectrum, may also initiate chemical reactions, though in this case ionization does not occur and reaction is brought about via electronically excited species. The reactions of these excited species, unaccompanied by ionization, make up the subject of photochemistry. The

[1] For clarity, the terms "α-, β-, and γ-ray" will be confined to the radiations emitted by radioactive nuclei while similar radiations produced by other means will be referred to as accelerated helium nuclei, accelerated electrons, and x-rays respectively. The separation of the radioactive and artificial radiations in this way has some further justification in the case of β- and γ-rays since their energy distribution will generally be different from that of the corresponding artificial radiations (see Chapter 2).

chief difference between radiation chemistry and photochemistry lies in the energy of the radiation which initiates the reaction, the energy of the particles and photons concerned in radiation chemistry being very much greater than the energy of the photons causing photochemical reactions. Thus in photochemistry each photon excites only one molecule and, by the use of monochromatic light, it is often possible to produce a single, well-defined, excited state in a particular component in the system. The excited species are distributed essentially uniformly in any plane at right angles to the direction of the beam of light. In radiation chemistry each photon or particle can (via secondary electrons in the case of photons) ionize or excite a large number of molecules, which are distributed along its track (Fig. 1.1). The high-energy photons and particles are not selective and may react with any molecule lying in their path, raising it to any one of its possible ionized or excited states. Subsequently the different energy-rich species react to give a complex mixture of products, in contrast to the relatively small number of products from a photochemical reaction. The radiation chemical reaction may be complicated further by effects due to the high initial concentration of ionized and excited species in the tracks, particularly in the liquid and solid phases.

Ions and excited molecules are also formed by electric discharges in gases and give rise to chemical effects similar to those produced by ionizing radiation. However it is not a simple matter to measure the energy transferred to the active species and the experimental results are qualitative rather than quantitative; they are generally treated separately from radiation chemistry.

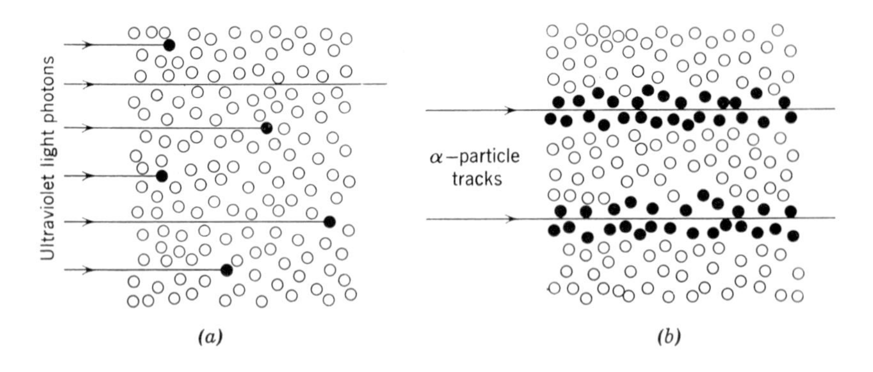

FIGURE 1.1 *Absorption by matter of (a) ultraviolet light photons; (b) α-particles.*

Closely related to radiation chemistry is the study of the chemical effects which accompany nuclear reactions, brought about, for example, by slow neutrons or by radioactive decay. In so far as the products are charged particles with excess kinetic energy, the ionization and excitation that they bring about in slowing down to thermal energies will initiate typical radiation-chemical changes. However, the nuclear reaction may make it possible to identify the nuclei involved and to trace the products in which they appear if, for example, the product nuclei are radioactive. The study of the chemical changes involving such nuclei is termed "hot-atom" chemistry, and is a branch of nuclear chemistry.

In the past, radiation chemistry was sometimes called radiochemistry. This is generally avoided at present, and the term "radiochemistry" is confined to chemical studies with radioactive isotopes where the isotope is not used as a source of radiation.

DEVELOPMENT OF RADIATION CHEMISTRY

Radiation chemistry can be said to have had its origin with the discovery of x-rays by Röentgen in 1895 and of radioactivity by Becquerel in the following year. The discoveries followed the observations that discharge tubes and uranium salts respectively give off penetrating rays that can pass through opaque materials and activate photographic emulsions. Both x-rays and the rays from uranium were found to render air electrically conductive, and by measuring the rate of discharge of a charged electroscope it was possible to estimate the intensity of the radiation. By comparing the amount of ionization produced by various uranium minerals and salts, Mme. Curie was led to the discovery of polonium and radium in 1898. The discovery of these elements and the isolation of radium in appreciable amounts was important to the study of radiation chemistry since it made available a relatively powerful source of radiation, and it was not long before the chemical effects induced by the α-rays from radium and radium emanation (radon) were being examined.

One of the first reactions to be observed and studied was the action of the radiation from radium on water. Curie and Debierne (1901) found that a hydrated radium salt produced gas continuously, and Giesel (1902) observed the evolution of gas from aqueous solutions of radium bromide. Ramsay and Soddy (1903) showed that the gas evolved was a mixture of hydrogen and oxygen, which led Cameron and Ramsay (1907) to suggest that the action of the radiation might be analogous to the electrolytic decomposition of water, though the analogy did not hold in other cases, and an attempt to deposit copper from a solution of copper sulfate with the α-particles from radon was unsuccessful. The quantitative data on the decomposition of water reported by Ramsay and Soddy was used by Bragg (1907) in making the first comparison between the chemical and ionizing effects of α-particles. Bragg calculated that the number of molecules of water decomposed was approximately equal to the number of ions that would have been produced in air by the radiation. Three years later Mme. Curie proposed that the primary effect of high-energy radiation on any substance is the formation of ions, which are the precursors of the chemical action.

The relationship between ionization and chemical action was put on a firmer basis by Lind (1) who studied the formation of ozone in oxygen under the influence of α-radiation, and was able to measure for the first time both the ionization produced and the amount of chemical change in the same medium. Yields of about 0.5 molecule of ozone per ion pair were found at this time. Lind (2) also collected the available data on the chemical action of α-rays and from them calculated values of the *ion-pair*, or *ionic, yield* (M/N), the ratio of the number of molecules undergoing change (M) to the number of ion-pairs formed (N), which was regarded as the radiation-chemical equivalent of the photochemical quantum yield. The results showed that ionization and chemical action were closely related and were proportional to each other.

It was later realized that the ion-pair yields were very often greater than the corresponding quantum yields and an explanation for this was found in the "ion-cluster" theory associated with the names of Lind (3) and Mund (4). The essential concept of this theory was that the ions could act as nuclei to which neutral molecules were drawn and held by polarization forces. When a cluster was neutralized by an ion, or cluster, of opposite charge the heat of neutralization was believed to be shared between the molecules in the cluster, which might then all undergo chemical reaction. Since the number of molecules reacting depended on the size of the clusters rather than on the number of ions formed, ion-pair yields greater than unity could readily be explained. For example, acetylene is polymerized by α-particles to give a polymer, cuprene, with an ion-pair yield of about twenty, and this could be visualized as taking place as follows:

$$C_2H_2 \overset{\alpha}{\rightsquigarrow} C_2H_2^+ + e^-$$

$$C_2H_2^+ + 19C_2H_2 \rightarrow (19C_2H_2, C_2H_2^+)$$

$$(19C_2H_2, C_2H_2^+) + e^- \rightarrow C_{40}H_{40} \qquad \text{(cuprene)}$$

(The symbol $\rightsquigarrow$ will be used to distinguish reactions brought about by the absorption of ionizing radiation.)

While a great many experimental observations were explained satisfactorily on the basis of the ion-cluster theory, more recent work has raised several major objections both to the adoption of the theory as a general mechanism for radiation-chemical reactions and to the supposition that ions are the sole precursors of the chemical effects. In the first place, Eyring, Hirschfelder, and Taylor (5) calculated that large clusters were theoretically improbable and drew attention to the fact that the average energy lost in forming an ion pair in a gas (denoted by the symbol W) is appreciably greater than the first ionization potential (I) for the gas, determined by means of the mass-spectrograph; W is often about twice as large as I. They concluded that the excess energy ($W - I$) could be used to form electronically excited molecules, such as are produced in photochemical reactions. Both the ions and excited molecules were considered capable of giving rise to free radicals. Free radical mechanisms based on these assumptions explained satisfactorily results obtained in earlier work on the α-particle-induced *ortho-para* hydrogen conversion and on the synthesis and decomposition of hydrogen bromide. Secondly, Essex and his co-workers (6) studied gaseous reactions induced by α-particles both in the presence and absence of an electric field. Their results showed that even in the presence of the field, when ion neutralization should be eliminated or very much reduced, the chemical yield is not greatly affected. Finally, both chemical and physical evidence has shown that atoms and free radicals, which are not accounted for on the basis of the ion-cluster theory, are present in a number of reaction systems. In consequence it is now accepted that both ions and excited molecules are formed initially during the absorption of the ionizing radiation and that free radicals are generally produced subsequently to play an important part in the chemical reactions which follow. Chemical reactions involving ions are not excluded, however, and ion-molecule reactions are believed to be important steps in many radiolyses.

During the early years of radiation chemistry, gas-phase studies proved most profitable but some work was also carried out on condensed systems. The chief source of radiation, radium, was generally used as a source of α-particles, though a few experiments were carried out with β- and γ-rays by using filters to remove the less-penetrating radiation. The sources available were not large and work was retarded by the long irradiation times needed to produce sufficient products for analysis (Kailan in Vienna irradiated samples for as long as three years); Kailan found the ion-pair yields in liquids to be much smaller than the corresponding quantum yields, in contrast to reactions in gases where the ion-pair yield was often greater than the quantum yield.

The development of powerful x-ray machines for industrial and medical purposes introduced an intense source of radiation that was more penetrating than α-particles and better suited to the irradiation of bulk liquid and solid samples. At the same time, interest in the biological effects of x-rays focused attention upon the chemical effects produced in water and aqueous solutions. For example, Fricke, in the United States, used x-rays to irradiate a variety of aqueous solutions, including solutions of simple organic compounds, and found that both oxidation and reduction might occur. In solutions, in contrast to reactions in gaseous systems, there was found to be a marked difference between radiation-chemical and photochemical reactions. Whereas in the latter energy is absorbed only by the solute, while the solvent itself is inert, in the former energy is absorbed by both solvent and solute and, at least in dilute solutions where the energy is absorbed almost entirely by the solvent, the direct action of the radiation on the solute molecules is relatively unimportant. This introduced the concept of *indirect action* in which, in a dilute solution, energy is absorbed from ionizing radiation by the solvent molecules and reaction between the "activated" solvent and the solute follows (7, 8), though the nature of the activation was not immediately known. Fricke (9) found that irradiation of aqueous solutions of ferrous sulfate, formic acid, and methanol with light of wavelengths between 2000 and 1850 Å produced oxidation similar to that produced by x-rays, suggesting that "activated water" was water in an excited state. Later work has led to the conclusion that irradiation of water gives hydrogen atoms (or some equivalent reducing species) and hydroxyl radicals, as suggested by Debierne in 1914 (10), and that the reactions of these radicals are responsible for most of the chemical results observed. However, highly excited water molecules may be intermediates in the formation of these radicals.

The ion-pair yield, M/N, used as a measure of radiation-chemical yields in the gas-phase was also used when referring to yields in liquids, though in this case the value of N, the number of ions formed, was not known and had to be calculated assuming a value of W, the mean energy loss in forming an ion pair in the liquid. This itself was not known and the value of W for air (32.5 ev) was usually taken, without any particular justification. An alternative way of representing the yield is to relate it to the energy absorbed, which in principle can be measured directly, and the term *G value* was introduced to denote the number of molecules changed for each 100 electron-volts of energy absorbed. Thus $G(\mathrm{X})$ refers to the number of molecules of a product X formed on irradiation per 100 ev of energy absorbed and $G(\text{-Y})$ refers in the same way to the loss of a material Y that is destroyed on irradiation. Subscripts are sometimes added to further identify the G value, e.g., $G_\alpha(\mathrm{X})$ to represent the yield of X formed on irradiation with α-particles. The use of G values has the advantage that it does not imply, as does the ion-pair yield, that the chemical action is controlled by the number of ions formed, and G values have now become the customary means of expressing radiation-chemical yields. The G value is related to the ion-pair yield by the following expression,

$$G = \frac{M}{N} \times \frac{100}{W}$$

where W (ev) is the mean energy required to form an ion pair in the material being irradiated. Thus for ion-pair yields calculated assuming W to be 32.5 ev,

$$G \sim 3M/N$$

Until about 1942 the number of workers studying radiation chemistry was limited; but in that year and succeeding years large groups were set up to meet the needs in this field of atomic energy programs. Indeed it was at this time that the subject received the name radiation chemistry, to distinguish it from the chemistry of the radioactive nuclides which retained the name radiochemistry.

With the development of atomic energy programs, a variety of particle accelerators became available and have been used to provide high-energy radiation for various specific radiation-chemical problems. Some machines, such as the Van de Graaff accelerator, have proved particularly adaptable to the needs of the radiation chemist and are used for more routine studies. Probably the greatest benefit to accrue to the radiation chemist has been the increasing availability of artificial radioactive isotopes; for example, cobalt-60 and strontium-90, which provide intense, adaptable, and relatively cheap sources of radiation. At the present time the subject is studied widely both because of its intrinsic interest and for its practical value in the fields of atomic energy and the industrial use of ionizing radiation.

REFERENCES

1. S. C. Lind, *Monatsh. Chem.*, **33,** 295 (1912); *Am. Chem. J.*, **47,** 397 (1912).
2. S. C. Lind, *J. Phys. Chem.*, **16,** 564 (1912).
3. S. C. Lind, *The Chemical Effects of Alpha-particles and Electrons,* Chemical Catalog Co., Inc., New York, 1928; G. Glockler and S. C. Lind, *The Electrochemistry of Gases and Other Dielectrics,* John Wiley and Sons, New York,

1939; R. S. Livingstone and S. C. Lind, *J. Am. Chem. Soc.,* **58,** 612 (1936); S. C. Lind, *J. Chem. Phys.,* **7,** 790 (1939).

4. W. Mund, *L'Action chimique des rayons alpha en phase gazeuze,* Hermann et Cie, Paris, 1935; W. Mund, *Bull. Soc. Chim. Belges,* **43,** 49 (1934).
5. H. Eyring, J. O. Hirschfelder, and H. S. Taylor, *J. Chem. Phys.,* **4,** 479, 570 (1936).
6. C. Smith and H. Essex, *J. Chem. Phys.,* **6,** 188 (1938); A. D. Kolumban and H. Essex, *ibid.,* **8,** 450 (1940); N. T. Williams and H. Essex, *ibid.,* **16,** 1153 (1948), **17,** 995 (1949); H. Essex, *J. Phys. Chem.,* **58,** 42 (1954).
7. O. Risse, *Ergebn. Physiol.,* **30,** 242 (1930).
8. H. Fricke, *Cold Spring Harbor Symp.,* **2,** 241 (1934).
9. H. Fricke and E. J. Hart, *J. Chem. Phys.,* **4,** 418 (1936).
10. A. Debierne, *Ann. Phys. (Paris),* (9) **2,** 97 (1914).

CHAPTER 2

Sources of Radiation

The sources of radiation used in radiation-chemical studies can be divided into two groups, those employing natural or artificial radioactive isotopes, and those which employ some form of particle accelerator. The first group includes the classical radiation sources, radium and radon, and also the more recently discovered artificial radioactive isotopes such as cobalt-60, caesium-137, and strontium-90. The earliest and the most widespread of the sources in the second group is the familiar x-ray tube, which was developed in its present form by Coolidge in 1913. Also included in this group are the linear and Van de Graaff accelerators, the betatron, the cyclotron, and other high-energy machines. Nuclear reactors may be considered as rather special members of the first group.

RADIOACTIVE ISOTOPE SOURCES

Table 2.1 lists the chief radioactive isotopes presently used as sources of radiation, the type and energy of the radiation which they emit, and the approximate price per curie. The prices given are probably of the right order of magnitude, though the cost of an isotope source will also depend upon its size since the cost of fabricating and handling a small source often exceeds the cost of the isotope itself. The processes by which the isotopes decay and the method of producing the artificial radioisotopes are shown in Table 2.2.

TABLE 2.1 *Radioactive Isotopes Commonly Used as Sources of Radiation*

Isotope	Half-life	Type and energy (in Mev) of principal radiation emitted		Approximate cost per curie* (dollars)
Natural isotopes				
Polonium-210	138 days	α, 5.304 (100%) γ, 0.8 (0.0012%)		150
Radium-226	1620 years	α, 4.777 (94.3%) α, 4.589 (5.7%) γ, 0.188 (~4%) (+ radiation from decay products if present)		20,000
Radon-222	3.83 days	α, 5.49 (+ radiation from decay products if present)		
Artificial isotopes				
Caesium-137	30 years	β, 1.18 (max) (8%) β, 0.52 (max) (92%) γ, 0.6616 (82%)	0.24 (av)	5
Cobalt-60	5.27 years	β, 0.314 (max) γ, 1.332 γ, 1.173	0.093 (av)	1–4
Hydrogen-3 (tritium)	12.26 years	β, 0.018 (max)	0.0055 (av)	7–30
Phosphorus-32	14.22 days	β, 1.710 (max)	0.70 (av)	0.70
Strontium-90 + Yttrium-90	28.0 years (Y^{90}, 64 hours)	β, 0.544 (max) β, 2.25 (max)†	0.205 (av) 0.93 (av)†	7.50
Sulfur-35	87.2 days	β, 0.167 (max)	0.049 (av)	1.50

* The *curie* (symbol "c") is the unit of radioactivity and is defined as the quantity of any radioactive nuclide in which the number of disintegrations per second is 3.700×10^{10}; this is very nearly equal to the rate of disintegration of one gram of radium or of the radon in equilibrium with this weight of radium.

† From yttrium-90.

TABLE 2.2 *Production and Decay of Commonly Used Radioactive Isotopes*

Isotope	Formation	Source	Decay
Polonium-210	–	Natural radioisotope and	$Po^{210} \xrightarrow{\alpha, \gamma} Pb^{206}$ (stable)
	$Bi^{209}(n,\gamma)Bi^{210}(RaE) \xrightarrow[5\ days]{\beta} Po^{210}$	Reactor	
Radium-226	–	Natural radioisotope	$Ra^{226} \xrightarrow{\alpha, \gamma} Rn^{222}$ (radioactive)
Radon-222	$Ra^{226} \xrightarrow{\alpha, \gamma} Rn^{222}$ (gas ↑)	Natural radioisotope	$Rn^{222} \xrightarrow{\alpha} Po^{218}(RaA)$ (radioactive)
Caesium-137	Separated from fission products	Reactor	$Cs^{137} \xrightarrow{\beta, \gamma} Ba^{137}$ (stable)
Cobalt-60	$Co^{59}(n,\gamma)$	Reactor	$Co^{60} \xrightarrow{\beta, \gamma} Ni^{60}$ (stable)
Hydrogen-3	$Li^{6}(n,\alpha)$	Reactor	$H^{3} \xrightarrow{\beta} He^{3}$ (stable)
Phosphorus-32	$P^{31}(n,\gamma)$ $S^{32}(n,p)$	Reactor Reactor	$P^{32} \xrightarrow{\beta} S^{32}$ (stable)
Strontium-90	Separated from fission products	Reactor	$Sr^{90} \xrightarrow{\beta} Y^{90} \xrightarrow[64\ hr]{\beta} Zr^{90}$ (stable)
Sulfur-35	$Cl^{35}(n,p)$ $S^{34}(n,\gamma)$	Reactor Reactor	$S^{35} \xrightarrow{\beta} Cl^{35}$ (stable)

Alpha-Ray

Alpha-particles are the nuclei of helium atoms, that is, helium atoms that have lost both electrons and hence have a double positive charge, ${}^{4}_{2}He^{2+}$. They are emitted by radioactive nuclei and have discrete energies which are characteristic of the radioisotope disintegrating. Polonium-210, for example, emits α-particles, each of which has an energy of 5.304 Mev.[1]

On passing through matter, α-particles lose energy principally by inelastic collisions with electrons lying in their path, leading to excitation and ionization of the atoms and molecules to which these electrons belong. The great difference in mass between the α-particle and the electron means that the α-particle loses only a small fraction of its energy and is virtually undeflected as a result of a collision. As a consequence α-particles are slowed down gradually as the result of a large number of small energy losses and travel in a very nearly straight path. Since each of the α-particles from a radioactive element has the same energy they will each have about the same range; the random nature of the collisions gives rise to small variations in the range of individual particles. This is shown by the solid curve in Fig. 2.1 where the number of α-particles is plotted against the distance traveled. If all the particles had exactly the

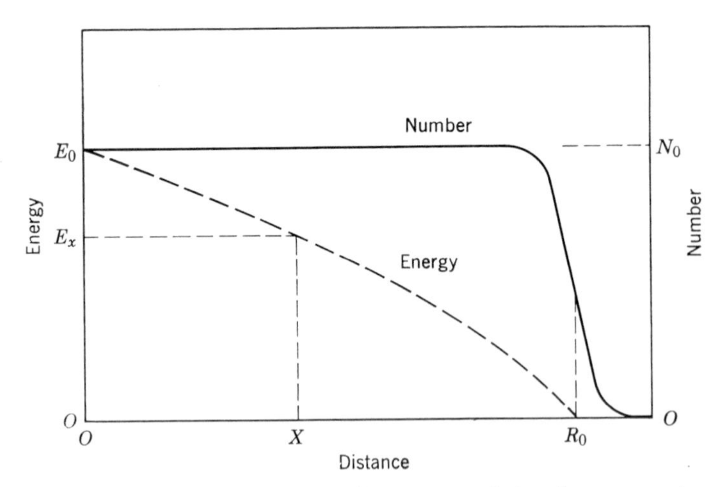

FIGURE 2.1 *Relationship between distance traveled and energy and number of α-particles.*

[1] One million electron-volts (1 Mev) is the kinetic energy an electron, or other singly charged particle, receives on being accelerated by a potential difference of one million volts. It should be noted that under these circumstances a helium nucleus, being doubly charged, would receive an energy increment of 2 Mev. The kilo electron-volt (kev) is equal to one thousandth of one Mev.

same range the curve would drop vertically (to $N = 0$) at the distance equal to the range. In practice some straggling occurs and the mean range (R_0) is found from the point of inflection of the curve.

The energy of the α-particles falls as the distance traveled increases. This is shown by the broken curve in Fig. 2.1 where the mean energy of all the α-particles is plotted against the distance they have traveled. If the α-particles are allowed to penetrate a thickness of material which is less than the mean range in that material they will be slowed down but not stopped. Advantage may be taken of this to obtain α-particles of lower energies than are normally available; for example, in Fig. 2.1 passage through an absorber of thickness X would lower the mean energy of the α-particles to E_x.

The energy lost by an α-particle in passing through matter produces considerable numbers of ions and excited molecules in the particle track. An α-particle from polonium-210, for example, gives a total of about 150,000 ion pairs and a rather greater number of excited molecules when slowed down in air. However, the extent of the chemical reaction which follows depends not only on the number of these active species formed but also upon their concentration in the particle track which, in turn, depends on the rate at which energy is lost as the particle is slowed down. The rate of energy loss is generally expressed in terms of the *linear energy transfer*, or LET, which is defined (1) as "the linear-rate of loss of energy (locally absorbed) by an ionizing particle traversing a material medium." The units in which LET values are expressed are usually kilo electron-volts per micron (kev/μ). Table 2.3 gives some values for the mean range in air and water and the average LET in water for some commonly used α-particles. The LET depends upon the energy of the α-particle and increases as the particle is slowed down, however a very rough approximation to the LET can be obtained by dividing the initial energy of the particle by its mean range. Values obtained in this way, and termed the "average LET", are included in Table 2.3. Such "average" values suffice to show the differences between the various types of radiation. A fuller discussion of LET will be deferred until Chapter 3.

TABLE 2.3 *Range and LET Values for Alpha-Particles*

Isotope	Energy of α-particle (Mev)	Mean range in air (15°C, 760 mm Hg) (cm)	Mean range in water (ref. 2) (microns)	Average LET in water (kev/micron)
Radium-226	4.795	3.3	33.0	145
Polonium-210	5.30	3.8	38.9	136
Radon-222	5.49	4.0	41.1	134

α-particles are the least penetrating of the radiations from radioactive isotopes, but they have the highest LET values and are of particular value where a high LET is desired.

α-particle sources may be constructed in various forms; one type, which employs polonium-210 as the active material, is shown in Fig. 2.2 (The Radiochemical Centre, Amersham, England). Polonium (1 millicurie to 1 curie) is electrodeposited onto a gold foil disc (*A*) which is mounted in a stainless steel holder (*B*). A thin mica sheet (*C*) is cemented onto the front face of the holder to protect the polonium deposit, and a steel handle is provided that can be screwed into either the back or the side of the holder. The mica window will absorb part of the energy of the α-particles so that the transmitted radiation will have a slightly lower energy than that given in Table 2.3 for polonium α-particles. The energy of the transmitted α-particles can be decreased further (and the LET increased) by placing thin sheets of mica between the source and the material being irradiated. This will also cause some straggling and the energies of the emerging particles will be distributed over a more or less broad band. The γ-rays which are emitted by polonium will be absorbed to a much smaller extent than the α-rays and their contribution to the energy absorption can be ignored.

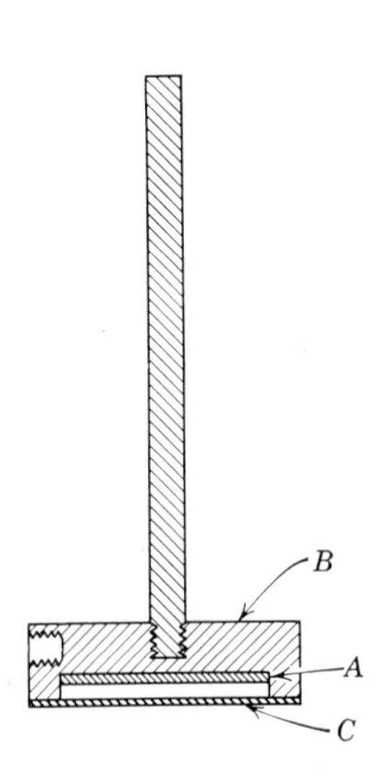

FIGURE 2.2 *Section through an α-particle source.*

Radon is also used as a source of α-radiation and may be used either mixed directly with the material to be irradiated or sealed in an extremely thin glass bulb which is surrounded by the material. The former has the advantage that it is possible to irradiate a relatively large bulk of material uniformly. It should be noted that radon decays rather quickly and gives a series of radioactive decay products which will contribute to the radiation emitted. Equilibrium between radon and its decay products is reached a few hours after the radon is separated from its parent radium. When used in radiation therapy radon is sealed into gold "seeds" which are sufficiently thick-walled to absorb all the α- and β-radiation and it is only the γ-radiation that is used.

α-particles can be produced in situ in the material to be irradiated by combining with it a compound of boron or lithium and irradiating the mixture with slow neutrons; the reactions $B^{10}(n, \alpha)Li^7$ and $Li^6(n, \alpha)H^3$ respectively occur with the liberation of α-particles and the formation of energetic nuclei.

Helium nuclei may also be accelerated to energies up to several hundred million electron volts by modern particle accelerators.

Beta-Ray

Beta-particles are fast electrons emitted by radioactive nuclei. In contrast to α-particles the β-particles from a particular radioactive element are not all emitted with the same energy but with energies ranging from zero up to a maximum value (E_β) which is characteristic of the element. These differences are explained by the fact that in β-decay the energy released is carried off partly by the β-particles and partly by antineutrinos, the total energy (E_β) being divided between these two particles. Antineutrinos have neither mass nor charge and produce a negligible effect on the matter through which they pass; their existence was postulated to allow the conservation of energy, momentum, and spin in β-decay.

The energy distributions, or energy spectra, of the β-particles emitted by phosphorus-32 and by an equilibrium mixture of strontium-90 and its daughter yttrium-90 are shown in Figs. 2.3 and 2.4 respectively.

The maximum energy of the β-particles (E_β) determines the greatest range that the β-radiation will have in matter. Only a small fraction of

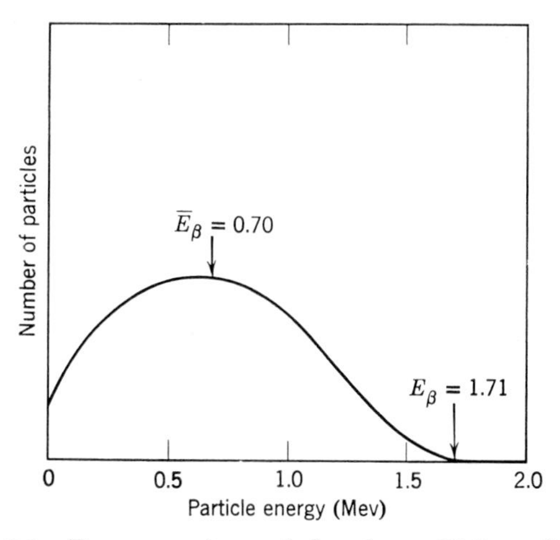

FIGURE 2.3 *Energy spectrum of phosphorus-32 β-particles (ref. 3).*

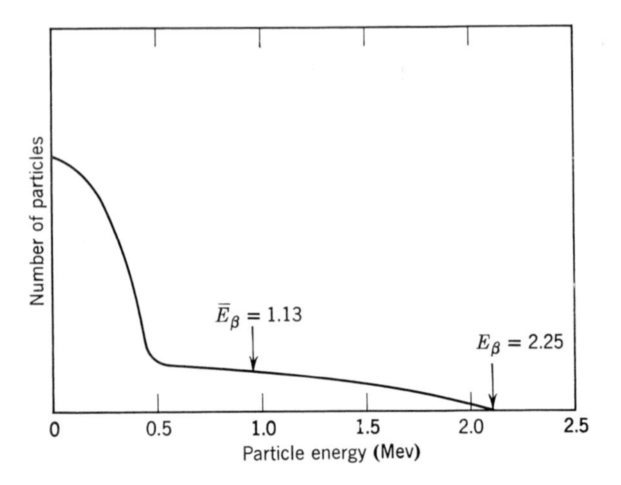

FIGURE 2.4 *β-particle energy spectrum of strontium-90–yttrium-90 pair (ref. 3).*

the β-particles actually have an energy close to E_β, however, and another quantity $\overline{E}_\beta$, the *average β-particle energy,* is more representative of the β-spectrum as a whole. The average energy is given by

$$\overline{E}_\beta = \frac{\int_0^{E_\beta} EN(E)\, dE}{\int_0^{E_\beta} N(E)\, dE} \tag{2.1}$$

where $N(E)$ is the number of particles with energy between E and $E + dE$; it is generally about one third of the maximum energy. The value of $\overline{E}_\beta$ for phosphorus-32 is 0.70 Mev and for the strontium-90–yttrium-90 pair 1.13 Mev. The latter is the sum of the individual $\overline{E}_\beta$ values for strontium-90 (0.205 Mev) and yttrium-90 (0.93 Mev) since the decay $Sr^{90} \rightarrow Y^{90} \rightarrow Zr^{90}$ is treated as a single process. Alternatively if the decay of the strontium-90 and yttrium-90 are treated separately, $\overline{E}_\beta$ for the pair is $(0.205 + 0.93)/2$, but the total activity (in curies) is twice as great. Generally the first alternative is used and a source which is said to be x curies of strontium-90 actually contains x curies of strontium-90 and also x curies of yttrium-90.

If a nucleus can disintegrate by either of two alternative routes, both of which give groups of β-particles, the average β-particle energy will be found by averaging the individual $\overline{E}_\beta$'s, weighting each according to the intensity of the group to which it belongs. For example, if an isotope gives in 60% of its disintegrations a group of β-particles with average energy $\overline{E}_\beta'$ and in the remainder of its disintegrations a group with average energy $\overline{E}_\beta''$ then the average β-energy for the isotope will be given by $(60\,\overline{E}_\beta' + 40\,\overline{E}_\beta'')/100$. Values of the average β-particle energy are included in Table 2.1.

Monoenergetic electrons known as *conversion electrons* and *Auger electrons* are produced by radioactive decay processes distinct from that which gives the continuous β-energy spectrum. Conversion electrons may accompany γ-ray emission from the nucleus and may be treated as though they arise from interaction between the γ-ray and electrons in the atomic shells of the atom. Their energies are equal to $E_\gamma - E_s$, where E_γ is the energy of the γ-photon and E_s is the energy required to separate the electron from its shell. Electrons may be ejected from any shell, though the process is more probable for the inner shells (i.e., K and L), and, since E_s is different for each shell, monoenergetic γ-rays will give several monoenergetic groups of conversion electrons. Auger electrons arise from electron rearrangements after the production of an electron vacancy in an inner shell. The vacancy will immediately be filled by an electron from an outer shell and the excess energy lost either by x-ray emission or by the ejection of one of the other electrons from the atom (Auger electron). The process may be repeated if the electron which moved to fill the inner shell did not come from the outermost shell, and so a number of Auger electrons may arise from the original vacancy. The energy of Auger electrons is limited since it cannot exceed the difference between the binding energies of the inner and outer shells of the atom; this limitation does not apply to conversion electrons which have energies approaching that of the γ-rays emitted by the nucleus. Conversion and Auger electrons do not add appreciably to the β-ray energy from the isotopes listed in Table 2.1 (conversion electrons are produced in about 2% of the disintegrations of radium-226), but in other cases it may be important to include their contribution.

On passing through matter β-particles lose energy predominantly by inelastic collisions with electrons, in a similar manner to α-particles. However, because the β-particle and the electron with which it collides have the same mass, the β-particle can lose up to half of its energy in a single collision and may be deflected through a large angle. Deflection also occurs when the particle passes close to an atomic nucleus. As a result even β-particles which start with the same energy may come to rest at widely separated points. Thus β-particles have no fixed range in matter but show a maximum distance of penetration, or maximum range. The experimental number-distance curve for a beam of β-particles with energies ranging from zero to a maximum has the form shown in Fig. 2.5; the background count is due to bremsstrahlung, i.e., secondary x-rays (cf. page 28). The maximum range, R_0, is taken as the point where the absorption curve merges with the background.

The range of β-rays and electrons is generally determined using aluminum absorbers; values for the maximum range of some β-rays in aluminum are given in Table 2.4 (3). Since the absorption and scattering of electrons is only slightly affected by changes in atomic number, ranges (in mg/cm^2)[2] in other low-atomic number materials (e.g., water, tissue, organic compounds) are very nearly the same as the range in aluminum; the values for the maximum range in water in Table 2.4 were calculated by making the assumption that the ranges in water and aluminum were identical. Ranges in air are taken from ref. 4. It should be emphasized that these ranges are for β-particles with the maximum energy (E_β) alone and that only a very small fraction of the β-particles will actually penetrate to this distance; the average penetration for all the β-particles emitted is about one fifth of the maximum range. It should also be noted that the term "range" used in connection with β-particles and electrons is used here to denote the penetration of the radiation straight through the absorber. Since even the β-particles and electrons which penetrate furthest suffer some deflection from the straight path, the *path length*, measured along the curved path, will be rather greater than the distance to which the particle penetrates. Both path length and penetration are referred to as the range, but we will reserve the term "range" for the penetration, and the path length will be referred to as such. For heavy charged particles, such as α-particles, which travel along almost straight paths, the range (i.e., penetration) and path length are the same.

The average LET values given in Table 2.4 were calculated for β-particles with the maximum energy by dividing this energy by the

[2] The thickness of material penetrated by radiation is very often expressed as the *mass per unit area* (e.g., mg/cm^2) of the material. Expressed in this way the thickness is independent of the density of the material and is related more directly to the fundamental absorption process. There is also the practical advantage that the thickness of very thin absorbers is easier to determine by weighing than by direct measurement. Mass per unit area can be converted into units of length by dividing by the density of the material.

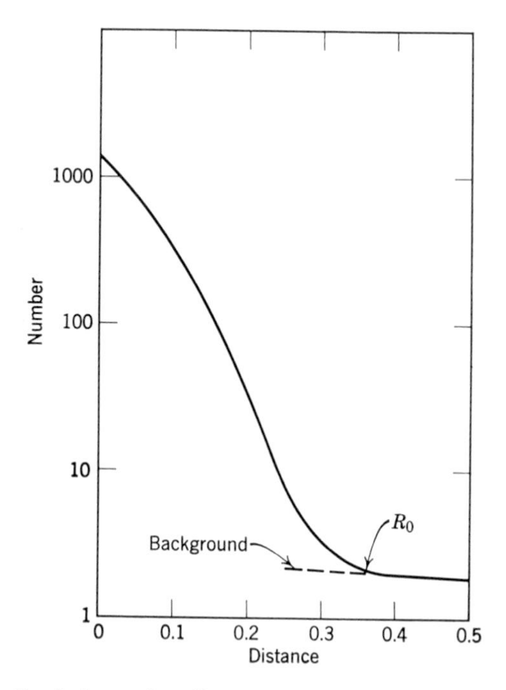

FIGURE 2.5 *Typical number-distance curve for β-rays. The number of β-particles transmitted through an absorber is plotted on a logarithmic scale against distance (the thickness of the absorber is g/cm²) on a linear scale.*

path length (4) for the particles. Average LET values over the whole β-ray energy spectrum will be rather greater than those given because of the increased contribution from lower energy particles.

TABLE 2.4 *Range and LET Values for Beta-Particles*

Isotope	Maximum energy of β-particles (Mev)	Path length in air (cm)	Maximum range in aluminum (cm)	Maximum range in water (cm)	Average LET in water (kev/micron)
Hydrogen-3	0.018	0.65	0.0002	0.00055	2.6
Sulfur-35	0.167	31.	0.012	0.032	0.52
Strontium-90	0.544	185.	0.066	0.18	0.27
Phosphorus-32	1.71	770.	0.29	0.79	0.21
Yttrium-90	2.25	1020.	0.40	1.1	0.20

β-ray sources used at the present time employ the artificial radioisotopes shown in Table 2.1 which are used either as external sources of radiation or, mixed with the material to be irradiated, as internal radiation sources.

Strontium-90 β-ray sources similar in design to the α-ray source shown in Fig. 2.2 are available with activities ranging from 5 millicurie to one curie of strontium-90. In this case the active disc contains strontium-90 bonded in silver and protected by a surface layer of silver; the mica window is not needed. The strontium-90 is in equilibrium with its daughter, yttrium-90, and β-particles characteristic of each isotope are emitted. Though neither the strontium-90 nor the yttrium-90 emits any γ-radiation, secondary x-rays (bremsstrahlung) may be formed by interaction of the β-particles with high-atomic number materials in the source. The secondary radiation is unlikely to contribute appreciably to the energy absorbed by material being irradiated but, because of its greater penetrating power, may constitute a health hazard in the neighborhood of the source.

Phosphorus-32, sulfur-35, and hydrogen-3 (tritium) have been used as internal sources of β-radiation. Phosphorus-32 and sulfur-35 have the advantages of being readily available with high specific activities and of decaying sufficiently rapidly that there is no serious difficulty in disposing of the active residues.

Gamma-Ray

Gamma-rays are electromagnetic radiation of nuclear origin with short wavelengths in the region of 3×10^{-9} cm to 3×10^{-11} cm. For the present purpose it is more convenient to describe the radiation in terms of energy than in terms of wavelength since it is the energy absorbed from the radiation that is basically of interest. The relationship between wavelength and energy is

$$E = hc/\lambda \qquad (2.2)$$

where h is Planck's constant, c is the velocity of light, and λ is the wavelength. Substituting for the constants

$$E \text{ (in electron volts)} = 12.4/10^5\lambda \text{ (in cm)} \qquad (2.3)$$

In terms of energy the wavelength range 3×10^{-9} cm to 3×10^{-11} cm becomes approximately 40 kev to 4 Mev.

The γ-rays emitted by radioactive isotopes are either monoenergetic or have a small number of discrete energies as, for example, has cobalt-60 which gives equal numbers of γ-photons of energy 1.332 Mev and 1.173 Mev.

Unlike α and β particles, which lose their energy gradually through a number of small energy transfers, γ-rays tend to lose the greater part of their energy through a single interaction. The result is that whereas monoenergetic α-particles and electrons are slowed down by thin absorbers, rather than absorbed, in the same situation a part of the incident γ-rays are completely absorbed but the remainder are transmitted with their full initial energy. The number (N) of γ-photons transmitted through a sheet of absorbing material (under narrow-beam conditions; see p. 56) is given by

$$N = N_i e^{-\mu x} \tag{2.4}$$

where N_i is the number of incident photons, x is the thickness of the absorber, and μ is the total absorption coefficient of the material for γ-rays of the appropriate energy. This is shown graphically in Fig. 2.6.

γ-rays do not have a definite range in matter; another term, the *half-thickness value* (or *half-value thickness*), is often used to relate the number of photons transmitted with the thickness of the absorber. The half-thickness value is the thickness of the absorber required to reduce the intensity of the γ-radiation (i.e., the number of photons transmitted) by one half. It can be calculated from Eq. 2.4 if the value of the absorption coefficient is known (the half-thickness value $= 0.693/\mu$), or read from

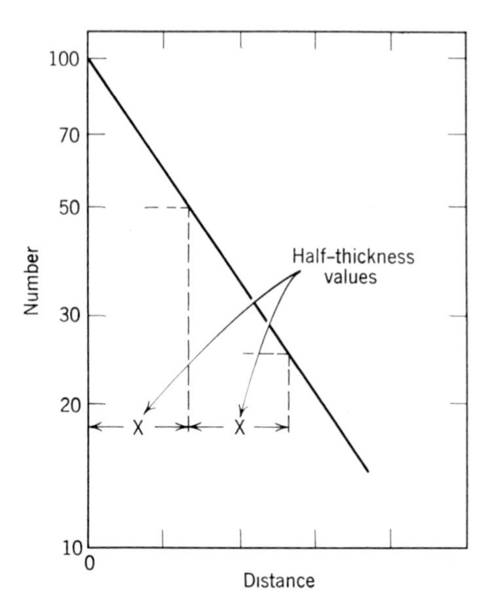

FIGURE 2.6 *Typical number-distance curve for γ-rays.*

a number-distance curve (Fig. 2.6). Some half-thickness values for cobalt-60 and caesium-137 γ-rays are given in Table 2.5.

Table 2.6 gives average values for the LET of the secondary electrons produced by the absorption of γ-radiation in water; γ-rays do not form a track of charged particles and hence the LET is not directly applicable to the γ-radiation itself. The values were calculated using an average energy for the secondary electrons.

In addition to absorption by matter both α and β particles and electromagnetic radiation, from point sources, decrease in intensity as the square of the distance from the source as this distance is increased — this is the familiar inverse-square relationship of photometry. The absorption of radiation by matter and the decrease in intensity with distance may be treated independently.

TABLE 2.5 *Half-Thickness Values for Gamma Radiation* (ref. 5)

Isotope	Photon energy (Mev)	Half-thickness values (cm)			
		Water	Aluminum	Concrete	Lead
Caesium-137	0.66	8.1	3.4	3.8	0.57
Cobalt-60	1.25 (mean)	11	4.6	5.2	1.06
Density of absorber (g/cm^3)		1.0	2.72	2.35	11.34

TABLE 2.6 *LET Values for Gamma Radiation*

Isotope	Photon energy (Mev)	Average LET in water (kev/micron)
Caesium-137	0.66	0.39
Cobalt-60	1.25 (mean)	0.27

The original source of γ-radiation for chemical studies was radium, enclosed in a container with walls of sufficient thickness to absorb the α and β radiation (e.g., 0.5 mm platinum). Within the last decade artificial γ-emitting radioisotopes have become available at reasonable cost and provide very convenient γ-ray sources. The most widely used isotope at the present time is cobalt-60. Caesium-137 has the advantage of a longer half-life but is more expensive than cobalt-60, though the cost of the two isotopes may become comparable if caesium-137 is extracted from fission products on a large scale.

Cobalt-60 can be obtained with activities as high as 20 to 40 curies per gram though an activity of 1 to 5 curies per gram is more usual. The cobalt-59 from which it is prepared is generally irradiated in a reactor in the form of pellets, small slugs, or thin discs to give a uniformly active material and these are assembled into radiation sources of the desired size. The containers in which the cobalt-60 is assembled also serve to filter out the β-rays emitted. Sources containing between 100 and 10,000 curies are in common use in university laboratories and sources in the region of 1000 curies for cancer therapy. Larger sources containing of the order of 100,000 to 1,000,000 curies have been designed for irradiating materials on an industrial scale.

γ-emitting isotopes must be surrounded by relatively thick shields of dense material to protect personnel working with them. Very many designs are available for cobalt-60 sources and the associated shielding but, in general, they can be divided into two groups. In the first the cobalt is arranged to irradiate a cavity, in which the sample to be irradiated is placed inside a compact mass of shielding material, and some form of movable shielding is provided so that the sample can be introduced into the cavity without exposing the cobalt-60. The shielding is generally lead and such sources can be quite compact. An example is the Atomic Energy of Canada "Gammacell" which is shown in Fig. 2.7. In this the cobalt is in the form of a hollow cylinder into which the sample is introduced by means of the moving drawer; spiral tubes through the drawer allow wires and small tubes to be led into the irradiation cavity without the escape of radiation. The "Gammacell" shown contains 1100 curies of cobalt-60 and weighs about 7500 lb.

The second group of cobalt-60 sources are the so-called "cave" type in which the cobalt-60 is stored in a shielded container and, when required, moved out of the container and close to the sample in a small shielded room or cave. An example of this arrangement is shown in Fig. 2.8; in other facilities the cobalt-60 may be stored in the floor or walls of the cave itself. In this case it is necessary to provide adequate shielding for the room and also for the entrance, which is usually built in the form of a labyrinth. The common shielding material for cave-type sources is concrete, but the distance between the active source and the outside of the shielding walls also contributes to the attenuation of the radiation because of the inverse-square relationship.

The cavity-type source has the advantage of compactness, so that it can be used in existing laboratories, but has the disadvantage that the size of samples and equipment that can be put into the cavity is limited. The intensity of the radiation inside the cavity is fixed. The cave type

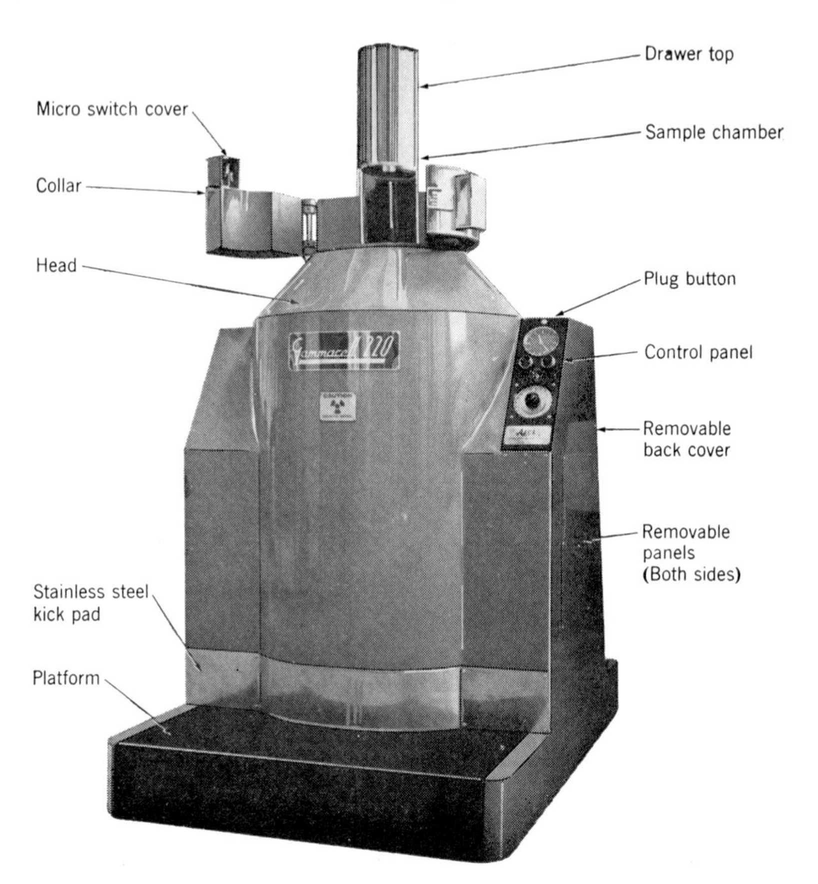

FIGURE 2.7 *Atomic Energy of Canada "Gammacell" cobalt-60 radiation source at the University of Saskatchewan. (Courtesy of Atomic Energy of Canada, Ltd., Commercial Prod. Div., Ottawa, Canada.)*

of source offers a very much greater area for equipment and it is possible, by varying the distance between the cobalt source and the sample, to irradiate materials at different radiation intensities. A disadvantage of the cave-type source is the greater space required and the bulk and weight of the concrete shielding needed. All very large cobalt-60 sources (over about 10,000 curies) are of the cave type.

Miscellaneous Sources

Fission of uranium in a nuclear reactor leads to the liberation of large amounts of energy of which about 80 to 85% appears as kinetic energy of the recoiling fission fragments, about 5 to 6% as the energy of neutrons

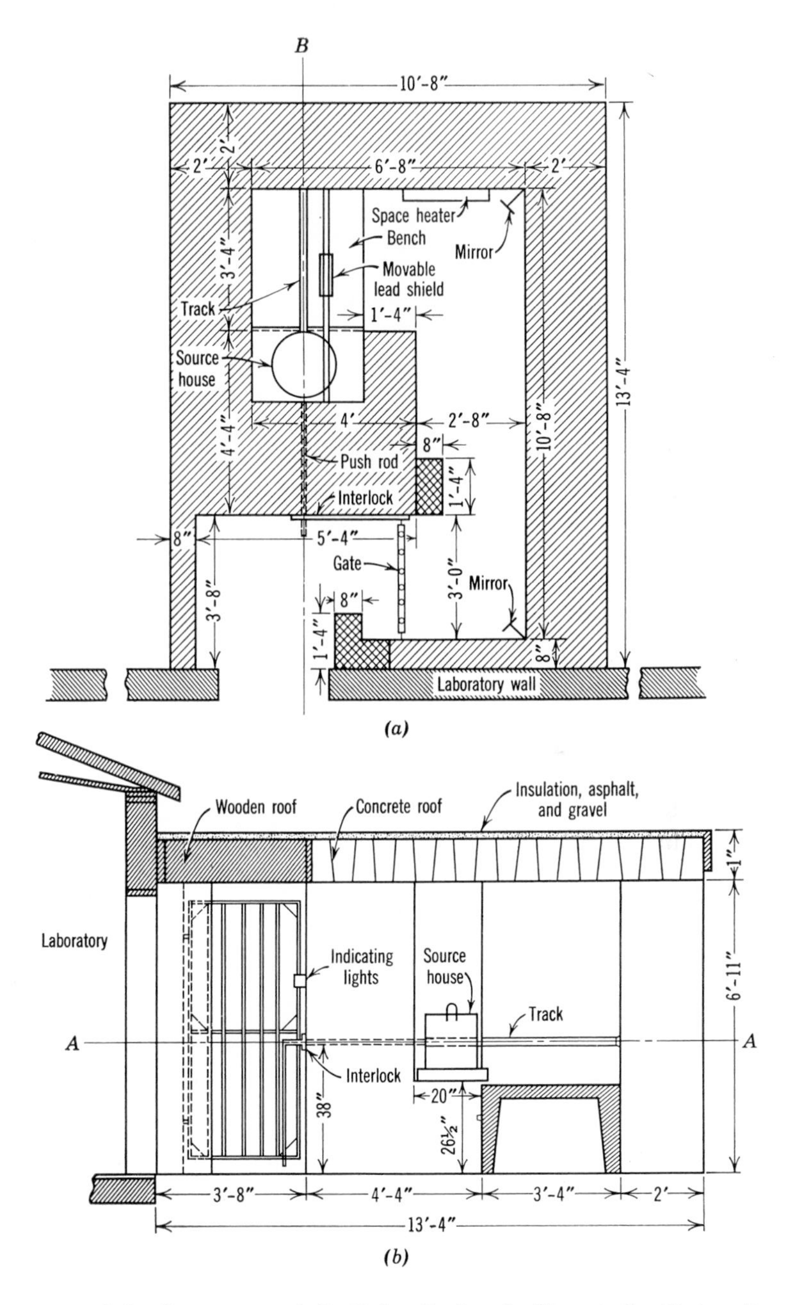

FIGURE 2.8 *Cave-type cobalt-60 irradiation facility at the University of Saskatchewan. A 90-curie cobalt-60 slug is stored in the lead source house and in use is pushed out along the track by means of the push rod. (a) Horizontal cross-section; (b) Vertical cross-section. (Courtesy 1959 Nuclear Congress.)*

and γ-rays produced during the fission reaction, and 5 to 6% as energy stored in radioactive fission products and liberated as β-or γ-radiation when these decay.

The range of the fission fragments is quite short and the kinetic energy associated with them is normally dissipated as heat within the fuel elements of the reactor. Several proposals have been made for utilizing this energy to initiate chemical reaction, using intimate mixtures of chemicals and reactor fuel. Harteck and Dondes (6), for example, proposed incorporating uranium enriched with uranium-235 in glass-wool fibers a few microns in diameter and passing gaseous reactants through the fiber mat exposed to the neutron flux of a reactor. Whatever method is used the products will be contaminated with fission fragments and may also contain radioactive impurities formed by the absorption of neutrons; radioactive material from both sources must be removed before the product can be used.

Neutron and γ-radiation within, or near, the reactor core might also be used to initiate chemical reaction by pumping the material to be irradiated through these regions. Neutron absorption would again be a possible source of radioactive contamination. An alternative approach, in which the neutron flux in the core is used indirectly as a radiation source, is possible if the reactor is cooled with liquid sodium. The function of the sodium is to transfer heat from the reactor core to an external heat exchanger, after which it is recycled through the reactor. In the core the sodium will also absorb neutrons forming radioactive sodium-24 which emits γ-rays with energies of 1.37 and 2.75 Mev with a half-life of about 15 hours. The stream of radioactive sodium can be used to irradiate materials outside the reactor before being recycled through the core. Use of the sodium in this way will not affect the operation of the reactor and has the advantage that the material being irradiated is only exposed to γ-radiation and will not itself become radioactive. Other elements can, of course, be exposed to neutrons in the reactor to produce longer-lived radioisotopes that can be used subsequently as radiation sources; the production of cobalt-60 from cobalt-59 is an example.

Fuel rods that have been exposed in a nuclear reactor for long periods contain a large proportion of fission products and are extremely radioactive. When they are replaced by fresh fuel the used fuel elements are allowed to stand for some time to let the short-lived activity decay; during this time they may be used directly as radiation sources, though the radioactivity decays rather rapidly, necessitating frequent replacement to maintain a reasonably constant radiation level. After most of the short-lived radioactivity has decayed the fuel rods are dissolved and processed chemically to recover fissionable material, leaving a solution containing the fission fragments and various salts and impurities. The mixture, generally with water removed, is known as the gross fission product and may be processed further to separate groups of chemically similar radioisotopes, which are known as mixed fission products. The mixed fission products will probably have higher specific activities than the gross fission product, be more specific in the type and energy of the radiation emitted, and have a more stable half-life. A final step is to separate the mixed fission products into individual isotopes, such as caesium-137 and strontium-90; these are referred to as separated fission products. Both the mixed and separated fission products have found use as sources of β- and/or γ-radiation.

Radioactive Decay

The activity of all radioactive radiation sources falls as the source grows older and it is often necessary to make allowance for this. The activity (C_t) after a period of decay (t) is related to the original activity (C_o) by the expression

$$C_t/C_o = e^{-\lambda t} \tag{2.5}$$

where λ is the decay constant (λ = 0.693/half-life). If a table of exponential functions is not available C_t/C_o can be calculated from

$$\log_{10} (C_t/C_o) = \bar{1}.(1.0 - 0.4343\lambda t). \tag{2.6}$$

For example, for cobalt-60, which has a half-life of 5.27 years or 63.24 months, λ is found to be 0.01096 month^{-1} and, by substitution in Eq. 2.6, the ratio C_t/C_o to be 0.989 after one month, 0.947 after five months, 0.896 after ten months, etc. Thus the activity of a cobalt-60 source falls by roughly 1% per month.

The expressions derived for the radioactive decay of a source apply equally to the fall in the intensity of the radiation from the source, so that Eqs. 2.5 and 2.6 can be rewritten

$$I_t/I_o = e^{-\lambda t} \tag{2.7}$$

and

$$\log_{10} (I_t/I_o) = \bar{1}.(1.0 - 0.4343\lambda t) \tag{2.8}$$

where I_o and I_t are the initial intensity and the intensity after time t respectively.

X-RAY GENERATORS AND HIGH-ENERGY PARTICLE ACCELERATORS

Many of the high-energy particle accelerators developed for nuclear research have been used to study particular radiation-chemical problems. However the very high energy radiation from these machines is not normally necessary, or even desirable, and the radiation chemist is more likely to be concerned with accelerators which are able to provide a very intense beam of radiation at moderate energies (the intensity may be several orders of magnitude greater than the intensity of the radiation available from a radioactive source). The main characteristics of x-ray machines and several particle accelerators are very briefly described below; fuller descriptions of the machines and their mode of operation are available in many physics textbooks and in almost all books on nuclear physics. The x-ray machine, cyclotron, Van de Graaff accelerator, and linear electron accelerator have been employed most frequently for radiation-chemical studies, but other accelerators are being developed for, and adapted to, this work as radiation becomes accepted as a useful industrial tool.

X-Ray Machines

X-rays are electromagnetic radiation with wavelengths less than about 10^{-6} cm, i.e., with energies greater than about 0.1 kev. They are produced whenever high-speed electrons are rapidly decelerated, as when they pass through the electric field of an atomic nucleus. The radiation produced in this way is known as *bremsstrahlung* (i.e., braking radiation) and its production offers an alternative means of energy loss by electrons to loss by collision, mentioned earlier in connection with the stopping of β-rays. For high-energy electrons the ratio of radiative to collision loss is given roughly by

$$\frac{(dE/dx)_{\text{rad}}}{(dE/dx)_{\text{coll}}} \approx \frac{EZ}{1600 m_0 c^2} \tag{2.9}$$

where m_0 is the rest mass of an electron, E is the electron energy, and Z is the atomic number of the target material. Radiative and collision energy losses are roughly equal, therefore, for low-Z materials (water, aluminum) when the incident electrons have an energy of about 100 Mev and for high-Z materials (lead, tungsten) when they have an energy of about 10 Mev.

The energy of the bremsstrahlung radiation ranges from near zero to the maximum energy of the incident electrons. The energy of an individual bremsstrahlung photon depends upon the amount by which the electron producing it is slowed down; if the electron is brought to rest (i.e., to thermal energy) the photon will have the full energy of the electron. A typical energy spectrum for x-rays is shown in Fig. 2.9.

The small peaks in Fig. 2.9 are not due to bremsstrahlung radiation but are x-rays characteristic of the target material. *Characteristic radiation* is caused by electrons from the outer shells of the target atoms dropping towards the nucleus to fill a vacancy in an inner shell. The energy that the electron gains in this way, which is equal to the difference between the energies of the initial and final shells, is emitted as a photon of x-radiation of characteristic energy or leads to the ejection of Auger electrons. Characteristic x-rays are produced with energies corresponding to the possible electron transitions from shell to shell, for example the tungsten lines shown in Fig. 2.9 at energies between 58 and 70 kev correspond to transitions between outer shells and the K shell; similar transitions between outer shells and the L shell give a series of lines at about 9 kev. Similar characteristic x-rays are produced with other target elements but at lower energies with elements of lower atomic number. Characteristic radiation often makes up only a small part of the total x-ray radiation, and the x-ray energy spectrum (e.g., Fig. 2.9) can generally be treated as a smooth curve.

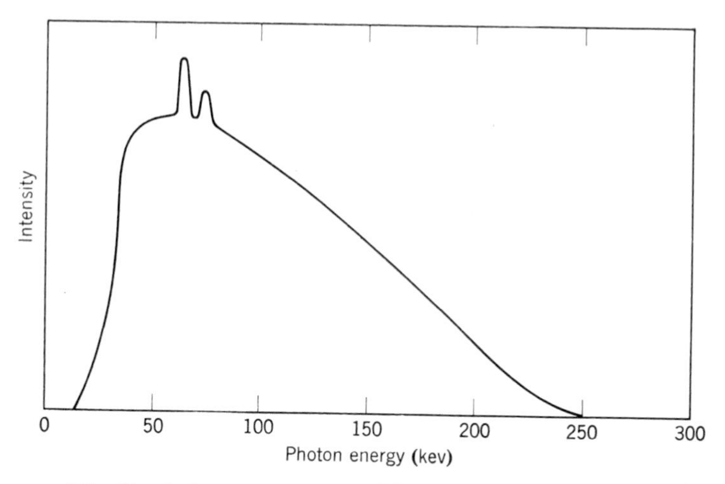

FIGURE 2.9 *Typical x-ray spectrum. (Energy distribution produced by 250 kev electrons striking a tungsten target; the characteristic radiation is not shown to scale.)*

The conventional x-ray tube used to produce x-rays consists of a tungsten wire cathode and a massive anode inside an evacuated glass envelope. The cathode is heated to provide a stream of electrons which are accelerated towards the anode by a potential applied between the cathode and the anode. The magnitude of the applied potential determines the maximum, or peak, energy of the x-rays produced. By making the anode of a high atomic number material as much as possible of the incident electron energy is converted to x-radiation, but the anode must also have a high melting point so that it will not melt under the intense electron bombardment (the collision energy loss appears in the target as

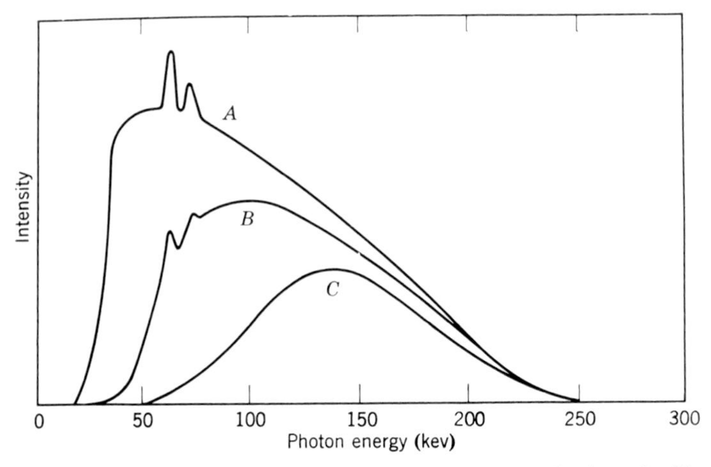

FIGURE 2.10 *The effect of filters on x-ray energy distribution. A: No filter except the inherent filtration of the x-ray tube; B and C: Curves showing the effect of filters upon the primary energy spectrum (curve A); the filtration is greatest for curve C.*

thermal energy). Tungsten is usually chosen as the target material and embedded in a heavy copper support to help dissipate the considerable amounts of heat produced; the support may be cooled by circulating liquid through it.

Figure 2.9 shows that an appreciable fraction of the x-rays produced are of relatively low energy. The penetrating power of these low-energy x-rays will be small and they will largely be absorbed near the surface of any material being irradiated. In many cases it is desirable to have essentially uniform irradiation throughout the sample and, in particular, to avoid the heavy surface dose. This can be achieved by placing metal filters between the x-ray tube and the sample to absorb the less penetrating, low-energy, x-rays as shown in Fig. 2.10; x-rays with very low energies are removed by the window of the x-ray tube itself (inherent filtration). The filters also reduce the intensity of the higher energy x-rays to some extent so that excessive filtration is also to be avoided (Table 2.7).

In describing an x-ray source used for irradiations, the accelerating voltage, target and window materials, and filters used should be specified and, wherever possible, the half-value layer for the beam of some standard absorber, e.g., aluminum, copper, or lead. The *half-value layer* (HVL)[3] is the thickness of the absorber required to reduce the intensity of the beam to one half its original value; it is usually expressed in millimeters.

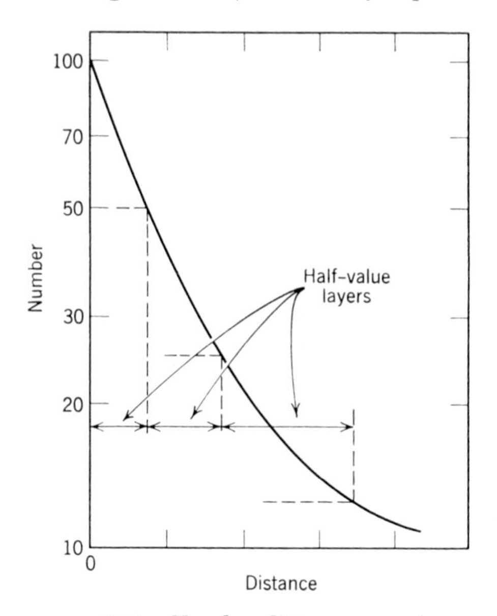

FIGURE 2.11 *Number-distance curve for x-rays.*

A typical number-distance curve for x-rays is shown in Fig. 2.11; the vertical broken lines mark off successive half-value layers. From Figure 2.11 and Table 2.7 it is seen that the half-value layer increases as the filtration of the x-ray beam is increased. In contrast the half-thickness value for monoenergetic γ-rays remains constant as the γ-ray beam is attenuated (Fig. 2.6).

[3] An arbitrary distinction will be made here between the two terms "half-value layer" and "half-thickness value" (page 21) by limiting the former to the absorption of x-rays, which have a continuous energy distribution, and the latter to the absorption of monoenergetic γ-rays. Both terms will be met in practice and it should be remembered that the meaning varies slightly according as x-rays or γ-rays are being discussed.

TABLE 2.7 *HVL and Relative Intensity for 200 Kvp X-Rays Filtered With Copper*

Filtration (mm copper)	Half-value layer (mm copper)	Relative intensity of x-ray beam
0.0	0.35	100
1.0	1.3	29
2.0	1.8	17
3.0	2.3	11
4.0	2.7	8

Conventional x-ray machines suitable for continuous operation are available with maximum operating potentials in the region of 40 kev to 300 kev. Higher voltage machines have been built but the large transformers which are necessary make them unwieldy. X-rays with higher peak energies can be obtained by stopping high-energy electrons from an accelerator with a tungsten target; the energy spectrum of the x-rays produced will be similar to that shown in Fig. 2.9 with the maximum energy equal to the energy of the accelerated electrons.

At high electron energies x-ray production is a more efficient process, consequently less heat will be produced in the target and the heavy anode assemblies used in conventional x-ray tubes are not necessary. At the same time the x-ray photons tend to be produced with the same direction of motion as the incident electrons, rather than at an angle to the electron beam, and the x-rays transmitted through a thin target are used rather than a reflected beam as in low-energy x-ray tubes. This tends to give a rather narrow beam of x-rays at high incident electron energies.

Resonant Transformer

The resonant transformer is a form of x-ray generator in which the heavy iron core of the high-voltage transformer is absent and the secondary, high-voltage, circuit of the transformer, which is in series with the x-ray tube, is tuned to resonance. High voltages can be obtained with a great saving in weight and size in the transformer, and compact x-ray generators built on this principle are available with peak energies ranging from 100 kev to 3.5 Mev.

Cockcroft-Walton Accelerator

The Cockcroft-Walton voltage-multiplier circuit uses a series of rectifiers and condensers to rectify and multiply the output voltage of a transformer, each rectifier-condenser unit doubling the voltage. The potential difference generated in this way (up to about 1.5 Mev) may be used to accelerate positive ions or, though this is not common, electrons.

Van de Graaff Accelerator

In the Van de Graaff accelerator an electrostatic charge, which may be either negative or positive, is carried to a high-voltage electrode by means of a rapidly moving belt, and the potential difference between the electrode and the ground used to accelerate electrons or positive ions (protons, deuterons, helium nuclei, etc.) to high velocities.

The Van de Graaff accelerator is able to accelerate electrons or positive ions to any energy within the range of the machine (the maximum energy is generally between 1 and 5 Mev) and to maintain the energy constant to within about 0.1%, or better.

Betatron

The betatron is a circular accelerator into which electrons are injected as a pulse and then continuously accelerated and held in a circular path by a changing magnetic field. When the electrons have reached their full energy they are allowed to impinge on a target, producing x-rays, or are extracted from the machine as a beam. The process is repeated to give a pulsed beam of radiation with several hundred pulses a second, each lasting of the order of one microsecond. Betatrons operating at maximum energies from 10 Mev to 300 Mev have been constructed. Lower energy radiation than the maximum for the machine can be obtained by extracting the electrons before they have completed the full number of circles.

Cyclotron

In the cyclotron light ions are introduced into the center of a flat, evacuated, hollow disc which is divided into two halves along a diameter and situated between the poles of an electromagnet designed to produce a uniform field across it. By rapidly alternating the potential applied to the two halves, or dees, the ions can be accelerated along a spiral path which increases in diameter as the energy of the ions increases. The accelerated ions are extracted as they near the outer edge of the dees as an essentially continuous beam. Deuterium ions and protons have been accelerated in the cyclotron to about 20 Mev and helium nuclei to about

40 Mev; at energies much above these the increase in mass of the particles causes them to get out of step with the alternating potential and modified forms of the cyclotron, the frequency modulated cyclotron and the proton synchrotron, are necessary if it is desired to accelerate the particles to higher energies.

Linear Electron Accelerator

The linear electron accelerator is a traveling wave accelerator; electrons are injected in pulses into a straight, segmented, waveguide and accelerated by the electric field of an electromagnetic wave that travels down the tube. Electron energies up to 630 Mev have been obtained in this way; lower energy linear electron accelerators are available commercially.

The accelerated electrons are delivered in pulses of a few microseconds duration, with a repetition rate of the order of 500 pulses per second.

Linear Ion Accelerator

In the linear ion accelerator positive ions are accelerated by passing through a series of tubes of increasing length to which an alternating potential is applied, the particles receiving an increment of energy each time they traverse a gap between two tubes.

Accelerators of this type have been used to accelerate the nuclei of light elements (helium to argon) to energies of about $10A$ Mev, where A is the atomic weight of the nucleus. These accelerated nuclei are of particular interest since they give LET's an order of magnitude greater than those usually available with accelerated particles.

The Radiation from Accelerators

Table 2.8 gives the main characteristics of the radiation from the particle accelerators mentioned above. All the accelerators which give high-energy electrons can be used as x-ray sources by stopping the electrons with a heavy-metal target, e.g., tungsten. The x-rays produced will have a continuous distribution of energies from zero up to the energy of the incident electrons; the x-ray energies given in the table refer to this maximum, or peak, energy.

The terms pulsed and continuous beam refer to the fact that the radiation may be received either as a beam of constant intensity (i.e., continuous) or broken up into a number of pulses which are separated by periods

TABLE 2.8 *Particle Accelerators*

Accelerator	Particles accelerated or radiation produced	Energy (Mev)	Remarks
X-ray machine	X-rays	0.05–0.3	Pulsed beam unless constant potential power supply used, continuous energy spectrum.
Resonant transformer	X-rays	0.1–3.5	Pulsed beam, continuous energy spectrum.
Cockcroft-Walton accelerator	Positive ions	0.1–1.5	Continuous beam, monoenergetic radiation.
Van de Graaff accelerator	X-rays	1–5	Continuous beam, continuous energy spectrum.
	Electrons and positive ions	1–5	Continuous beam, monoenergetic radiation.
Betatron	X-rays	10–300	Pulsed beam, continuous energy spectrum.
	Electrons	10–300	Pulsed beam, monoenergetic radiation.
Cyclotron	Positive ions	10–20	Essentially continuous beam, monoenergetic radiation.
Linear electron accelerator	X-rays	3–630	Pulsed beam, continuous energy spectrum.
	Electrons	3–630	Pulsed beam, essentially monoenergetic radiation.
Linear ion accelerator	Positive ions	4–400	Pulsed beam, essentially monoenergetic radiation.
Radioactive sources	α-ray	0–5.5	Monoenergetic.
	β-ray	0.02–2.25	Continuous energy spectrum.
	γ-ray	0.5–2	Monoenergetic or small number of discrete energies.

in which no radiation is being received from the machine. Pulsed beams often give instantaneous radiation intensities much greater than are obtained with a continuous beam.

When positive ions are being accelerated the energies given in the table refer to singly charged ions; for example, protons and deuterons. Ions with more than one positive charge will receive multiples of the energy shown, in proportion to their charge. A helium nucleus with two positive charges would, for example, be accelerated to twice the energy of a proton by the same accelerating potential. The properties of some accelerated particles are given in Table 2.9.

Neutron Sources

Neutrons are uncharged nuclear particles with a mass of one mass unit. They are not stable in the free state and, unless captured by a nucleus, decay spontaneously into a proton and electron with a half-life of about 13 minutes. Reaction with a nucleus is, however, their normal fate.

There are no long-lived[4] radioisotopes that emit neutrons directly with the exception of a few isotopes of heavy elements which undergo spontaneous fission. Neutrons can, however, be produced by stopping accelerated positive particles or high-energy electromagnetic radiation with suitable target materials. A number of these nuclear reactions are listed in Table 2.10.

TABLE 2.9 *Range and LET Values for Accelerated Particles*

Particle	Energy (Mev)	Range in air (cm; 15°C, 760 mm Hg)	Range in aluminum (mm)	Range in water (mm)	Average LET in water (kev/micron)
Electron	1	405	1.5	4.1	0.24
	3	1400	5.5	15	0.20
	10	4200	19.5	52	0.19
Proton	1	2.3	0.013	0.023	43
	3	14	0.072	0.14	21
	10	115	0.64	1.2	8.3
	30	820	4.3	8.5	3.5
Deuteron	1	1.7	0.0096		
	3	8.8	0.049	0.088	34
	10	68	0.37	0.72	14
	30	480	2.65	5.0	6
Helium nucleus	1	0.57	0.0029	0.0053	190
	3	1.7	0.0077	0.017	180
	10	10.5	0.057	0.11	92
	30	71	0.375		

[4] Rather less than one percent of the neutrons released during a nuclear chain reaction are produced by the decay of radioactive fission products and appear up to about a minute after the fission event. These are known as *delayed neutrons*.

TABLE 2.10 *Nuclear Reactions Used to Produce Neutrons*

Incident radiation	Target	Threshold energy (Mev)	Product
α-particles	Beryllium-9		Carbon-12
	Boron-10 (18.8%)*		Nitrogen-13
	Boron-11 (81.2%)*		Nitrogen-14
	Lithium-7 (92.5%)*		Boron-10
Deuterons	Deuterium		Helium-3
	Tritium		Helium-4
	Beryllium-9		Boron-10
Protons	Tritium	1.19	Helium-3
	Beryllium-9		Boron-9
	Lithium-7 (92.5%)*	1.88	Beryllium-7
x- or γ-rays	Deuterium	2.23	Hydrogen-1
	Beryllium-9	1.67	Beryllium-8
	Uranium-238	6.0	Uranium-237

* Natural abundance.

The threshold energy is the minimum energy that the incident radiation needs to initiate the nuclear reaction. Accelerated electrons produce similar reactions to x-rays via the bremsstrahlung radiation produced in the target.

The energy of the neutrons produced in nuclear reactions is governed solely by the energy balance of the reaction and depends upon the type and energy of the incident radiation and on the target material; by selecting the appropriate reaction and conditions monoenergetic neutrons with any desired energy, within a broad range, can be obtained. Generally the efficiency of the nuclear reactions is not high, a large part of the incident radiation energy being lost by ionization and excitation in the target.

Small neutron sources may use radioisotopes as sources of alpha or gamma radiation, or small ion sources producing accelerated deuterons in conjunction with a target containing tritium (7). The most frequently used radioisotope-target pairs are intimate mixtures of Ra^{226}-Be, Po^{210}-Be, and Sb^{124}-Be, employing (α, n), (α, n), and (γ, n) reactions respectively. Of these the polonium-beryllium source has the advantage that very little γ-radiation accompanies the neutrons. Larger neutron fluxes can be obtained by using particle accelerators to provide the incident radiation or from nuclear reactors.

Both radioisotopes and particle accelerators are widely used as radiation sources and they are, to a certain extent, complementary. The radioisotope sources have the advantage of relatively low cost and of adaptability where small sources are required or large volumes are to be irradiated. The particle accelerators have a much greater range of energies and are able to produce much greater radiation intensities than are normally available from isotope sources. In addition the accelerators are able to accelerate particles which are not available naturally from radioactive isotopes.

REFERENCES

1. Report of the International Commission on Radiological Units and Measurements (ICRU), 1959, *Nat. Bur. St. (U.S.) Handbook* 78 (1961).
2. D. E. Lea, *Actions of Radiations on Living Cells,* Cambridge University Press, Cambridge, 1946, p. 25.
3. L. Slack and K. Way, *Radiations from Radioactive Atoms in Frequent Use,* U.S. Atomic Energy Commission, 1959.
4. A. T. Nelms, *Energy Loss and Range of Electrons and Positrons, Nat. Bur. St. Circ.* 577 (1956).
5. G. W. Grodstein, *X-ray Attenuation Coefficients from 10 kev to 100 Mev, Nat. Bur. St. (U.S.) Circ.* 583 (1957) and R. T. McGinnies, *Supplement to Nat. Bur. St. (U.S.) Circ.* 583 (1959).
6. P. Harteck and S. Dondes, *Nucleonics,* **14,** (July), 22 (1956); P. Harteck, S. Dondes and J. W. Michener, *Proc. Second Intern. Conf., Peaceful Uses of Atomic Energy,* United Nations, Geneva, **7,** 544 (1958).
7. *Nucleonics,* **18,** (Dec.), 69, 72, 75 (1960).

CHAPTER 3

The Interaction of Radiation with Matter

Some knowledge of the processes by which radiation interacts with matter is essential to an understanding of radiation-chemical phenomena, since the chemical effects are a direct consequence of the absorption of energy from the radiation. In this chapter the principal interactions of electrons, heavy charged particles, neutrons, and electromagnetic radiation with matter will be outlined.

ELECTRONS

Electrons interact with matter by a number of processes of which the most important are the emission of electromagnetic radiation and inelastic and elastic collisions. The relative importance of these processes varies strongly with the energy of the incident electrons and, to a smaller extent, with the nature of the absorbing material; at high energies energy is lost predominantly by radiation emission and at low energies through inelastic collisions. Elastic scattering (change in the direction of motion without conversion of kinetic energy to any other form of energy) is of greatest importance at low energies.

Energy Loss by Radiation

High speed charged particles passing close to the nucleus of an atom may be decelerated and, according to classical physics, will radiate electromagnetic energy (*bremsstrahlung*) with a rate, $-dE/dx$, proportional to z^2Z^2/m^2, where z and Z are the charge on the particle and the nucleus respectively and m is the mass of the particle. Thus the energy loss by radiation will be greatest for light particles and for stopping materials of high atomic number.

For electrons, bremsstrahlung emission is negligible below 100 kev but increases rapidly with increasing energy, becoming the predominant mode of energy loss at an electron energy between 10 and 100 Mev (the exact energy depends on the stopping material). The bremsstrahlung energy spectrum extends from zero to the energy of the incident electrons and is, in fact, the continuous x-ray spectrum (Fig. 2.9).

Bethe and Ashkin (1) and Heitler (2) have calculated expressions for the energy loss by electrons from deceleration in the field of nuclei and atomic electrons. For incident electrons of kinetic energy E, where $m_0c^2 \ll E \ll 137m_0c^2Z^{-1/3}$, the screening effect of the atomic electrons on the nuclear charge can be neglected and the energy loss per unit path length is given by

$$-\left(\frac{dE}{dx}\right)_{\text{rad}} = N(E + m_0c^2)\,\frac{Z(Z+1)}{137}\left(\frac{e^2}{m_0c^2}\right)^2 \left(4\ln\frac{2(E+m_0c^2)}{m_0c^2} - \frac{4}{3}\right)\ \text{ergs/cm} \quad (3.1)$$

where N is the number of atoms per cubic centimeter, e is the charge on an electron in electrostatic units, m_0 is the rest mass of an electron in grams, c is the velocity of light in cm/sec, and Z is the atomic number of the stopping material.[1] When $E \gg 137m_0c^2Z^{-1/3}$ the screening is assumed to be complete and the rate of energy loss is given by

$$-\left(\frac{dE}{dx}\right)_{\text{rad}} = N(E + m_0c^2)\,\frac{Z(Z+\zeta)}{137}\left(\frac{e^2}{m_0c^2}\right)^2 \left(4\ln\frac{183}{Z^{1/3}} + \frac{2}{9}\right)\ \text{ergs/cm} \quad (3.2)$$

where ζ is a function of the atomic number and ranges between 1.1 and 1.4.

[1] A list of symbols is given in Appendix C.

Bremsstrahlung formation does not produce any significant changes in the stopping material (e.g., excitation or ionization) unless the bremsstrahlung is subsequently absorbed by it.

Energy Loss through Inelastic Collisions

Charged particles can also lose energy in matter through Coulomb interactions with electrons of the stopping material. Interaction in this way, which produces excitation and ionization in the stopping material, is the dominant process whereby electrons are slowed down at electron energies below those at which bremsstrahlung emission occurs.

Bethe (1, 3) derived an expression for the energy loss from electrons by excitation and ionization

$$-\left(\frac{dE}{dx}\right)_{\text{coll}} = \frac{2\pi N e^4 Z}{m_0 v^2}\left[\ln \frac{m_0 v^2 E}{2I^2(1-\beta^2)} - (2\sqrt{1-\beta^2} - 1 + \beta^2)\ln 2 + 1 - \beta^2 + \tfrac{1}{8}(1 - \sqrt{1-\beta^2})^2\right] \text{ ergs/cm} \quad (3.3)$$

where v is the velocity of the electron in cm/sec, β is v/c, I is the mean excitation potential for the atoms of the stopping material in ergs, and the other symbols have the same meaning as in Eq. 3.1. The energy loss per unit path, $-(dE/dx)_{\text{coll}}$, is known as the *specific energy loss*, or *stopping power*. It should be noted that this is a function of the electron velocity, and changes as the electron is slowed down. A quantity which will be referred to later is the *mass stopping power*, ${}_mS$, given by

$${}_mS = -\left(\frac{dE}{dx}\right)_{\text{coll}} \times \frac{1}{\rho} \text{ ergs cm}^2/\text{g} \quad (3.4)$$

where ρ is the density of the material.

The mean excitation potential, I, takes into account the effect of the electron binding energies on the energy loss, and is given by $I = kZ$, where k is a "constant" that can be determined experimentally for different elements and which lies between 8 and 16. Experimental values of I are determined using heavy particles since the strong scattering of electrons in matter make them unsuitable for this determination.

For an electron of energy E Mev the ratio of the energy loss by radiation to the loss by collision is given roughly (in the Mev range of energies) by

$$\frac{(dE/dx)_{\text{rad}}}{(dE/dx)_{\text{coll}}} \approx \frac{EZ}{1600 m_0 c^2} \quad (3.5)$$

Elastic Scattering

Charged particles may be deflected by the Coulomb (electrostatic) field of an atomic nucleus. This is particularly important in the case of electrons because of their small mass, and they frequently experience such elastic scattering. Scattering is greatest for low electron energies and for high atomic number materials.

Range of Electrons

The range, or penetration, of β-particles (groups of electrons of mixed energy) has been discussed briefly in Chapter 2. Monoenergetic electrons are also characterized by an indefinite range due to frequent scattering and the possibility of large energy losses; a typical number-distance curve for monoenergetic electrons is shown in Fig. 3.1. The extrapolated or practical range, R_p, is found by extrapolating the more or less linear portion of the curve to intersect the background and the maximum range, R_0, from the point where the curve merges with the background. Both ranges are characteristic of the original electron energy.

Several empirical formulae have been used to relate the range and energy of electrons. Katz and Penfold (4) for example found that in

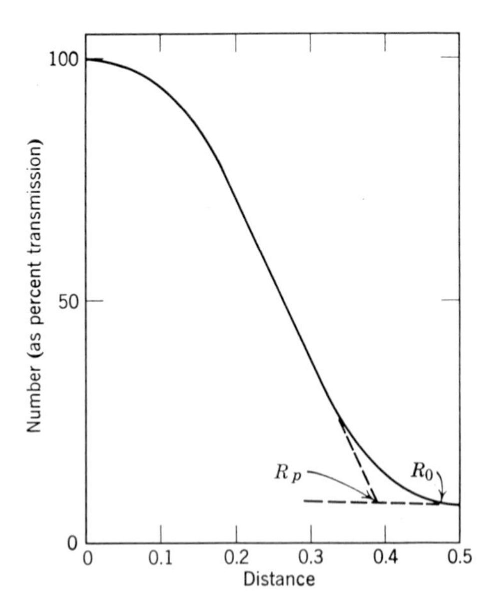

FIGURE 3.1 *Typical number-distance curve for monoenergetic electrons.*

aluminum both the maximum range of β-rays and the extrapolated range of monoenergetic electrons could be represented by

$$\text{Range (mg/cm}^2) = 412E^n \tag{3.6}$$

where E (Mev) is the maximum β-ray energy or the energy of the monoenergetic electrons and $n = 1.265 - 0.0954 \ln E$, for energies from 0.01 to 2.5 Mev. For energies from 2.5 Mev to about 20 Mev

$$\text{Range (mg/cm}^2) = 530E - 106 \tag{3.7}$$

Though these formulae fit the data for aluminum best they also apply reasonably well to other materials, especially other light elements, since the range (in mg/cm^2) varies only slightly with atomic number.

The mean energy loss due to ionization and excitation and the range for electrons and positrons in a number of materials have been tabulated by Nelms (5).

HEAVY CHARGED PARTICLES

Heavy charged particles (protons, deuterons, α-particles, etc.) interact with matter in the same way as electrons, that is, by bremsstrahlung emission, inelastic collisions, and elastic scattering. However, bremsstrahlung emission is only important at very high energies (of the order of 1000 Mev) and elastic scattering is relatively unimportant, so that energy loss is principally by inelastic collisions with the electrons of the stopping material.

For heavy charged particles the linear rate of energy loss by collision, or the stopping power, is given by Eq. 3.8 (1, 3, 6)

$$-\frac{dE}{dx} = \frac{4\pi z^2 e^4}{m_0 v^2} NZ \left[\ln \frac{2m_0 v^2}{I(1 - \beta^2)} - \beta^2 \right] \text{ergs/cm} \tag{3.8}$$

where ze is the charge on the particle and v its velocity; the other symbols are as previously defined. At energies below about 0.1 Mev for protons and 1 Mev for α-particles, the moving particles are slowed down sufficiently to alternately capture and lose electrons and Eq. 3.8 no longer applies.

The calculated linear rate of energy loss (Eq. 3.8) increases as the particle slows down since the factor v^2 outside the logarithmic term is more effective than the v^2 inside. Furthermore, if two particles of equal energy but different mass are compared the heavier will have the smaller velocity and hence a larger linear rate of energy loss. The ion density along the track of an α-particle, for example, is several hundred times greater than that along the track of an electron of the same energy.

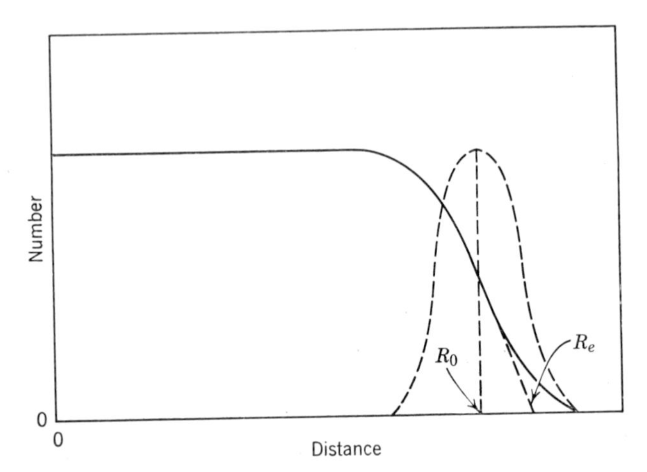

FIGURE 3.2 *Typical number-distance curve for heavy particles. (The number of particles left in the beam is plotted against the distance from the source.)*

Range of Heavy Particles

A typical number-distance curve for heavy particles is shown in Fig. 3.2. The broken line is obtained by differentiating the solid curve with respect to distance and represents the distribution of the range of individual particles about the mean range, R_0. The mean range can be found from the position of the maximum of the differential curve or the point of inflection of the solid, integral, curve. In practice the extrapolated range, R_e, is more readily determined (by drawing a tangent to the steepest part of the number-distance curve and extrapolating it to cut the distance axis) and the mean range calculated from this (1, 6). The difference between the mean and extrapolated range is a measure of the straggling of the particles and usually amounts to about 1 or 2% of the total range.

Data on the range of heavy particles are available from a number of sources, (1, 6, 7, 8). Frequently ranges are given for only one type of particle. However the range of other heavy particles can be found quite readily since for particles of the same velocity the linear rate of energy loss is proportional to the square of their charge (except at very low energies). The range is proportional to $E/(-dE/dx)$ and by considering particles with the same velocity the expressions

$$\text{Range of particle } A = \frac{m_A Z_B^2}{m_B Z_A^2} \times \text{Range of particle } B \qquad (3.9a)$$

when

$$\text{Energy of particle } A = \frac{m_A}{m_B} \times \text{Energy of particle } B \qquad (3.9b)$$

are obtained relating the range of particles A and B of mass and atomic number m_A and Z_A, and m_B and Z_B, respectively, in the same stopping material. For example, the range of an α-particle ($m = 4, Z = 2$) is related to the range of a proton ($m = 1, Z = 1$) of energy E_p by

$$\text{Range of } \alpha\text{-particle} = \frac{4}{4} \times \text{Range of proton} \qquad (3.10)$$

$$(\alpha\text{-particle energy} = 4E_p)$$

i.e., in a particular stopping material the range of an α-particle is equal to the range of a proton with one quarter the energy (both parts of Eq. 3.9, a and b, are required to obtain this result). Ranges for deuterons ($m = 2, Z = 1$) and α-particles in air calculated from the range of protons in air (6) using Eq. 3.9 are tabulated in Table 3.1. The calculated

TABLE 3.1 *Range (cm) of Protons, Deuterons, and Alpha-Particles in Air (15°C, 760 mm Hg)*

Energy (Mev)	Proton	Deuteron	α-Particle
0.5	0.86	—	—
1.0	2.30	1.72	—
2.0	7.20	4.61	0.86 (1.05)
4.0	23.1	14.4	2.30 (2.49)
8.0	77.3	46.2	7.20 (7.35)

α-particle ranges are smaller by a small constant value than the ranges found experimentally (shown in parentheses). This constant, found by experiment to be 0.20 cm, takes into account the capture and loss of electrons at low energies, which affects α-particles more than protons. Other multiply charged particles require a similar correction at low energies for exact results.

NEUTRONS

Neutrons, since they are uncharged, do not produce ionization directly in matter but interact almost exclusively with atomic nuclei. However, the products of neutron interactions often do produce ionization and thus give rise to typical radiation-chemical changes. The main ionizing species are protons, or heavier positive ions, and the chemical effects of neutron irradiation are similar to those produced by beams of these charged particles. Neutrons can, however, penetrate much greater thicknesses of material, and the consequences of neutron irradiation are not confined to the surface regions of the absorber.

The main processes by which neutrons and nuclei interact are elastic scattering, inelastic scattering, nuclear reaction, and capture. The type of interaction taking place depends to a large extent upon the energy of the neutron and for this reason it is convenient to divide neutrons into groups according to their energy. The groups are (9)[2]: thermal neutrons, in thermal equilibrium with their surroundings and having energies of the order of 0.025 ev at room temperature; intermediate neutrons, with energies from 0.5 ev to 10 kev; fast neutrons, with energies from 10 kev to 10 Mev; and relativistic neutrons with energies greater than 10 Mev.

Elastic Scattering

Elastic scattering is the most probable interaction of fast neutrons with matter and is also important for neutrons in the intermediate range of energies. The energy of the incident neutron is shared between the recoiling neutron and nucleus according to the laws of conservation of energy and momentum and, apart from gaining kinetic energy, the nucleus is unchanged. The fraction of the energy of the neutron that is transferred to the recoiling nucleus (atomic weight A) varies from zero up to a maximum which is given by

$$\left(\frac{\Delta E}{E_0}\right)_{\max} = \frac{4A}{(A + 1)^2} \tag{3.11}$$

This fraction is greatest for hydrogen ($A = 1$) and decreases with increasing atomic weight. In biological tissues and other materials containing a large proportion of hydrogen the most important interaction of fast neutrons is elastic scattering with hydrogen nuclei. The recoiling hydrogen nuclei (protons) subsequently produce excitation and ionization in the substrate.

The slowing down of neutrons in the moderator of a nuclear reactor is due mainly to elastic scattering and is accomplished most efficiently by low atomic weight materials. Thus the average number of collisions to reduce the energy of a neutron from 2 Mev, the average energy of neutrons produced by the fission process, to thermal energy (0.025 ev) is 18 in hydrogen, over 100 in graphite, and about 2000 in lead (10). The cross section for elastic scattering increases as the energy of the neutron decreases.

[2] Other authors may use different limits and names.

Inelastic Scattering

Inelastic scattering occurs if the neutron is absorbed by the nucleus and then a neutron with lower energy re-emitted, leaving the original nucleus in an excited state which eventually returns to the ground state by emitting one or more γ-rays. Inelastic scattering is not possible for neutron energies below that of the lowest excited state of the nucleus (generally a few hundred kev) but increases in importance as the neutron energy is increased; it may be as probable as elastic scattering at energies above about 10 Mev. Inelastic scattering can be considered as a (n, n) reaction.

Nuclear Reactions

At high energies the colliding neutron may be incorporated into the nucleus and another particle such as a proton or α-particle emitted. Nuclear reactions (other than capture) only occur when the neutron has an energy in excess of the threshold energy for the reaction and they are generally not significant at neutron energies below several Mev. The energy of the emitted particle depends not only on the neutron energy but also on the energy liberated or absorbed by the nuclear reaction taking place.

One nuclear reaction which can take place at thermal neutron energies is reaction with the mass-10 isotope of boron, $B^{10}(n, \alpha)Li^7$, and this is widely used in detectors for low-energy neutrons. The same reaction may also be used to produce α-particles and recoiling Li^7 nuclei in situ in a material containing boron, by irradiating it with low-energy neutrons. A second important thermal-neutron reaction is that with nitrogen-14 to give carbon-14, $N^{14}(n, p)C^{14}$.

Capture

At thermal energies the most probable interaction process is capture of the neutron by the nucleus to give an isotope of the target element. Often the compound nucleus is formed in an excited state and returns to the ground state with the emission of one or more γ-rays; the reaction in this case can be classed as a (n, γ) reaction.

The cross section for capture is generally low at high neutron energies but frequently rises in a series of (resonance) peaks at energies within the intermediate range, increasing again in the thermal region in inverse proportion to the neutron velocity.

In biological tissue and similar systems (for example, organic compounds containing only C, H, O, and N) the important reactions are $H^1(n, \gamma)H^2$, which yields a 2.2 Mev γ-ray, and $N^{14}(n, p)C^{14}$, which produces a 0.66 Mev proton; the capture cross sections of oxygen and carbon are small.

ELECTROMAGNETIC RADIATION

Unlike charged particles, which generally lose energy almost continuously through a large number of small energy transfers as they pass through matter, photons of electromagnetic radiation tend to lose a relatively large amount of energy whenever they interact with matter. However, not all incident photons will interact with any finite thickness of matter, and those which do not interact suffer no change and are transmitted with their original direction and energy. The effect of the absorbing matter (neglecting for the moment the photons which do interact) is therefore to reduce the number of photons transmitted, and thus to reduce the *intensity* of the radiation passing through it. By intensity is meant the radiation energy (the number of photons multiplied by their average energy) passing through a sphere of unit (maximum) cross-sectional area in unit time at the point of interest; the units of intensity are generally ergs per square centimeter per second.

The reduction in electromagnetic radiation intensity (dI) on passing through a small thickness (dx) of absorber is given by

$$dI = -I_i \mu \, dx \tag{3.12}$$

where I_i is the intensity of the incident radiation and μ is the total *linear absorption coefficient* (units cm^{-1}) of the material. The linear absorption coefficient is thus the fraction of the incident photons diverted from the incident beam by unit thickness of absorber; it is a constant for a given material and for radiation of a given energy but varies from material to material and for different photon energies. Equation 3.12 only applies when dI and dx are very small but integration gives an expression which is not restricted in this manner

$$I = I_i e^{-\mu x} \tag{3.13}$$

where I is the intensity of the radiation transmitted through a thickness x of absorber.

If the linear absorption coefficient is divided by density the *mass absorption coefficient* (symbol μ/ρ, units cm^2/g) is obtained, which is independent of the density and physical state of the material. Also useful are the *atomic absorption coefficient* (symbol ${}_a\mu$, units cm^2/atom) and the *electronic absorption coefficient* (symbol ${}_e\mu$, units cm²/electron) which are the absorption coefficients per atom and per electron respectively. They are related to the linear and mass absorption coefficients in the following manner

$$ {}_a\mu = \frac{\mu A}{\rho N_0} \text{ cm}^2/\text{atom} \tag{3.14}$$

$$ {}_e\mu = \frac{\mu A}{\rho N_0 Z} \text{ cm}^2/\text{electron} \tag{3.15}$$

where ρ is the density, A the atomic weight and Z the atomic number of the stopping material, and N_0 is Avogadro's number. The atomic and electronic absorption coefficients have the dimensions of an area and are often referred to as *cross sections*. The term "cross section" is used interchangeably with "absorption coefficient" to denote the probability of absorption. Numerical values of the atomic and electronic absorption coefficients or cross sections are of the order of 10^{-24} cm² per atom or electron and are often given in terms of barns/atom or barns/electron where one *barn* is 10^{-24} cm².

The total absorption coefficient is the sum of a number of partial coefficients representing various processes of absorption. These processes are the photoelectric effect, the Compton effect, pair production, coherent scattering, and photonuclear reactions. The first three of these processes are the most important, though the relative importance of each process depends very much on the photon energy and the atomic number of the stopping material.

The Photoelectric Effect

Low-energy photons are absorbed mainly by photoelectric absorption. In this type of interaction the entire energy of the photon (E_0) is transferred to a single atomic electron, which is ejected from the atom with an energy equal to the difference between the photon energy and the binding energy (E_s) of the electron in the atom,

$$E_e = E_0 - E_s \tag{3.16}$$

At low photon energies the electrons are ejected predominantly at right angles to the direction of the incoming photon, but as the energy increases the distribution shifts increasingly toward the forward direction. Energy and momentum must be conserved and this is made possible by the recoil of the remainder of the atom, so that photoelectric interaction is not possible with free electrons.

If the incident photon has sufficient energy it is generally the most tightly bound electron in the atom that is ejected, i.e., an electron from the K shell. Interactions with K-electrons account for about 80% of the photoelectric absorption for photons with energies greater than the K shell binding energy; most of the remainder of the interactions are with L-electrons. The vacancy created by loss of an electron from an inner atomic shell will be filled by an electron from an outer shell, with emission of characteristic x-radiation (fluorescent radiation) or of low-energy Auger electrons. For low atomic number (often referred to as "low-Z") materials the binding energy of the inner electron shells is relatively small (of the order of 500 ev for water, for example) and the secondary x-rays and electrons will have low energies and will be absorbed in the immediate vicinity of the original interaction. On the other hand materials of high atomic number may give moderately energetic secondary radiation (for tungsten, for example, the secondary x-rays have energies up to 70 kev) which can travel some distance from the original interaction before being completely absorbed.

Photoelectric absorption is most probable for high atomic number materials and for low photon energies. The *electronic* absorption coefficient varies from element to element approximately as Z^3 and for a given element decreases rapidly with increasing photon energy. Photoelectric absorption shows a marked increase as the photon energy increases from a value just below the K shell binding energy to a value just above this energy, a plot of the photoelectric absorption coefficient against photon energy having a distinct edge at the binding energy (cf., Fig. 3.7).

The Compton Effect

In the Compton effect a photon interacts with an electron, which may be loosely bound or free, so that the electron is accelerated and the photon deflected with reduced energy. The energy and momentum of the incident photon are shared between the scattered photon and the recoil electron.

From the equations for the conservation of energy and momentum it is possible to calculate three of the four variables, θ, ϕ, E_γ, and E_e (Fig. 3.3) representing the Compton process if the energy of the incident photon is known and the remaining variable is assumed. For example, the energy of the scattered photon is related to the angle θ by

$$E_\gamma = \frac{E_0}{1 + (E_0/m_0c^2)(1 - \cos\theta)} \tag{3.17}$$

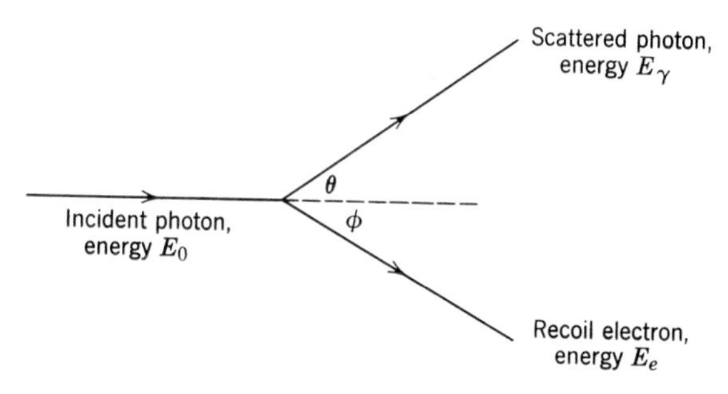

FIGURE 3.3 *The Compton effect.*

where E_0 and E_γ are the energies of the incident and scattered photon respectively and m_0c^2 is the rest energy of the electron. This equation shows that when the angle θ is small the photon is scattered with little reduction in energy and that the greater the deflection θ the greater the energy loss from the photon.

The energy of the recoil electron is equal to the difference between the energy of the incident and scattered photon

$$E_e = E_0 - E_\gamma \tag{3.18}$$

and may have any value from zero up to a maximum which can be calculated from Eqs. 3.17 and 3.18 by putting $\theta = 180°$. The most probable electron energies are those near zero and near the maximum energy, energies near the maximum being particularly favoured when the energy of the incident photon is high. The direction in which the electron recoils is predominantly that of the incident photon, and is more nearly so the higher the fraction of the photon energy it carries away and the higher the incident photon energy.

The probability of the photon being scattered with a definite energy or direction and the probability of Compton interaction as a whole were derived quantum mechanically by Klein and Nishina (11). The Klein-Nishina formula for the total electronic Compton absorption coefficient is

$$_e\sigma = \frac{2\pi e^4}{m_0^2c^4}\left\{\frac{1+\alpha}{\alpha^2}\left[\frac{2(1+\alpha)}{1+2\alpha} - \frac{\ln(1+2\alpha)}{\alpha}\right] + \frac{\ln(1+2\alpha)}{2\alpha} - \frac{1+3\alpha}{(1+2\alpha)^2}\right\} \text{ cm}^2/\text{electron} \tag{3.19}$$

where $\alpha = E_0/m_0c^2$. This absorption coefficient gives the fraction of the photons of energy E_0 which interact by the Compton process, per electron/cm^2. However, an appreciable part of the energy of these photons is retained by the scattered photons. The fraction of the incident photon energy, per electron/cm², that the scattered photons retain is given by the Compton *scattering coefficient*, ${}_e\sigma_s$,

$$ {}_e\sigma_s = \frac{2\pi e^4}{m_0^2 c^4}\left[\frac{\ln(1+2\alpha)}{2\alpha^3} + \frac{(1+\alpha)(2\alpha^2 - 2\alpha - 1)}{\alpha^2(1+2\alpha)^2} + \frac{4\alpha^2}{3(1+2\alpha)^3}\right] \text{ cm}^2/\text{electron} \quad (3.20) $$

The fraction of the incident photon energy transferred to the recoil electrons, per electron/cm², is given by the *true* or *energy* Compton absorption coefficient, ${}_e\sigma_a$, where

$$ {}_e\sigma_a = {}_e\sigma - {}_e\sigma_s \quad (3.21) $$

The ratio of the true to the scatter absorption coefficient varies with the energy of the incident photons (Fig. 3.4).

Compton electronic absorption coefficients are independent of the atomic number of the stopping material and can be applied to any material, though separate coefficients must be determined for each different incident photon energy. Conversion of the electronic absorption coefficients to the atomic, mass, or linear coefficients will involve one or more of the constants, atomic number, atomic weight, and density of the stopping material.

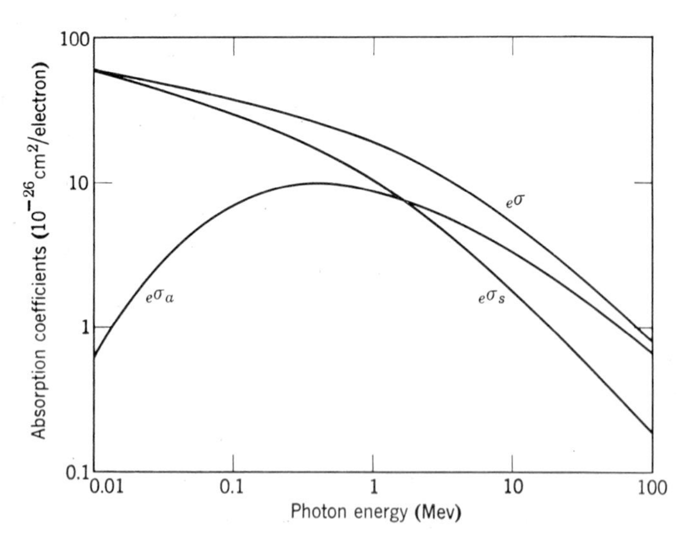

FIGURE 3.4 *Variation of Compton absorption coefficients with photon energy.*

Compton interactions predominate for photon energies between 1 and 5 Mev in high atomic number (high-Z) materials and over a much wider range of energies in low-Z materials. In water, for example, Compton interactions predominate from about 30 kev to 20 Mev (Fig. 3.6).

Graphs of the angular and energy distributions for the Compton process have been published by Nelms (12).

Pair-Production

Pair production involves the complete absorption of a photon in the vicinity of an atomic nucleus or, less frequently, an electron[3] with the production of two particles, an electron and a positron (Fig. 3.5). The energy of the photon less the rest energies of the two particles (each m_0c^2) is divided between the kinetic energy of the electron and positron (the small amount of energy transferred to the nucleus is nearly always neglected), i.e.,

$$E_0 = E_e + E_p + 2m_0c^2 \tag{3.22}$$

Momentum is shared by the recoiling nucleus. The positron is slowed down in a similar manner to an electron and eventually combines with an electron, the two particles being replaced by two 0.51 Mev γ-rays (*annihilation radiation*) emitted in opposite directions.

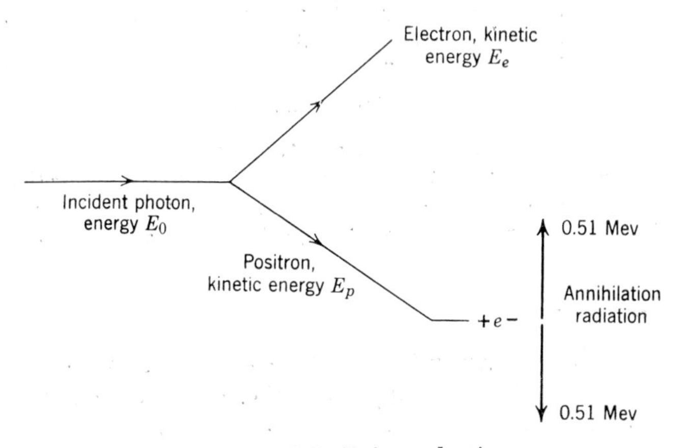

FIGURE 3.5 *Pair-production.*

[3] When the photon is absorbed in the field of an electron, this electron also is set in motion and hence the process is often referred to as *triplet production*. Triplet production is less common than pair production and will not be considered here, the discussion which follows applies particularly to pair-production in the field of a nucleus.

Pair production cannot occur at photon energies less than 1.02 Mev (i.e., $2m_0c^2$). Above this energy the *electronic* absorption coefficient or cross section varies with the photon energy and is very nearly proportional to the atomic number (Z) of the stopping material. Since the atomic cross section is equal to the electronic coefficient multiplied by Z (Eqs. 3.14 and 3.15) the atomic cross section will vary as Z^2.

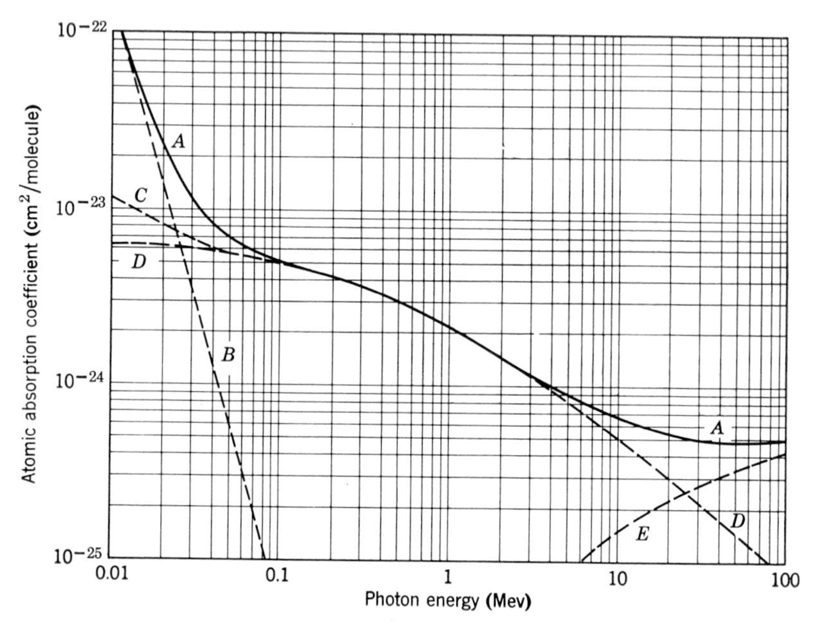

FIGURE 3.6 *Atomic absorption coefficients for water. Curve A: total absorption coefficient (with coherent scattering). B: photoelectric absorption coefficient. C: total Compton coefficient (with coherent scattering). D: total Compton coefficient (without coherent scattering). E: pair-production coefficient.*

Coherent Scattering

A photon may be scattered with little loss of energy by several processes, the chief process involving interaction with the atomic electrons (*Rayleigh scattering*). Rayleigh scattering is most probable at low photon energies (less than 0.1 Mev) and in high-Z materials; it is included in Fig. 3.6 for water and Fig. 3.7 for lead as *coherent scattering*. The term "coherent" refers to the fact that the effects combine coherently, i.e., by the addition of amplitudes, since there is a definite phase relationship between the incident and scattered radiation. Compton scattering effects combine incoherently by the addition of the intensities of the effects since there is a random phase relationship between the incident and scattered radiation; hence the term *incoherent scattering* that is sometimes applied to Compton scattering.

Rayleigh scattering occurs in an energy range where the photoelectric cross section is large and it can often be neglected without introducing a very large error. Furthermore, the angle of deflection is generally small

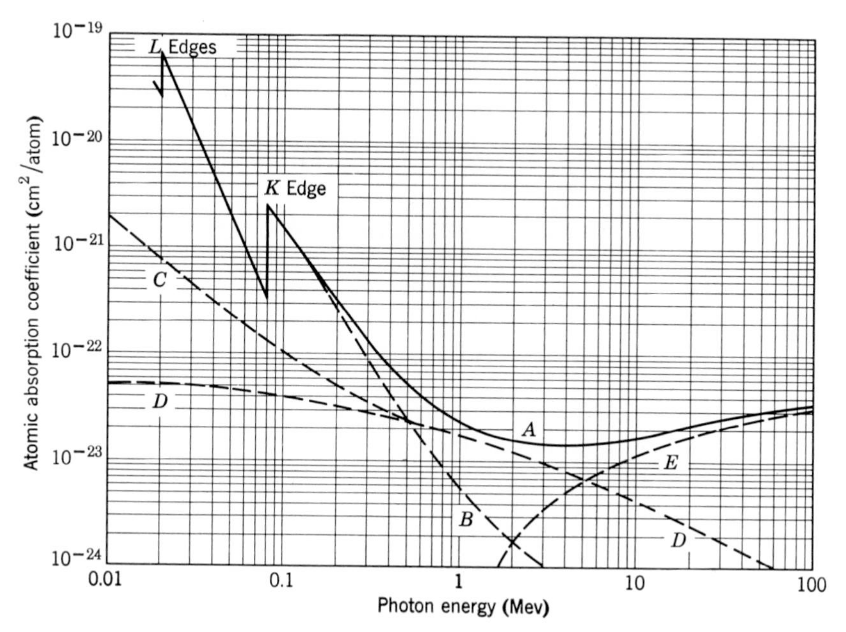

FIGURE 3.7 *Atomic absorption coefficients for lead.*

and since it is not accompanied by any significant energy loss the scattered photon will only be distinguished from the primary beam under "narrow-beam" conditions (see page 56).

In crystals, coherent scattering may be particularly intense in certain directions due to interference between waves scattered by different atoms; this is the basis for the determination of crystal structure by x-ray diffraction.

Photonuclear Reactions

At energies above about 8 Mev for high-Z materials, and in the region of 10 to 20 Mev for low-Z materials, photons have sufficient energy to eject a proton or neutron from the nucleus of an atom. The cross section for these reactions is zero for photon energies below the binding energy of the particles and then generally rises to a maximum at energies two to four times the binding energy, falling again at higher energies. Photonuclear cross sections are generally small compared with the Compton and pair-production cross sections at the same energy, though the neutrons which are ejected may be significant in practice because of their considerable range.

Natural lead, for example, can undergo a (γ, n) reaction with a threshold energy of 7.9 Mev. The photonuclear cross section shows a maximum at 13.7 Mev and at this energy has a value about 4.3% of that for the combined Compton and pair-production processes (13).

Photonuclear reactions have been reviewed by Strauch (14).

The Attenuation of Monoenergetic Radiation in Matter

Absorption coefficients for the processes outlined above may be added to give a total absorption coefficient, i.e.,

$$\mu = \tau + \sigma + \kappa \tag{3.23}$$

where τ, σ, and κ are the linear absorption coefficients for the photoelectric, Compton, and pair-production processes respectively, neglecting the small contributions from coherent scattering and photonuclear reaction. The total mass and the total atomic and total electronic absorption coefficients can be obtained in the same way by adding the appropriate partial coefficients. It should be emphasized however that a value for a total absorption coefficient refers only to one material and one photon energy; separate values must be determined for every different material and for each photon energy. Figures 3.6 and 3.7 show the variation of the total and partial atomic absorption coefficients for water and lead respectively with photon energy. The two curves are reasonably characteristic of those for other low-Z and high-Z materials respectively.

Figure 3.8 illustrates the experimental arrangement for measuring absorption coefficients under *narrow-beam* conditions, i.e., where the radiation impinging on the absorber is restricted to a narrow beam by means of a collimator. Ideally, the radiation intensity measured by the detector under these conditions is due only to that part of the primary beam which has not interacted with the absorbing material in any way; scattered radiation due to both incoherent and coherent scattering being deflected away from the detector and not measured. Under narrow-beam conditions the intensity measured by the detector (I) is given by

$$I = I_i e^{-\mu x} \tag{3.13}$$

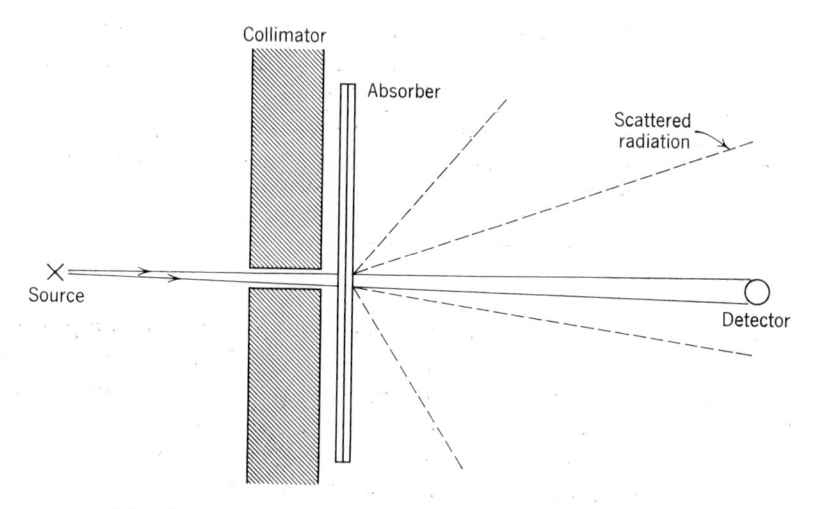

FIGURE 3.8 *Experimental arrangement for measuring narrow-beam attenuation coefficients.*

where I_i is the intensity measured in the absence of the absorber and x is the thickness of the absorber; μ is the total linear absorption coefficient.

Tables of absorption coefficients are given by Grodstein (15) and McGinnies (16).

Combination of Absorption Coefficients

In general the probability of a photon interacting with an atom is independent of the environment of the atom. Absorption coefficients for atoms of different elements present in an absorbing material can therefore be treated separately and, weighted in proportion to the abundance of the element (in appropriate units), added to give the absorption coefficient for the material as a whole.

Electronic absorption coefficients are weighted in proportion to the number of electrons each element contributes to the total number of electrons present in the compound. For example, a water molecule contains 10 electrons, one from each of the hydrogen atoms and 8 from the oxygen atom, and therefore

$$({}_e\mu)_{H_2O} = 2/10({}_e\mu)_H + 8/10({}_e\mu)_O \tag{3.24}$$

Substituting numerical values from Table 3.2 for 1 Mev γ-rays

$$\begin{aligned}({}_e\mu)_{H_2O} &= 0.2 \times 0.211 + 0.8 \times 0.211 \\ &= 0.211 \text{ barn/electron}\end{aligned} \tag{3.25}$$

TABLE 3.2 *Total Absorption Coefficients for 1 Mev Gamma-Rays* (ref. 15)

Coefficient	Hydrogen	Oxygen	Water	Units
Electronic, ${}_e\mu$	0.211	0.211	0.211	Barn*/electron
Atomic, ${}_a\mu$	0.211	1.69	2.11	Barn*/atom or molecule
Mass, μ/ρ	0.126	0.0636	0.0706	cm^2/g
Linear, μ	—	—	0.0706	cm^{-1}

* 1 barn = 10^{-24} cm².

In this particular example absorption is entirely by the Compton process and, since the Compton electronic absorption coefficient is the same for all materials at any given photon energy, the electronic absorption coefficient for water is the same as that for both hydrogen and oxygen. Electronic absorption coefficients can, however, be combined in this way regardless of the process by which absorption takes place.

Atomic absorption coefficients are combined after weighting them in proportion to the number of atoms of each element present. For water, containing two atoms of hydrogen and one of oxygen, this is simply

$$({}_a\mu)_{H_2O} = 2({}_a\mu)_H + ({}_a\mu)_O \tag{3.26}$$

For 1 Mev γ-rays

$$\begin{aligned}({}_a\mu)_{H_2O} &= 2 \times 0.211 + 1.69 \\ &= 2.11 \text{ barn/molecule}\end{aligned} \tag{3.27}$$

Mass absorption coefficients are weighted in proportion to the weight of each element present. Water contains 2/18 part by weight of hydrogen and 16/18 part of oxygen and the mass absorption coefficient of water is given by

$$(\mu/\rho)_{H_2O} = 2/18(\mu/\rho)_H + 16/18(\mu/\rho)_O \tag{3.28}$$

For 1 Mev γ-rays

$$\begin{aligned}(\mu/\rho)_{H_2O} &= 2/18 \times 0.126 + 16/18 \times 0.0636 \\ &= 0.0706 \text{ cm}^2/\text{g}\end{aligned} \tag{3.29}$$

Linear absorption coefficients cannot be combined quite as simply since they depend also upon the density of the elements and the compound. The linear absorption coefficient (μ) of a compound (density ρ_c) containing two elements is given by

$$\mu = w_1(\rho_c/\rho_1)\mu_1 + w_2(\rho_c/\rho_2)\mu_2 \tag{3.30}$$

where w_1, ρ_1, and μ_1 are the weight fraction, density, and linear absorption coefficient respectively for the first element. It is better to avoid using the densities of the elements altogether. This can be accomplished by adding their electronic, atomic, or mass absorption coefficients to get the corresponding coefficient for the compound and converting this to the required linear absorption coefficient. Only the density of the compound is needed.

The electronic, atomic, mass, and linear absorption coefficients can be interconverted at any stage using the relationships

$$ {}_a\mu = Z({}_e\mu) \tag{3.31} $$

$$ \mu/\rho = \frac{N_0 Z}{A}({}_e\mu) = \frac{N_0}{A}({}_a\mu) \tag{3.32} $$

$$ \mu = (\mu/\rho)\rho \tag{3.33} $$

where Z is the atomic number or, for a compound, the sum of the atomic numbers of the elements present (e.g., 10 for water), A is the atomic or molecular weight, N_0 is Avogadro's number, and ρ is the density of the material.

Absorption coefficients for mixtures of compounds are derived in the same way, combining the absorption coefficients for the elements present or, if known, for the compounds making up the mixture. Energy and scatter coefficients (see page 64) can be combined in the same way as the total absorption coefficients.

Broad-Beam Attenuation

When a sheet of absorbing material is put in a beam of radiation the intensity measured by a detector placed in the transmitted beam depends, in part, on the amount of scattered radiation that reaches the detector. Narrow-beam experiments (Fig. 3.8) are designed to keep to a minimum the amount of scattered radiation measured. If, however, the collimator is removed, as shown in Fig. 3.9, or the detector is moved close to the absorber, an appreciable amount of scattered radiation can enter the detector, which will then give a higher reading for the transmitted radiation intensity than under narrow-beam conditions; i.e., the measured absorption coefficient under these broad-beam conditions is spuriously low.

Under broad-beam conditions Eq. 3.13 for the attenuation of the radiation is replaced by

$$ I = I_i B e^{-\mu x} \tag{3.34} $$

where μ is the narrow-beam attenuation coefficient and B is the *build-up factor*. The build-up factor is the ratio of the measured (transmitted) intensity under broad-beam conditions (i.e., attenuated primary radiation plus scattered radiation entering the detector) to the measured intensity under narrow-beam conditions (attenuated primary radiation only). It is dependent on the kind and thickness of the absorber, the photon energy, and also on the type of detector used and its position relative to the absorber. Typical broad-beam and narrow-beam attenuation curves for monoenergetic radiation are shown in Fig. 3.10.

Data on build-up factors have been tabulated by Fano (17) and Goldstein and Wilkins (18).

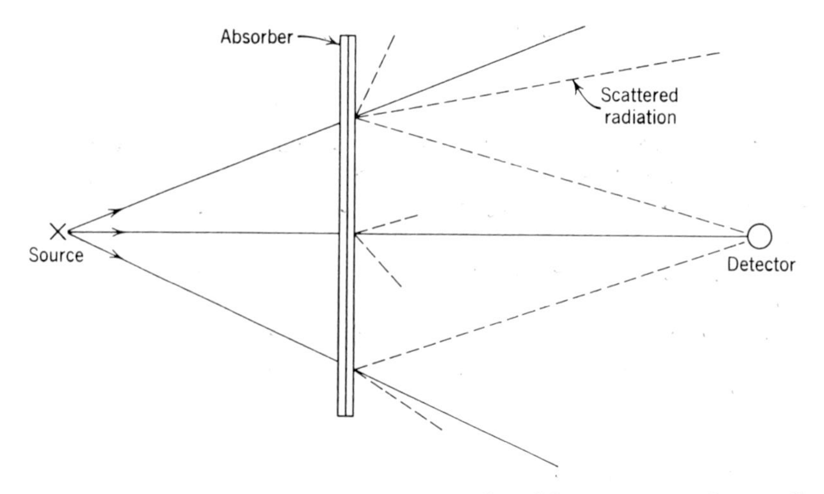

FIGURE 3.9 *Arrangement for measuring broad-beam attenuation coefficients.*

Build-Up of Secondary Radiation

When a beam of electromagnetic radiation penetrates an absorber, the secondary electron radiation builds up to a maximum at a distance below the surface that is roughly equal to the greatest range of the secondary electrons, and then falls as the primary beam is attenuated. The reason for the build-up is readily seen. Immediately below the surface a small volume of the absorber contains the electron tracks of secondary electrons generated in the volume and the tracks of electrons generated outside the volume but scattered into it (Fig. 3.11). The volume thus receives scattered electrons from all directions but the direction of the surface. As the distance of the volume element from the surface is increased the volume of absorber from which it receives scattered electrons also increases, until the depth of the volume element below the surface corresponds to the greatest range of the secondary electrons. At this point it is receiving the maximum number of scattered electrons, since electrons produced at a greater distance from the volume element will not reach it. At greater depths the number of secondary electrons falls as the primary beam of radiation is attenuated. Scattered electromagnetic radiation will build up in a similar manner but in general its effect will be small compared to that of the secondary electrons.

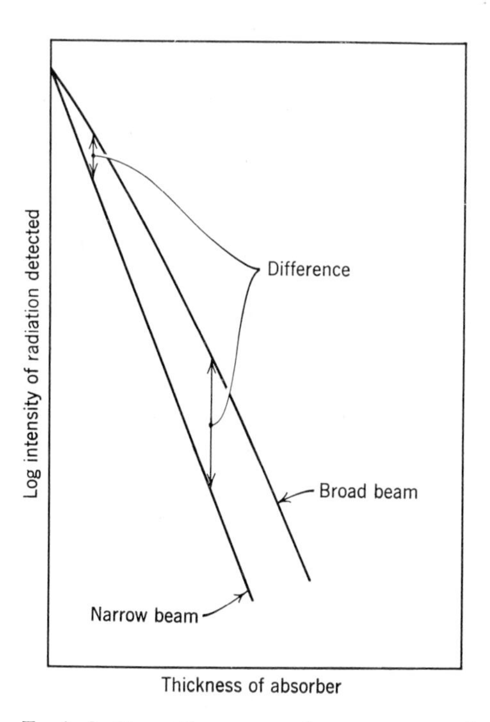

FIGURE 3.10 *Typical attenuation curves for monoenergetic γ-radiation determined under broad-beam and narrow-beam conditions.*

If the greatest range of the secondary electrons is small the build-up effect can be neglected, though it may be quite large with high-energy radiation. Typical curves relating the energy absorbed per unit volume with the depth (*depth-dose curves*) are shown in Fig. 3.12 for radiation of different energies absorbed in water. The vertical axis gives the depth dose as a percentage of the maximum dose.

Part of the scattered electromagnetic radiation and secondary electrons will be directed back across the surface and will increase the measured intensity at a point P (Fig. 3.11), in front of the surface, to a greater value than it would have had in the absence of the absorber. The amount of this *backscattered radiation* depends upon the energy of the incident radiation, the nature of the absorbing material, and the area of the surface irradiated. Scattered electromagnetic radiation will generally be the most effective part of the backscattered radiation because of its greater range, and the term backscatter normally refers to this alone, the secondary electron contribution being neglected.

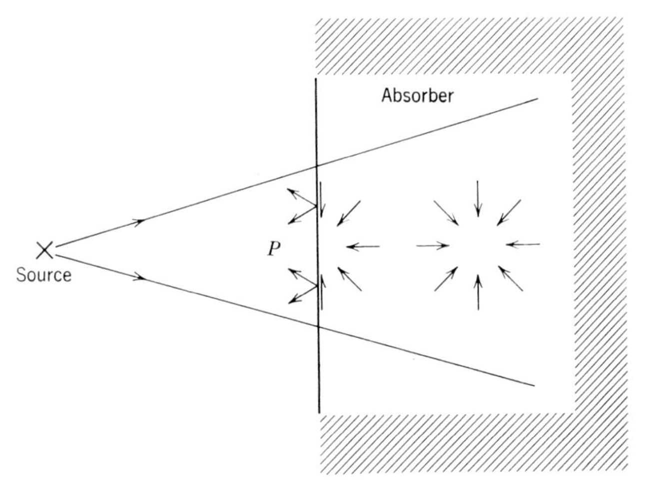

FIGURE 3.11 *Build-up of secondary electrons in an absorber.*

Energy Absorption from Monoenergetic Radiation

The total absorption coefficient (μ) relates to the attenuation of a narrow beam of monoenergetic radiation passing through an absorber. It is not directly a measure of the energy transferred to the absorbing material — the quantity that is primarily of interest in radiation chemistry — since part of the incident photon energy may be diverted from the primary beam as scattered or secondary radiation.

Processes which lead to photon scattering or to secondary electromagnetic radiation are:

(i) secondary x-ray (fluorescent radiation) emission from an atom that has lost an electron by the photoelectric process,
(ii) radiation scattering as a result of Compton interaction,

(iii) formation of annihilation radiation by the combination of a positron produced by pair-production and an electron,
(iv) coherent scattering,
(v) bremsstrahlung emission by high-energy secondary electrons (cf. ref. 17, Table 5).

For moderate photon energies (0.1 to 5 Mev) and low-Z materials only Compton scattering (ii) is important. At lower energies and for high-Z

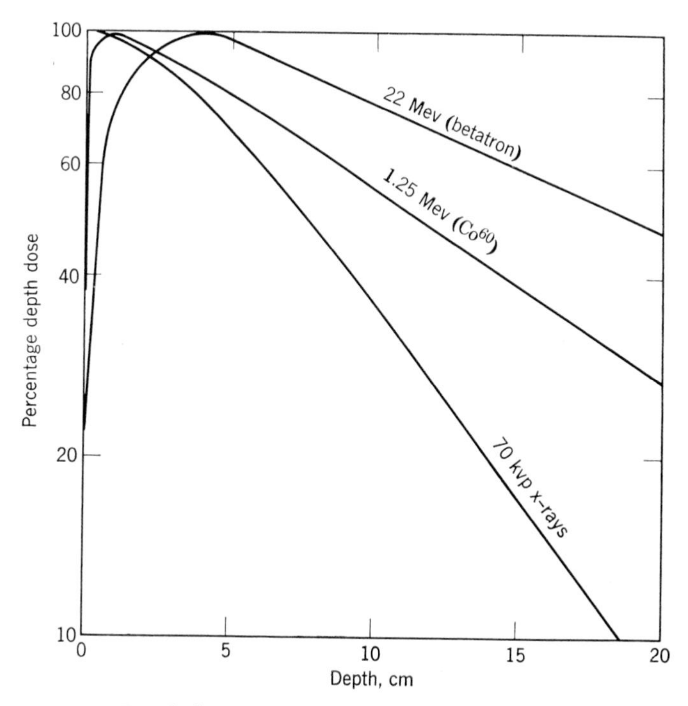

FIGURE 3.12 *Depth-dose curves for electromagnetic radiation in water. (Distance between radiation source and water surface, 80 cm; area of beam at surface of water, 100 cm².)*

materials processes (i) and (iv) may be significant, and at high energies processes (iii) and (v) become important. The energy actually absorbed is equal to the energy lost from the primary beam (found via the total absorption coefficient) less the energy scattered by the five processes listed above; it is assumed that scattered and secondary electromagnetic radiation escape from the absorbing material without reacting further, which may often be true for small samples but is less likely to be true for large ones.

The energy absorbed may be equated with the energy transferred to the secondary electrons if these do not subsequently lose energy by bremsstrahlung emission (v) and if they remain within the absorbing material. However, if the range of the secondary electrons is greater than the dimensions of the sample, an appreciable number will escape and carry off part of the energy that would otherwise have been absorbed. This can be alleviated by surrounding the sample with similar material to a distance roughly equal to the greatest range of the secondary electrons. Under these conditions, as many electrons enter the sample from the surrounding material as escape from it, and the sample is said to be in a state of *electronic equilibrium.*

A series of absorption coefficients[4] relate to the scattered radiation and the energy transferred to the secondary electrons (equating this with the energy absorbed, but bearing in mind the two qualifying conditions given in the last paragraph), these are the *scatter* (absorption) *coefficients,* identified by the subscript s, and the *true,* or *energy, absorption coefficients* identified by the subscript a. These subscripts are placed *after*[5] the symbol for the appropriate absorption coefficient, e.g., μ_s, μ_a, etc. (cf. Table 3.3).

[4] The term absorption coefficient is widely used; however, with the exception of the true or energy absorption coefficient, it does not refer to the energy absorbed but rather to the attenuation or scattering of the incident radiation. There appear to be no standardized names for the various coefficients and a number of terms that have the same meaning are gathered below; the groups refer to the total, scatter, and energy coefficients respectively.

Total absorption coefficient; absorption coefficient; attenuation coefficient; (atomic or electronic) total cross section (i.e., the fraction of the incident radiation energy lost by the transmitted primary beam, and the fraction of the incident photons transmitted with change of energy or direction).

Scatter absorption coefficient; scatter coefficient; (atomic or electronic) scattering cross section (i.e., the fraction of the incident radiation energy scattered).

True absorption coefficient; real absorption coefficient; energy absorption coefficient; energy transfer coefficient (19); (atomic or electronic) absorption cross section (i.e., the fraction of the incident radiation energy transferred to secondary electrons).

When necessary these terms can all be qualified further to show the units involved (as in linear, mass, atomic, and electronic coefficients) and to identify the interaction process — photoelectric, Compton, etc. (cf. Table 3.3).

[5] It is particularly important to put the subscript a in the right position, that is after the symbol (as in μ_a), since the subscript a before the symbol (e.g., ${}_a\mu$) means the *atomic* absorption coefficient.

The symbols μ_{en} and ${}_m\mu_{en}$ are also used to represent the total linear and total mass energy absorption coefficients respectively (cf. 19). We have preferred to use the symbols μ_a and μ_a/ρ for these quantities as being rather more systematic and better suited to an introductory text.

TABLE 3.3 *Absorption Coefficients*

Coefficient	Linear	Mass	Atomic	Electronic
Units	cm^{-1}	cm^2/g	cm^2/atom	cm^2/electron
Units in which absorber thickness is measured	cm	g/cm^2	atoms/cm^2	electrons/cm^2
Total absorption coefficient	μ	μ/ρ	$_a\mu$	$_e\mu$
scatter component	μ_s	μ_s/ρ	$_a\mu_s$	$_e\mu_s$
energy absorption component	μ_a	μ_a/ρ	$_a\mu_a$	$_e\mu_a$
Compton absorption coefficient	σ	σ/ρ	$_a\sigma$	$_e\sigma$
scatter component	σ_s	σ_s/ρ	$_a\sigma_s$	$_e\sigma_s$
energy absorption component	σ_a	σ_a/ρ	$_a\sigma_a$	$_e\sigma_a$
Photoelectric absorption coefficient*	τ	τ/ρ	$_a\tau$	$_e\tau$
Pair-production coefficient*	κ	κ/ρ	$_a\kappa$	$_e\kappa$

N.B. considering only the three main absorption processes

$$\mu = \tau + \sigma + \kappa$$
$$= \mu_s + \mu_a$$
$$\mu_s = \tau_s + \sigma_s + \kappa_s$$
$$\mu_a = \tau_a + \sigma_a + \kappa_a$$

* Scatter and energy absorption components are represented as shown for the Compton absorption coefficient.

The linear scatter (μ_s) and linear energy (μ_a) absorption coefficients are defined in a similar manner to the total linear absorption coefficient, that is, by

$$dI_s = -I'\mu_s\,dx \tag{3.35}$$

and

$$dI_a = -I'\mu_a\,dx \tag{3.36}$$

where dI_s is the reduction in intensity due to scattering and dI_a the reduction due to energy absorption when radiation with intensity I' passes through a very small thickness dx of absorber. Since these two processes account for all the energy lost from the incident radiation it is clear that the total reduction in intensity (dI), which is given by

$$dI = -I'\mu\,dx \tag{3.12}$$

is also given by

$$dI = dI_s + dI_a \tag{3.37}$$

and that

$$\mu = \mu_s + \mu_a \tag{3.38}$$

The quantity with which we are mainly concerned is the energy absorbed by a sample placed in a beam of radiation of known intensity. This can be derived as follows: Consider an absorber made up of a large number of very thin layers, perpendicular to the direction of the incident radiation and each dx thick. Then the energy absorbed by any one layer is a function of the reduction in intensity as the radiation passes through it as given by Eq. 3.36; I' is now the radiation intensity at the position occupied by the layer. However the intensity at any depth in the absorber is given by Eq. 3.13, i.e.,

$$I' = I_i e^{-\mu x} \tag{3.13}$$

where I_i is the radiation intensity at the surface. Thus, at any depth x, dI_a is given by

$$dI_a = -I_i \mu_a e^{-\mu x}\, dx \tag{3.39}$$

The total reduction in intensity due to energy absorption as the radiation passes through the entire thickness of absorber, x cm, is found by integrating Eq. 3.39,

$$I_a = \int_0^x -I_i \mu_a e^{-\mu x}\, dx \tag{3.40}$$

$$= I_i \mu_a/\mu (1 - e^{-\mu x}) \text{ ergs/cm}^2 \text{ sec} \tag{3.41}$$

The reduction in intensity due to energy scattered is found in a similar manner to be

$$I_s = I_i \mu_s/\mu (1 - e^{-\mu x}) \text{ ergs/cm}^2 \text{ sec} \tag{3.42}$$

The total reduction in intensity of the radiation beam as it passes through the absorber, due to both scattering and energy absorption, can be found by adding Eqs. 3.41 and 3.42

$$I_a + I_s = I_i(1 - e^{-\mu x}) \text{ ergs/cm}^2 \text{ sec} \tag{3.43a}$$

(since $\mu = \mu_a + \mu_s$) or by subtracting the intensity of the transmitted radiation (from Eq. 3.13) from the incident radiation intensity

$$I_i - I = I_i(1 - e^{-\mu x}) \text{ ergs/cm}^2 \text{ sec} \tag{3.43b}$$

The energy lost from the beam as it passes through the absorber is found by integrating Eq. 3.43 with respect to time, i.e.,

$$E_{\text{lost}} = E_i(1 - e^{-\mu x}) \text{ ergs/cm}^2 \tag{3.44}$$

where E_i is the energy incident upon the absorber in units of ergs/cm^2. In the same way the energy absorbed (E_a) can be derived from Eq. 3.41

$$E_a = E_i \mu_a/\mu (1 - e^{-\mu x}) \text{ ergs/cm}^2 \tag{3.45}$$

A simplified form of Eq. 3.45 can be used if μx is small, i.e., if the radiation is not appreciably attenuated by passage through a thickness x of the stopping material. Under these conditions

$$1 - e^{-\mu x} \sim \mu x$$

and Eq. 3.45 becomes

$$E_a = E_i \mu_a x \text{ ergs/cm}^2 \tag{3.46}$$

For some purposes it is convenient to express this in terms of the mass energy absorption coefficient, μ_a/ρ, when

$$E_a(\text{ergs/g}) = E_i(\text{ergs/cm}^2)\mu_a/\rho \tag{3.47}$$

Values for the energy absorbed from a beam of radiation calculated using both Eq. 3.45 and Eq. 3.46 are compared in Table 3.4. As the thickness of absorber is increased the approximate value given by Eq. 3.46 deviates from the true value to an increasing extent. In using these equations it is assumed that none of the energy scattered is subsequently absorbed by the sample.

TABLE 3.4 *Absorbed Energy Calculations*

Calculations of the energy absorbed from 1.25 Mev (Co^{60}) γ-rays when the energy incident upon the absorber (water) is 100 ergs/cm². For 1.25 Mev γ-rays in water $\mu = 0.064$ cm^{-1} and $\mu_a = 0.03$ cm^{-1}.

Thickness of absorber (water) (cm)	Total energy lost from beam (Eq. 3.44) (ergs/cm²)	Energy absorbed by water (ergs/cm²)	
		(Eq. 3.45)	(Eq. 3.46)
1	6.2	2.9	3
2	12	5.6	6
3	17.5	8.2	9
5	27	13	15
10	47	22	30
20	72	34	60

Equations 3.46 and 3.47 are only true for thin absorbers which do not attenuate the radiation appreciably. However they may be used to find the ratio of the energies absorbed by two different stopping materials, exposed to the same beam of radiation, over a much wider range of thicknesses since the errors in the numerator and denominator largely nullify each other. Thus

$$\frac{(E_a)_A}{(E_a)_B} = \frac{E_i(\mu_a/\rho)_A}{E_i(\mu_a/\rho)_B} = \frac{(\mu_a/\rho)_A}{(\mu_a/\rho)_B} \tag{3.48}$$

The total energy absorption coefficient μ_a, like the total absorption coefficient μ, is the sum of three partial coefficients relating to the three major absorption processes:

$$\mu_a = \tau_a + \sigma_a + \kappa_a \tag{3.49}$$

For the photoelectric process

$$\tau_a = \tau \frac{E_0 - fE_s}{E_0} \tag{3.50}$$

where f is the probability that the binding energy E_s of the electron ejected from the atom will be re-emitted as a secondary x-ray photon. If the energy of the incident photon, E_0, is much greater than the binding energy, then for all practical purposes $\tau_a = \tau$. The derivation of the Compton electronic energy absorption coefficient ${}_e\sigma_a$ has already been given in the description of the Compton effect. It is related to the linear coefficient by

$$\sigma_a = {}_e\sigma_a \frac{\rho N_0 Z}{A} \tag{3.51}$$

The pair-production linear energy absorption coefficient is

$$\kappa_a = \kappa \frac{E_0 - 2m_0c^2}{E_0} \tag{3.52}$$

where $2m_0c^2$ (=1.02 Mev) is that part of the absorbed energy which reappears as annihilation radiation.

Values of the total energy absorption coefficient for a number of materials and photon energies are given by Fano (17), Berger (19), and in the 1959 report of the ICRU (20). The values are corrected for energy loss through bremsstrahlung production by secondary electrons.

For low-Z materials there is a range of energies for which the only significant absorption process is the Compton effect; for water this range is about 0.1 Mev to 4 Mev (Fig. 3.6). In this region

$$\mu = \sigma \tag{3.53}$$

and

$$\mu_a = \sigma_a \tag{3.54}$$

The absorption of cobalt-60 and caesium-137 γ-rays by aqueous, biological, and most organic systems comes in this region.

Attenuation of X-Rays

In the preceding sections, factors governing the absorption of monoenergetic electromagnetic radiation have been described. In practice, radiation made up of photons with a wide range of energies may be encountered, as in the case of an x-ray beam. The absorption of such polyenergetic radiation can be treated in a manner similar to the absorption of monoenergetic radiation by considering it as a number of superimposed monoenergetic beams, whose radiation penetrates independently. Calculation of the absorption characteristics of a polyenergetic beam involves integration over the range of energies represented in the beam and requires a knowledge of the number of photons of each energy present, i.e., of the energy spectrum of the beam.

Low-energy photons tend to have higher absorption coefficients than those of higher energies and will be removed from the primary beam faster than the high-energy components. Thus as the beam penetrates to greater depths the energy spectrum of the attenuated primary beam changes, the proportion of low-energy photons falling (neglecting any build-up of low-energy scattered radiation). At the same time the average absorption coefficient for the beam decreases. Consequently it is not possible to calculate a single average absorption coefficient for an x-ray beam at all depths in an absorber, but only an average coefficient applicable to the energy spectrum as it exists at a particular point, and which will only be effective over a limited range of thicknesses. This is shown in Fig. 2.11 by the increase in the half-value layer for an x-ray beam as the beam penetrates further through the absorber.

The energy absorbed from an x-ray beam can be calculated in a similar manner to the energy absorption from a beam of monoenergetic γ-rays by using, for example

$$E_a = \int_{E_m}^{E_0} EN_E(\mu_a)_E x \, dx \tag{3.55}$$

(based on Eq. 3.46) where N_E is the number of photons of energy E incident upon the absorber, $(\mu_a)_E$ is the energy absorption coefficient for photons of energy E, x is the thickness of the absorber, and E_0 and E_m are the highest and lowest photon energies present in the x-ray beam respectively. The integration can be solved graphically.

IONIZATION AND EXCITATION PRODUCED BY RADIATION

The energy lost when a moving charged particle is slowed down in matter gives rise to a trail of excited and ionized atoms and molecules in the path of the particle. Excited states are produced when bound electrons in atoms and molecules of the stopping material gain energy and are raised to higher energy levels, and ions when the energy gained is sufficient, and the transient excited states produced such, that electrons are expelled. Electromagnetic radiation produces a similar result since the energy absorbed is transferred to electrons and positrons and then dissipated along the paths of these particles. The over-all result of the absorption of any type of ionizing radiation by matter is thus the formation of tracks of excited and ionized species. These species will, in general,[6] be the same in a particular material regardless of the type or energy of the radiation responsible. All ionizing radiation will, therefore, give rise to qualitatively similar chemical effects. However, radiation of different types and energy will lose energy in matter at different rates, and consequently will form tracks that may be densely or sparsely populated with the active species. The differences observed in the chemical effect of different radiations — differences in the quantities and proportions of the chemical products — stem from the different density of active species in the particle tracks. Expressions which reflect this changing density, such as specific ionization and linear energy transfer, are therefore useful in evaluating the over-all chemical effect. Track effects of this sort are more important in the case of liquids, where the active species are hindered from moving apart by the proximity of other molecules, than in gases, where they can move apart with relative ease. In gases the different types of radiation do not give the markedly different yields of products that they may in liquid systems.

Electrons ejected as a consequence of the ionization produced by radiation may themselves be sufficiently energetic to produce further ionization and excitation. If the energy of these secondary electrons is relatively small, less than about 100 ev, their range in liquid or solid materials will be short and any secondary ionizations that they produce will be situated close to the original ionization, giving a small cluster or spur[7] of excited and ionized species. Some of the secondary electrons will have enough energy to travel further from the site of the original ionization and will form tracks of their own, branching off from the primary track. Such electrons are known as δ-rays (Fig. 3.13); their tracks will be similar to those of other electrons with the same energy. Lea (21) has calculated that about one half of the total number of ionizations produced by a primary particle, whether electron, proton, or α-particle, are to be found in the tracks of δ-rays with energy exceeding 100 ev. The

[6] The relative proportions of the various excited and ionized states produced may vary with the type and energy of the radiation. However, for the purposes of radiation chemistry, these differences are generally ignored.

[7] We will use the term spur rather than the alternative, cluster, when referring to these small groups of excited and ionized species.

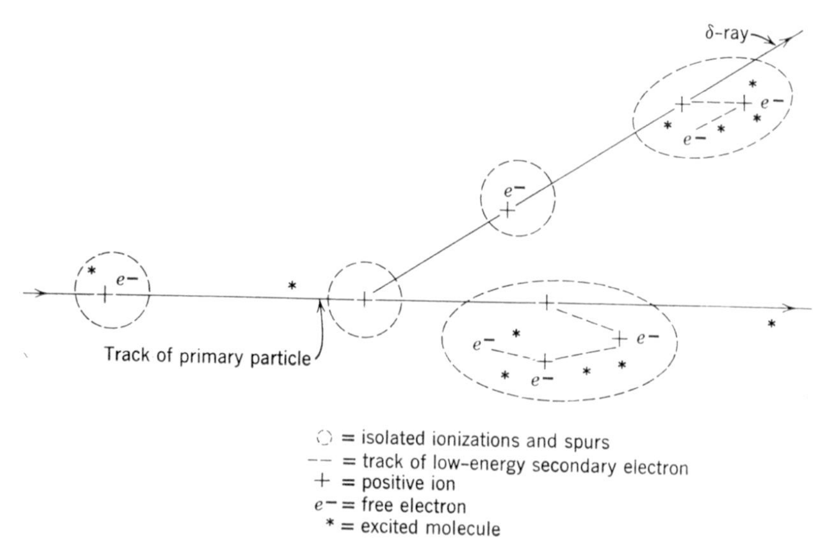

FIGURE 3.13 *Distribution of ions and excited molecules in the track of a fast electron (not to scale).*

remaining ionization events are distributed along the primary track as isolated single ionizations or in small spurs. Wilson (22), using cloud-chamber photographs, counted the ion pairs formed along the track of fast electrons in water vapor and found the following distribution of ion pairs in the spurs

Number of ion pairs in the spur:	1	2	3	4	over 4	Total
Frequency of spurs of each size:	0.44	0.22	0.12	0.10	0.12	1.00

The average spur contains 2-3 ion pairs and corresponds to an energy loss of about 100 ev. The spurs will also contain excited species (Fig. 3.13).

With densely ionizing radiation (e.g., α-particles) the spurs overlap and form a column of ions and excited species about the track (so-called *columnar ionization*); less densely ionizing radiation gives spurs at intervals along the track (Fig. 3.14). For fast particles, such as the secondary electrons formed when energetic γ-rays are absorbed in water and organic liquids, Samuel and Magee (23) have calculated that the spurs occur at intervals of about 10^4 Å and that they have an initial diameter of about 20 Å.

Once the electrons have slowed down to thermal energies they will probably either neutralize a positive ion directly or add to a neutral molecule to form a negative ion, which subsequently neutralizes a positive ion.

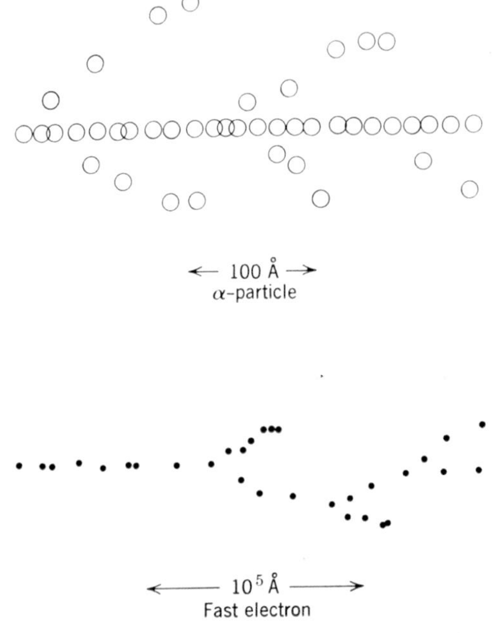

FIGURE 3.14 *Distribution of spurs in particle tracks. The spurs will have a diameter of the order of 20 Å. (Not to scale.)*

Specific Ionization

An indication of the linear rate of energy loss by a charged particle and the density of ionization in the particle track is given by the *specific ionization*, the total number of ion pairs produced in a gas per unit length of track. The specific ionization includes both ions produced in the primary particle track and those produced by δ-rays. In Fig. 3.15 the specific ionization for protons and α-particles are plotted as a function of the distance from the end of the particle track (*Bragg curve*). The most intense ionization is produced near the end of the track where the particle velocity is low, though the ion density falls when the velocity becomes low enough for the particle to capture electrons.

The energy loss is related to the specific ionization by the important quantity W, the mean energy loss per ion pair formed

$$\text{specific ionization} = \frac{dE/dx}{W} \tag{3.56}$$

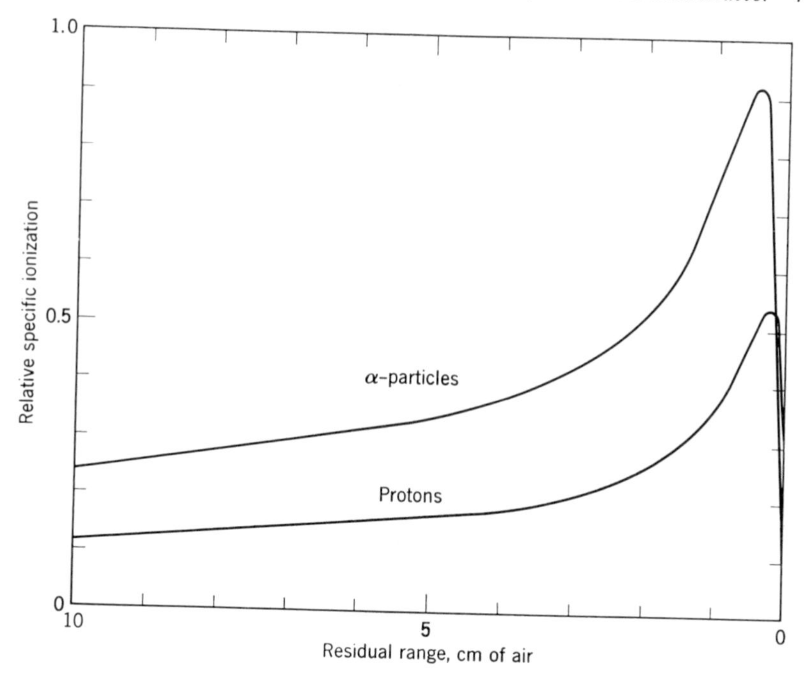

FIGURE 3.15 *Bragg curves for protons and α-particles.*

where dE/dx is the specific energy loss or stopping power. W is the total energy consumed per ion pair formed; that is, the energy to eject an electron plus the energy, per ion pair, used in producing excited molecules. Some experimentally determined values of W for gases are given in Table 3.5; the International Commission on Radiological Units and Measurements has suggested that W_{air} be taken as 34.0 ev for electromagnetic radiation with quantum energies greater than 20 kev (20).

Values of W are very nearly independent of the energy of the radiation and are practically the same for all types of radiation; electromagnetic radiation and electrons give the same values.

Linear Energy Transfer

Linear energy transfer was defined in Chapter 2 as the linear-rate of loss of energy (locally absorbed) by an ionizing particle traversing a material medium (20), and a rough average value calculated by dividing

TABLE 3.5 *Experimental Values of W for Gases*

Gas	*W* (ev/ion pair)	
	Electrons (ref. 24)	α-Particles (ref. 25)
Air	34.0*	35.1
Helium	42.3	44
Argon	26.4	26.4
Hydrogen	36.3	36.5
Nitrogen	34.9	36.4
Oxygen	30.8	32.4
Carbon Dioxide	32.8	34.4
Methane	27.3	29.3
Ethane	24.5	26.6
Ethylene	26.1	28.0
Acetylene	25.7	27.5

* Ref. 20.

the total energy of a particle by its path length. Several factors contribute to the roughness of this average value. In the first place, the rate of energy loss by a particle changes as it is slowed down, as is shown by the Bragg curves (Fig. 3.15), and the LET will vary at different positions along the track. Secondly, energy lost by the primary particle in a particular section of the track is not necessarily absorbed locally but may be transferred in part to δ-rays or to secondary electromagnetic radiation. γ- and x-rays transfer all their energy to the medium through secondary electrons having a wide range of energies and LET.

In practice some sort of mean value may be derived for the LET (26, 27, 28, 29) or the complete distribution of LET values calculated for particles of all energies present (28, 29). In either case the nature of the calculations and the assumptions made depend upon the author, so that it is essential to use care when comparing LET values from different sources. Some mean LET values in liquid water are presented in Table 3.6; average values were determined as described in the previous paragraph. Burch used a different method of calculating the mean LET to the other authors listed and his values are quite different. They can, however, be recalculated in the more usual manner and are then similar to those of the other workers (30).

TABLE 3.6 *Mean LET Values in Water*

Radiation	Mean LET (kev per micron)			
	Average LET	Gray (26)	Cormack and Johns (27)	Burch (28)
25 Mvp betatron x-rays	—	0.28	0.202	18.4
2 Mev electrons	0.21	—	—	18.6
Co^{60} γ-rays (1.25 Mev)	—	0.36	0.25	19.6
200 kvp x-rays	—	3.25	1.79	25.8
tritium β-particles (0.018 Mev)	3.2	—	—	30.1
Po^{210} α-particles (5.3 Mev)	136	158	—	84.5
1 Mev α-particles	189	—	—	128.4

For charged particle radiation the LET at any given energy can be calculated using the stopping power equations, Eq. 3.3 for electrons and Eq. 3.8 for heavy charged particles, if the mean excitation potential for the stopping material is known.

Regardless of the manner in which the LET is derived, the values increase in the order shown below, assuming the protons and heavier particles to have about the same energy,

LET increases ↓

- γ-rays, high-energy electrons
- low-energy x-rays, β-particles
- protons
- deuterons
- α-particles
- heavy ions (ionized N, O, etc.)
- fission fragments from nuclear reactions

The increase in LET for electrons in water as the electron energy decreases is shown in Fig. 3.16 (28, 31). The LET plotted here is the average energy dissipated per unit track length by electrons having the energy shown, and not the energy loss averaged over the entire path length; energy transfers giving δ-rays with more than 100 ev were not included as part of the energy locally dissipated. Above 1 Mev the LET is practically constant, and little difference in biological or chemical effect would be expected of radiations giving secondary electrons with energies in this range.

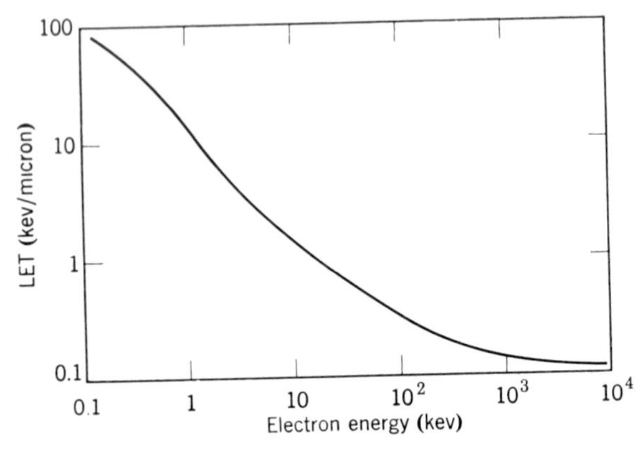

FIGURE 3.16 *Average linear energy transfer (LET) for electrons in water.*

REFERENCES

The topics included in this section are discussed more fully in ref. 1, in *Radiation Dosimetry*, (ed. G. J. Hine and G. L. Brownell), Academic Press Inc., New York, 1956, and by G. N. Whyte, *Principles of Radiation Dosimetry*, John Wiley and Sons, New York, 1959.

1. H. A. Bethe and J. Ashkin in *Experimental Nuclear Physics*, (ed. E. Segrè), Vol. 1, John Wiley and Sons, New York, 1953, pp. 166, *et seq.*
2. W. Heitler, *Quantum Theory of Radiation*, 3rd Ed., Oxford University Press, 1954.
3. H. A. Bethe, *Handbuch der Physik*, Julius Springer, Berlin, Vol. 24, 1933, p. 273; *Ann. Physik*, **5**, 325 (1930) ; *Z. Physik*, **76**, 293 (1932).
4. L. Katz and A. S. Penfold, *Rev. Mod. Phys.*, **24**, 28 (1952).
5. A. T. Nelms, *Energy Loss and Range of Electrons and Positrons, Nat. Bur. St. (U.S.), Circ.* 577 (1956).
6. M. S. Livingston and H. A. Bethe, *Rev. Mod. Phys.*, **9**, 245 (1937).
7. W. A. Aron, B. G. Hoffman, and F. C. Williams, *Range-Energy Curves*, AECU 663 (1951).
8. *American Institute of Physics Handbook*, (ed. D. E. Gray), McGraw-Hill, New York, 1957. Section 8c.
9. *Measurement of Absorbed Dose of Neutrons, and of Mixtures of Neutrons and Gamma Rays, Nat. Bur. St. (U.S.), Handbook* 75 (1961).
10. G. N. Whyte, *Principles of Radiation Dosimetry*, John Wiley and Sons, New York, 1959.
11. O. Klein and Y. Nishina, *Z. Physik*, **52**, 853 (1929).
12. A. T. Nelms, *Graphs of the Compton Energy-Angle Relationship and the Klein-Nishina Formula from 10 kev to 500 Mev, Nat. Bur. St. (U.S.), Circ.* 542 (1953).
13. R. Montalbetti, L. Katz, and J. Goldemberg, *Phys. Rev.*, **91**, 659 (1953).
14. K. Strauch, *Ann. Rev. Nucl. Sci.*, **2**, 105 (1953).

15. G. W. Grodstein, *X-ray Attenuation, Coefficients from 10 kev to 100 Mev, Nat. Bur. St. (U.S.), Circ.* 583 (1957).
16. R. T. McGinnies, *X-ray Attenuation Coefficients from 10 kev to 100 Mev, Supplement to Nat. Bur. Std. (U.S.), Circ.* 583 (1959).
17. U. Fano, *Nucleonics,* **11,** (Aug.), 8, (Sept.), 55 (1953).
18. H. Goldstein and J. E. Wilkins, *USAEC Report NYO-3075* (1954).
19. R. T. Berger, *Radiation Res.,* **15,** 1 (1961).
20. *Report of the International Commission on Radiological Units and Measurements (ICRU),* 1959, *Nat. Bur. St. (U.S.), Handbook* 78 (1961).
21. D. E. Lea, *Actions of Radiations on Living Cells,* Cambridge University Press, Cambridge, 1946, p. 27.
22. C. T. R. Wilson, *Proc. Roy. Soc. (London), Ser. A,* **104,** 192 (1923).
23. A. H. Samuel and J. L. Magee, *J. Chem. Phys.,* **21,** 1080 (1953).
24. R. L. Platzman, *Intern. J. Appl. Radiation Isotopes,* **10,** 116 (1961).
25. J. Weiss and W. Bernstein, *Radiation Res.,* **6,** 603 (1957).
26. L. H. Gray, *Brit. J. Radiol. Suppl. 1,* **7** (1947).
27. D. V. Cormack and H. E. Johns, *Brit. J. Radiol.,* **25,** 369 (1952).
28. P. R. J. Burch, *Brit. J. Radiol.,* **30,** 524 (1957).
29. H. E. Johns in *Radiation Dosimetry,* (ed. G. J. Hine and G. L. Brownell), Academic Press, Inc., New York, 1956. Chapter 12.
30. D. V. Cormack, personal communication.
31. P. R. J. Burch, *Radiation Res.,* **6,** 289 (1957).

CHAPTER 4

Radiation Dosimetry

Quantitative studies in radiation chemistry require a knowledge of the amount of energy absorbed from the radiation; the determination of this quantity constitutes radiation dosimetry. Before describing the ways in which this measurement can be made it is necessary to introduce a number of terms and units peculiar to this field. Where possible these follow the 1959 recommendations of the International Commission on Radiological Units and Measurements (ICRU)(1).

Dosimetric Terms and Units

The *absorbed dose* of *any* ionizing radiation is the energy imparted to matter by ionizing particles per unit mass of irradiated material at the place of interest. The unit of absorbed dose is the *rad*; 1 rad is 100 ergs per gram. It is also common practice in radiation chemistry to give the absorbed dose in units of *electron volts per gram* or *electron volts per cubic centimeter*, though these units are not included in the recommendations of the

1959 commission;[1] 1 rad is equal to 6.24×10^{13} ev/g or $6.24 \times 10^{13} \times \rho$ ev/cm^3, where ρ(g/cm^3) is the density of the material. The absorbed dose is generally the quantity sought when making dosimetric measurements, and is a direct measure of the energy transferred to the irradiated material. It is determined by the composition of the absorbing material as well as by the radiation field.

The *integral absorbed dose* in a certain region is the energy imparted to matter by ionizing particles in that region. The unit of integral absorbed dose is the *gram rad;* 1 gram rad is equal to 100 ergs, or 6.24×10^{13} ev.

The *absorbed dose rate* is the absorbed dose per unit time, and has the units *rads per unit time* (e.g., rads per minute) or electron volts per gram, or per cm^3, per unit time.

The *exposure dose of x- or γ-radiation* at a certain place is a measure of the radiation that is based upon its ability to produce ionization. The unit of exposure dose of x- or γ-radiation is the *roentgen* (symbol r). One roentgen is an exposure dose of x- or γ-radiation such that the associated corpuscular emission per 0.001293 g of air produces, in air, ions carrying 1 electrostatic unit of quantity of electricity of either[2] sign. (0.001293 g is the weight of 1 cm^3 of dry air at 0°C and 760 mm of mercury pressure, i.e., at NTP.) Though the roentgen as defined (1) applies only to x- and γ-radiation, Lea (2) has suggested that it may be applied to charged-particle radiation by describing 1 roentgen of this radiation as being that exposure dose which in 0.001293 g of dry air liberates ions carrying 1 e.s.u. of charge of either sign.

The *exposure dose rate* is the exposure dose per unit time, and is expressed in *roentgens per unit time.*

The *intensity of radiation* (radiant energy flux density) at a given place is the energy per unit time entering a small sphere centered at that place per unit cross-sectional area of the sphere. The unit of intensity of radiation may be *ergs per square centimeter second* (ergs/cm^2 sec), or *watts per square centimeter.* The radiation intensity has also been defined as the energy per unit time crossing a unit area perpendicular to the direction

[1] There is a clear relationship between the absorbed dose in terms of ev/g or ev/cm^3 and the chemical yield in terms of the G value, the number of molecules undergoing change per 100 ev of energy absorbed. However the rad appears to be in general use among medical-physicists, who are responsible for much of the basic work in the field of radiation dosimetry, and it also has the advantage of being a larger unit than ev/g or ev/cm^3. For materials of low atomic number, the absorbed dose in rads will often have roughly the same numerical value as the exposure dose in roentgens, which can be determined quite readily by means of ionization measurements.

[2] Either negative ions or positive ions, but not both together.

of propagation of the radiation; the units are, as above, ergs/cm^2 sec. The (spherical) radiation intensity is the product of the number of particles or photons entering the unit sphere per unit time and their energy. The quantity of radiation energy entering the unit sphere, or the energy flux, is the time integral of the intensity and has the units ergs per square centimeter.

The *flux* (flux density) of particles or photons at a point is the number of particles or photons entering a sphere of unit cross-sectional area at that point in unit time. The units of flux are *particles* (or *photons*) *per square centimeter second.*

Mass stopping power is the loss of energy per unit mass per unit area by an ionizing particle traversing a material medium. Mass stopping power may be conveniently expressed in *kilo electron volts per milligram/square centimeter* (kev cm^2/mg).

The indefinite term "dose" is used in general statements which apply equally to the absorbed dose and the exposure dose; apart from this the more specific terms ought always to be used.

Techniques for measuring ionizing radiation can be divided into absolute and secondary methods. Absolute methods involve direct determination of the radiation intensity or dose from physical measurements of, for example, the ionization produced in a gas, the energy absorbed (by calorimetry), or the charge carried by a beam of charged particles of known energy. The absolute methods are often not suited to routine use and, in practice, convenient secondary dosimeters are used, whose response to radiation is known from comparison with an absolute dosimeter. Thimble ionization chambers and chemical dosimeters are two examples of secondary dosimeters.

IONIZATION MEASUREMENTS (ELECTROMAGNETIC RADIATION)

Measurements of the ionization produced in a gas by radiation have been used for the purposes of dosimetry since the discovery of x-rays and radioactivity. Such measurements are still the favored means of dosimetry when x- and γ-rays are used for medical purposes.

Ionization is measured by means of an ionization chamber, which may be either an absolute or a secondary instrument. Basically, an ionization chamber consists of two electrodes separated by a gas-filled space, in which the incident radiation produces ionization. A potential is applied to the electrodes to attract the ions to them, and the resulting current, or the discharge of the electrodes, is measured by some appropriate means. The quantity measured in this way is an exposure dose, from which we can calculate the absorbed dose by knowing the composition of the medium and the energy, or energy spectrum, of the radiation.

Standard Free-Air Chamber

For absolute ionization measurements a free-air chamber, represented by Fig. 4.1, is used. The photon beam (generally an x-ray beam) enters the air-filled chamber through a diaphragm, which defines the cross section of the beam inside the chamber, and then passes between the parallel-plate electrodes. The lower plate consists of a collecting section, in the center, and guard plates on either side to define the (shaded) *sensitive volume* — the volume of air irradiated by the beam for which the ionization will be measured. All ions of the appropriate sign (negative in Fig. 4.1) produced in the *collecting volume*, i.e., between the verticals through A and B, will be attracted to the collecting electrode. Some of the ions produced in this volume may arise from secondary electrons produced outside of the sensitive volume. However, these will be compensated for by electrons which are scattered from the sensitive volume outside the collecting volume. To ensure that this electronic equilibrium is set up the distance between the walls of the chamber and the nearest edge of the sensitive volume must be more than the greatest range of the secondary electrons. The distance between the x-ray beam and the elec-

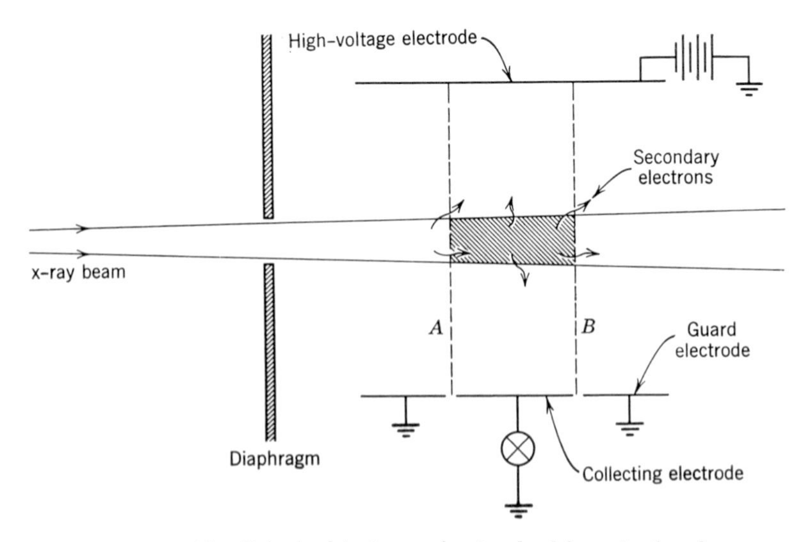

FIGURE 4.1 *Principal features of a standard free-air chamber.*

trodes must also be greater than this range, so that the secondary electrons are not collected before they have completed their tracks and produced their full complement of ions. If these conditions are satisfied, the charge collected (in e.s.u.), divided by the sensitive volume (cm^3), is numerically equal to the exposure dose in roentgens. After applying a number of corrections, including corrections to bring the temperature and pressure to NTP, the exposure dose should be accurate to better than 1%.

Free-air chambers are used as standards of exposure dose for x-rays in the range 10 to 300 kv. At higher energies the long range of the secondary electrons entails the use of very large chambers, or of chambers operating under pressures of several atmospheres; both of which present practical difficulties.

Thimble Ionization Chambers

An alternative to the use of air itself to produce electronic equilibrium in the air in the sensitive volume is the use of a much thinner layer of solid material with the same chemical composition as air. Such a material, whose physical properties (except density) are the same as those of air for the purposes of radiation absorption, is referred to as an *air-equivalent* material. Materials having mean atomic numbers close to that of air approximate an air-equivalent material; these include such organic polymers as Bakelite (a phenolformaldehyde resin), Lucite (polymethylmethacrylate), and nylon (adipic acid-hexamethylenediamine polyamide). Thimble ionization chambers in which a small volume of air (the sensitive volume) is surrounded by a thin shell of polymer are available in a wide variety of forms, are both rugged and portable, and offer a convenient and sensitive means of measuring the exposure dose of x- and γ-radiation.

An example of a thimble ionization chamber is the Victoreen condenser r-meter, shown in Fig. 4.2. The small air volume is enclosed by a Bakelite cap, which is made conducting on the inside by a coating of colloidal carbon, and in the center is an aluminum electrode, insulated from the cap. The instrument acts as a small condenser and before use is charged to an appropriate voltage with the device shown. When the chamber is irradiated, the charge is partly neutralized and the drop in voltage, multiplied by the capacitance of the instrument, gives a measure of the ionization produced by the radiation. The charging device is also used to measure the voltage drop, and is calibrated in roentgens; corrections are applied to the observed exposure dose for temperature and

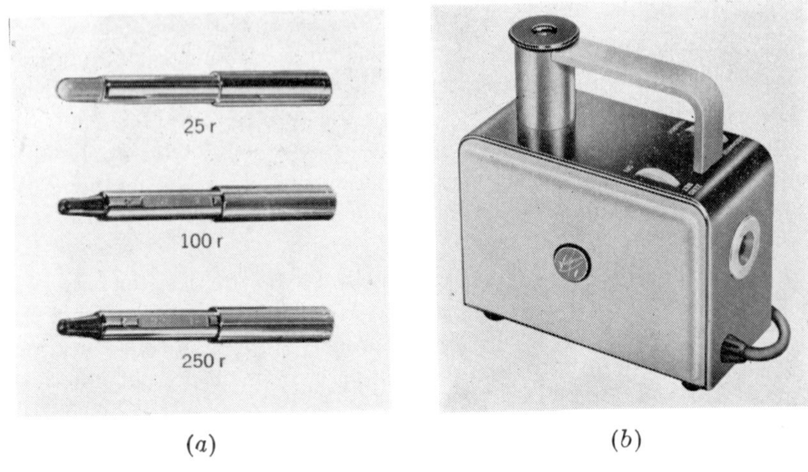

(a) (b)

FIGURE 4.2 *Victoreen condenser r-meter. (a) Ionization chambers for measuring doses up to 25 r, 100 r, and 250 r respectively (the dose which can be measured is increased as the ionization chamber — the plastic cap on the left of the instrument — is made smaller). (b) The charging and reading device. (Courtesy of Victoreen Instrument Co., Cleveland, Ohio.)*

barometric pressure, and also an instrument correction found by comparing the thimble chamber with a standard air chamber. The calibration is generally independent of energy over a considerable range of x-ray energies.

At high photon energies the thickness of the thimble chamber wall is not sufficient to ensure electronic equilibrium and the chamber must be surrounded by sufficient air-equivalent material to fulfill this condition (Table 4.1, column 2). Large thicknesses of the air-wall material will attenuate the radiation (Table 4.1, column 3), and a correction for this must be applied to obtain the exposure dose in free air at the point of interest. Up to energies of a few Mev the correction may be made by plotting the observed ionization against the thickness of the absorber surrounding the thimble chamber, using various thicknesses, and extrapolating the curve back to zero thickness. The necessity for electronic equilibrium makes it increasingly difficult to determine the exposure dose in roentgens as the energy of the x- or γ-radiation approaches very high values. For this reason 3 Mev is sometimes arbitrarily taken as the upper limit of the energy range over which the roentgen should be used (1).

Ritz and Attix (4) have described a graphite cavity ionization chamber suitable with kilocurie cobalt-60 sources which allows the absolute determination of exposure dose rates to within 2% at dose rates up to 10^7 r/hr.

TABLE 4.1 *Typical Values of Equilibrium Thickness and Wall Attenuation for X-Rays* (ref. 3)

Tube potential (millions of volts)	Equilibrium thickness (g/cm²)	Approximate wall attenuation (%)
0.2	<0.05	<0.2
1.0	0.2	0.6
2.0	0.4	1
5.0	1.0	3
10	2.0	7
20	4	10
50	7	20
100	11	30
Co^{60} γ-rays (1.25 Mev)	0.4	1

Calculation of Absorbed Dose from Ionization Measurements

The absorbed dose in air, or air-equivalent material, exposed to x- or γ-radiation and in electronic equilibrium can be calculated from the definition of the roentgen. By definition, 1 roentgen of x- or γ-radiation produces in 0.001293 g of air at NTP electrons, or positive ions, carrying 1 e.s.u. of charge, and therefore,

$$1 \text{ roentgen} \equiv \frac{1}{0.001293}\,\frac{(\text{e.s.u.})}{(\text{g})} \times 2.082 \times 10^{9}\,\frac{(\text{electrons})}{(\text{e.s.u.})}$$
$$\times\, 34\,\frac{(\text{ev})}{(\text{electron, or ion pair})} \times 1.602 \times 10^{-12}\,\frac{(\text{erg})}{(\text{ev})} \times \frac{1}{100}\,\frac{(\text{rad})}{(\text{ergs/g})}$$
$$\equiv 0.87_{7} \text{ rad (in air)} \tag{4.1}$$

This can also be expressed by saying that one roentgen is equivalent to an energy absorption of 87.7 ergs per gram in air.

A value of 34.0 ev/ion pair has been used here for W_{air}, as recommended in ref. 1 for x- or γ-radiation with quantum energies greater than 20 kev, and this value will be used in all subsequent calculations involving W_{air}. It should be remembered, however, that other values of W_{air}, notably 32.5 ev/ion pair, have been used widely in the past. Where values other than 34.0 have been used it is necessary to make a correction to bring the results in line with current calculations. For example, if W_{air} is taken as 32.5 ev/ion pair, the constant in Eq. 4.1 becomes 0.838 rads/r, but this is converted to the currently accepted value by multiplying by the ratio of the values of W used, in this case by 34/32.5.

The relationship expressed in Eq. 4.1 is true for x- and γ-radiation of all energies greater than 20 kev (i.e., photon energies for which W is assumed to be constant) when absorbed in air. For other materials the value of the constant varies with the atomic composition of the material and the energy of the radiation.

Ionization measurements can be used to determine the absorbed dose in media other than air in either of two ways: first, by measuring the exposure dose in air at a point, using an ionization chamber, and then substituting the material to be irradiated at the same position, so that it is exposed to the same beam of radiation; secondly, by taking measurements of the ionization with a thimble chamber actually inside the material. The two problems differ somewhat and will be treated separately.

Case I. EXPOSURE DOSE MEASURED IN AIR. It will be assumed that:

(i) both the ionization chamber and the sample are small enough not to attenuate the radiation appreciably,
(ii) both the ionization chamber and the sample are in electronic equilibrium,
(iii) the scattered electromagnetic radiation is not absorbed by either the chamber or the sample,
(iv) the thimble chamber has been calibrated by comparison with a standard chamber for radiation of the appropriate energy, and the exposure dose correctly measured at the point to be occupied by the sample.

Given these conditions the energy absorbed by the sample and by air are proportional to their mass energy absorption coefficients (Eq. 3.48) and

$$D_M = D_A \times \frac{(\mu_a/\rho)_M}{(\mu_a/\rho)_A} \text{ rads} \tag{4.2}$$

where D_M and D_A are the absorbed dose in the medium and in air respectively and $(\mu_a/\rho)_M$ and $(\mu_a/\rho)_A$ are the corresponding mass energy absorption coefficients. From Eq. 4.1

$$D_A = 0.87_7 R_A \text{ rads} \tag{4.3}$$

where R_A is the exposure dose in roentgens, and, therefore,

$$D_M = 0.87_7 R_A \times \frac{(\mu_a/\rho)_M}{(\mu_a/\rho)_A} = fR_A \text{ rads} \tag{4.4}$$

For a given material, the value of f is constant in the range of photon energies where only Compton interactions occur, but varies with the energy of the incident radiation in the energy regions where photoelectric absorption and pair-production predominate. If the radiation is not monoenergetic, values of f must be calculated for all energies present and combined to give a mean value, $\bar{f}$; typical values of f and $\bar{f}$ for some materials of medical interest are presented in Tables 4.2 and 4.3 respectively. The values are fairly close to unity except at low energies and for materials of moderately high, or high, atomic number (bone contains about 15% of calcium, which has $Z = 20$).

TABLE 4.2 *Conversion Factors from Roentgens to Rads for γ-Rays* (ref. 1)

Photon energy (Mev)	$f = 0.87_7 \times \frac{(\mu_a/\rho)_M}{(\mu_a/\rho)_A}$ rads/r		
	Water	Muscle	Bone
0.01	0.92	0.93_5	3.6
0.1	0.95_5	0.95_5	1.5
1.0	0.97_5	0.96_5	0.92_5
3.0	0.97	0.96_5	0.93_5
Cs^{137} γ-ray (0.66 Mev)	0.97_5	0.96_5	0.93
Co^{60} γ-rays (1.25 Mev)	0.97_5	0.96_5	0.93

TABLE 4.3 *Conversion Factors from Roentgens to Rads for X-Rays* (ref. 5)

Tube potential (kv)	Filter (mm)	HVL (mm)	$\bar{f}$, rads/r		
			Water	Muscle	Bone
100	0.18Cu	5.5Al or 0.25Cu	0.91	0.94	3.1
200	0.20Cu	0.5Cu	0.94	0.95	2.05
400	—	4.2Cu	0.97	0.97	1.11

In the Compton absorption region the *total* mass energy absorption coefficient (μ_a/ρ) is equal to the *Compton* mass energy absorption coefficient (σ_a/ρ) (Eq. 3.54) and this is related to the Compton electronic energy absorption coefficient by

$$\sigma_a/\rho = {}_e\sigma_a(Z/A)N_0 \tag{4.5}$$

(The symbols have their usual meanings; cf. Appendix C.) For radiation of a given energy, the Compton electronic energy absorption coefficient ($_e\sigma_a$) is the same for all materials (Eqs. 3.19 to 3.21), and therefore,

$$\sigma_a/\rho \propto (Z/A)N_0 \text{ (the number of electrons per gram)} \tag{4.6}$$

or

$$\sigma_a/\rho \propto Z/A \tag{4.7}$$

since N_0 is a constant (Avogadro's number). Thus, for radiation energies at which both air and the material in question absorb energy predominantly by the Compton process, either $(Z/A)N_0$ or Z/A can replace μ_a/ρ in Eq. 4.4, e.g.,

$$D_M = 0.87_7 R_A \times \frac{(Z/A)_M}{(Z/A)_A} = fR_A \text{ rads} \tag{4.8}$$

The Compton region for air extends from about 100 kev to about 5 Mev. For materials other than elements a mean value of Z/A is used, calculated from

$$\overline{Z/A} = \sum w_i(Z/A)_i \tag{4.9}$$

w_i being the fraction by weight of the ith element in the medium. For a chemical compound this is simply the sum of the atomic numbers of the atoms present divided by the molecular weight of the compound, e.g., for water $\overline{Z/A} = (2 \times 1 + 8)/18 = 0.556$. Table 4.4 lists some values of f calculated using Eq. 4.8.

TABLE 4.4 *Conversion Factors from Roentgens to Rads in the Compton Region*

Material	$\overline{Z/A}$	$f = 0.87_7 \times \frac{\overline{(Z/A)}_M}{\overline{(Z/A)}_A}$
Air	0.499	0.87_7 rads/r
Water	0.556	0.97_5
0.8N sulfuric acid	0.553	0.97
Methane	0.623	1.09_5
Methanol	0.562	0.99
Acetic acid	0.533	0.93_5
Chloroform	0.486	0.85_5

To calculate the absorbed dose by means of Eq. 4.4, a knowledge of the mass energy absorption coefficients of air and the medium are required. If these are not available, it is possible to utilize the known variation of electronic absorption coefficients with atomic number (Chapter 3) in the regions where photoelectric absorption and pair-production predominate. The electronic and mass absorption coefficients are related by

$$\mu_a/\rho = {}_e\mu_a(Z/A)N_0 \tag{4.10}$$

In the range of photon energies where photoelectric interaction is the predominant absorption process

$$_e\tau \propto Z^m \tag{4.11}$$

where m is about 3. Substituting for the mass absorption coefficients in Eq. 4.4,

$$D_M = 0.87_7 R_A \times \frac{(_e\tau)_M}{(_e\tau)_A} \times \frac{(Z/A)_M}{(Z/A)_A} \text{ rads} \tag{4.12}$$

$$= 0.87_7 R_A \times \left(\frac{Z_M}{Z_A}\right)^m \times \frac{(Z/A)_M}{(Z/A)_A} \text{ rads} \tag{4.13}$$

Often it is convenient to keep the term $(Z/A)_M/(Z/A)_A$ separate from $(Z_M/Z_A)^m$ since the former is the ratio of the number of electrons per gram in the material and in air. If the two terms containing Z are combined the absorbed dose is proportional to $(Z_M/Z_A)^{m+1}$.

When pair production is the dominant process

$$_e\kappa \propto Z \tag{4.14}$$

and

$$D_M = 0.87_7 R_A \times \left(\frac{Z_M}{Z_A}\right) \times \frac{(Z/A)_M}{(Z/A)_A} \text{ rads} \tag{4.15}$$

For materials other than elements, a mean atomic number must be used in equations 4.13 and 4.15. The *effective atomic number* in the photoelectric region ($\bar{Z}_\tau$) is a function of $(Z_1{}^m, Z_2{}^m, \ldots)^{1/m}$ where Z_1, Z_2, etc., are the atomic numbers of the elements present. When pair-production is the main absorption process, the effective atomic number ($\bar{Z}_\kappa$) is a linear function of $(Z_1, Z_2, \ldots)$. In both cases the ratio $\overline{Z/A}$ is calculated separately, as described earlier (Eq. 4.9); the ratio has a value near 0.5 for all materials (cf. Table 4.4). The calculation of energy absorption using effective atomic numbers is described by Spiers (6).

In large samples of material, all the scattered and secondary electromagnetic radiation may not escape from the material, and allowance must be made for the extra energy absorbed from such radiation. The nature of the corrections and the use of backscatter tables are discussed by Johns (7, 8). With large samples the exposure dose is best measured at the position to be occupied by the surface of the sample, and the exposure dose at different depths in the material calculated from attenuation data, or from depth-dose curves if these are available.

Case II. ABSORBED DOSE BY CAVITY IONIZATION. Ionization measurements made inside the irradiated medium with a gas-filled thimble chamber, or other cavity ionization chamber, can be used to calculate the absorbed dose by means of the *Bragg-Gray cavity principle* (9, 10). This is expressed by the equation

$$E_M = J_G W_G (s_m)_{\text{gas}}^{\text{medium}} \tag{4.16}$$

where E_M is the energy absorbed by the medium in ergs/g, J_G is the ionization produced in the gas-filled cavity in e.s.u./g, W_G is the mean energy expended by the secondary electrons crossing the cavity per ion pair formed in the gas (ergs/ion pair), and $(s_m)_{\text{gas}}^{\text{medium}}$ is the ratio of the mass stopping power of the medium to that of the gas for these secondary electrons.[3] The principle follows from the assumption that if the cavity is sufficiently small it will not alter the electron flux in the medium when it is introduced. For the principle to be valid, (1) the cavity must be small compared to the range of the ionizing particles (i.e., electrons for electromagnetic radiation) in the gas, (2) direct interaction between the incident radiation and the gas should contribute little to the ionization in the cavity and, (3) the incident radiation must not be appreciably attenuated in the medium over a distance equal to the dimensions of the cavity. The conditions for validity are discussed by Spiers (6) and Boag (13). From the definition of the rad it follows that the absorbed dose in the medium is

$$D_M = 0.01 E_M \text{ rads} \tag{4.17}$$

If the cavity gas is air ($W = 34$ ev/ion pair) and the ionization produced is expressed in terms of Q, the charge in e.s.u. carried by ions of either sign per 0.001293 g of air

$$D_M = 0.01 \frac{\text{(rad)}}{\text{(erg/g)}} \times \frac{Q}{0.001293} \frac{\text{(e.s.u.)}}{\text{(g air)}} \times 2.082 \times 10^9 \frac{\text{(electrons)}}{\text{(e.s.u.)}} \times 34 \frac{\text{(ev)}}{\text{(electron, or ion pair)}} \times 1.602 \times 10^{-12} \frac{\text{(erg)}}{\text{(ev)}} \times (s_m)_{\text{air}}^{\text{medium}}$$

$$= 0.87_7 Q \times (s_m)_{\text{air}}^{\text{medium}} \text{ rads} \tag{4.18}$$

[3] The mass stopping power ratio can be calculated approximately from the stopping power equation derived by Bethe (Eq. 3.3 for electrons):

$$(s_m)_{\text{gas}}^{\text{medium}} \sim {}_mS_{\text{medium}}/{}_mS_{\text{gas}}$$

The quantity is more complex than this equation would suggest, however, and it is influenced by other factors such as the size and shape of the cavity (11, 12).

Electronic equilibrium, which is so important when measuring the exposure dose, is no longer essential when the absorbed dose is determined by cavity ionization. The cavity ionization measurements are determined by the flux of secondary electrons at the point of interest, and these also determine the energy absorbed at that point. Near the surface of an absorber, where electronic equilibrium has not yet been reached, the electron flux will be smaller than at a greater depth in the medium, but both the observed ionization[4] and the energy absorbed will also be smaller. For the same reason, scattered and secondary electromagnetic radiation absorbed in the medium need not be corrected for separately, since electrons produced by such radiation, and passing through the point of interest, will contribute to the measured ionization. It might be pertinent to point out also that cavity ionization measurements can be used to measure other ionizing radiation provided that the requirements for the Bragg-Gray principle to be valid can be met.

Equation 4.18 is derived making the assumption that the secondary electrons crossing the cavity originate in the medium. That is to say, either the walls of the ionization chamber are of the same composition as the medium or else are very thin, compared to the range of the secondary electrons crossing them. If this assumption is not true, and the secondary electrons crossing the cavity are produced entirely within the walls of the ionization chamber itself, then,

$$D_M = 0.87_7 Q \times (s_m)_{\text{air}}^{\text{wall}} \times \frac{(\mu_a/\rho)_M}{(\mu_a/\rho)_{\text{wall}}} \text{ rads} \tag{4.19}$$

When, under these circumstances, the walls of the ionization chamber are made of an air-equivalent material, the stopping power ratio $(s_m)_{\text{air}}^{\text{wall}}$ has the value 1, and Eq. 4.19 becomes

$$D_M = 0.87_7 Q \times \frac{(\mu_a/\rho)_M}{(\mu_a/\rho)_A} \text{ rads} \tag{4.20}$$

In this equation Q is equal to the exposure dose in roentgens measured at the point of interest in the medium[5]; apart from this the equation is similar to Eq. 4.4. It should be noted, however, that because of the

[4] An ionization chamber with a very thin wall, or a wall of material similar in composition to the medium, would be used.

[5] Q is also equal to the exposure dose in roentgens, even if the wall material is not air-equivalent, provided the ionization chamber has been calibrated against a standard chamber. In this case $(s_m)_{\text{air}}^{\text{wall}}$ is included in the calibration correction. The secondary electrons crossing the cavity must, however, still be produced entirely within the walls of the ionization chamber.

attenuating and scattering effect of the medium the exposure dose Q will not be the same as the exposure dose in air (R_A) at the same point if the medium were removed. The thickness of absorber in front of the ionization chamber may attenuate the radiation reaching the chamber to a very much greater extent than an equal thickness of air, in which case Q would be very much smaller than R_A, though both could be termed an exposure dose at that particular point. A distinction can be made between the two types of exposure dose if the exposure dose measured in air is referred to as an *air-dose*.

Between the limits where the secondary electrons crossing the cavity are produced entirely within the medium or entirely within the walls of the ionization chamber, the observed ionization will lie between that found for the two limiting cases, and the absorbed dose will lie between that given by Eq. 4.18 and that given by Eq. 4.19 or Eq. 4.20. Whether or not a given ionization chamber can be classed as thin or thick walled depends, of course, upon the energy of the incident radiation. A chamber with walls of air-equivalent material of thickness about 0.5 g/cm^2 would be thick walled with respect to Co^{60} γ-rays but thin walled with respect to 100 Mvp x-rays (Table 4.1).

Tables of mass stopping-power ratios relative to air, and other data useful in determining the absorbed dose from cavity-ionization measurements with air-filled chambers, are given in ref. 1. Whyte (14) and Spiers (6) also discuss current values of mass stopping-power ratios. Some values of the mean mass stopping-power ratio relative to air are given in Table 4.5; the data were taken from Whyte (14) with the exception of those for water, which are from ref. 1. The values given are mean values for the absorption of photons of the energy shown; the values will be slightly different for electrons with initial energies equal to those given in column 1.

TABLE 4.5 *Mean Mass Stopping-Power Ratios Relative to Air,* $(s_m)_{air}^{M}$ or $(s_m)_{air}^{wall}$

Photon energy (Mev)	Graphite	Polystyrene	Lucite	Bakelite	Aluminum	Water
0.1	1.01	1.14	1.12	1.09	0.85	1.17
0.5	1.01	1.12	1.11	1.08	0.88	1.16
1.0	1.00	1.11	1.11	1.08	0.88	1.15
3.0	0.99	1.09	1.09	1.05	0.89	1.13
Co^{60} γ-rays (1.25 Mev)	1.00	1.11	1.11	1.07	0.89	1.15

Energy Absorption by the Components of a Mixture

If a mixture of elements or compounds is irradiated with x- or γ-rays, the fraction of the total absorbed dose absorbed by each component of the mixture is proportional to the fraction of the component present, by weight, and to the mass energy absorption coefficient for the component. For example, the fraction of the total dose absorbed by the first component of a mixture is given by

$$\frac{D_1}{D_{\text{mix}}} = w_1 \times \frac{(\mu_a/\rho)_1}{(\mu_a/\rho)_{\text{mix}}} \tag{4.21}$$

where

$$(\mu_a/\rho)_{\text{mix}} = w_1(\mu_a/\rho)_1 + w_2(\mu_a/\rho)_2 + \ldots w_n(\mu_a/\rho)_n \tag{4.22}$$

for a mixture with n components; w_1 is the weight of the first component divided by the weight of the mixture. The relationship is equally true whether the component selected is an element, a compound, or a group of compounds present in the medium, provided that the proper weight fractions and absorption coefficients are chosen.

In the Compton absorption region μ_a/ρ is proportional to Z/A and Eq. 4.21 becomes

$$\frac{D_1}{D_{\text{mix}}} = w_1 \times \frac{(Z/A)_1}{(\overline{Z/A})_{\text{mix}}} \tag{4.23}$$

where $(\overline{Z/A})_{\text{mix}}$ is a mean value given by Eq. 4.9. If any of the components are not elements the value of Z/A for the component will also be a mean value, which can be calculated in the same manner. Equation 4.23 states, in effect, that in the Compton region the energy absorbed by each component is proportional to the number of electrons it contributes to the total number of electrons present.

Implicit in these calculations is the assumption that the secondary electrons transfer energy to each component in the same proportion as that component interacts with the primary electromagnetic radiation. That is to say that the total energy absorbed by a particular component is governed entirely by the extent to which it interacts with the primary radiation, and is independent of the subsequent reactions of the secondary electrons. This assumption appears to be reasonably valid, particularly for compounds which are chemically similar (the members of a homologous series for example), though there are some exceptions. For example, subexcitation electrons (p. 155) may interact with only one of the substances present and thereby increase its share of the absorbed energy. Furthermore it appears that the π electrons present in unsaturated organic compounds (e.g., aromatic compounds) may be more readily excited by fast electrons than the σ electrons of saturated compounds (15). Thus, in a mixture of saturated and unsaturated compounds rather more energy may be transferred to the unsaturated components than would be anticipated on the basis of the equations given in this section (16).

Conversion of Absorbed Dose Measurements for Different Materials

A problem that frequently arises is how to determine the absorbed dose in a particular material from the measured absorbed dose in some other material. For example, in chemical dosimetry the dosimeter and the material to be irradiated may not have the same composition and may not absorb the same amount of energy from the incident radiation. It is convenient to consider this problem here since, for x- and γ-rays, the relevant equations are derived from those already given.

FOR THE ABSORPTION OF MONOENERGETIC RADIATION IN THE COMPTON REGION OF ENERGIES FOR BOTH MATERIALS. It is assumed that both materials are exposed to the same beam of incident radiation and are in electronic equilibrium. Then, from Eq. 4.8,

$$D_2 = D_1 \times \frac{(Z/A)_2}{(Z/A)_1} \text{ rads} \tag{4.24}$$

where D_1 and D_2 are the absorbed dose in materials 1 and 2 respectively and $(Z/A)_1$ and $(Z/A)_2$ are the ratio of the atomic number to the atomic weight for these two materials; if the materials are not pure elements, mean values of Z/A must be used. These are calculated from Eq. 4.9.

For Eq. 4.24 to be valid it is necessary to assume that the incident radiation does not interact appreciably by photoelectric absorption or pair-production in either material. This assumption can be verified by examination of graphs (e.g., Figs. 3.6 and 3.7) or tables (17) which give the attenuation coefficients for these three processes (Compton, photoelectric, and pair-production) over the energy range concerned. If the material being irradiated contains a number of elements, energy absorption must be by the Compton process for those elements which are major constituents. Fortunately the absorption of cobalt-60 and caesium-137 γ-radiation by aqueous, biological, and most organic systems is well within the Compton region for these materials.

FOR THE ABSORPTION OF MONOENERGETIC RADIATION AT ENERGIES WHERE COMPTON ABSORPTION IS UNIMPORTANT. From Eq. 4.2

$$D_2 = D_1 \times \frac{(\mu_a/\rho)_2}{(\mu_a/\rho)_1} \text{ rads} \tag{4.25}$$

where $(\mu_a/\rho)_1$ and $(\mu_a/\rho)_2$ are the mass energy absorption coefficients for materials 1 and 2 respectively. Values of the mass energy absorption coefficients for materials other than elements can be calculated using the coefficients for the elements present (cf. Eq. 3.28), if these are known (1, 18, 19).

If the necessary mass energy absorption coefficients are not available, the variation of these coefficients with the effective atomic number of the material can be utilized in the photon energy regions where photoelectric interactions and pair-production are important (Eqs. 4.13 and 4.15; cf. refs. 6, 7).

FOR THE ABSORPTION OF POLYENERGETIC RADIATION. When photons of more than one energy are present in the incident radiation, this can be considered as made up of a number of monoenergetic beams, which are absorbed independently. The mean absorption coefficient for the beam as a whole is a function of the photon energies present and the numbers of photons in each energy range. If the energy spectrum of the incident beam and the variation in the mass energy absorption coefficient over this range of energies are known, they can be combined graphically to give a mean absorption coefficient for the beam as a whole. This must be done for both materials and then the mean absorption coefficients substituted in Eq. 4.25.

In the event that all the photon energies represented in the x-ray beam are within the Compton region for both materials this procedure is unnecessary, and the required result can be found using Eq. 4.24.

Equations 4.24 and 4.25 only apply when the absorbed dose is measured in terms of the energy absorption per unit mass of absorber, for example, in units of rads. If the measured absorbed dose is in units of energy absorption per unit volume, e.g., ev/cm^3, the calculated dose is a function of the densities (ρ_1 and ρ_2 g/cm^3) of the two media. Equation 4.24 then becomes

$$(D_v)_2 = (D_v)_1 \times \frac{(Z/A)_2}{(Z/A)_1} \times \frac{\rho_2}{\rho_1} \tag{4.26}$$

and Eq. 4.25,

$$(D_v)_2 = (D_v)_1 \times \frac{(\mu_a/\rho)_2}{(\mu_a/\rho)_1} \times \frac{\rho_2}{\rho_1}$$

$$= (D_v)_1 \times \frac{(\mu_a)_2}{(\mu_a)_1} \tag{4.27}$$

where D_v is an absorbed dose per unit volume and μ_a a linear energy absorption coefficient.

These equations (4.24 to 4.27) are strictly true only when the x- or γ-rays are not appreciably attenuated by passing through the absorbing media (this is the condition for Eq. 3.48, and hence Eq. 4.2, to be true). However, they are generally useful in practice even when an appreciable fraction of the incident radiation is absorbed.

CHARGED PARTICLE RADIATION. If the incident radiation is a beam of charged particles (electrons, protons, etc.) and the two absorbing media are irradiated as thin layers, then the ratio of the energy absorbed is simply the ratio of the stopping powers of the two substances (cf. Eqs. 3.3 and 3.8). If the samples are relatively thick the incident radiation may be absorbed completely by both media.

CALORIMETRIC METHODS

The most direct way of measuring the amount of energy in a beam of x- or γ-radiation is by measuring the increase in temperature in a block of material placed in the beam. The material must be such that all the absorbed energy is converted to heat, none, for example, being used to initiate chemical reaction. Good thermal conductivity is also necessary and in practice graphite or metals are used for this purpose. The block must be of sufficient size to completely absorb the radiation, and the size will increase as the energy of the radiation is increased. When all the radiation energy is absorbed by the material, the rate of temperature rise of the block is directly related to the *intensity* (ergs/cm^2 sec) of the beam of radiation (20). In practice the amount of heat generated in the block is extremely small, and calorimetry is not a convenient method of dosimetry for routine use. However, since the results are obtained in absolute energy units, calorimetry does provide an important check on other, less direct, methods.

The *absorbed dose* at any depth in the material can be calculated from the measured intensity of the radiation (20) or it may be measured directly (21), also by calorimetry. The direct calorimetric measurement of absorbed dose is rather more difficult than the measurement of the radiation intensity by this means. A smaller sample of material is used, so that the radiation is only partially absorbed, and the sample is surrounded by the same, or similar, material so that it is in electronic equilibrium with its surroundings. The principle of calorimeters designed to measure radiation intensity and absorbed dose is shown in Fig. 4.3. Preliminary work on the development of a graphite sphere calorimeter, which could serve as a primary standard of absorbed dose, has been described by Hart and his colleagues (22).

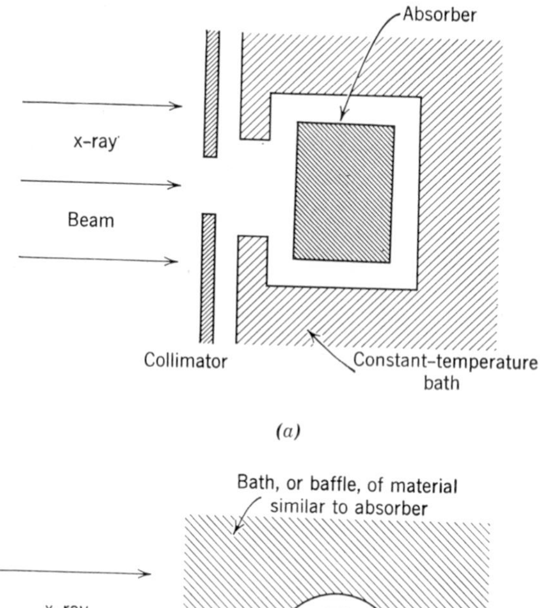

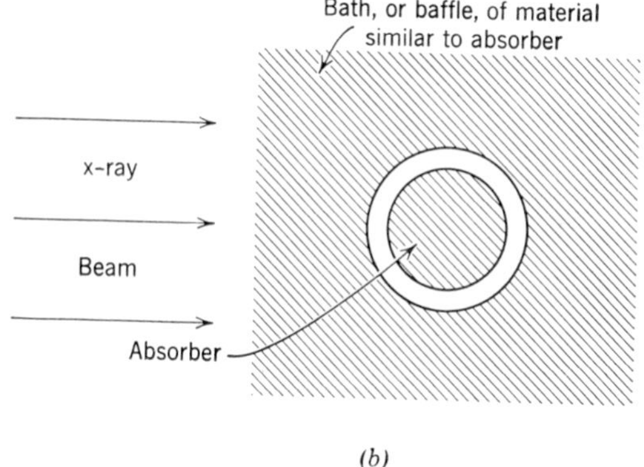

FIGURE *4.3* *Principle of calorimeters to measure (a) radiation intensity and (b) absorbed dose.*

Calorimetric determination of the energy absorbed from beams of accelerated charged particles is simpler because much greater radiation intensities are involved (23). However, other practical difficulties have limited the use of the method with particle beams at the present time.

DOSIMETRY OF CHARGED PARTICLES

Two features distinguish charged-particle dosimetry from that of x- and γ-radiation. First, the fact that the particles are charged means that information about the beam can be gained by collecting their charge and measuring it. The second feature arises from the greater rate of energy loss by charged particles. This leads to large variations in the absorbed dose over comparatively small distances, and to the complete stopping of a charged-particle beam by a thickness of absorber that would barely attenuate an x- or γ-ray beam. Regardless of other considerations, the latter must obviously influence the design of instruments for use with these less-penetrating radiations.

Charge-Collection Measurements

The particle flux (particles/cm² sec) in a beam of charged particles from an accelerator can be determined by measuring the total charge carried by the beam by means of a Faraday cup (or Faraday cage). A Faraday cup consists of a metal block thick enough to stop the beam completely, supported on insulators inside an evacuated chamber (Fig. 4.4). The block acquires the charge of every particle absorbed, and the current flowing from it is a direct measure of the number of particles entering the chamber. (It may be necessary to correct for the loss of charge due to particles scattered out of the block.)

In order to obtain the intensity of the radiation the energy of the particles is also required. This will often be known from the characteristics of the accelerator, or it can be determined from the range of the particles or from magnetic-deflection measurements. Then

$$I \text{ (ergs/cm}^2 \text{ sec)} = N \text{ (particles/cm}^2 \text{ sec)} \times E \text{ (ergs/particle)} \quad (4.28)$$

where I is the intensity of the radiation, N the particle flux, and E the particle energy.

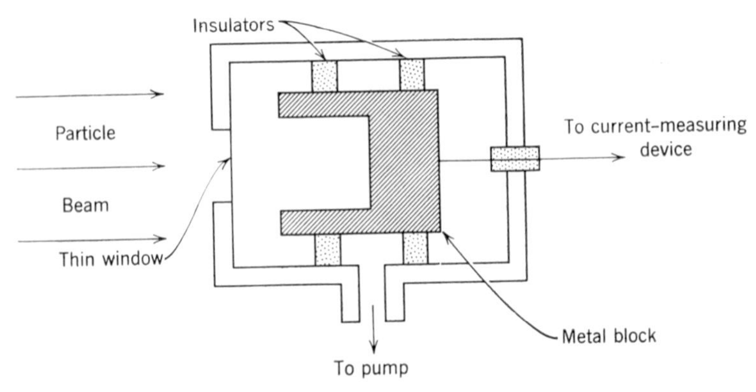

FIGURE 4.4 *Faraday cage.*

Ionization Measurements

Ionization chambers are generally used as secondary instruments with charged-particle radiation, and calibrated against a Faraday cup. They may be either parallel-plate chambers, similar to the standard free-air chamber used with x-rays, or cavity chambers; in either case the design is influenced by the need to keep absorbing material in the path of the beam to a minimum. Chambers for use with electron beams have been described by Boag (13) and Laughlin (24), and for heavy charged-particle beams by Birge, Anger, and Tobias (25).

Absorbed Dose Measurements

The dose absorbed by a thin absorber can be calculated from the particle flux, measured using a Faraday cup, the energy of the radiation, and the stopping power of the absorber. When the sample is sufficiently thick and the range of the particles great enough, the absorbed dose is generally measured by cavity ionization using a very thin-walled ionization chamber. The Bragg-Gray principle is valid provided that the conditions concerning the size of the cavity are met (cf. 6, 13), and the absorbed dose is given by

$$D_M = 0.87_7 Q \times (s_m)_{\text{air}}^{\text{medium}} \text{ rads} \tag{4.18}$$

where Q is the charge (in e.s.u.) produced in 0.001293 g of air. The numerical term, 0.87_7, was calculated assuming W_{air} to be 34 ev per ion pair. This assumption is still valid if the charged particles concerned are electrons, but it will not be quite true if the ionization in the cavity is produced largely by heavier charged particles; in the latter case the numerical term will be $0.87_7 \times W_{\text{air}}/34$, where W_{air} is the value appropriate to the radiation being used. The mass stopping-power ratio will vary according to the type and mean energy of the particles producing ionization in the cavity.

Other Measurements

At energies above about 20 Mev the flux of heavy particles can be measured by means of the nuclear reactions giving radioactive products that the particles can initiate in suitable stopping materials. The number of radioactive nuclei formed can be determined by standard counting techniques and then used to calculate the particle flux (25).

NEUTRON DOSIMETRY

Neutrons do not, themselves, produce ionization in matter, and they are detected by means of their interactions with nuclei. The absorbed dose from neutron irradiation may be calculated if the number and energy distribution of the incident neutrons are known. A discussion of the methods by which these quantities can be determined is beyond the scope of this book but is included in many which deal with nuclear physics and reactor technology (26, 27, 28). Ionization measurements can also be used to determine the absorbed dose and these are briefly described below.

Ionization Measurements

The Bragg-Gray principle (Eq. 4.16) is applicable to cavity ionization measurements made in neutron fields and it enables the absorbed dose to be calculated from such measurements.

In practice, cavity ionization measurements have been used most frequently to determine the absorbed dose for fast neutrons in biological tissue, where most of the neutron energy is transferred to hydrogen nuclei (protons). Ionization chambers for this purpose are made with walls of hydrogen-rich material so that the ionization in the gas-filled cavity, like the energy deposition in the tissue, is brought about by recoil protons. Tissue-equivalent ionization chambers are described in several places (26, 28).

The quantity W_G in Eq. 4.16 is the mean energy expended in producing an ion pair in the cavity gas. It will not be the same for neutron irradiation as for x- and γ-ray irradiation since the particles causing ionization, protons and electrons respectively, are not the same. When the cavity gas is air it is generally assumed that W_{air} (protons) is 35 ev/ion pair, or 5.6×10^{-11} ergs/ion pair (1).

The stopping-power ratio, $(s_m)_{\text{gas}}^{\text{medium}}$, will also be different when ionization in the cavity gas is brought about by protons rather than electrons. However, uncertainty regarding the stopping-power ratio may be avoided by choosing gas and wall materials with the same atomic composition, e.g., ethylene and polyethylene, when $(s_m)_{\text{gas}}^{\text{medium}} = 1$. This has the further advantage that restrictions on the cavity size (for the Bragg-Gray principle to be valid), which are particularly stringent for neutrons because of the short range of the recoil protons, are removed.

If the gas filling the cavity has the same composition as the wall material, and the ions, of either sign, produced in the cavity carry a charge of Q e.s.u./cm³ at NTP, the absorbed dose in the wall material is given by

$$D_{\text{wall}} = 0.01\,\frac{\text{(rad)}}{\text{(erg/g)}} \times Q\,\frac{\text{(e.s.u.)}}{\text{(cm}^3\text{)}} \times \frac{1}{\rho}\,\frac{\text{(cm}^3\text{)}}{\text{(g)}}$$

$$\times\, 2.08 \times 10^{9}\,\frac{\text{(electrons)}}{\text{(e.s.u.)}} \times W_G\,\frac{\text{(ev)}}{\text{(electron, or ion pair)}}$$

$$\times\, 1.60 \times 10^{-12}\,\frac{\text{(erg)}}{\text{(ev)}}$$

$$= 3.34 \times 10^{-5} Q W_G/\rho \text{ rads} \tag{4.29}$$

where ρ is the density of the gas (g/cm^3).

The absorbed dose in the medium surrounding the ionization chamber is equal to D_{wall} if both the medium and the wall material have the same atomic composition. However, if their composition is different the absorbed dose in the medium is

$$D_{\text{medium}} = D_{\text{wall}} \times \frac{(\Sigma \sigma_i k_i N_i)_{\text{medium}}}{(\Sigma \sigma_i k_i N_i)_{\text{wall}}} \tag{4.30}$$

where N_i is the number of atoms of type i per gram, σ_i is the scattering cross section for atoms of this type, and k_i is the average fraction of the neutron energy transferred to the medium in such interactions. The summation is extended to cover all types of atoms in the material. When neutrons of more than one energy are present, values of $\sigma_i k_i$ must be averages covering the whole neutron-energy spectrum. Values of σk for H, C, N, O, S, and P and for neutron energies between 0.1 and 10 Mev are given in ref. 1 (Table 8.8).

Neutron dosimetry is complicated by the fact that neutrons are very often accompanied by electromagnetic radiation which, for many purposes, must be estimated separately. When the incident radiation is a mixture of neutrons and γ-rays, cavity ionization chambers of the type considered above (i.e., with gas and walls of similar hydrogenous material) will respond to both types of radiation. The measured ionization, Q, will be related to the total absorbed dose by Eq. 4.29, though W_G should now be a mean value since both protons and electrons will be ionizing the cavity gas. The appropriate mean value for W_G can be estimated if the relative contribution to the total absorbed dose from neutrons and γ-rays is known approximately. If the wall material and the surrounding medium have the same composition $D_{\text{medium}} = D_{\text{wall}}$, otherwise the absorbed dose in the wall due to neutron interactions can be converted to the absorbed dose in the medium using Eq. 4.30, and the absorbed dose due to the γ-rays similarly converted using the ratio of the mass energy absorption coefficients for the medium and wall material

(Eq. 4.2). Some knowledge of the relative neutron and γ-ray contributions to the absorbed dose is needed to make this conversion from D_{wall} to D_{medium}.

The γ-ray contribution to the absorbed dose can be estimated by using a second cavity ionization chamber, similar in size and shape to the first, but with thick walls of a material that contains no hydrogen (e.g., aluminum, graphite, or teflon). The second chamber will have a lower response to neutrons than the first but a roughly similar response to γ-rays, so that it is possible to discriminate between the effects due to these two types of radiation (1, 26, 28).

DOSIMETRY OF INTERNAL RADIATION SOURCES

The short range of α- and β-particles limits the quantity of material that can be irradiated by an external α- or β-source, and it is sometimes convenient to mix the radioactive material with the material to be irradiated, and so achieve uniform irradiation of a large sample. The most frequently used isotopes for this purpose are the β-emitting phosphorus-32 and sulfur-35 and, rather less often, α-emitting radon and β-emitting tritium; it is usually a prerequisite that the isotope decay quickly, and that the decay products are stable, so that radioactive residues from the experiment do not present a disposal problem.

Generally the sample irradiated will be large, compared to the range of the ionizing particles in the medium, and the absorbed dose in the sample can be assumed to be the total energy liberated by the disintegrating nuclei.[6] Loss of energy by the escape of secondary electromagnetic radiation from the sample can usually be disregarded. If the concentration of the radioactive isotope present in the sample is C millicuries per gram (equivalent to $3.7 \times 10^7\, C$ disintegrations/g sec) and the mean energy released by each disintegration and transferred to the ionizing particles is $\overline{E}$ Mev, then the absorbed dose rate, T_M, is given by

$$T_M = 3.7 \times 10^7\, C \,\frac{\text{(disintegrations)}}{\text{(g sec)}} \times \overline{E}\, \frac{\text{(Mev)}}{\text{(disintegration)}} \times 1.602 \times 10^{-8}\, \frac{\text{(g rad)}}{\text{(Mev)}}$$

$$= 0.593 \times C \times \overline{E} \text{ rads/sec} \tag{4.31}$$

[6] Actually that part of the total energy liberated that is transferred to ionizing particles; energy liberated in the form of energetic γ-rays or antineutrinos does not contribute to the absorbed energy being considered in this section.

The concentration of the radioisotope (C) can be found by counting the number of particles emitted per unit time by a small aliquot of the radioactive material. Any counting technique can be used, but the result must be corrected to give an absolute value of the activity present; i.e., the total number of nuclei disintegrating per gram-second rather than the number of disintegrations per gram-second that happen to be observed. Allowance must also be made for radioactive decay in the period between counting the activity and mixing the active material with the sample.

Radioactive decay will also occur during the irradiation itself. For irradiations which last a much shorter time than the half-life of the isotope being used, it is sufficient to calculate the dose rate (T_M) from the activity present at the midpoint of the irradiation and to use this value to calculate the total absorbed dose. For longer irradiations, for example longer than the half-life of the isotope, the absorbed dose rate should be integrated over the period of the irradiation (t) to give the true absorbed dose (D_M), i.e.,

$$D_M = \int_0^t T_M \, dt \tag{4.32}$$

Substituting for T_M from Eq. 4.31,

$$D_M = 0.593\bar{E} \int_0^t C \, dt \text{ rads} \tag{4.33}$$

For radioactive decay,

$$C_t = C_0 e^{-\lambda t} \tag{4.34}$$

where C_0 and C_t (millicuries per gram) are the concentration of radioactive material present in the sample at the start of the irradiation and after time t (sec) respectively, and λ (sec^{-1}) is the decay constant for the isotope being used. Substituting for C the integration (Eq. 4.33) becomes

$$D_M = 0.593 \times \bar{E} \times C_0 \int_0^t e^{-\lambda t} \, dt \text{ rads} \tag{4.35}$$

and, integrating,

$$D_M = \frac{0.593 \times \bar{E} \times C_0}{\lambda} (1 - e^{-\lambda t}) \text{ rads} \tag{4.36}$$

for an irradiation lasting t seconds. If λ and t are expressed in min^{-1} and minutes respectively the numerical constant in Eq. 4.36 becomes 35.6, and if the units are days^{-1} and days, the constant has the value

5.12×10^4. The greatest absorbed dose is obtained if the mixture is left until the radioactivity has decayed completely. In this case $t \to \infty$ and Eq. 4.36 becomes

$$D_M = (0.593 \times \overline{E} \times C_0)/\lambda \text{ rads} \tag{4.37}$$

Values for the energy of the particles emitted by radioactive nuclei can be found in most collections of nuclear data; a few values are given in Table 2.1. For β-particles the average β-particle energy is used in equations 4.31 to 4.37. When more than one particle is expelled for each disintegration of the parent isotope (i.e., when the daughter elements are radioactive and have much shorter half-lives than the parent element), $\overline{E}$ is the mean energy carried by all these particles, per disintegration of the parent. An example of this is the energy released by radon when it is in equilibrium, in the sample, with its daughter elements (Table 4.6). The energy released was calculated using Eq. 4.31, taking $\overline{E}$ as the sum of the energies of the individual particles.

TABLE 4.6 *Energy Release by Radon in Equilibrium with its Daughter Elements*

Element	Half-life	Particle emitted	Particle energy (Mev)		Rate of energy release per millicurie of radon per gram (rads/sec)
Radon	3.83 days	α	5.49	Total	
RaA (Po^{218})	3.05 min	α	6.00	energy	11.4
RaC′ (Po^{214})	10^{-4} sec	α	7.68	$\overline{E} = 19.17$	
				Total	
RaB (Pb^{214})	26.8 min	β	0.23 (av)	energy	0.59
RaC (Bi^{214})	19.7 min	β	0.76 (av)	$\overline{E} = 0.99$	

Energy transferred to the recoiling nucleus by the expulsion of an α- or β-particle ought also to be included in the mean energy of the disintegration ($\overline{E}$), though in practice this may not be very significant. The energy transferred to the nucleus by loss of an α-particle, calculated from the equation for the conservation of momentum, is

$$E_{\text{nucleus}} = E_\alpha \times (\text{mass } \alpha\text{-particle/mass recoiling nucleus}) \tag{4.38}$$

In the example given in Table 4.6 the energy transferred to the nuclei by the loss of the three α-particles totals 0.36 Mev; inclusion of this energy raises the absorbed dose rate for α-particle absorption from 11.4 to 11.6 rads/sec. The fraction of the energy transferred to the nucleus by the loss of a β-particle will be less than that resulting from the loss of an α-particle, and can be disregarded.

CHEMICAL DOSIMETRY

In chemical dosimetry the radiation dose is determined from the chemical change produced in a suitable substrate. Calculation of the dose requires a knowledge of the G value for the reaction or product estimated, and this is found by comparing the chemical system with some form of absolute dosimeter. Chemical dosimeters are therefore secondary dosimeters, and are used because of their greater convenience. The quantity which they measure is the absorbed dose (or absorbed dose rate) in the material composing the dosimeter, which can be converted to the absorbed dose (or dose rate) in other materials using equations 4.24 to 4.27.

In view of the large number of chemical systems that might conceivably be used for dosimetry it may be helpful to list some of the features desirable in a dosimeter. The response of the dosimeter should be:

(i) proportional to the radiation dose over a wide range of dose (the range of interest in radiation chemistry is about 10 to 10^8 rads, though no one dosimeter is likely to cover more than a part of this range),

(ii) independent of dose rate (this may range from a few rads per minute to as high as 10^{10} rads per second during the individual radiation pulses from an accelerator),

(iii) independent of the energy and LET of the radiation,

(iv) independent of temperature,

(v) reproducible; for most purposes a precision of between $\pm 2\%$ and $\pm 5\%$ is acceptable.

In addition the dosimeter should be:

(vi) stable under normal conditions, such as exposure to light and air, both before and after irradiation,

(vii) simple to use.

Two other desirable characteristics are applicable to chemical dosimeters:

(viii) the dosimeter should be easy to prepare from standard shelf reagents and solvents (i.e., the system should be insensitive to small amounts of impurities and not require elaborate purification of the reagents used),

(ix) the response should not be dependent upon minor changes in the composition of the dosimeter, for example, upon small changes in the concentration of the reagents.

In practice, no one dosimeter meets all these demands. Of the chemical systems the Fricke, or ferrous sulfate, dosimeter probably comes closest, and at the present time it is the most widely used chemical dosimeter. Other systems may be superior for some purposes, and a number of these, together with the Fricke dosimeter, are described below.

Fricke (Ferrous Sulfate) Dosimeter

The reaction involved in the Fricke dosimeter is the oxidation of an acid solution of ferrous sulfate to the ferric salt, in the presence of oxygen and under the influence of radiation.

Fricke (29) proposed this system as an x-ray dosimeter as early as 1929, and chose $0.8N$ sulfuric acid as the solvent so that the response to x-rays should be the same as that of standard air ionization chambers over a range of x-ray energies. Various procedures are available for preparing the dosimeter solution, Weiss, Allen, and Schwarz (30) have recommended the following: dissolve 2 g $FeSO_4 \cdot 7H_2O$ or $Fe(NH_4)_2(SO_4)_2 \cdot 6H_2O$, 0.3 g NaCl, and 110 ml conc. (95–98%) H_2SO_4 (analytical reagent grade) in sufficient distilled water to make 5 liters of solution; the solution is then $0.0014M$ with respect to ferrous sulfate ($0.001M$ ferrous ammonium sulfate), $0.001M$ with respect to sodium chloride, and $0.8N(0.4M)$ with respect to sulfuric acid. Alternatively, a stock solution $0.5M$ in ferrous ammonium sulfate and $0.5M$ in sodium chloride can be made up and diluted (2 ml to 1 liter) with $0.8N$ sulfuric acid when required (31). The stock solution should be stable for up to three months when stored in an amber bottle out of direct sunlight.

Chloride is added to the dosimeter solution to inhibit the oxidation of ferrous ions by organic impurities (32), and it is unnecessary if both the water and the reagents used are purified exhaustively. The purity of the water used as a solvent is a major consideration whenever aqueous solutions are irradiated. Ordinary distilled water is commonly purified by redistillation from an alkaline permanganate solution, and then from an acid dichromate solution, to reduce the amount of organic impurities present; the product is "triply distilled" water. It is even better to reflux the alkaline and acid solutions for extended periods, though even this does not suffice to remove all organic material, and final traces are best removed by irradiating the triply distilled water (33). De-ionized water is not an acceptable substitute for distilled water for radiation-chemical purposes.

The care taken in purifying solvents and reagents should be equaled by the attention given to cleaning glassware which will be in contact with aqueous solutions before, and during, their irradiation. The glassware is generally freed of organic matter by treatment with a strong acid-oxidizing agent mixture (e.g., conc. sulfuric acid + CrO_3, $Na_2Cr_2O_7 \cdot 2H_2O$, etc., or nitric acid + oxidizing agent), and then thoroughly washed with tap, distilled, and triply distilled water. Contact between the solution to be irradiated and any organic material (e.g., rubber stoppers or tubing) is best avoided. Nevertheless, Haybittle, Saunders, and Swallow (34) found that polymethylmethacrylate (Lucite) vessels could be used for ferrous sulfate dosimetry, though polystyrene vessels gave spuriously high yields if the solution was allowed to stand in contact with the vessel for several hours before irradiation.

To determine the absorbed dose (in 0.8*N* sulfuric acid) using the Fricke dosimeter, a sample of the dosimeter solution in a container thick enough to ensure electronic equilibrium[7] is placed in the radiation field for a measured length of time, and then the yield of ferric ions measured. To avoid undue wall effects (i.e., so that practically all the secondary electrons contributing to the energy absorption originate in the solution) glass containers for the solution should have an inner diameter of at least 8 mm when γ-radiation is being determined (30, 35). The most common method of measuring the ferric ion formed is by spectrophotometric analysis, comparing the optical density of the irradiated and nonirradiated dosimeter solutions at the wavelength at which ferric ions show maximum absorption (about 304 mμ, or 3040 Å). The optical readings should be taken soon after the irradiation, so that adventitious oxidation of the solutions is minimized. The mean absorbed dose (D_D) for the volume occupied by the dosimeter solution is derived as follows. For any chemical system, by definition,

[7] This applies particularly to high energy radiation, since at low and moderate energies (e.g., for Co^{60} γ-rays) the walls of most glass vessels represent an adequate thickness; for true electronic equilibrium the walls should have the same atomic composition as the dosimeter solution.

Electronic equilibrium and wall effects can be ignored if a liquid dosimeter is chosen which has essentially the same atomic composition as the material to be irradiated and both dosimeter and sample are irradiated in the same vessel.

$$G(\text{product}) = \text{molecules product formed/100 ev energy absorbed} \quad (4.39)$$

and

$$1 \text{ rad} = \text{an energy absorption of 100 ergs/g} \quad (4.40)$$

Combining these two equations,

$$\text{Energy absorbed} = \frac{100 \times (\text{molecules product formed/g})}{G(\text{product})} \frac{(\text{ev})}{(\text{g})} \times 1.602 \times 10^{-12} \frac{(\text{erg})}{(\text{ev})} \times \frac{1}{100} \frac{(\text{g rad})}{(\text{ergs})}$$

$$= 1.602 \times 10^{-12} \times \frac{\text{molecules product formed/gram}}{G(\text{product})} \text{ rads} \quad (4.41)$$

Equation 4.41 may be applied to any chemical system. For the ferrous sulfate dosimeter, when the yield of ferric ions is measured spectrophotometrically,

$$\text{Ferric ion formed (moles/liter)} = \frac{(O.D_i - O.D_b)}{\epsilon d} \quad (4.42)$$

where $O.D_i$ and $O.D_b$ are the optical density of the irradiated and nonirradiated dosimeter solution respectively, ϵ is the molar extinction coefficient for ferric ions at the wavelength of maximum absorption (liters/mole cm), and d is the thickness of the sample used when measuring the optical density (cm). Whence,

$$\text{Ferric ion formed (molecules/g)} = \frac{(O.D_i - O.D_b)}{\epsilon d} \frac{(\text{moles})}{(\text{liter})} \times \frac{1}{1000\rho} \frac{(\text{liter})}{(\text{g})} \times 6.023 \times 10^{23} \frac{(\text{molecules})}{(\text{mole})} \quad (4.43)$$

By substituting for the number of ferric ions formed per gram (Eq. 4.43) in Eq. 4.41,

$$\text{Energy absorbed} = \frac{O.D_i - O.D_b}{\epsilon d G(Fe^{3+})} \times \frac{6.023 \times 10^{20}}{\rho} \times 1.602 \times 10^{-12}$$

(i.e., absorbed dose, D_D, in the dosimeter solution)

$$= \frac{0.965 \times 10^{9}(O.D_i - O.D_b)}{\epsilon d \rho G(Fe^{3+})} \text{ rads} \quad (4.44)$$

The value of ϵ should be determined (31, 36, 37) with the spectrophotometer used for the optical density measurements, making the determination at the wavelength at which the absorption by ferric ions is greatest (302-305 mμ, depending on the instrument calibration). The extinction coefficient has a rather large temperature coefficient of +0.7 percent per degree centigrade[8] (34, 37) so that the optical measurements should be made at a constant temperature or, if this is not possible, corrected using the expression

$$\text{Absorbed dose (corr.)} = \frac{\text{absorbed dose (measured at } t_2\text{°C)}}{1 + 0.007(t_2 - t_1)} \qquad (4.45)$$

where t_1°C is the temperature at which the extinction coefficient was determined. A typical value of the extinction coefficient is 2174 ± 6 liters/mole cm at 23.7°C (30, 36, cf. 37).

The density of the dosimeter solution is essentially that of 0.8*N* sulfuric acid, i.e., $1.024_5 \pm 0.001_5$ between 15° and 25°C (40); the density used is that at the temperature at which the optical densities are measured, rather than the temperature of the solution during irradiation.

Substituting $\epsilon = 2174$, $\rho = 1.024$, and $G(Fe^{3+}) = 15.5$ (for Co^{60} γ-rays) in Eq. 4.44,

$$D_D = 2.80 \times 10^4 \,(O.D_i - O.D_b)/d \text{ rads} \qquad (4.46)$$

$$= 1.75 \times 10^{18} \,(O.D_i - O.D_b)/d \text{ ev/g} \qquad (4.47)$$

and, assuming the density of the dosimeter solution during irradiation to be 1.024,

$$(D_D)_v = 1.79 \times 10^{18} \,(O.D_i - O.D_b)/d \text{ ev/cm}^3 \qquad (4.48)$$

These equations should be accurate to within a few percent for radiation for which $G(Fe^{3+})$ is 15.5; more accurate values are obtained by substituting the appropriate values of ϵ, ρ, and $G(Fe^{3+})$ in Eq. 4.44 and, if necessary, correcting the result for temperature as shown in Eq. 4.45.

[8] According to Hochanadel and Ghormley (reported in ref. 38) the extinction coefficient at 275 mμ is almost independent of temperature and there is no need to measure or control the temperature when measurements are made at this wavelength; the molar extinction coefficient of ferric ions at 275 mμ is 1830. These authors also recommend using an absorption cell with pure fused silica windows, which do not color under irradiation, so that both irradiation and measurement of the optical density can be carried out in the same vessel.

Rather more recently, Scharf and Lee (39) have recommended making measurements at 224 mμ. The molar extinction coefficient for ferric ion absorption at this wavelength is greater (4565 liter/mole cm) than at 304 mμ, enabling smaller doses to be measured without loss of accuracy, and the temperature dependence of the extinction coefficient is smaller at 224 mμ (+0.10%) than at 304 mμ.

The $G(Fe^{3+})$ values depend upon the LET of the radiation, and are greatest when the LET is low; a rather arbitrary selection of values from the current literature is given in Table 4.7. In several cases other authors give values slightly different from those in the table (though the G value for cobalt-60 γ-radiation can be given with fair certainty as 15.5 or 15.6). In practice the particular G value chosen is not of major importance, as long as the figure used is recorded, since yields derived using a particular value can be corrected quite readily as more exact values become available.

The processes by which ferrous ions are oxidized to ferric consume oxygen, and exhaustion of the oxygen present in solution marks an upper limit beyond which the yield of the dosimeter falls. The highest dose that an air-saturated solution can register accurately is about 50,000 rads, and in practice the absorbed dose is usually kept between 4000 and 40,000 rads; the maximum dose is about four times as great if dissolved air is displaced by pure oxygen before the solution is irradiated. The lower limit is the dose that produces sufficient oxidation to be accurately measured. Using a 1 cm absorption cell ($d = 1$ in Eq. 4.44), this is about 4000 rads, but rather lower doses can be measured with the same accuracy by using longer cells. Lower doses can also be measured by increasing the sensitivity of the analytical method. In the photometric method this can be achieved, at the expense of convenience, by making a derivative of ferric iron that has a higher extinction coefficient than ferric ions alone. Ehrenberg and Sæland, for example, used the thiocyanate complex ($\epsilon = 8500$ at 465 mμ) for this purpose (41). By adding Fe^{59} to the dosimeter solution as a radioactive tracer, and subsequently isolating and counting the ferric ions formed, Rudstam and Svedberg (52) were able to measure doses of 1 to 100 rads to better than 2 rads.

The response of the dosimeter is independent of the dose rate up to about 10^7 to 10^8 rads/sec (53, 54), but falls at higher dose rates. Rotblat and Sutton (53) found $G(Fe^{3+}) = 13.1 \pm 0.4$ for electron irradiation at a dose rate of 8×10^9 rads/sec, compared with a value of 15.45 at lower dose rates (36). Anderson (54) gives a G value of 11.4 ± 0.5 for the dose rate range from 2 to 3×10^9 rads/sec.

The response is independent of the ferrous ion concentration between 5×10^{-2} and $10^{-4}M$ (35, 43), and of sulfuric acid concentration between 1.5 and $0.1N$ (55). However, altering the acid concentration will alter the density of the solution (e.g., in Eq. 4.44) and, by changing the absorption coefficient for the solution, will also alter the amount of energy absorbed.

TABLE 4.7 *G Values for the Ferrous Sulfate Dosimeter*

Radiation	$G(Fe^{3+})$	Method of energy measurement	Ref.
160 Mev protons	16.5 ± 1	Proton flux from induced radioactivity	41
30 Mvp x-rays (filtered, $\bar{E}$ = 7.6 Mev)*	16.3 ± 0.6	Ionization	34
2 Mvp x-rays	16.0 ± 0.5	Ionization†	42
Co^{60} γ-rays (1.25 Mev)	15.5 ± 0.5	Ionization	34
	15.6 ± 0.3	Calorimetry	43
	15.7	Ionization†	43
	15.8 ± 0.3	Calorimetry	44
2 Mev electrons	15.45 ± 0.11	Charge collection	36
P^{32} β-particles (E_{av} = 0.70 Mev)	15.21 ± 0.04	4π scintillation counting	45
	15.39 ± 0.04	4π proportional counting	45
220 kvp x-rays (filtered 0.65 mm Al, $\bar{E}$ = 56 kev)*	15.0 ± 0.5	Ionization	34
100 kvp x-rays (filtered 0.65 mm Al, $\bar{E}$ = 33 kev)*	14.7 ± 0.5	Ionization	34
50 kvp x-rays (unfiltered)	14.0 ± 0.8	(Not an absolute calibration)	46
8 kvp x-rays	13.4 ± 0.6	Ionization	47
Tritium β-particles (E_{av} = 5.5 kev; internal source)	12.9 ± 0.2	Counting and gas density determination	48
12 Mev deuterons	9.81	Charge collection	49
1.99 Mev protons	8.00	Charge collection	49
3.47 Mev deuterons	6.90	Charge collection	49
0.63 Mev protons	6.89	Charge collection	49
$Li^6(n,\alpha)H^3$ recoil nuclei	5.69 ± 0.12	Neutron flux measurement	50
Po^{210} α-particles (5.3 Mev; internal source)	5.10 ± 0.10	Absolute counting	51
$B^{10}(n,\alpha)Li^7$ recoil nuclei	4.22 ± 0.08	Neutron flux measurement	49
U^{235} fission fragments	3.0 ± 0.9	Neutron flux measurement	41

* Effective mean energy of radiation (author).

† *G* values based on ionization measurements have been adjusted assuming W_{air} = 34·0 ev/ion pair where the authors have used another value for this constant.

The yield of the dosimeter is not significantly affected by the temperature of the solution during irradiation in the range of temperatures from 0° to 65°C (43, 56). Increasing the temperature of the solution will lower its density, resulting in a lower energy absorption per unit volume, but it will not affect the energy absorption per gram, on which the absorbed dose is based.

Barr, Geisselsoder, and Laughlin (57) have suggested adding high-atomic-number zinc or cadmium sulfate to the dosimeter solution when low-energy radiation (e.g., low-energy x-rays), which interacts mainly by the photoelectric process, is to be measured. The solutes cause no significant change in $G(Fe^{3+})$ but increase the mean atomic number of the dosimeter solution, making it possible to match the mean atomic number of the dosimeter to that of the system being studied.

In common with other liquid dosimeters, the ferrous sulfate dosimeter has the advantage that it may be irradiated in a container of any size or shape, duplicating in these respects the sample to be irradiated.

Ceric Sulfate Dosimeter

The use of ceric sulfate in dosimetry is based on the reduction of ceric ions to cerous under the influence of radiation.

The response of this dosimeter is the same whether or not oxygen is present, and consequently exhaustion of the dissolved oxygen does not impose an upper limit to the dose that can be measured. Acid ceric sulfate solutions can, in fact, be used to measure absorbed doses as large as 10^8 rads (58), the upper limit being set by the solubility of ceric salts and the complete reduction of the ceric ions present.

The yield of cerous ions is measured by the difference in ceric ion concentration before and after irradiation. At low ceric ion concentrations this is determined from the change in optical density at the ceric absorption maximum at 320 mμ (the exact wavelength should be determined with the instrument being used for dosimetry); the molar extinction coefficient for ceric ions at this wavelength, 5565 (37), is not temperature dependent. At higher concentrations of ceric ion the change can be measured using standard analytical techniques; for example, by titration with ferrous sulfate (58). The absorbed dose is calculated from Eq. 4.41 or, when spectrophotometric analysis is used, from Eq. 4.44. In the latter case $O.D_i$ and $O.D_b$ are now the optical density of the nonirradiated and irradiated ceric sulfate solutions respectively, and $G(Fe^{3+})$ becomes $G(Ce^{3+})$.

Since the cerous ion concentration is determined by difference, it is advantageous to start with a ceric ion concentration that is of the same order as, but slightly larger than, the expected change in concentration. Reduction of between 20% and 80% of the ceric ions originally present is generally desirable, and concentrations of ceric sulfate between 10^{-5} and $0.4M$ are used. Solutions are made up in $0.8N$ sulfuric acid and it is important in ceric dosimetry that triply distilled water and high-purity reagents be used, since the system is very sensitive to traces of impurities (20 ppm of formic acid, for example, is reported to increase $G(Ce^{3+})$ from 2.50 to 3.55 (59)). To the present time no additives that will counteract the effect of impurities have been reported. Impurities can be detected by comparing the absorbed dose measured with the suspect ceric sulfate solution with the absorbed dose measured with the Fricke dosimeter; if the results differ by more than the experimental error, the presence of impurity in the ceric sulfate solution can be inferred. Scrupulous care must be taken in cleaning glassware to be used in ceric dosimetry.

The dosimeter is generally calibrated against the Fricke dosimeter; some recent $G(Ce^{3+})$ values for ceric sulfate solutions, 10^{-5} to $0.03M$, are given in Table 4.8.

The $G(Ce^{3+})$ values are independent of the initial ceric ion concentration from 10^{-5} to $0.05M$ (35, 59), but are concentration dependent above about $0.05M$. Cerous ions may also affect the yield as they build up in

TABLE 4.8 *G Values for the Ceric Sulfate Dosimeter*

Radiation	$G(Ce^{3+})$	Assumed $G(Fe^{3+})$, or method of energy measurement	Ref.
8–14 Mev electrons	2.5 ± 0.18	Calorimetry	59
Co^{60} γ-rays (1.25 Mev)	2.5 ± 0.026	15.6	59
	2.33 ± 0.03	15.45	60
	2.45 ± 0.08	15.5	61
	2.44 ± 0.03*	15.6	62
200 kvp x-rays	3.15 ± 0.10	15.5	61
10 Mev deuterons	2.80 ± 0.04	Charge collection	60
11 Mev helium ions	2.90 ± 0.06	Charge collection	60
Po^{210} α-particles (5.3 Mev; internal source)	3.20 ± 0.06	Absolute counting	63
Po^{210} α-particles (3.4 Mev; filtered through mica)	2.88 ± 0.02	4.7	64
$B^{10}(n,\alpha)Li^7$ recoil nuclei	2.94 ± 0.12	4.22	60

* This is the average of six independent literature values normalized to a standard set of conditions, taking 5609 liter/mole cm as the molar extinction coefficient for ceric ion at 320 mμ.

the irradiated solution, particularly when concentrated ceric solutions are given large doses of radiation. Harlan and Hart (58) found that $G(Ce^{3+})$ for a 0.39M solution fell from an initial value of 3.1 to 1.7 as the solution absorbed a total dose of about 10^8 rads. For lower doses, in the region of 10^5 to 10^7 rads, the response is essentially linear with absorbed dose.

Taimuty, Towle, and Peterson (59) found the yield to be independent of dose rate up to 2×10^8 rads/sec,[9] using pulsed electron radiation from a linear accelerator, and independent of temperature from 7° to 35°C; the yield falls slightly at higher temperatures.

Nicksic and Wright (66) have drawn attention to the need to avoid unnecessary exposure of ceric ion solutions to light in order to avoid photoreduction. Two hours exposure to daylight, for example, reduced the ceric ion concentration of a $2.5 \times 10^{-4}M$ solution by 32%.

Other Chemical Dosimeters

Many other chemical systems have been proposed and, to a limited extent, used as chemical dosimeters, but to the present time none has been adopted as widely as the Fricke dosimeter and, to a lesser degree, the ceric sulfate dosimeter. A few of these systems are listed in Table 4.9.

When the ferrous sulfate dosimeter is modified by the inclusion of cupric sulfate, the ferrous ions are oxidized without the consumption of oxygen and the range of the dosimeter is extended up to 10^7 rads. With the modified dosimeter, $G(Fe^{3+})$ increases with increasing LET; the opposite is true for the Fricke dosimeter.

An advantage claimed for the sodium formate dosimeter is that neither the dosimeter solution nor the irradiated solution corrode common metals, so that the dosimeter may be used for irradiations carried out in metal vessels. A similar claim may be made for the calcium benzoate system, though this is useful at a much lower dose range. Both the calcium benzoate and the quinine sulfate systems employ extremely sensitive fluorescence measurements in order to determine the small chemical changes produced by low doses of radiation. The oxalic acid and D(+)maltose systems are also noncorrosive, and the former is recommended for use in nuclear reactors since it can measure large doses without becoming radioactive; G(-oxalic acid) for the secondary protons produced by fast neutrons in a reactor core varies from 0.7 to 0.3 according to the irradiation conditions. The polyacrylamide dosimeter is

[9] Rotblat and Sutton (53) and Pikaev and Glazunov (65) give a rather lower limit of about 10^7 rads/sec.

TABLE 4.9 *Systems Used, or Suggested for Use, In Chemical Dosimetry*

Dosimeter	Chemical change measured, and G value	Method of measurement	Dose range (rads)	Ref.
Aqueous ferrous + cupric sulfates (aerated; 1mN $FeSO_4$, 10mM $CuSO_4$, 10mN H_2SO_4)	$Fe^{2+} \rightarrow Fe^{3+}$ $G(Fe^{3+}) = 0.66$(Co^{60} γ-rays) $= 2.0(B^{10}(n,\alpha)Li^7$ recoil nuclei)	Spectrophotometry (at 302 mμ)	to 10^7	49, 67
Aqueous sodium formate (deaerated)	$HCOONa \rightarrow$ oxidizable products G(equiv. $KMnO_4$ reduced) $= 3.40$(3 Mev electrons)	Titration with acid permanganate at a temperature above 80°C	10^6 to 8×10^7	68
Aqueous calcium benzoate (aerated; $6 \times 10^{-4}M$)	COO^- → COO^-, OH G(salicylic acid) approx. 0.7	Fluorescence	5 to 5000 ($\pm 5\%$)	69
Aqueous quinine sulfate (0.1 to 1 ppm in 0.8N H_2SO_4)	G(-quinine) approx. 2.3	Fluorescence	10 to 1000	70
Aqueous oxalic acid (aerated; 0.025–0.6M)	Loss of oxalic acid G(-oxalic acid) $= 4.9 \pm 0.4$ (Co^{60} γ-rays)	Spectrophotometry	1.6×10^6 to 1.6×10^8	71
Aqueous $D(+)$maltose (aerated; 10% solution + 0.02% NH_4OH)	Degradation of the sugar	Polarimetry	2.5×10^7 to 10^8	72

TABLE 4.9 (*Continued*)

Dosimeter	Chemical change measured, and G value	Method of measurement	Dose range (rads)	Ref.
Aqueous polyacrylamide (aerated; 0.078% material mol. wt. 5 to 6×10^6)	Degradation of the polymer to smaller molecules	Viscosity	50 to 7500	73
Aqueous chloroform (single phase) (aerated; saturated solution, i.e., about 0.07M)	Formation HCl $G(HCl)$ approx. 26	Any method for estimating either strong acid or Cl^-, e.g., titration, conductivity, or pH measurements	10^3 to 4×10^4 (±5%)	74, 75
Chloroform + water (two phase) (air-saturated)	Formation HCl $G(HCl)$ approx. 6000 or, if inhibitor (alcohol or phenol) present, approx. 35–90	Titration or (+ dye) colorimetry	(+ inhibitor) 50 to 1000	75
Cyclohexane	Formation gaseous products (H_2) $G(H_2) = 5.25$	Pressure increase measured by vacuum techniques	10^4 to 10^8 (±3 to 6%)	76, 77, 78
Nitrous oxide	$N_2O \rightarrow N_2, O_2, NO_2$ $G(\text{-}N_2O)$ approx. 12	Pressure increase measured by vacuum techniques or, at doses greater than 3×10^7 rad, colorimetric estimation of NO_2	5×10^4 to 3×10^9 (±5%)	79, 80
Acetylene	Condensation to liquid or solid products (benzene + cuprene) $G(\text{-}C_2H_2) = 71.9$ $G(C_6H_6) = 5.1$	Pressure decrease measured by vacuum techniques and corrected for benzene formed		81, 82

almost unaffected by fast and thermal neutrons and since it is particularly simple and inexpensive has been suggested for use in personnel monitoring and for Civil Defense purposes.

Organic halogen compounds liberate acid products on irradiation and have formed the basis for several chemical dosimeters. The simplest of these is merely water saturated with pure chloroform. Hydrochloric acid is formed on irradiation, and can be determined by titration with dilute alkali, from the conductivity of the solution, or by any other of the many standard analytical methods for strong acids and chloride ions. $G(HCl)$ is relatively independent of the dose rate and energy of the radiation but, since the radiolysis reaction consumes oxygen, exhaustion of the dissolved oxygen imposes an upper limit to the dose that can be measured. A similar restriction applies to the two-phase chloroform-water system, which consists of a layer of pure chloroform covered with a layer of water. Most of the radiation-induced reaction here takes place in the organic layer, and the acid products are subsequently extracted into the water layer and estimated. Radiation initiates a chain reaction in pure chloroform and consequently very high yields of acid can be obtained and rather small doses of radiation detected. However, chain reactions have the disadvantage of being generally very dependent upon the radiation dose rate, and upon such factors as the temperature and the presence of impurities. These undesirable features can be overcome in part by adding inhibitors, generally organic alcohols or phenols, which limit the chain length of the reaction. By adding carefully controlled amounts of inhibitors the characteristics of the two-phase chloroform-water dosimeter can be improved, and it may be used to measure doses in the range 50 to 1000 rads. Two-phase systems of tetra chloroethylene and water, containing varying amounts of inhibitor, can be prepared so as to have a useful range over some part of the region from 1 to 10^6 rads. The response of the two-phase dosimeters is energy dependent at low x- and γ-ray energies since they contain a high proportion of the relatively high-Z element chlorine, and they are of limited use in the laboratory. Taplin (75) has published a comprehensive review of chlorinated-hydrocarbon dosimeters and their applications.

Gels containing water-soluble chlorine compounds and a pH-sensitive dye give a three-dimensional picture of the dose distribution when they are irradiated (83, 84). The gel can be cut into sections after irradiation and the local doses estimated from the color change, or from conductivity measurements, at the point of interest.

Cyclohexane is one of a number of chemical dosimeters proposed in order to cover the important high-dose range above 10^6 rads.

Dosimetry with nitrous oxide and acetylene provides a useful method of estimating the energy absorption in gaseous systems. The nitrous oxide dosimeter has a further advantage in being stable at temperatures up to about 200°C, and it may prove a useful general dosimeter at temperatures in the range −80° to 200°C at which other chemical dosimeters cannot be used.

Glass Dosimetry

Though the changes involved are physical rather than chemical, it is convenient to include a brief description of glass dosimeters at this stage.

On exposure to radiation glasses darken, and the degree of darkening may be used as a measure of the dose. At the same time fluorescent centers may be created in certain sensitized glasses, and the fluorescence (radiophotoluminescence) excited when the glass is afterwards exposed to light of a suitable wavelength used to estimate the dose. Both techniques have proved useful in dosimetry, the former for large doses and the latter for smaller doses.

The glass generally used for fluorescence measurements is a silver-activated phosphate glass containing 50% $Al(PO_3)_3$, 25% $Ba(PO_3)_2$, and 25% KPO_3, with 8% $AgPO_3$ added. Small plates, about 1 × 1 × 0.2 cm, and small needles, about 1 mm in diameter and 6 mm long, of the sensitized glass have been used for dosimetry (85, 86, 87, 88), though any other convenient shape or size can be used. After irradiation the glass is exposed to ultraviolet light with a wavelength in the region of 3650 Å, and the orange fluorescence is measured with a photomultiplier tube fitted with an orange filter. Under controlled conditions of ultraviolet illumination, the intensity of the luminescence is proportional to the radiation dose, which can be determined by calibrating the device against some form of standard dosimeter. Doses between 10 and 1000 rads can be measured in this way with an accuracy of about 5%. The response of the dosimeter is linear with dose, cumulative, and independent of dose rate over a wide range of dose rates. It is, however, energy dependent at low x- and γ-ray energies because of the inclusion of relatively high-Z elements in the glass. The energy dependence at low energies (80 kev to 1 Mev) can be improved by placing lead filters about the glass, though this adversely affects the response at energies higher than 1 Mev. The temperature during irradiation and the temperature at which the fluorescence is measured also affect the response. The unirradiated glass is quite stable and the irradiated glass retains its ability to fluoresce for a reasonable period after irradiation if it is stored in the dark at room temperature; the intensity of the fluorescence is reduced if the irradiated glass is exposed to strong light and also if it is stored at temperatures well above room temperature. Fluorescence intensities determined immediately after irradiation are 10–20% lower than the values reached after standing several hours, so that it is necessary to store the irradiated glass for about 24 hours before taking any measurements.

The silver-activated phosphate glass may also be used for measuring doses from 10^3 to 2×10^6 rads by utilizing the coloration produced by radiation; the quantity measured here is the change in optical absorption at 3500 Å, or longer wavelengths (89, 90). Some fading of the coloration occurs on standing, but this can be allowed for by making the optical measurements at a set time after the irradiation, or by heating the glass for a few minutes at a temperature between 100° and 150°C. Such relatively mild heating destroys the more unstable color centers, which are mainly responsible for the initial fading, leaving more stable centers that fade only gradually. The response is not linear over the whole of the dose range, the change in optical density with increasing dose becoming smaller at doses greater than 10^5 rads, and it is energy dependent, particularly below 200 kev. However the response is dose-rate independent up to at least 10^8 rads/hr. When the irradiated glass is heated at about 450°C for a few minutes the color is erased and the glass can be reused for dosimetry; the response of the dosimeter is not altered by this procedure.

Dosimetry in the range above 1000 rads is not restricted to the silver-activated phosphate glass; other glasses also darken upon irradiation and may be used for this purpose. Kreidl and Blair (91), for example, have suggested the use of a sodium borosilicate glass containing 0.1% of cobalt oxide which is usable over the range 100 to 10^7 rads. The response of this glass should be less dependent on the radiation energy at low photon energies since the high-*Z* elements barium and silver, present in the phosphate glass, are absent.

Glass dosimeters have several points in their favor, including their size (they may be made quite small), chemical inertness, rigidity, and their indefinite shelf life, and they would seem well suited to routine dose measurements as applied, for example, to industrial irradiations.

MEASUREMENT OF VERY SMALL AND VERY LARGE DOSES

Most of the dosimeters already mentioned cover the range of doses between 1 and 10^6 or 10^7 rads. Doses both below and above this range are important, and the methods of measuring them deserve some mention.

Doses below 1 rad, down to the dose absorbed due to natural background radiation, are of concern to all radiation workers since they represent the most common hazard in this field. Consequently some knowledge of the dose absorbed by the worker, over fairly long periods of time, and of the dose-rate in working areas, are essential to health and safety.

Low exposure dose rates, of the order of milliroentgens per hour, that may be found in working areas, are controlled by means of survey instruments. These include portable instruments based on ionization measurements, and capable of indicating dose rates in ranges varying from 0 to 25 mr/hr to (for Civil Defense purposes) 0 to 500 r/hr, portable Geiger counters, which are rather more sensitive and have operating ranges varying from 0 to 0.2 mr/hr to 0 to 10 r/hr, and scintillation counters, which can be made even more sensitive than the Geiger counters.

Low exposure doses, accumulated over a period of time, can be measured with sensitive ionization chambers reading up to a few hundred milliroentgens. The sensitive volume of these chambers is generally only one or two cubic centimeters and the whole instrument no larger than a fountain pen, so that they are aptly named *pocket dosimeters*. Some form of separate charging device is necessary, but the dosimeters are often designed to include a calibrated scale that can be read without other instrumentation. The fogging produced in photographic film by exposure to ionizing radiation is also used to determine the accumulated dose to persons working with radiation sources (92, cf. 93). The films are subsequently developed under carefully controlled conditions and the degree of darkening provides a measure of the exposure dose. Careful control of the developing procedure is essential and this is usually carried out at a central laboratory devoted to this purpose.

Both the survey instruments and the pocket dosimeters will be energy dependent and their response may vary with such conditions as the temperature and barometric pressure, or the direction in which they are exposed to the radiation. Great accuracy cannot be expected from them unless they are calibrated and used under controlled conditions. Generally, for the purposes for which they are intended, an accuracy of 25% is adequate. Survey instruments and pocket dosimeters are reviewed by Bemis (92).

Large doses, in the range above 10^6 rads, are becoming increasingly important as the industrial use of radiation expands and as accelerators capable of producing very high doses and dose rates are developed. In addition to the dosimetric procedures already mentioned, which can in some cases be extended to cover the high-dose range, other methods become feasible which, because of low yields or small response, are not practicable for lower doses.

At high dose rates the accuracy of ionization measurements suffers because of recombination of the ions before they can be collected; the limiting dose rate appears to be about 10^7 rads/hr. Calorimetric measurements are applicable to high doses and high dose rates, but experimental difficulties generally preclude the use of calorimetry for routine purposes and at the present time it is limited to absolute energy-absorption and intensity measurements under laboratory conditions. Charge collection, again, is independent of the dose and dose rate, and is widely used for measurements with accelerated electron and heavy ion beams. Several of the chemical dosimeters are applicable to high doses and dose rates; for example the ceric sulfate, cyclohexane, and nitrous oxide systems, and others will undoubtedly be developed. Glass dosimetry is also likely to be extended to cover higher ranges of dose.

An interesting development in the use of photographic films for dosimetry is the use of print-out emulsions, which contain an excess of silver ions and do not require wet processing. On irradiation the silver ions deposit on the sites where absorption of the radiation has produced silver atoms, with the result that the emulsion is darkened. The darkening can be estimated either visually (through an orange filter) or by means of a densitometer, and has been used to determine doses from 10^4 to several million rads (94); the range can probably be extended to greater doses by using less sensitive emulsions (95).

Degradation of luminescent organic compounds (e.g., anthracene and *p*-quaterphenyl) has also been proposed as a means of measuring large doses (96, 97). The absorbed dose is a function of the decrease in intensity of the fluorescence (excited by ultraviolet illumination) from the compound after irradiation. Doses in the range 5×10^5 to 5×10^9 rads can be determined in this way with an accuracy of better than 10%. The degradation of polystyrene-based plastic scintillators (98) is an alternative means of dosimetry; in this case the extent of the radiation damage can be measured by the change in response of the scintillator to ionizing radiation, rather than the change in ultraviolet-excited fluorescence.

The useful dose and dose-rate ranges for a number of dosimeters are compared in Table 4.10.

TABLE 4.10 *Dosimeter Characteristics*

Dosimeter	Maximum dose rate (rads/hr)	Dose range (rads)	Reproducibility
Ionization chambers (thimble)	10^7		±2%
Fricke (ferrous sulfate)	4×10^{10}	4000 to 40,000	±1%
Ceric sulfate	7×10^{11}	10^5 to 1.4×10^8	±1 to 4%
Ferrous + cupric sulfate	8×10^5	up to 10^7	
Nitrous oxide	10^9	5×10^4 to 3×10^9	±5%
Cyclohexane	10^6	10^4 to 10^8	±3 to 6%
Silver-activated phosphate glass:			
fluorescence	over 10^8	10 to 1000	±5%
optical density	over 10^8	10^3 to 2×10^6	±2 to 5%
Cobalt glass (ref. 91)	over 10^{10}	100 to 10^7	±2%
Degradation of luminescent organic compounds:			
anthracene	10^9	3×10^5 to 2×10^8	±10%
p-quaterphenyl	3×10^8	5×10^5 to 5×10^9	±5 to 10%

REFERENCES

Many of the topics included in this section are discussed more fully by G. N. Whyte, *Principles of Radiation Dosimetry*, John Wiley and Sons, New York, 1959, and in *Radiation Dosimetry*, (eds. G. J. Hine and G. L. Brownell) Academic Press Inc., New York, 1956. Further useful information is contained in *Selected Topics in Radiation Dosimetry*, International Atomic Energy Agency, Vienna, 1961.

1. *Report of the International Commission on Radiological Units and Measurements (ICRU), 1959, Nat. Bur. St. (U.S.), Handbook* 78 (1961).
2. D. E. Lea, *Actions of Radiations on Living Cells,* Cambridge University Press, Cambridge, 1946. Chapter 1.
3. G. N. Whyte, *Principles of Radiation Dosimetry,* John Wiley and Sons, New York, 1959, p. 64.
4. V. H. Ritz and F. H. Attix, *Radiation Res.,* **16,** 401 (1962).
5. *Report of the International Commission on Radiological Units and Measurements (ICRU), 1956, Nat. Bur. St. (U.S.), Handbook* 62 (1957).
6. F. W. Spiers in *Radiation Dosimetry,* (eds. G. J. Hine and G. L. Brownell) Academic Press Inc., New York, 1956. Chapter 1.
7. H. E. Johns, *The Physics of Radiology,* Second Edition, Charles C. Thomas, Springfield, Illinois, 1961.
8. H. E. Johns in *Radiation Dosimetry,* (eds. G. J. Hine and G. L. Brownell) Academic Press Inc., New York, 1956. Chapter 12.
9. W. H. Bragg, *Studies in Radioactivity,* Macmillan and Co., London, 1912, p. 94.

10. L. H. Gray, *Proc. Roy. Soc. (London), Ser. A,* **156,** 578 (1936) ; *Brit. J. Radiol.,* **10,** 600, 721 (1937).
11. P. R. J. Burch, *Radiation Res.,* **3,** 361 (1955).
12. L. V. Spencer and F. H. Attix, *Radiation Res.,* **3,** 239 (1955).
13. J. W. Boag in *Radiation Dosimetry,* (eds. G. J. Hine and G. L. Brownell) Academic Press Inc., New York, 1956, Chapter 4.
14. G. N. Whyte, *Principles of Radiation Dosimetry,* John Wiley and Sons, New York, 1959, p. 68 (Table 5.2).
15. M. Inokuti, *J. Phys. Soc. Japan,* **13,** 537 (1958); *Isotopes and Radiation (Tokyo),* **1,** 82 (1958).
16. J. Lamborn and A. J. Swallow, *J. Phys. Chem.,* **65,** 920 (1961).
17. G. W. Grodstein, *X-ray Attenuation Coefficients from 10 kev to 100 Mev, Nat. Bur. St. (U.S.), Circ.* 583 (1957; R. T. McGinnies, *Nat. Bur. St. (U.S.), Supplement to Circ.* 583 (1959)
18. U. Fano, *Nucleonics,* **11** (Aug.), 8 (Sept.), 55 (1953).
19. R. T. Berger, *Radiation Res.* **15,** 1 (1961).
20. J. S. Laughlin and S. Genna in *Radiation Dosimetry,* (eds. G. J. Hine and G. L. Brownell) Academic Press Inc., New York, 1956, Chapter 9.
21. W. B. Reid and H. E. Johns, *Radiation Res.,* **14,** 1 (1961).
22. E. J. Hart, H. W. Koch, B. Petree, J. H. Schulman, S. I. Taimuty, and H. O. Wyckoff, *Proc. Second Intern. Conf. Peaceful Uses Atomic Energy,* United Nations, Geneva, **21,** 188 (1958).
23. S. I. Taimuty, *Nucleonics,* **15,** (Nov)., 182 (1957).
24. J. S. Laughlin in *Radiation Dosimetry,* (eds. G. J. Hine and G. L. Brownell) Academic Press Inc., New York, 1956, Chapter 13.
25. A. C. Birge, H. O. Anger, and C. A. Tobias in *Radiation Dosimetry, ibid.,* Chapter 14.
26. H. H. Rossi in *Radiation Dosimetry, ibid.,* Chapter 15.
27. *Measurement of Neutron Flux and Spectra for Physical and Biological Applications, Nat. Bur. St. (U.S.), Handbook* 72 (1960).
28. *Measurement of Absorbed Dose of Neutrons, and Mixtures of Neutrons and Gamma Rays, Nat. Bur. St. (U.S.), Handbook* 75 (1961).
29. H. Fricke and S. Morse, *Am. J. Roentgenol,* **18,** 430 (1927); H. Fricke and S. Morse, *Phil. Mag.,* **7,** 129 (1929) ; H. Fricke and E. J. Hart, *J. Chem. Phys.,* **3,** 60 (1935).
30. Jerome Weiss, A. O. Allen, and H. A. Schwarz, *Proc. Intern. Conf. Peaceful Uses Atomic Energy,* United Nations, New York, **14,** 179 (1956).
31. American Society for Testing Materials, *Proposed Tentative Method of Test for Gamma Radiation by Chemical Dosimetry* (1959).
32. H. A. Dewhurst, *J. Chem. Phys.,* **19,** 1329 (1951) ; *Trans. Faraday Soc.,* **48,** 905 (1952).
33. H. Fricke, E. J. Hart, and H. P. Smith, *J. Chem. Phys.,* **6,** 229 (1938).
34. J. L. Haybittle, R. D. Saunders, and A. J. Swallow, *J. Chem. Phys.,* **25,** 1213 (1956).
35. Jerome Weiss, *Nucleonics,* **10,** (July), 28 (1952).
36. R. H. Schuler and A. O. Allen, *J. Chem. Phys.,* **24,** 56 (1956).
37. C. M. Henderson and N. Miller, *Radiation Res.,* **13,** 641 (1960).

38. J. A. Ghormley in *Radiation Chemistry of Gases* by S. C. Lind, Reinhold Publishing Corporation, New York, 1961, p. 59.
39. K. Scharf and R. M. Lee, *Radiation Res.,* **16,** 115 (1962).
40. *International Critical Tables,* (United States) National Research Council, 1928, Vol. 3, p. 56.
41. L. Ehrenberg and E. Sæland, *JENER Publications No.* 8 (1954).
42. Jerome Weiss, W. Bernstein, and J. B. H. Kuper, *J. Chem. Phys.,* **22,** 1593 (1954).
43. C. J. Hochanadel and J. A. Ghormley, *J. Chem. Phys.,* **21,** 880 (1953).
44. R. M. Lazo, H. A. Dewhurst, and M. Burton, *J. Chem. Phys.,* **22,** 1370 (1954).
45. M. Peisch and J. Steyn, *Nature,* **187,** 58 (1960).
46. M. H. Back and N. Miller, *Nature,* **179,** 321 (1957).
47. M. Cottin and M. Lefort, *J. Chim. Phys.,* **53,** 267 (1956).
48. W. R. McDonell and E. J. Hart, *J. Am. Chem. Soc.,* **76,** 2121 (1954).
49. E. J. Hart, W. J. Ramler, and S. R. Rocklin, *Radiation Res.,* **4,** 378 (1956).
50. R. H. Schuler and N. F. Barr, *J. Am. Chem. Soc.,* **78,** 5756 (1956).
51. C. N. Trumbore and E. J. Hart, *J. Phys. Chem.,* **63,** 867 (1959).
52. G. Rudstam and T. Svedberg, *Nature,* **171,** 648 (1953).
53. J. Rotblat and H. C. Sutton, *Proc. Roy. Soc. (London), Ser.* A **255,** 490 (1960).
54. A. R. Anderson, *J. Phys. Chem.,* **66,** 180 (1962).
55. H. A. Dewhurst, *Trans. Faraday Soc.,* **49,** 1174 (1953).
56. H. A. Schwarz, *J. Am. Chem. Soc.,* **76,** 1587 (1954).
57. N. F. Barr, J. Geisselsoder, and J. S. Laughlin, *Radiation Res.,* **14,** 291 (1961).
58. J. T. Harlan and E. J. Hart, *Nucleonics,* **17,** (Aug.), 102 (1959).
59. S. I. Taimuty, L. H. Towle, and D. L. Peterson, *Nucleonics,* **17,** (Aug.), 103 (1959).
60. N. F. Barr and R. H. Schuler, *J. Phys. Chem.,* **63,** 808 (1959).
61. G. R. A. Johnson and J. Weiss, *Proc. Roy. Soc. (London), Ser. A,* **240,** 189 (1957).
62. J. W. Boyle, *Radiation Res.,* **17,** 427 (1962).
63. M. Lefort and X. Tarrago, *J. Phys. Chem.,* **63,** 833 (1959).
64. Jerome Weiss and N. Miller, *J. Phys. Chem.,* **63,** 888 (1959).
65. A. K. Pikaev and P. Ya. Glazunov, *Izv. Akad. Nauk SSSR, Otd. Khim. Nauk,* 940 (1960).
66. S. W. Nicksic and J. R. Wright, *Nucleonics,* **13,** (Nov.), 104 (1955).
67. E. J. Hart and P. D. Walsh, *Radiation Res.,* **1,** 342 (1954); E. J. Hart, *ibid.,* **2,** 33 (1955).
68. T. J. Hardwick and W. S. Guentner, *J. Phys. Chem.,* **63,** 896 (1959); T. J. Hardwick, *Radiation Res.,* **12,** 5 (1960).
69. W. A. Armstrong and D. W. Grant, *Nature,* **182,** 747 (1958); *Can. J. Chem.,* **38,** 845 (1960); W. A. Armstrong, R. A. Facey, D. W. Grant, and W. G. Humphreys, *Radiation Res.,* **19,** 120 (1963).
70. N. F. Barr and M. B. Stark, *Radiation Res.,* **12,** 1 (1960).
71. I. Draganić, *Nucleonics,* **21,** (Feb.), 33 (1963).
72. A. L. Glass, *Nucleonics,* **20,** (Dec.), 66 (1962).
73. A. L. Boni, *Radiation Res.,* **14,** 374 (1961).
74. J. Teplý and J. Bednář, *Proc. Second Intern. Conf. Peaceful Uses Atomic Energy,* United Nations, Geneva, **29,** 71 (1958).

75. G. V. Taplin in *Radiation Dosimetry,* (eds. G. J. Hine and G. L. Brownell) Academic Press Inc., New York, 1956, Chapter 8.
76. R. H. Schuler and A. O. Allen, *J. Am. Chem. Soc.,* **77,** 507 (1955).
77. H. A. Dewhurst, *J. Phys. Chem.,* **61,** 1466 (1957).
78. J. Prévé and G. Gaudemaris, *Compt. Rend.,* **250,** 3470 (1960).
79. P. Harteck and S. Dondes, *Nucleonics,* **14,** (Mar.), 66 (1956).
80. R. E. Simpson, *Health Phys.,* **8,** 143 (1962).
81. L. M. Dorfman and F. J. Shipko, *J. Am. Chem. Soc.,* **77,** 4723 (1955).
82. F. W. Lampe, *Nucleonics,* **18,** (Apr.), 60 (1960).
83. H. L. Andrews, R. E. Murphy, and E. J. LeBrun, *Rev. Sci. Instr.,* **28,** 329 (1957).
84. L. H. Gevantman, *Radiation Res. Supplement* **2,** 608 (1960).
85. A. L. Riegert, H. E. Johns, and J. W. T. Spinks, *Nucleonics,* **14,** (Nov.), 134 (1956); A. L. Riegert and J. W. T. Spinks, *Intern. J. Appl. Radiation Isotopes,* **3,** 125 (1958).
86. J. H. Schulman and H. W. Etzel, *Science,* **118,** 184 (1953); J. H. Schulman, W. Shurcliff, R. J. Ginther, and F. H. Attix, *Nucleonics,* **11,** (Oct.), 52 (1953).
87. N. F. Barr, M. B. Stark, J. Hands, and J. S. Laughlin, *Health Phys.,* **7,** 48 (1961).
88. S. Kondo, *Health Phys.,* **7,** 25 (1961).
89. J. H. Schulman, C. C. Klick, and H. Rabin, *Nucleonics,* **13,** (Feb.), 30 (1955).
90. S. Davison, S. A. Goldblith, and B. E. Proctor, *Nucleonics,* **14,** (Jan.), 34 (1956).
91. N. J. Kreidl and G. E. Blair, *Nucleonics,* **14,** (Mar.), 82 (1956).
92. E. A. Bemis in *Radiation Dosimetry,* (eds. G. J. Hine and G. L. Brownell) Academic Press Inc., New York, 1956, Chapter 10.
93. R. A. Dudley in *Radiation Dosimetry,* (eds. G. J. Hine and G. L. Brownell), Academic Press Inc., New York, 1956, Chapter 7.
94. H. F. Nitka and D. P. Jones, *Nucleonics,* **15,** (Oct.), 128 (1957); H. F. Nitka, *ibid.,* **17,** (Oct.), 58 (1959).
95. W. L. McLaughlin, *Radiation Res.,* **13,** 594 (1960).
96. F. H. Attix, *Nucleonics,* **17,** (Apr.), 142 (1959).
97. J. H. Schulman, H. W. Etzel, and J. G. Allard, *J. Appl. Phys.,* **28,** 792 (1957).
98. I. M. Rozman and K. G. Zimmer, *Intern. J. Appl. Radiation Isotopes,* **3,** 36 (1958).

CHAPTER 5

Ions and Excited Molecules

In the earlier chapters ions and excited molecules were introduced as the first species formed when ionizing radiation is absorbed by matter. Their formation is related to the absorption of energy by the material and their numbers are directly proportional to the absorbed dose; for most molecules in the gas phase, approximately equal numbers of ionized and excited molecules are produced (1). At a later period these primary species may break down and (or) react with the substrate to bring about chemical change. Free radicals formed from the excited and ionized molecules are largely responsible for these changes and generally dominate mechanisms postulated for radiation-induced reactions. In subsequent chapters we will of necessity concentrate more on the free radicals than on their precursors but, to emphasize that these precursors are not unimportant, brief descriptions of the properties and reactions of excited and ionized molecules are given here.

EXCITED MOLECULES

The properties of excited atoms and molecules are known from spectroscopic and photochemical studies in which the excited species are produced by the absorption of visible or ultraviolet light. The same excited species are formed by the interaction of ionizing radiation with matter, though ionizing radiation may also produce more highly excited states, with more intrinsic energy, and states (e.g., triplet) which are not formed directly by the absorption of light. Reactions observed in photochemistry, therefore, are not necessarily the only ones stemming from excited molecules which occur upon radiolysis. The distribution of excited species in media exposed to light and to ionizing radiation is also different (Fig. 1.1); photochemically produced species are distributed randomly in any plane perpendicular to the direction of the incident light but those produced by ionizing radiation are concentrated along the tracks of charged particles.

Ionizing radiation can produce excited molecules in matter directly (Eq. 5.1) and also indirectly by neutralization of the ions formed (Eq. 5.2).

$$\mathrm{A} \rightsquigarrow \mathrm{A}^* \tag{5.1}$$

$$\mathrm{A} \rightsquigarrow \mathrm{A}^+ + e^- \text{ (or } (\mathrm{A}^+)^* + e^-\text{)} \tag{5.2}$$

$$\mathrm{A}^+ + e^- \rightarrow \mathrm{A}^{**} \rightarrow \mathrm{A}^*$$

(an asterisk will be used to designate a molecule or ion in an excited state). The highly excited molecules formed on neutralization (A^{**}) often lose rapidly part of their energy through collisions with other molecules and drop to lower excited states (A^*) similar to those formed photochemically.

The absorption of ultraviolet and visible light by matter can be represented by

$$\mathrm{A} + h\nu \rightarrow \mathrm{A}^* \tag{5.3}$$

where $h\nu$ (Planck's constant multiplied by the frequency of the radiation) is the energy of a light quantum (photon). This is similar to photoelectric absorption of x- and γ-radiation in the sense that the photon disappears completely and its energy is transferred to the molecule. However, it differs from photoelectric absorption in two important respects. First, the incident photon does not have sufficient energy to eject an electron from the molecule and an electron is merely moved to a new orbit, farther from the nucleus, corresponding to a higher energy than the original stable orbit. (The electron excited will be a loosely bound electron in an outer orbit rather than one from an inner shell as is generally the case with photoelectric absorption.) Second, in photoelectric absorption an electron is liberated which can carry off energy of the photon in excess of the binding energy of the electron. This is not so in the process represented by Eq. 5.3, and all the photon energy must be transferred to the excited molecule. Since the possible energy states of the molecule are strictly regulated by quantum-mechanical considerations it also follows that only light quanta can be absorbed whose energy is equal to the difference between the energies of two of these states, and then only if the transition between these two states is allowed. Light absorption is therefore selective and the energy of the light absorbed depends upon the molecular structure of the absorbing matter. A corollary to this is that absorption of light of a given wavelength will raise the absorbing molecule to a particular, well-defined, energy state. Furthermore, in complex molecules light absorption is often limited to one of the functional groups present. Ionizing radiation, on the other hand, is not selective and can excite any part of the molecule.

The formation and properties of excited molecules can be illustrated by considering a simple diatomic molecule. Figure 5.1 represents the potential-energy of such a molecule plotted against the distance between the two nuclei. Potential-energy in this context comprises the electronic energy associated with electron orbits other than the stable ground orbits,

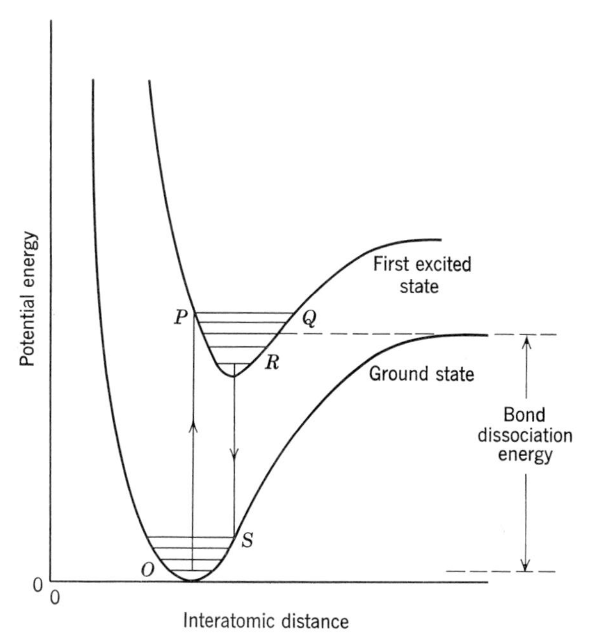

FIGURE 5.1 *Potential-energy curves for a diatomic molecule in its ground state and in an electronically excited state.*

vibrational energy of the two nuclei as they move together and apart along the line joining their centers, and rotational energy of the molecule as a whole; translational (thermal) energy associated with the movement of the molecule from place to place is not included. Quanta of rotational energy are small and will not concern us further since they do not contribute materially to the energy available for bringing about chemical change. The figure shows the stable ground state of the molecule in which the electrons are in their lowest orbits and the first (singlet) excited state in which one of the electrons is raised to a higher orbit. Higher, more energetic, electronic states also exist and would be represented in the figure by other curves lying above the first excited state. The minima in the curves in Fig. 5.1 show that in this instance a stable (covalent) bond is formed between the two nuclei in both ground and excited states. The vertical distance between the horizontal portion of the ground state curve and the x axis (or, more accurately, the horizontal through O) is a measure of the bond dissociation energy in the ground state, while the interatomic distance at the minimum of the curve is the equilibrium bond length. Excited states which have potential-energy curves similar to the ground state curve, as does the excited state shown in Fig. 5.1, generally have a smaller dissociation energy than the ground state, corresponding with a weaker bond.

The normal state of the molecule is represented by the lowest vibrational level of the ground state, i.e., by the lowest horizontal line within the ground state curve, where the vibrational quantum number is zero and the molecule has only zero-point vibrational energy. For the sake of brevity, states in which the molecule has only zero-point vibrational energy will be called vibrationless states. Absorption of light with an energy corresponding to the vertical distance between O and P can raise the molecule to the upper curve at P. The most probable transitions between different electronic energy states are those that can be represented as a vertical line on a potential-energy diagram. This restriction, which is known as the Franck-Condon Principle, can also be expressed by saying that the two nuclei are unlikely to move, relative to one another, during the transition; the transition from the ground to the excited state takes place in about 10^{-15} sec whereas a complete vibration of the molecule takes about 10^{-13} sec. Other near-vertical transitions are not completely excluded but they occur with a smaller probability. Furthermore, transitions are possible with a lower probability from positions other than the center of the lowest vibrational level so that a series of absorption bands are obtained rather than a single absorption line.

At P the excited molecule is compressed since P lies to the left of the minimum in the excited curve, which represents the stable internuclear distance for the excited state, and the molecule subsequently vibrates with an amplitude equal to the distance PQ. The vibrational energy that the molecule gains in this way is also quantized, that is it can only have a certain number of definite values, and these are represented in Fig. 5.1 by the horizontal lines (e.g., PQ) contained in the two curves. Vibrational energy can be lost quite readily by transfer to other molecules as thermal (translational) energy when these collide with the vibrationally excited molecule. On the potential energy diagram this is shown by the molecule dropping from the vibrationally excited state PQ to lower vibrational levels and eventually to the vibrationless state R.

Electronic excitation energy is not lost as readily as vibrational energy by collisional processes and the excited molecule may remain at R for a relatively long time (e.g., with a half-life of about 10^{-8} sec) before emitting a photon and returning to the ground state at S. A vertical transition is again most probable and the energy of the emitted radiation (*fluorescence*) is given by the distance RS. Since RS is shorter than OP the fluorescent radiation has a longer wavelength than the radiation originally absorbed or, in other words, the emission (fluorescent) radiation bands occur at longer wavelengths than the absorption bands. At S the molecule has excess vibrational energy which will rapidly be lost by collisions with other molecules, returning the molecule to its original state, O.

Fluorescence is only one of several ways in which an electronically excited molecule can return to the ground state. Including fluorescence these are:

(i) fluorescence (radiative conversion to the ground state),
(ii) internal conversion (nonradiative conversion to a lower state of the same multiplicity),[1]
(iii) intersystem crossing (nonradiative conversion to a state of different multiplicity),
(iv) nonradiative energy transfer to a neighboring molecule,
(v) unimolecular reaction (dissociation or isomerization of the excited molecule),
(vi) bimolecular reaction (chemical reaction involving a second molecule).

[1] The multiplicity of a state is a type of degeneracy which is determined by the total electron spin. Most stable molecules have singlet ground states and singlet and triplet excited states.

Influences external to the excited molecule may favor one or another of the alternatives. If they restrict or prevent fluorescence the fluorescence is said to be quenched.

Internal Conversion

If the potential-energy curve of the excited state crosses or comes close to that of the ground state at a vibrational level lower than that to which the molecule is originally excited (Fig. 5.2), there is a finite possibility that the molecule will cross from the excited to the ground state at this point. In the ground state the molecule will be highly vibrationally excited but will rapidly lose this energy by collision with other molecules; the degraded energy will appear as thermal energy. Internal conversion to the ground state may not be complete, but any such conversion which does take place will reduce the intensity of the fluorescence observed.

More common than conversion from an excited state to the ground state is internal conversion from higher electronically excited states to the lowest excited state of the same multiplicity (e.g., singlet or triplet). This is particularly true for polyatomic molecules because the potential-energy surfaces corresponding with the many excited states will have numerous intersections. Conversion to the lowest excited state takes place rapidly within 10^{-13} sec (2). Fluorescence is therefore characteristic of the lowest electronically excited state of a given multiplicity even though higher excited states may be formed initially. Chemical reactions

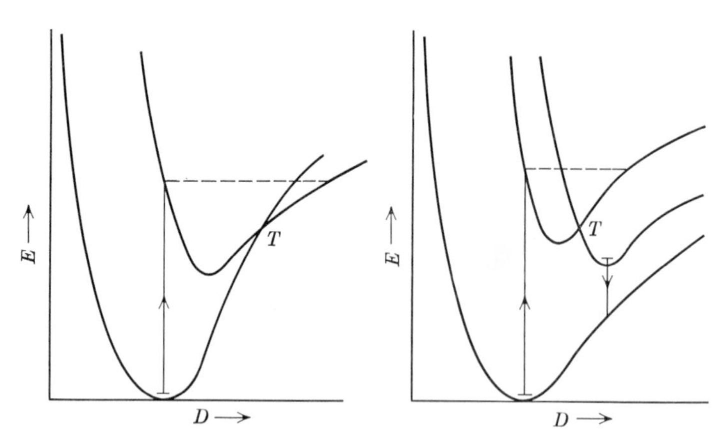

FIGURE 5.2 *Internal conversion from an electronically excited state to the ground state.*

FIGURE 5.3 *Intersystem crossing from singlet to triplet excited state.*

of electronically excited molecules are also those of the lowest excited state unless the first step is rapid unimolecular dissociation of the excited molecule. Higher excited states may dissociate before they have lost energy through internal conversion and in this case the extra energy is carried away by the dissociation products.

Intersystem Crossing

Figure 5.3 shows the potential-energy curve of a second electronically excited state of different multiplicity crossing the original excited state curve. The second curve corresponds to a lower energy than the first and, since the curves cross at a point (T) whose vibrational level is below that to which the molecule is originally excited, the excited molecule is in a position to cross to the second curve at T. Some of the excited molecules may do this, thereby decreasing the intensity of the fluorescence, but allowing the possibility of radiative transfer from the second curve to the ground state. This phenomenon has been found in molecular spectroscopy and the original and second (lower energy) excited curves have been identified as singlet and triplet excited states respectively.

Electronically excited states formed directly by the absorption of light are normally singlet states while triplet excited states are formed from these by intersystem crossing, the process shown in Fig. 5.3. In general, triplet excited states are not formed directly from the ground state by the absorption of light, and the transition from singlet ground state to triplet excited state is said to be forbidden.

Triplet excited states have longer lifetimes than singlet excited states because the triplet → singlet emission is highly forbidden. Lifetimes from 10^{-4} to 10^{-3} sec are usual but the lifetime may be as long as several seconds. The radiation emitted when an excited triplet state drops to the ground state has a longer wavelength than the corresponding fluorescence and is known as *phosphorescence*. Some of the triplet excited molecules may gain enough energy through collisions with other molecules to raise them to the vibrational level at T (Fig. 5.3), so that they can return to the singlet excited state and fluoresce in the normal way. Fluorescence due to molecules which have spent some time in the triplet state will be delayed beyond the normal half-life of the singlet excited molecules (about 10^{-8} sec) and is known as *delayed* or *slow fluorescence;* the effect is enhanced by heating the triplet-excited medium.

The lifetime of triplet excited states is influenced by the physical state of the medium and is longest in very viscous or solid systems; singlet excited states differ in this respect and their lifetimes are not affected by the nature of the surrounding medium. Phosphorescence is not observed at all in nonviscous solutions where, in the absence of other nonradiative processes such as bimolecular reaction, the triplet state is deactivated in a radiationless process involving both the triplet excited molecule and the solvent.

Structurally the triplet state is distinguished by inversion of the spin of the excited electron (Fig. 5.4). In stable molecules the electrons are normally grouped in pairs in each of which the two electrons have opposite spins. Excitation to an excited singlet state results in the translation of one of the electrons to a higher-energy orbit, but without change in the direction of spin. Excitation to an excited triplet state involves both transfer of an electron to a higher orbit and inversion of the spin of the excited electron. The triplet state will therefore contain two electrons whose spins are parallel, and for many purposes it can be treated as a diradical. The two unpaired electrons associated with the triplet state have been detected by magnetic susceptibility and electron spin resonance measurements similar to those used to detect the single unpaired electron present in free radicals. In Fig. 5.4 the energy of the molecule in the triplet excited state is shown as rather less than the energy of the excited molecule in the singlet state since a system in which the electron spins are parallel has a lower energy than one in which they are all paired (Hund's rule); a triplet level is normally the lowest electronically excited state of the molecule.

Interconversion of singlet and triplet states is facilitated by the presence of paramagnetic atoms or heavy nuclei. The lifetime of triplet excited states for example is shorter when the excited compound contains heavy elements which facilitate conversion to the singlet ground state.

Triplet excited molecules are important in radiation chemistry both because of their relatively long lifetimes and diradical character, which

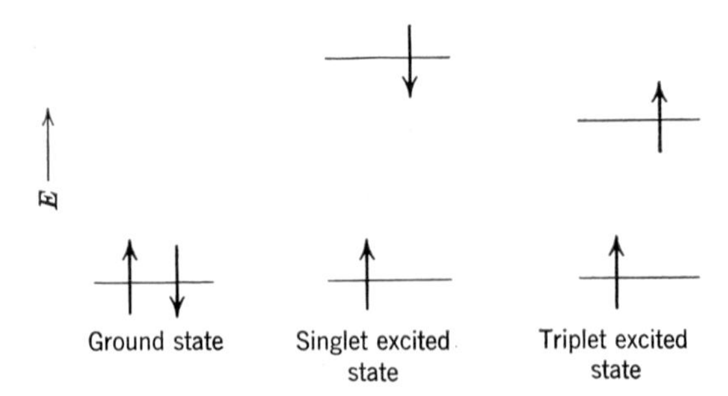

FIGURE 5.4 *Electron distribution and spin in molecules in the ground (singlet) state, excited singlet, and excited triplet states.*

favor chemical reaction with the substrate rather than energy loss by phosphorescence and internal conversion, and because they are formed in the tracks of charged particles in rather greater numbers than might be anticipated by analogy with photochemistry. Swiftly moving charged particles can produce only optically allowed transitions — from singlet ground states only singlet excited states — but slowly moving charged particles, particularly electrons, can induce optically forbidden transitions — e.g., give triplet excited states from singlet ground states. Furthermore, neutralization of positive ions with electrons (Eq. 5.2) in the presence of other ions, i.e., under the conditions present in the clusters or spurs found along the track of a charged particle, can give both singlet and triplet excited molecules (3). Finally, slow secondary electrons which do not have quite enough energy to excite a molecule to its lowest singlet excited state may have sufficient energy to raise it to the lowest triplet state.

Representative lifetimes for the processes described above are given in the following diagram. The lifetimes are in seconds and refer to condensed (liquid) systems excited photochemically.

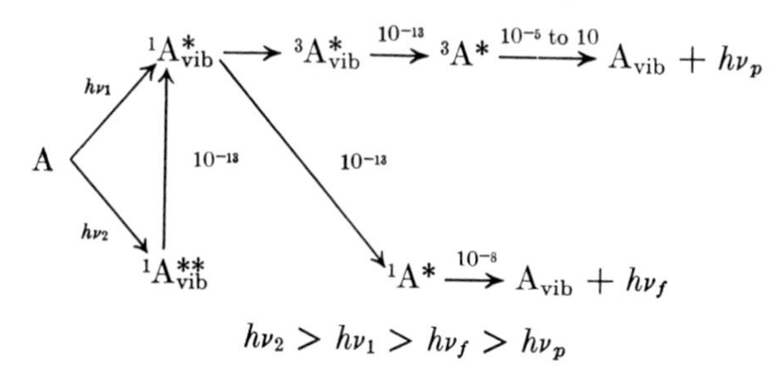

$$h\nu_2 > h\nu_1 > h\nu_f > h\nu_p$$

A is the molecule in the ground state, the superscripts 1 and 3 denote the singlet and triplet states respectively, the subscript "vib" a molecule with excess vibrational energy, and * indicates the lowest electronic excited states (either singlet or triplet), and ** any higher electronic excited state.

Nonradiative Energy Transfer

The transfer of electronic excitation energy from one molecule to another can take place in several ways, but the over-all process is represented simply by,

$$A^* + B \rightarrow A + B^* \tag{5.4}$$

The electronically excited molecule produced, B*, may revert to the ground state by any of the processes listed earlier in this chapter. Transfer of excitation energy is only possible if the energy necessary to excite B is equal to or less than the excitation energy of A*, i.e., if the excitation potential of B is equal to or less than the excitation potential of A. Energy of A* in excess of that necessary to excite B appears as vibrational or translational energy of the two molecules.

In its simplest form reaction 5.4 occurs when an excited molecule collides directly with a molecule able to accept the excitation energy; so-called "collisions of the second kind." Photochemistry offers many examples of this process including a large number of reactions, mainly in the gas phase, in which the first step is collision of an excited mercury atom with another molecule. When this second molecule is hydrogen, for example, the energy transferred is sufficient to cause it to dissociate into two hydrogen atoms; light of wavelength 2537 Å raises mercury to a triplet excited state with an energy of 113 kcal per mole while the bond dissociation energy of molecular hydrogen is 103 kcal per mole. Similar reactions can take place in liquid media but in condensed systems the two processes described below may play a significant part in the energy transfer. A well-known example of energy transfer in liquid media occurs with liquid scintillators in which energy is absorbed by a solvent and transferred to a dissolved organic compound which subsequently fluoresces.

Transfer of excitation energy also occurs if the excited molecule A* fluoresces and the fluorescent radiation is absorbed by the molecule B, raising it to the excited state B*. Qualitatively similar to this picture but more efficient is nonradiative resonance, or dipole-dipole, transfer of excitation energy between the two molecules (4). The requirements are similar to those for the emission and reabsorption of fluorescent radiation, i.e., that there be maximum overlap of the emission spectrum of the sensitizing molecule (A) and the absorption spectrum of the accepting molecule (B), but the process is pictured as involving both molecules simultaneously. The particular interest of the resonance-transfer process is that it is not restricted to collisions of the two molecules concerned but can take place when these are separated by distances large by comparison with molecular dimensions, that is by distances of the order of 50-100 Å. It is applicable to gas, liquid, and solid systems.

A further energy transfer process is possible if the excited molecule is one of an orderly array of similar molecules, e.g., one molecule in a molecular crystal. In this case it is possible to treat the system as though the electronic excitation energy (or exciton) moved rapidly from one molecule to another, spending a very short time (less than the period of one vibration) on each. The energy of the exciton is that of the vibrationless lowest excited state, since extra electronic or vibrational energy will be lost quite rapidly, and its lifetime will be about the same as if it were located on a single molecule, i.e., about 10^{-8} sec. If the crystal contains an impurity molecule which has an excited state with a lower energy than the host molecules, the exciton, if it becomes located on the impurity, will raise it to an excited state with both electronic and vibrational energy. If now the vibrational energy is lost the exciton will no longer have sufficient energy to return to the host molecules and will be trapped on the impurity and, if the excited impurity fluoresces, the fluorescence will be characteristic of the impurity and not of the host molecules which make up the bulk of the crystal. Trapping of the absorbed radiation energy in this way and the subsequent emission of fluorescence from a minor component in the solid is frequently observed with the solids used as organic scintillators.

Energy transfer by exciton migration is most likely in crystals and in large molecules such as polymers, but it appears that it may also occur in liquids. Burton and his colleagues (5) have proposed, in order to explain high rates of excitation transfer in certain scintillator solutions, that in liquid hydrocarbons small groups of ordered molecules (domains) may exist. Exciton transfer can occur within these groups of perhaps 10 or 15 molecules, so that collision with any molecule of a domain containing an excited molecule is equivalent to collision with the initially excited molecule itself.

A review of energy transfer in radiation chemistry has been given by Matheson (6).

Unimolecular Reaction

Polyatomic excited molecules may reach a stable state through some form of molecular rearrangement (7). A simple example is the conversion of a *trans* compound into an equilibrium mixture of the *cis* and *trans* forms on irradiation with ultraviolet light, i.e.,

$$\underset{trans}{\text{HC}=\text{CH}} \xrightarrow{h\nu} \underset{cis}{\text{HC}=\text{CH}} \tag{5.5}$$

If the excited state has sufficient energy the molecule may break at a covalent bond to give two free radical fragments,

$$(\text{R} : \text{S})^* \rightarrow \text{R}\cdot + \cdot\text{S} \tag{5.6}$$

The two electrons comprising the bond are divided one to each radical, and the least excitation energy that will produce dissociation is equal to the dissociation energy of the bond. Frequently rather more energy than this is required and the excess appears as kinetic energy of the fragments. Two situations which lead to dissociation are illustrated by the potential-energy curves in Fig. 5.5. In the first (*a*) the molecule is excited directly into a repulsive state and dissociation occurs in less time than the period of one vibration (less than about 10^{-13} sec); the excited state involved may be the lowest or a higher electronic excited state. In the second figure (*b*) the molecule is raised to a stable excited state but it may cross to a repulsive state at T. The excited molecules will not necessarily all pass into the repulsive state and dissociate; some may drop past T and fluoresce in the normal manner. Dissociation of the excited molecule after crossing into a second excited state, as in (*b*), is called *predissociation*.

Dissociation is very often the first step in photochemical reaction, the chemical changes being brought about subsequently by the free radicals produced. With light of short wavelength, i.e., of relatively high energy, the radicals themselves may be excited or may have an appreciable amount of kinetic energy. Radicals formed with very little extra energy may not, in liquid media, be able to escape through the close-packed molecules which surround them. In this case they will recombine, dissipating the energy of recombination as heat and producing no over-all

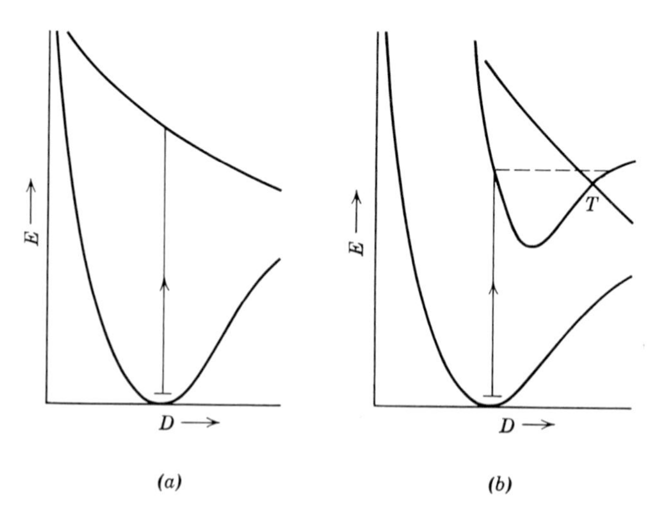

FIGURE 5.5 *(a) transition to an unstable (repulsive) state, (b) predissociation.*

chemical change. The caging and recombination of free radicals from an excited molecule before they have become separated is often referred to as the *Franck-Rabinowitch* or *cage* effect (8). A good example of the cage effect has been provided by Lampe and Noyes (9) who determined the quantum yields for the photodissociation of iodine in various solvents. They found that the quantum yield decreased in the series hexane, carbon tetrachloride, hexachlorobutadiene as the mass of the solvent molecules increased. In all solvents the quantum yields were below that found in the gas phase where the dissociation products can move apart without hindrance. More recently Meadows and Noyes (10) have drawn attention to the fact that the cage effect will operate in the opposite sense once a dissociation product is past the first layer of solvent molecules; thereafter the cage will act to keep the fragments apart.

Another feature of photochemical dissociation is the possibility of intramolecular energy transfer prior to dissociation. The bond breaking is not necessarily the site at which light was absorbed; often it is the weakest bond in the molecule which breaks. Aldehydes and ketones for example absorb light at a wavelength characteristic for the carbonyl group, but subsequently dissociate in such a manner that a carbon-carbon bond breaks and not the carbon-oxygen bond responsible for the light absorption. Acetone dissociates to give an acetyl and a methyl radical,

$$CH_3COCH_3 \xrightarrow{h\nu} CH_3CO\cdot + \cdot CH_3 \tag{5.7}$$

Aldehydes and ketones with longer hydrocarbon chains break between the α and β carbon atoms; thus methyl butyl ketone decomposes almost entirely into acetone and propylene,

$$CH_3(CH_2)_3COCH_3 \xrightarrow{h\nu} CH_3CH{=}CH_2 + CH_3COCH_3 \tag{5.8}$$

The redistribution of electronic energy within a molecule is a rapid process and often it is necessary to consider the molecule as a whole to be excited rather than associate excitation with a particular location in the molecule.

Dissociation of excited molecules into molecular products is possible (reaction 5.8 is an example) though less common than dissociation into free radicals. Another example is the dehydrogenation of excited ethane to give ethylene,

$$C_2H_6^* \rightarrow C_2H_4 + H_2 \tag{5.9}$$

Rearrangement and dissociation may involve either singlet or triplet excited states.

Bimolecular Reaction

Excited molecules may react directly with a second molecule to form new chemical products. Reactions of this type can be classified under the headings, electron transfer, abstraction, addition, and Stern-Volmer reactions.

ELECTRON TRANSFER: An electron may be transferred between the excited molecule and a second molecule or ion;

$$A^* + B \rightarrow A^+ + B^- \text{ (or } A^- + B^+) \tag{5.10}$$

Ferrous ions quench the fluorescence of methylene blue in aqueous solution by a mechanism that is believed to include transfer of an electron from a ferrous ion to an excited dye molecule (D^*) on collision,

$$D^* + Fe^{2+} \rightarrow D\cdot^- + Fe^{3+} \tag{5.11}$$

$$D\cdot^- + H^+ \rightarrow DH\cdot \tag{5.12}$$

$$2DH\cdot \rightarrow D + DH_2 \tag{5.13}$$

The excited dye is converted by electron transfer to the radical-ion $D\cdot^-$, and then, by combination with a hydrogen ion, to the radical $DH\cdot$. Disproportionation between two of these radicals regenerates a molecule of the dye and gives a reduced form of the dye (the leuco dye), DH_2 (11). Oxidizing agents (e.g., Fe^{3+}, Ce^{4+}, O_2) may also quench the fluorescence, accepting an electron in the electron transfer step and being reduced.

Reaction frequently takes place between two molecules or ions that form a complex and are already loosely bound together when one of the species is excited. Photochemical electron transfer reactions between transition metal ions and anions or water molecules are well established, e.g.,

$$Fe^{3+}X^- \xrightarrow{h\nu} Fe^{2+} + X\cdot \tag{5.14}$$

and

$$M^{z+}H_2O \xrightarrow{h\nu} M^{(z+1)+}OH^- + H\cdot \tag{5.15}$$

where X = F, Cl, Br, OH, N_3, C_2O_4 and M = Fe, Cr, V, or Ce, etc. In both reactions one of the products is a free radical.

ABSTRACTION: Abstraction reactions generally involve reduction of the excited molecule through hydrogen abstraction from the substrate,

$$A^* + RH \rightarrow AH\cdot + R\cdot \tag{5.16}$$

Both products are free radicals. Bolland and Cooper (12) have investigated the oxidation of ethanol in neutral or acid aqueous solution photosensitized by the anthraquinone-2,6-disulfonate ion. The singlet excited quinone abstracts hydrogen from the ethanol and in the absence of oxygen the process is represented as

$$Q^* + CH_3CH_2OH \rightarrow QH\cdot + CH_3\dot{C}HOH \tag{5.17}$$

$$CH_3\dot{C}HOH + Q \rightarrow CH_3CHO + QH\cdot \tag{5.18}$$

$$2QH\cdot \rightarrow Q + QH_2 \tag{5.19}$$

The quinone is reduced to the hydroquinone and the ethanol oxidized to acetaldehyde. Oxygen, when present, adds to the free radical intermediates to give peroxy-radicals which interact to give hydrogen peroxide, acetaldehyde, and acetic acid as the final products; the initial step, hydrogen abstraction by the singlet excited quinone, remains the same.

ADDITION: Addition reactions appear to be characteristic of the triplet rather than the singlet excited state. Typical of these reactions is the addition of oxygen, which itself has a triplet ground state, to triplet excited linear polynuclear aromatic hydrocarbons (except naphthalene) to form transannular peroxides

$$+ O_2 \xrightarrow{h\nu} \tag{5.20}$$

anthracene

Schenck and his collaborators (13) have shown that photochemical oxidations sensitized by dyes (e.g., eosin, methylene blue, etc.) can produce transannular peroxides from cyclic dienes and hydroperoxides from mono-olefins. The hydroperoxides formed are very often isomers of those formed by autoxidation, which is known to proceed through a free radical mechanism, and a different process must be involved in the sensitized oxidations. Schenck has suggested that the triplet excited sensitizer (D*) adds oxygen to form an intermediate diradical peroxide, DO_2, which subsequently reacts with the substrate (P)

$$D^* + O_2 \rightarrow DO_2 \tag{5.21}$$

$$DO_2 + P \rightarrow D + PO_2 \tag{5.22}$$

Addition reactions are not limited to photo- or photosensitized oxidations. Dainton and Ivin (14) have shown that excited sulfur dioxide will add to both saturated and unsaturated aliphatic hydrocarbons. Excited sulfur dioxide apparently adds directly to the saturated compounds to give sulfinic acids

$$SO_2^* + RH \rightarrow R\text{—}SO_2H \tag{5.23}$$

Addition to the unsaturated hydrocarbons is believed to give an intermediate diradical which in the gas phase rearranges to give a sulfinic acid,

$$SO_2^* + R{-}CH{=}CH_2 \rightarrow R{-}\dot{C}H{-}CH_2{-}SO_2\cdot \tag{5.24}$$

$$R{-}\dot{C}H{-}CH_2{-}SO_2\cdot \rightarrow R{-}CH{=}CH{-}SO_2H \tag{5.25}$$

In the liquid phase the diradical initiates polymerization to give a polysulfone with the repeating unit $-(RCH{-}CH_2{-}SO_2)-$.

STERN-VOLMER REACTIONS: These reactions involve an interchange of atoms between two molecules, one or both of which are excited,

$$2A^* \rightarrow P + Q \tag{5.26}$$

It has been suggested (15) that a reaction of this type may account in part for the production of hydrogen and hydrogen peroxide in water irradiated with densely ionizing radiation:

$$2H_2O^* \rightarrow H_2 + H_2O_2 \tag{5.27}$$

IONS

Ionization is the distinctive consequence of the absorption of ionizing radiation by matter. The ions are produced by the process,

$$A \rightsquigarrow A^+ + e^- \text{ (or } (A^+)^* + e^-) \tag{5.28}$$

In this section we will consider the fate of both the positive ion and the electron and the results that follow recombination of a positive ion with either an electron or a negative ion. Much of the available information about ions is the result of gas phase studies with the mass spectrometer and the principle of this instrument will first be described briefly.

The Mass Spectrometer

The mass spectrometer enables ions of different mass and different charge to be separated and collected. In the instrument (Fig. 5.6) the gas or vapor to be examined is ionized and the ions accelerated by a potential difference V and subjected to a magnetic field (strength H) perpendicular to the direction of motion of the ions. In the magnetic field the ions follow a circular path of radius r given by

$$r^2 = \frac{2Vm}{H^2e} \tag{5.29}$$

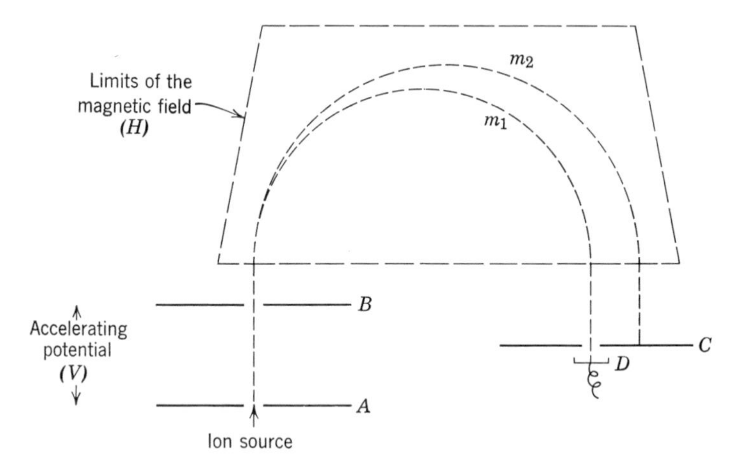

FIGURE 5.6 *Principle of the mass spectrometer.*

where m and e are the mass and charge of the ion respectively. When V and H are constant, r depends upon the ratio m/e or, for singly charged ions (which predominate), upon m only.

Considering Fig. 5.6, ions formed in the ion source pass in succession through slits in two parallel plates, A and B, which are maintained at a potential difference V (the accelerating potential). The ions passing through B emerge into the magnetic field and in it follow circular paths of radius r_1, r_2, etc., depending on their masses, m_1, m_2, etc. By altering the accelerating potential (V) or the magnetic field (H) groups each containing ions of the same mass are made to fall, one group at a time, on a slit in the plate C. Ions passing through the slit in C are collected in a metal cup (Faraday cup) and the charge that they carry measured. Thus the charge collected per unit time gives a measure of the number of ions of that mass present.

The ion source (Fig. 5.7) is basically a box which the material under examination is led into as a gas or vapor. A collimated beam of electrons from a heated filament is drawn through the box by a potential (the ionizing potential, V_i) applied between the filament and an electron collecting electrode F. The vapor is ionized by the electron beam, and the ions urged towards the plate A by a small potential between A and a repeller electrode E; once through the slit in A the ions are accelerated by the accelerating potential V (Fig. 5.6). The pressure in the instrument is generally kept as low as possible (usually 10^{-7} to 10^{-5} mm mercury) in order to prevent ion-ion and ion-molecule collisions. Under these conditions the ions collected are formed only by direct electron impact,

$$A + e^- \rightarrow A^+ + 2e^- \quad (5.30)$$

In practice the ions collected are almost invariably the positive ions, though negative ions can be examined by reversing the polarity of the electrodes and the direction of the magnetic field.

The number of positive ions collected, expressed in the form of an ion current, is dependent upon the energy of the ionizing electrons (V_i ev). No current flows until the ionizing potential (V_i) exceeds a critical value which is characteristic of the material to be ionized. Fig. 5.8 shows the

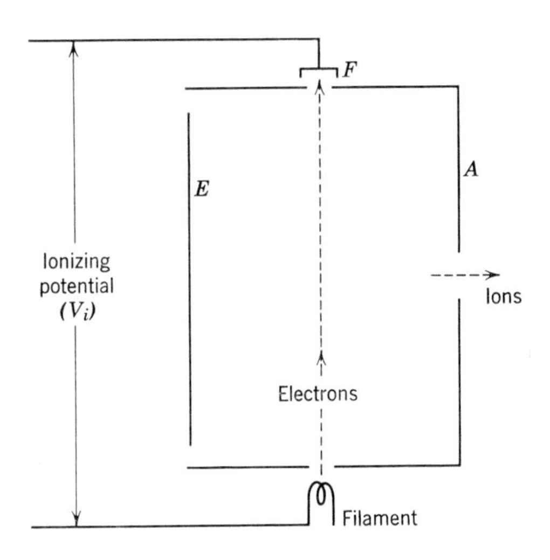

FIGURE 5.7 *Ionization chamber of a mass spectrometer.*

effect upon the ion current of increasing ionizing potential when the gas being examined is hydrogen; the experiment is conducted with V and H constant but with such values that (*a*) ions of mass 2 (i.e., H_2^+) are collected and (*b*), in a separate experiment, ions of mass 1 (H^+) are collected. The first curve shows that no H_2^+ ions are formed until the ionizing potential reaches 15·4 v; 15·4 ev is therefore the energy required (i.e., absorbed) by the reaction,

$$H_2 + e^- \rightarrow H_2^+ + 2e^- \quad (5.31)$$

and 15·4 v is in fact the *ionization potential* of molecular hydrogen. As the ionizing potential is increased further the ion current also increases, but it levels off when V_i reaches about 50 v. At slightly higher electron energies than the ionization potential, the hydrogen molecule may split into two hydrogen atoms, one of which is ionized,

$$H_2 + e^- \rightarrow H^+ + H\cdot + 2e^- \quad (5.32)$$

The H^+ ions are not detected until the ionizing potential reaches 18.05 v, the *appearance potential* for this ion. The appearance potential is the dissociation energy of the H—H bond plus the ionization potential of the hydrogen atom, provided that the reactants and products are in their ground states, i.e.,

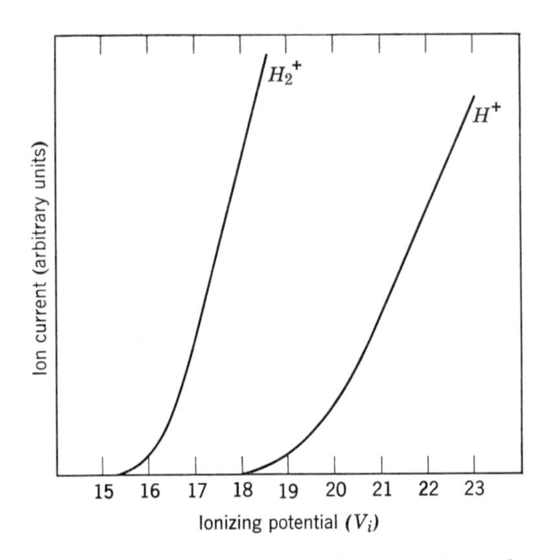

FIGURE 5.8 *Ion current* vs *ionizing potential curves for hydrogen.*

$$H_2 \rightarrow 2H\cdot \qquad 4.45 \text{ ev} \quad (5.33)$$

$$H\cdot + e^- \rightarrow H^+ + 2e^- \qquad 13.60 \text{ ev} \quad (5.34)$$

$$H_2 + e^- \rightarrow H^+ + H\cdot + 2e^- \qquad 18.05 \text{ ev} \quad (5.35)$$

Values of the H—H bond dissociation energy and hydrogen atom ionization potential are 4.45 and 13.60 ev respectively. Similar methods have been used to estimate unknown bond dissociation energies.

Mass spectrometry is used extensively to identify organic compounds using for this purpose ionizing potentials in the region of 50 to 75 v. Potentials in this range are great enough to ionize any organic material and to bring about dissociation reactions similar to that shown in Eq. 5.32 for hydrogen so that the mass spectra of complex organic compounds are made up of a large number of peaks (each due to an ion of different mass/charge ratio) of varying intensity.

Mass spectra are almost independent of electron energy from the conventional energy range, 50 to 75 v, up to energies of several kev (16, 17). Small differences that are observed at the higher energies are consistent with rather less fragmentation of the parent ion under these conditions. High-energy radiation has also been used to produce ionization in the ion source of a mass spectrometer. Melton and Rudolph (18) used both polonium α-particles and 75 ev electrons to bring about ionization of acetylene, methanol, and *n*-butane and showed that both types of radiation produced similar mass spectra, though spectra produced by the α-particles had fewer peaks than those produced by the electrons. In addition to these high-energy experiments, other developments in mass spectrometry of particular interest to radiation chemists include the construction of instruments capable of operating at ionization chamber pressures of up to 1 mm mercury (19), and the use of coupled mass spectrometers (20). In the latter case, ions produced by one mass spectrometer are allowed to interact with neutral molecules and the ionic products are analysed by a second mass spectrometer. Both these developments allow a more detailed study of the reactions between ions and neutral molecules (ion-molecule reactions) than is possible with conventional instruments.

The mass spectra of organic compounds have also been correlated with the products obtained from them by irradiation in the gas phase (21, 22, 23). The results confirm that ions are important intermediates in gas-phase radiolysis and the correlation is surprisingly good considering that the mass spectra tell nothing about the contribution of excited molecules to the radiolysis reactions. It is more debatable whether the mass spectrum of an organic vapor is closely related to the products and yields obtained by the irradiation of the same compound in the liquid phase. In the mass spectrometer the ions formed are essentially isolated from one another and from the parent molecules. This condition is approached, though not closely, in gas phase radiolyses at low to moderate pressures but is quite different from the situation in liquid systems. In the condensed phase bimolecular collisions (e.g., ion-molecule) will be many times more probable than in the gas and may lead to far more bimolecular reaction and to the stabilization by energy loss of ions that do not survive in the mass spectrometer. Unimolecular reactions (e.g., fragmentation) will be favored in the mass spectrometer by retention by the ion of its original energy and by the longer lifetime of the ions (about 10^{-5} sec compared to a lifetime of about 10^{-13} sec for ions formed by irradiation in the liquid phase (24)).

Ion Recombination

The normal fate of ions is to react with an ion of opposite sign to reform a neutral entity:

$$A^+ + e^- \rightarrow A^{**} \tag{5.36}$$

or

$$A^+ + A^- \rightarrow A^* + A \tag{5.37}$$

The electron ejected during ionization may have considerable energy and this will be lost through interactions with other molecules before the electron neutralizes a positive ion; in other words the electron is reduced to thermal or near thermal energy before recombination occurs. The immediate product of the recombination is a neutral but highly excited molecule which may be in either the singlet or the triplet state and which contains sufficient energy for spontaneous re-ionization. However, re-ionization is unlikely except perhaps in the case of a gas at very low pressures where the excited molecule is effectively isolated. In other cases internal conversion will rapidly convert the molecule to the lowest (singlet or triplet) excited state. Dissociation of the excited molecule often occurs to give either molecular products (Eq. 5.38) or, more frequently, free radicals (Eq. 5.39).

$$A^* \text{ (or } A^{**}) \rightarrow M^* + N \tag{5.38}$$

$$A^* \text{ (or } A^{**}) \rightarrow R\cdot^* + S\cdot \tag{5.39}$$

One or other of the products will most probably be excited (25).

Highly excited radicals can be formed by the neutralization of an ion which is also a free radical,

$$R\cdot^+ + e^- \rightarrow R\cdot^{**} \tag{5.40}$$

Excited radicals are often more reactive than those with only thermal energy and they are distinguished from the latter by the name *hot radicals*. The term also applies to radicals which are formed with a large amount of kinetic energy.

If the ionized molecule is closely associated with another molecule, as in a molecular complex or a transient ion-molecule collision complex, and neutralization occurs, chemical reaction between the two molecules may result:

$$A.B^+ + e^- \rightarrow C + D \tag{5.41}$$

The initial ion-molecule combination is similar to the ion-clusters postulated by Lind and Mund as intermediates in gas-phase radiolysis reactions, though smaller and possibly transient. However reaction 5.41 is likely to be only one of several simultaneous reactions which contribute to the over-all chemical change. The reaction is similar to the Stern-Volmer reaction (Eq. 5.26) mentioned in the section on excited molecules.

Other processes, dissociation, charge transfer, ion-molecule reaction, or electron addition, may intervene between the formation of an ion pair and ultimate recombination of two oppositely charged ions but, in all cases, neutralization with an ion of opposite sign also occurs and may lead to further chemical reaction.

Dissociation

Positive ions formed in the mass spectrometer and by ionizing radiation are nearly always vibrationally excited since they are formed by vertical Franck-Condon transitions from the ground state of the neutral molecule, and internuclear distances in the ion will in general be different to those in the neutral molecule. This is similar to the formation of vibrationally excited states of electronically excited molecules (Fig. 5.1). The positive ions may also be electronically excited if the radiation initiating ionization has an energy greater than the lowest ionization potential of the molecule; a condition which is true in the mass spectrometer when ionizing potentials in the usual range of 50 to 75 v are used and is also true for a large proportion of the ionizing events produced by ionizing radiation. It must be emphasized however that the mass spectrometer does not distinguish between excited and nonexcited ions of the same mass.

In common with electronically excited molecules, excited polyatomic ions may dissociate and (or) rearrange. Dissociation can be represented by,

$$(A^+)^* \rightarrow M^+ + N \tag{5.42}$$

or

$$(A^+)^* \rightarrow R\cdot^+ + S\cdot \tag{5.43}$$

The fragments may be either both molecules or both free radicals but in each case one has a positive charge. The charge normally remains with the fragment having the lowest ionization potential, which is generally the larger of the two fragments. Excited ionized ethane dissociates into the molecular products ethylene and hydrogen,

$$(C_2H_6^+)^* \rightarrow C_2H_4^+ + H_2 \tag{5.44}$$

In this instance the charge remains with the ethylene which has an ionization potential of 10.5 v rather than with the hydrogen for which the ionization potential is 15.4 v. (Ionization potentials are listed in Table 5.1.) Large ions may break down in stages to give progressively smaller fragment ions, though this is a feature of mass spectrometry rather than radiation chemistry since the ion and its breakdown products will need to escape neutralization for a relatively long time.

TABLE 5.1 *Ionization Potentials (volts)*

Atoms (ref. 26)			
H·	13.6	He	24.6
F·	17.4	Ne	21.6
Cl·	13.0	Ar	15.8
Br·	11.8	Kr	14.0
I·	10.4	Xe	12.1
Molecules (ref. 27)			
H_2	15.4	Cl_2	11.5
N_2	15.6	Br_2	10.6
O_2	12.1	I_2	9.3
CO	14.0	HCl	12.7
CO_2	13.8	HBr	11.6
SO_2	12.3	HI	10.4
H_2O	12.6	NO	9.2
NH_3	10.2	N_2O	12.9
CH_4	13.0	$CH_2{=}CH{-}CH_2{-}CH_3$	9.6
C_2H_6	11.7	C_2H_2	11.4
C_3H_8	11.1	C_6H_6	9.2
n-C_4H_{10}	10.6	$C_6H_5{-}CH_3$	8.8
iso-C_4H_{10}	10.6	$C_6H_5{-}C_2H_5$	8.8
C_2H_4	10.5	naphthalene	8.1
C_3H_6	9.7	cyclohexane	9.9
$CHCl_3$	11.4	CH_3OH	10.9
CH_3Cl	11.3	HCHO	10.9
CH_3Br	10.5	HCOOH	11.1
CH_3I	9.5	CH_3COCH_3	9.7
Radicals (ref. 28)			
·OH	13.7	$\cdot C_2H_5$	8.7
$\cdot O_2H$	11.5	$\cdot C_4H_9(t)$	6.9
$\cdot CH_3$	10.0	$\cdot C_6H_5$	9.9

As with excited molecules, the bond breaking in the dissociation of an ion is not necessarily the site of the original interaction. The electrons remaining in the ion may readily change their position, resulting in a migration of charge within the molecule. Furthermore, the excitation energy is also redistributed within the molecule among the various vibrational and electronic excited states in an essentially random fashion. If at any instant sufficient energy is concentrated in a single bond the molecule can dissociate at that bond. Dissociation is therefore not immediate and not specific (a group of similarly excited molecules will not all break at the same bond) though it will be favored with respect to weak bonds that require less than the average amount of energy to break them. Aliphatic halogen compounds for example frequently break preferentially at the relatively weak carbon-halogen bond both in the mass spectrometer and upon irradiation. Studies with the mass spectrometer have shown that fragmentation of complex ions may be delayed as long as 10^{-5} sec which, particularly in condensed systems, would allow ample time for other processes to compete with the dissociation.

Ions may rearrange before or during the fragmentation process and give products which cannot be obtained from the parent ion by fission of a single bond; the formation of ethylene from the ion $C_2H_6^+$ for example involves the migration of a hydrogen atom. Hydrogen is particularly liable to migrate and the mass spectra of many organic compounds show evidence of this. Isobutane for example gives a peak at mass 29 due to the ion $C_2H_5^+$, which is accounted for by migration of hydrogen and the subsequent splitting of two carbon-carbon bonds. Alcohols (R—CH_2OH) frequently give a peak at mass 19 due to the hydronium ion, H_3O^+, which is formed in a rearrangement involving two hydrogen atoms. Other groups may also migrate. Rearrangement is very common in the mass spectra of unsaturated hydrocarbons; for example, the four compounds shown below have almost indistinguishable mass spectra, as though the molecular structure were lost on ionization and the bonds redistributed in a random manner before fragmentation occurs (29).

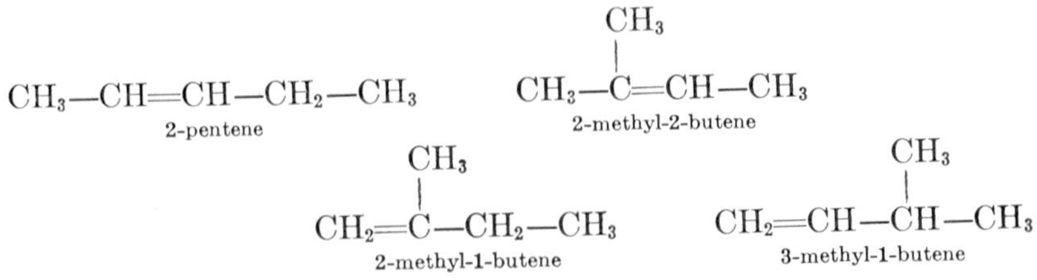

$$CH_3{-}CH{=}CH{-}CH_2{-}CH_3$$

2-pentene

$$CH_3{-}\underset{}{\overset{CH_3}{\overset{|}{C}}}{=}CH{-}CH_3$$

2-methyl-2-butene

$$CH_2{=}\overset{CH_3}{\overset{|}{C}}{-}CH_2{-}CH_3$$

2-methyl-1-butene

$$CH_2{=}CH{-}\overset{CH_3}{\overset{|}{C}H}{-}CH_3$$

3-methyl-1-butene

Charge transfer[2]

In charge-transfer reactions (30, 31) a positive ion removes an electron from an adjacent neutral molecule

$$A^+ + B \rightarrow A + B^+ \tag{5.45}$$

For the reaction to take place the ionization potential of the neutral molecule must be equal to or less than the ionization potential of the neutral counterpart of the ion, i.e., $I_B \leqq I_A$. The reaction

$$He^+ + Ne \rightarrow He + Ne^+ \tag{5.46}$$

for example is possible because the ionization potential of helium (24.6 v) is greater than that of neon (21.6 v). When the ionization potentials of the two neutral molecules differ, energy will be liberated in the process and may be retained by the products as vibrational or electronic energy, though the process is most favored when the energy difference is small. In some cases the energy liberated may be sufficient to bring about dissociation of the newly formed ion, e.g.,

$$Ar^+ + CH_4 \rightarrow Ar + \cdot CH_3^+ + H\cdot \tag{5.47}$$

Charge transfer between like molecules will not produce any observable change in liquid systems where the molecules are free to diffuse but it is a form of energy migration that may be significant in the solid state.

It may be pertinent to point out in connection with the table of ionization potentials (Table 5.1) that the values quoted are for materials in the gas phase and may not be true in liquid media. However, the relative values are believed to be the same in both phases and so the individual values can be used to decide the likelihood of charge transfer in liquid systems.

Ion-Molecule Reactions

Ion-molecule reactions are those between an ion and a neutral molecule,

$$A^+ + B \rightarrow C^+ + D \tag{5.48}$$

[2] Charge transfer is frequently treated as a special case of energy transfer, which in this case embraces both the transfer of excitation energy and of an electron. In this book, however, we have preferred to make a clear distinction between the two processes, and therefore limit the term "energy transfer" to the transfer of excitation energy, using "charge transfer" where an electron moves from one molecule to another.

Reactions of this type are not normally detected by the mass spectrometer since these operate at low pressures at which ion-molecule collisions will be scarce. However, by increasing the gas pressure in the instrument this sort of collision can be rendered more probable and the products of ion-molecule reactions detected. As the pressure is increased the ion-current due to the ions formed directly will increase in proportion to the pressure while the ion-current due to ions formed by bimolecular ion-molecule reactions will increase in proportion to the square of the pressure and can thereby be identified.

Ion-molecule reactions are believed to be important steps in the radiolysis of many compounds, and they can take a number of different courses. Hydrogen abstraction by an ion is common and leads to ions one mass unit heavier than the parent compound, e.g.,

$$HBr^+ + HBr \rightarrow H_2Br^+ + Br\cdot \tag{5.49}$$

$$H_2O^+ + H_2O \rightarrow H_3O^+ + \cdot OH \tag{5.50}$$

$$CH_4^+ + CH_4 \rightarrow CH_5^+ + \cdot CH_3 \tag{5.51}$$

Other ion-molecule reactions involve transfer of a proton (H^+) or (32) a hydride ion (H^-),

$$H_2^+ + O_2 \rightarrow HO_2\cdot^+ + H\cdot \tag{5.52}$$

$$C_3H_5^+ + \text{neo-}C_5H_{12} \rightarrow C_3H_6 + C_5H_{11}^+ \tag{5.53}$$

or the formation and rupture of carbon-carbon bonds,

$$CH_3^+ + CH_4 \rightarrow C_2H_5^+ + H_2 \tag{5.54}$$

$$C_2H_4^+ + C_2H_4 \rightarrow C_3H_5^+ + \cdot CH_3 \tag{5.55}$$

It should perhaps be pointed out that ions are not bound by the laws of valency in quite the same way as neutral molecules and ions such as CH_5^+ are stable.

Exothermic ion-molecule reactions with very few exceptions require no activation energy, reaction taking place at the first collision, and consequently the reactions are very fast even at low temperatures. Collisions between polyatomic ions and molecules are facilitated by the attraction that the ion exerts on the molecule by virtue of its charge. The collision complex formed when the molecular ion and molecule collide is also likely to be longer lived than that between two neutral molecules (e.g., 10^{-5} sec compared to 10^{-13} sec); the ion-molecule complex is an example of so-called *sticky collisions*.

Electron Addition

In most systems the only negatively charged entities with which we will be concerned are the electrons produced by ionization. However, a minority of chemical compounds are able to form negative ions by capture of a slow electron (33), accompanied in some cases by dissociation,

$$A + e^- \rightarrow A^- \tag{5.56}$$

or

$$A + e^- \rightarrow B^- + C \tag{5.57}$$

Compounds showing such electron affinity include the halogens and organic halogen compounds, oxygen, liquid water, and alcohols, e.g.,

$$I_2 + e^- \rightarrow I^- + I\cdot \tag{5.58}$$

$$C_2H_5I + e^- \rightarrow \cdot C_2H_5 + I^- \tag{5.59}$$

$$O_2 + e^- \rightarrow O_2^- \tag{5.60}$$

In liquid water

$$H_2O_{aq} + e^- \rightarrow OH_{aq}^- + H\cdot \tag{5.61}$$

The dissociation is endothermic and possible only in liquid water where solvation of the ions provides the necessary energy.

Reaction 5.56 differs from simple ionization (Eq. 5.30) in having no means of dissipating any excess energy that the electron might have. Following ionization the two electrons are able to remove energy and therefore electrons with any energy greater than the ionization potential of the molecule are effective. Since there is no process of energy removal in reaction 5.56 the captured electron can only have energies that can accommodate to the various energy levels in the negative ion formed (i.e., electron capture is a resonance process). Reaction 5.57 occurs if attachment of the electron to A, or to a fragment formed by the dissociation of A, liberates enough energy to break one of the bonds in the molecule. Capture of electrons with kinetic energy much above thermal energy always leads to dissociation.

A third process, detected in the mass spectrometer, results in the formation of an ion pair and is analogous to simple ionization,

$$A + e^- \rightarrow B^+ + C^- + e^- \tag{5.62}$$

This is not a resonance process and is possible over a much wider range of electron energies than electron capture. Reactions of this type have been detected in the mass spectra of organic halogen compounds and are attributed to the large electron affinities of the halogens. Ethyl chloride for example undergoes the following reaction at electron energies near 9 ev,

$$C_2H_5Cl + e^- \rightarrow C_2H_5^+ + Cl^- + e^- \tag{5.63}$$

though the ionization potential of ethyl chloride, the lowest electron energy for reaction 5.64 to take place, is 11.2 ev.

$$C_2H_5Cl + e^- \rightarrow C_2H_5Cl^+ + 2e^- \tag{5.64}$$

Magee and Burton (33) have pointed out that electron capture by a neutral molecule competes with capture by a positive ion, and the relative probability of these two processes in the track of densely ionizing particles in condensed systems will change as the track gets older and the ions diffuse further apart. Soon after the track is formed the positive ions and electrons will be concentrated near the track and electrons will be captured predominantly by positive ions. Later, as the ions diffuse outwards and get further apart, capture by neutral molecules (assuming that this is possible) will become increasingly important.

However it is formed the negative ion will eventually neutralize a positive ion (34)

$$A^+ + A^- \rightarrow A^* + A \tag{5.37}$$

One or both of the neutral molecules formed will be excited, though the excitation energy will be less than that gained by a positive ion neutralized by an electron and will decrease as the electron affinity of A increases.

Electron capture has been demonstrated experimentally by Hamill and his colleagues (35) by irradiating frozen solutions of biphenyl or naphthalene in organic solvents (e.g., hydrocarbons, ethers). Ultraviolet absorption spectra characteristic of the products of electron attachment, the ions $C_{12}H_{10}^-$ and $C_{10}H_8^-$ respectively from biphenyl and naphthalene, are observed. Furthermore, when a second solute is present which competes with the biphenyl or naphthalene for electrons, the decrease in $G(C_{12}H_{10}^-)$ or $G(C_{10}H_8^-)$ gives a measure of the electron-attaching efficiency of the second solute. Of a number of solutes tested by Hamill, those showing the greatest relative efficiency were iodine (the most efficient), carbon tetrabromide, sulfur dioxide, benzaldehyde, bromoform, carbon tetrachloride, and benzyl acetate.

Electron attachment by a minor component in an irradiated mixture may lead to a disproportionately high rate of decomposition. When dilute solutions of carbon tetrachloride in benzene are irradiated, for example, the carbon tetrachloride decomposes to a greater extent than would be anticipated from the radiolysis of the two components separately. The effect can be accounted for by assuming that the carbon tetrachloride captures electrons produced by ionization of both components (36).

Subexcitation Electrons

Platzman (37) has shown that electrons lose energy in a medium much more slowly once they have fallen to an energy (about 0.5 to 4 ev) below that of the lowest excitation energy of the medium. The rates of energy loss ($-dE/dt$) for an electron with energy 10 or 20 ev and one with an energy slightly less than E_p, the minimum excitation energy of the molecules of the medium, are approximately 10^{16} and 10^{13} ev/sec respectively in liquid water. On the basis of their longer lifetimes Platzman suggested treating these *subexcitation electrons* separately from the more energetic electrons.

Subexcitation electrons are likely to be most important in systems containing one or more minor components which have a lower excitation energy (E_m) than that of the principal component (E_p). In this case practically all the subexcitation electrons with energies between E_m and E_p may cause excitation of the minor component, which might therefore play a larger part in the radiolysis reactions than would be anticipated from its concentration. In these circumstances (and in the event of electron capture by a minor component) the equations given earlier for calculating the fraction of the total absorbed energy absorbed by a single component in a mixture (Eqs. 4.21 and 4.23) will not be true because part of the energy will be channeled selectively to the minor components, and the energy actually absorbed by these will be greater than that calculated from the equations. Platzman estimated that for high-energy radiations about 15 to 20% of the absorbed energy might be dissipated by subexcitation electrons.

SUMMARY OF THE REACTIONS OF IONS AND EXCITED MOLECULES

Excited Molecules

$$A \rightsquigarrow A^* \tag{5.1}$$

(excitation to singlet and triplet excited states)

$$A^* \rightarrow A$$

(radiative or nonradiative conversion to the ground state; no chemical reaction)

$$A^* + B \rightarrow A + B^* \qquad (5.4)$$
(nonradiative energy transfer)

$$A^* \rightarrow R\cdot + S\cdot \qquad (5.6)$$
(dissociation into free radicals)

$$A^* \rightarrow M + N \qquad (5.9)$$
(dissociation into molecular products)

$$A^* + B \rightarrow A^+ + B^- \text{ (or } A^- + B^+\text{)} \qquad (5.10)$$
(electron transfer)

$$A^* + RH \rightarrow AH\cdot + R\cdot \qquad (5.16)$$
(hydrogen abstraction)

$$A^* + B \rightarrow AB \qquad (5.20)$$
(addition)

$$A^* + B \rightarrow P + Q \qquad (5.26)$$
(Stern-Volmer reaction)

Ions

$$A \rightarrow A^+ + e^- \text{ (or } (A^+)^* + e^-\text{)} \qquad (5.28)$$
(ionization)

$$A^+ + e^- \rightarrow A^{**} \rightarrow A^* \qquad (5.36)$$
(neutralization producing both singlet and triplet excited states)

$$A^+ + A^- \rightarrow A^* + A \qquad (5.37)$$
(neutralization by a negative ion)

$$A^* \text{ (or } A^{**}\text{)} \rightarrow M^* + N \qquad (5.38)$$
(dissociation into molecular products following neutralization)

$$A^* \text{ (or } A^{**}\text{)} \rightarrow R\cdot^* + S\cdot \qquad (5.39)$$
(dissociation into free radicals following neutralization)

$$A.B^+ + e^- \rightarrow C + D \tag{5.41}$$

(neutralization of complex with reaction)

$$(A^+)^* \rightarrow M^+ + N \tag{5.42}$$

(dissociation of an excited ion into an ion and a molecule)

$$(A^+)^* \rightarrow R\cdot^+ + S\cdot \tag{5.43}$$

(dissociation of an excited ion into a radical-ion and a radical)

$$A^+ + B \rightarrow A + B^+ \tag{5.45}$$

(charge transfer)

$$A^+ + B \rightarrow C^+ + D \tag{5.48}$$

(ion-molecule reaction)

$$A + e^- \rightarrow A^- \tag{5.56}$$

(electron capture)

$$A + e^- \rightarrow B^- + C \tag{5.57}$$

(electron capture with dissociation)

REFERENCES

A more extensive discussion of excited states is given by C. Reid, *Excited States in Chemistry and Biology*, Butterworths Scientific Publications, London, 1957, and of mass spectrometry by J. H. Beynon, *Mass Spectrometry and its Applications to Organic Chemistry*, Elsevier, Amsterdam, 1960. D. P. Stevenson and D. O. Schissler have reviewed "Mass Spectrometry and Radiation Chemistry" in *Actions Chimiques et Biologiques des Radiations* (ed. M. Haissinsky), Masson et Cie, Paris, Vol. 5, 1961. Also pertinent to this chapter is *Electron Impact Phenomena* by F. H. Field and J. L. Franklin, Academic Press Inc., New York, 1957.

1. R. L. Platzman, *Internat. J. Appl. Radiation Isotopes,* **10,** 116 (1961).
2. M. Kasha, *Discuss. Faraday Soc.,* **9,** 14 (1950).
3. J. L. Magee in *Comparative Effects of Radiation,* (ed. M. Burton, J. S. Kirby-Smith, and J. L. Magee), John Wiley and Sons, New York, 1960, p. 130.
4. Th. Förster, *Discuss. Faraday Soc.,* **27,** 7 (1959).
5. S. Lipsky and M. Burton, *J. Chem. Phys.,* **31,** 1221 (1959); J. M. Nosworthy, J. L. Magee, and M. Burton, *J. Chem. Phys.,* **34,** 83 (1961).
6. M. S. Matheson, *Ann. Rev. Phys. Chem.,* **13,** 77 (1962).
7. P. De Mayo and S. T. Reid, *Quart. Rev.,* **15,** 393 (1961).

8. J. Franck and E. Rabinowitch, *Trans. Faraday Soc.,* **30,** 120 (1934).
9. F. W. Lampe and R. M. Noyes, *J. Am. Chem. Soc.,* **76,** 2140 (1954).
10. L. F. Meadows and R. M. Noyes, *J. Am. Chem. Soc.,* **82,** 1872 (1960).
11. J. Weiss, *Trans. Faraday Soc.,* **35,** 48 (1939).
12. J. L. Bolland and H. R. Cooper, *Proc. Roy. Soc. (London), Ser. A,* **225,** 405 (1954).
13. G. O. Schenck, *Angew. Chem.,* **64,** 12 (1952); G. O. Schenck, K. G. Kinkel, and H-J. Mertens, *Annalen,* **584,** 125 (1953); G. O. Schenck, *ibid.,* p. 156; G. O. Schenck, H. Eggert, and W. Denk, *ibid.,* p. 177.
14. F. S. Dainton and K. J. Ivin, *Trans. Faraday Soc.,* **46,** 374, 382 (1950); *Proc. Roy. Soc. (London), Ser. A,* **212,** 96 (1952).
15. H. A. Dewhurst, A. H. Samuel, and J. L. Magee, *Radiation Res.,* **1,** 62 (1954); P. Kelly, T. Rigg, and J. Weiss, *Nature,* **173,** 1130 (1954).
16. P. Kebarle and E. W. Godbole, *J. Chem. Phys.,* **36,** 302 (1962).
17. C. E. Melton, *J. Chem. Phys.,* **37,** 562 (1962).
18. C. E. Melton and P. S. Rudolph, *J. Chem. Phys.,* **30,** 847 (1959).
19. T. W. Martin, R. E. Rummel, and C. E. Melton, *Science,* **138,** 77 (1962).
20. H. Von Koch and E. Lindholm, *Arkiv Fys.,* **19,** 123 (1961); cf. refs. cited by P. Wilmenius and E. Lindholm, *Arkiv Fys.,* **21,** 97 (1962).
21. G. G. Meisels, W. H. Hamill, and R. R. Williams, *J. Phys. Chem.,* **61,** 1456 (1957).
22. L. M. Dorfman and M. C. Sauer, *J. Chem. Phys.,* **32,** 1886 (1960).
23. L. Reinisch, *J. Chim. Phys.,* **57,** 1064 (1960).
24. A. H. Samuel and J. L. Magee, *J. Chem. Phys.,* **21,** 1080 (1953).
25. J. L. Magee and M. Burton, *J. Am. Chem. Soc.,* **72,** 1965 (1950).
26. *American Institute of Physics Handbook,* (ed. D. E. Gray), McGraw-Hill, New York, 1957, section 7c.
27. K. Watanabe, *J. Chem. Phys.,* **26,** 542 (1957).
28. F. H. Field and J. L. Franklin, *Electron Impact Phenomena,* Academic Press Inc., New York, 1957, Table 10a, p. 106.
29. J. H. Beynon, *Mass Spectrometry and its Applications to Organic Chemistry,* Elsevier, Amsterdam, 1960, p. 263.
30. J. L. Magee, *J. Phys. Chem.,* **56,** 555 (1952).
31. M. Burton and J. L. Magee, *J. Phys. Chem.,* **56,** 842 (1952).
32. F. H. Field and F. W. Lampe, *J. Am. Chem. Soc.,* **80,** 5587 (1958).
33. J. L. Magee and M. Burton, *J. Am. Chem. Soc.,* **73,** 523 (1951).
34. J. L. Magee, *Discuss. Faraday Soc.,* **12,** 33 (1952).
35. P. S. Rao, J. R. Nash, J. P. Guarino, M. R. Ronayne and W. H. Hamill, *J. Am. Chem. Soc.,* **84,** 500 (1962); J. P. Guarino, M. R. Ronayne, and W. H. Hamill, *Radiation Res.,* **17,** 379 (1962).
36. W. Van Dusen and W. H. Hamill, *J. Am. Chem. Soc.,* **84,** 3648 (1962).
37. R. L. Platzman, *Radiation Res.,* **2,** 1 (1955).

CHAPTER 6

Free Radicals

Free radicals are atoms or molecules which have one or more unpaired electrons available to form chemical bonds. They are formed for instance when a molecule is divided at a covalent bond in such a manner that one of the bonding electrons remains with each fragment,

$$R:S \rightleftharpoons R\cdot + \cdot S \tag{6.1}$$

The process is reversible, the back reaction representing combination of two radicals to give a stable molecule. Free radicals are generally electrically neutral, although this is not necessarily so. Examples of charged radicals are the negative radical-ion O_2^- and the positive radical-ion $\cdot CH_3^+$. Triplet excited states, which were discussed in the last chapter, often react as though they are biradicals, with two separate unpaired electrons in the molecule.

Relatively stable free radicals have been known since the beginning of the century, the earliest being triphenylmethyl, $Ph_3C\cdot$,[1] discovered by Gomberg (1). More recently, reactive radicals have been shown to be transient intermediates in many reactions, including such diverse processes as autoxidation, electrolysis,

[1] "Ph" will be used to represent the phenyl group, C_6H_5.

polymerization, and pyrolysis. Consequently the properties and reactions of free radicals are well established, having been investigated by a variety of techniques and under many different conditions.

In radiation chemistry, free radicals are produced by the dissociation of excited molecules and by ion reactions (e.g., dissociation, ion-molecule reaction, neutralization) in or near the tracks of ionizing particles. Radicals which do not undergo radical-radical reactions in this region of high radical concentration diffuse into the bulk of the medium and generally react with the substrate. However, the initial high concentration of radicals close to the particle tracks can lead to radical phenomena in radiation chemistry different from those where the radicals are formed by other means (e.g., chemically or photochemically) and are more randomly distributed.

In this chapter the formation, properties and reactions, and, with particular reference to radiation chemistry, detection of radicals are discussed.

FORMATION

Methods used to produce free radicals are of more than theoretical interest in radiation chemistry since, judiciously applied, they allow the effect upon a system of a single radical species (normally one of the several formed upon irradiation) to be studied. They may also be applied to convert relatively large amounts of material to products similar to those produced by irradiation.

Preparative methods, other than the use of ionizing radiation, involve either the transfer of sufficient energy to a molecule to cause unimolecular dissociation (e.g., thermal or photodissociation) or an oxidation-reduction process. The latter entails transfer of a single electron, or an atom or group with an unpaired electron, from one atom or molecule to another. Mechanical stress (e.g., ultrasonic vibration) can sometimes disrupt molecules and produce radicals.

Thermal Dissociation

Covalent bonds can be broken if a molecule is heated to a sufficiently high temperature. A well-known instance is the thermal dissociation of molecular iodine:

$$I_2 \rightleftharpoons 2I\cdot \tag{6.2}$$

The reaction is reversible and the equilibrium lies completely to the left at low temperatures (below about 700°C at normal pressures) and to the right at high temperatures (above about 1700°C). At intermediate temperatures both molecular and atomic iodine are present in the equilibrium mixture. Organic molecules dissociate in a similar manner, and free radicals are important intermediates in the high-temperature pyrolysis of organic compounds. With organic compounds, however, the reverse, recombination reaction is only one of a number of possible radical-radical and radical-molecule reactions, and pyrolysis will give a variety of products.

Compounds with relatively weak covalent bonds may break down at moderate temperatures and provide a useful source of radicals. Organic peroxides, for example, contain weak 0—0 bonds and are convenient radical sources both in the gaseous state and in solution. In the gas phase di-tert-butyl peroxide is used as a source of methyl radicals:

$$(CH_3)_3CO\text{—}OC(CH_3)_3 \xrightarrow{120\text{–}200°C} 2(CH_3)_3CO\cdot \rightarrow 2\cdot CH_3 + 2CH_3COCH_3 \quad (6.3)$$

At the temperatures shown the intermediate *t*-butoxy radicals dissociate and the final products are methyl radicals and acetone. In solution the reaction can be used as a source of *t*-butoxy radicals by working at rather lower temperatures at which these are stable. Acetyl and benzoyl peroxides are also used in solution as radical sources,

$$CH_3COO\text{—}OOCCH_3 \xrightarrow{95\text{–}100°C} 2CH_3COO\cdot \rightarrow 2\cdot CH_3 + 2CO_2 \quad (6.4)$$

$$PhCOO\text{—}OOCPh \xrightarrow{\text{about } 70°C} 2PhCOO\cdot \quad (6.5)$$

The intermediate acetoxy radicals, $CH_3COO\cdot$, lose carbon dioxide very readily to give methyl radicals, but the benzoyloxy radicals are more stable and will probably react before they are decarboxylated. Azo compounds (R—N=N—R) and certain organometallic compounds (e.g., dimethyl mercury and tetraethyl lead) are also useful thermal sources of radicals.

Though a variety of different radicals are available from thermal decompositions, these suffer as radical sources from the disadvantage that experiments must be conducted at temperatures high enough to bring about fission of the radical precursor, restricting the range of possible reaction conditions.

Photodissociation

Several examples were given in the previous chapter of molecules which are excited by the absorption of light and then dissociate into free radical fragments. In some cases these provide a convenient source of radicals. Acetone, for example, is frequently used as a photochemical source of methyl radicals, both in the vapor state and in solution:

$$CH_3COCH_3 \xrightarrow{h\nu} CH_3CO\cdot + \cdot CH_3 \tag{6.6}$$

$$CH_3CO\cdot \rightarrow \cdot CH_3 + CO \tag{6.7}$$

Acetyl radicals readily decarbonate, and above 100°C methyl radicals and carbon monoxide are the major products. Furthermore, most of the compounds which are useful thermal sources of radicals dissociate at room temperature when irradiated with ultraviolet light.

Molecules which do not absorb light in a convenient range of wavelength can often be induced to dissociate by energy transfer from an atom that can be excited with the available light. Mercury is a common sensitizing atom and has been employed to induce dissociation in a variety of systems, mainly gaseous. An example is the photosensitized dissociation of hydrogen, where

$$Hg + h\nu \rightarrow Hg^* \tag{6.8}$$

$$Hg^* + H_2 \rightarrow Hg + 2H\cdot \tag{6.9}$$

With more complicated molecules more than one type of radical may be produced, limiting the usefulness of photosensitization in these cases.

Oxidation-Reduction Processes

Oxidation-reduction reactions which involve the transfer of a single electron between two reactants may produce free radicals. Probably the best known radical source of this nature is the Fenton reagent (2), a mixture of hydrogen peroxide and ferrous ion which produces hydroxyl radicals,

$$H_2O_2 + Fe^{2+} \rightarrow Fe^{3+} + \cdot OH + OH^- \tag{6.10}$$

Similar reactions occur with persulfate ($S_2O_8^{2-}$) and with the organic analogues of hydrogen peroxide, hydroperoxides (ROOH) and peroxides (ROOR). Organic hydroperoxides for instance give alkoxy radicals with ferrous ion

$$RO_2H + Fe^{2+} \rightarrow Fe^{3+} + RO\cdot + OH^- \tag{6.11}$$

Ions of other metals of variable valency, in their lower valence states, can often be substituted for ferrous ion in these reactions. Hydroxyl radicals generated by Fenton's reagent can produce similar effects to irradiation in aqueous solution (3), where hydroxyl radicals are among the active intermediates formed from the water.

Other oxidation-reduction systems which give radicals are

$$NH_3OH^+ + Ti^{3+} \rightarrow Ti^{4+} + \cdot NH_2 + H_2O \quad \text{(ref. 4)} \qquad (6.12)$$

$$Br^- + Ce^{4+} \rightarrow Ce^{3+} + Br\cdot \quad \text{(ref. 5)} \qquad (6.13)$$

$$PhCHO + Co^{3+} \rightarrow Co^{2+} + PhCO\cdot + H^+ \quad \text{(ref. 6)} \qquad (6.14)$$

There are many others. Cobaltic ions react with hydroperoxides to give peroxy radicals (6), $ROO\cdot$, in contrast to cobaltous ions which give alkoxy radicals, $RO\cdot$, with these compounds (as in Eq. 6.11):

$$RO_2H \rightleftharpoons RO_2^- + H^+ \qquad (6.15)$$

$$RO_2^- + Co^{3+} \rightarrow Co^{2+} + ROO\cdot \qquad (6.16)$$

Photo-initiated electron transfer has been mentioned in Chapter 5 and occurs between a water molecule and an anion or cation, or between loosely bound anions and cations, on irradiation with ultraviolet light; for example,

$$M^{z+}H_2O \xrightarrow{h\nu} M^{(z+1)+}OH^- + H\cdot \qquad (6.17)$$

$$Fe^{3+}X^- \xrightarrow{h\nu} Fe^{2+} + X\cdot \qquad (6.18)$$

where M = Fe, Cr, V, Ce, etc., and X = F, Cl, Br, OH, N_3, C_2O_4, etc.

Electrolysis can also produce free radicals. Solutions containing salts of carboxylic acids for example form radicals at the anode upon electrolysis

$$RCOO^- \xrightarrow{-e^-} RCOO\cdot \qquad (6.19)$$

The radicals formed normally lose carbon dioxide and dimerize to give a hydrocarbon (R—R)(Kolbe reaction). Radical-radical reactions are favored by the high radical concentration at the electrode and predominate over other radical reactions. Nevertheless, products obtained from a compound by electrolysis often resemble those obtained upon irradiation.

The preceding processes involve one-electron transfer steps, but reactions in which atoms are transferred may also lead to radicals. The sodium-flame technique originated by Polanyi (cf. 7) is an interesting example and occurs in the vapor phase between sodium and organic halides, e.g.,

$$Na + RCl \rightarrow NaCl + R\cdot \qquad (6.20)$$

The same reaction has been adapted to the preparation of specific hydrocarbon radicals for electron paramagnetic resonance study (8) by condensing alternately very thin layers of sodium and an organic halide (preferably an iodide) on a rotating surface at liquid nitrogen temperature. The radicals formed are trapped as the frozen matrix is built up and thereby preserved for subsequent examination. A somewhat similar atom-transfer reaction takes place in solution between cobaltous chloride and organic halides:

$$CoCl + RCl \rightarrow CoCl_2 + R\cdot \tag{6.21}$$

PROPERTIES AND REACTIONS

The most characteristic property of free radicals is the instability associated with the presence of an unpaired electron. Radicals are often extremely reactive, reacting in such a manner that the odd electron is paired with a similar electron in another radical or eliminated by an electron-transfer reaction. Alternatively, the radical may react so as to produce a second, more stable, free radical. The reactivity and, in the opposite sense, the stability of radicals depends to a great extent upon their structure. Taking the two extremes, radicals may be either very reactive under normal conditions or else unreactive and relatively stable. Some examples of these two types are listed below:

Reactive radicals; $H\cdot$, $\cdot OH$, $Cl\cdot$, $\cdot CH_3$, $Ph\cdot$

Stable radicals; $Ph_3C\cdot$ and substituted triphenylmethyl radicals,

$^-O-C_6H_4-O\cdot$ (semiquinone),

$(O_2N)_3C_6H_2-\dot{N}-NPh_2$ (diphenylpicrylhydrazyl, DPPH)

NO, NO_2, O_2

The radicals in the first group have only a transient existence under normal reaction conditions and are generally atoms or are formed from relatively small molecules. However, they can be trapped and preserved in solids, usually at low temperatures, where they are unable to diffuse and react together (9). Organic radicals in the second, stable, group are generally formed from large molecules where the odd electron is distributed over a much greater volume; in some cases steric factors may enhance the radical stability by hindering dimerization. Nitric oxide and nitrogen dioxide are included since each has a single unpaired electron and behaves as a rather unreactive free radical. Oxygen has a triplet ground state and behaves in radical reactions as a diradical. Needless to say the two groups contain radicals of varying stability and many other radicals are known which fall between the two extremes.

In Table 6.1 a number of reactive radicals are arranged in order of decreasing reactivity (increasing stability) as the table is descended. The relative positions are only approximate[2] and no clear distinction can be made between radicals in adjacent levels. Nevertheless the divisions, rough as they are, should help to clarify radical reactions.

The stability of organic radicals is increased when hydrogen attached to the carbon atom carrying the free electron is replaced by any other atom or group. Radical stability increases for example in the series primary ($—CH_2\cdot$) < secondary ($=CH\cdot$) < tertiary ($\equiv C\cdot$). Stability will also be affected by the nature of the substituents. Fluorine has only a small effect when it replaces hydrogen, but the effectiveness of the halogens increases in the series F < Cl < Br < I; stability increases also as the number of halogen substituents is increased. Unsaturated substituents increase stability when they involve carbon atoms adjacent to that carrying the odd electron, but not when this carbon atom itself is part of the unsaturated grouping. For instance $CH_2=CH—CH_2\cdot$ is very much more stable than $CH_2=CH\cdot$ or $Ph\cdot$. In all cases the effectiveness of the stabilizing substituent falls as it is moved farther from the carbon with the odd electron.

Radicals which are high in Table 6.1 tend to be less selective in their reaction with stable molecules than those which are lower in the table. Hydrogen atoms for example tend to react with the first molecule with which they collide. Chlorine atoms are more selective in their attack on the substrate than hydrogen atoms, but are less selective than bromine atoms. In general radicals are less selective at high temperatures but, conversely, even very reactive radicals may be quite selective at very low temperatures. Other factors affecting radical reactions with a substrate besides temperature include the reactivities of the attacking and displaced radicals, the dissociation energies of the bonds broken and formed, and polar effects.

[2] The radicals (R) were grouped by comparing the bond dissociation energies in the compounds R—H and R-halogen and assuming that the largest dissociation energies signified the most reactive radicals.

TABLE 6.1 *Relative Stability of Reactive Free Radicals*

(The radicals are arranged from top to bottom in order of increasing stability and decreasing reactivity. The relative positions are approximate and, for the radicals in parentheses, questionable.)

R = alkyl radical	Atoms and inorganic radicals	Alkyl radicals	Halogen derivatives	Unsaturated and oxygenated radicals	Aromatic compounds
—	$H\cdot$, $\cdot OH$	—	—	$CH_2{=}CH\cdot$	$Ph\cdot$ *o, m, p,* $CH_3C_6H_4\cdot$
$R\cdot$, $RCO_2\cdot$	$F\cdot$	$\cdot CH_3$, $\cdot C_2H_5$	—	$(CH_3CO_2\cdot)$	—
$RCO\cdot$	—	n-$C_3H_7\cdot$ n-$C_4H_9\cdot$	$\cdot CF_3$ $ClCH_2CH_2\cdot$	$CH_3CO\cdot$	—
$RO\cdot$	$Cl\cdot$	i-$C_3H_7\cdot$	$ClCH_2\cdot$	$(CH_3O\cdot)$	—
—	—	t-$C_4H_9\cdot$	$Cl_2CH\cdot$	—	—
—	—	—	$\cdot CCl_3$, $Br_2CH\cdot$	—	$PhCO\cdot$
—	$Br\cdot$	—	$\cdot CBr_3$	$CH_2{=}CH{-}CH_2\cdot$	$PhCH_2\cdot$
$RS\cdot$, $RO_2\cdot$	$I\cdot$, $(HO_2\cdot)$	—	—	$(CH_3S\cdot)(CH_3O_2\cdot)$	—

Representing radical attack on a substrate by the reaction

$$A\cdot + B\text{—}C \rightarrow A\text{—}B + C\cdot \qquad (6.22)$$

it is generally true that the newly formed radical is less reactive than the attacking radical. To take an extreme example, hydrogen atoms will react with molecular iodine to give hydrogen iodide and an iodine atom,

$$H\cdot + I_2 \rightarrow HI + I\cdot \qquad (6.23)$$

but the back reaction,

$$I\cdot + HI \rightarrow H\cdot + I_2 \qquad (6.24)$$

which would replace a relatively stable iodine atom by a very reactive hydrogen atom, is most unlikely. The relative radical reactivities (Table 6.1) were estimated by comparing bond dissociation energies in representative compounds; the same conclusions can be reached by considering these energies directly. The over-all energy change in reaction 6.23 is the difference between the energy released in forming a hydrogen-iodine bond and that absorbed in breaking an iodine-iodine bond, i.e., the difference between the bond dissociation energies for these two bonds. Thus, from Table 6.2, the energy change is

$$\text{D}(H\text{—}I) - \text{D}(I\text{—}I) = 70.5 - 35.6 = +34.9 \text{ kcal/mole}$$

Energy is in fact released and the reaction is perfectly feasible in the direction shown. The reverse reaction between iodine atoms and hydrogen iodide (Eq. 6.24) is very much less likely because 35 kcal of energy per mole must be supplied from the thermal energy of the system, or from an external source, for the reaction to take place.

Though the difference between the bond dissociation energies gives the over-all energy change for a radical-molecule reaction such as 6.23, a certain amount of activation energy may be required to initiate the reaction (Fig. 6.1). Activation energies may be an important factor if the attacking radical can react with the substrate in more than one way, when the reaction with the lowest activation energy will be favored. Normally the activation energy is provided from the thermal energy of the system, but in the case of radicals with extra energy (i.e., hot radicals) it can be provided by the radical itself and this will be more reactive than similar radicals in thermal equilibrium with the system. For most radical reactions the activation energies are appreciably lower than for nonradical reactions.

Polar factors, that is, effects due to differences in electron density in the reactants and media, such as the type of solvent, pH, inductive, and hyperconjugation effects, may influence radical reactions, though to a

TABLE 6.2 *Bond Dissociation Energies*

The values are largely taken from *The Strengths of Chemical Bonds*, by T. L. Cottrell, 2nd edition, Butterworths Scientific Publications, London, 1958. Values for ions are given assuming that the charge remains with the fragment having the lower ionization potential; they are taken from *Electron Impact Phenomena and the Properties of Gaseous Ions* by F. H. Field and J. L. Franklin, Academic Press Inc., New York, 1957. (1 ev/molecule = 23.06 kcal/mole)

Bond	Bond dissociation energy		Bond	Bond dissociation energy	
	kcal/mole	ev/molecule		kcal/mole	ev/molecule
H—H	103.2	4.5	F—F	36	1.6
$(H—H)^+$	61	2.6	Cl—Cl	57.1	2.5
HO—H	117.5	5.1	Br—Br	45.5	2.0
$(HO—H)^+$	142	6.2	I—I	35.6	1.5
·O—H	101.5	4.4	H—F	134	5.8
HO—OH	51	2.2	H—Cl	102.2	4.4
HO_2—H	90	3.9	$(H—Cl)^+$	108	4.7
$·O_2$—H	47	2.0	H—Br	86.5	3.8
O═O	118	5.1	$(H—Br)^+$	93	4.0
HS—H	$\sim$90	$\sim$3.9	H—I	70.5	3.1
H_2N—H	102	4.4	$(H—I)^+$	74	3.2
CH_3—H	101	4.4	CH≡CH	230	10.0
$(CH_3—H)^+$	31	1.3	CH≡C—H	<121	<5.2
$·CH_2$—H	88	3.8	CH_2═CH_2	140	6.1
CH_3—CH_3	83	3.6	CH_2═CH—H	104–122	4.5–5.3
C_2H_5—H	96	4.2	benzene C$\cdots$C	193	8.4
$(C_2H_5—H)^+$	25	1.1	C_6H_5—H	102	4.4
n-C_4H_9—H	101	4.4	$(C_6H_5—H)^+$	110	4.8
t-C_4H_9—H	89	3.9	$C_6H_5CH_2$—H	83	3.6
CH_3—F	107	4.6	Cl_3C—H	90	3.9
CH_3—Cl	81	3.5	Cl_3C—Cl	68	2.9
CH_3—Br	67	2.9	Cl_2CH—Cl	72	3.1
CH_3—I	53	2.3	Br_3C—Br	49	2.1
n-C_4H_9—I	49	2.1	CH_3—CN	103	4.5
t-C_4H_9—I	45	2.0	CH_3—NH_2	80	3.5
C_6H_5—I	57	2.5	CH_3—SH	74	3.2
$C_6H_5CH_2$—I	39	1.7	CH_3S—H	89	3.9
			CH_3S—SCH_3	73	3.2
OHC—H	76	3.3	CH_3CO_2—H	112	4.9
HCO—OH	$\sim$90	$\sim$3.9	CH_3CO—OH	90	3.9
CH_3—OH	91	3.9	CH_3—$CO_2·$	−17	−0.7
CH_3O—H	100	4.3	CH_3O—OCH_3	37	1.6
CH_3CO—H	$\sim$85	$\sim$3.7	CH_3CO—$OCCH_3$	57	2.5
CH_3—CO·	$\sim$17	$\sim$0.7	CH_3CO_2—O_2CCH_3	30	1.3
CH_3CO—CH_3	72	3.1			

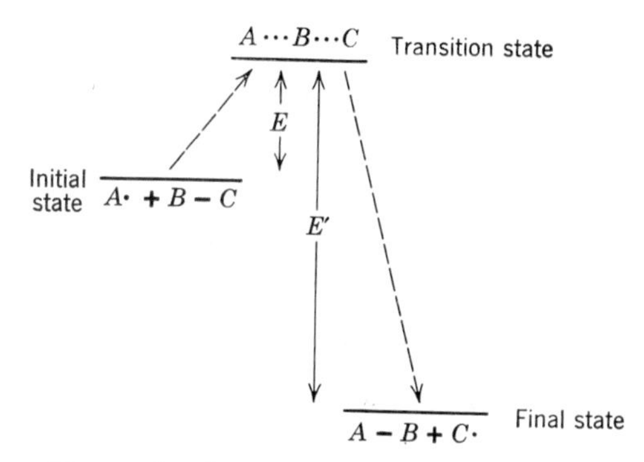

E = *activation energy for forward reaction*
E' = *activation energy for back reaction*
$$E' - E = \mathrm{D}(A\text{—}B) - \mathrm{D}(B\text{—}C)$$

FIGURE 6.1 *Energy diagram for the reaction* $A\cdot + B\text{—}C \rightarrow A\text{—}B + C\cdot$ *(Potential energy increases with increasing distance from the bottom of the figure).*

smaller extent than heterolytic reactions, which involve transfer of electron pairs in bond breaking and bond formation. Radicals can be classed as electron-acceptors or electron-donors according to their tendency to gain or lose electrons respectively. Halogen atoms tend to gain electrons and attack preferentially, though generally not exclusively, points of high electron density in the substrate. Methyl radicals on the other hand are relatively nucleophilic, and tend rather to donate electrons and seek electron deficient centers in the substrate. This is illustrated by the attack of chlorine atoms and methyl radicals on compounds $\cdots CH_2 \cdots CH_2\text{—}R$ where R is an electron attracting group (either Cl or COOH) (e.g., 10); the reactions are

$$Cl\cdot + \cdots CH_2 \cdots CH_2\text{—}R \rightarrow HCl + \cdots \dot{C}H \cdots CH_2\text{—}R \quad (6.25)$$

and

$$\cdot CH_3 + \cdots CH_2 \cdots CH_2\text{—}R \rightarrow CH_4 + \cdots CH_2 \cdots \dot{C}H\text{—}R \quad (6.26)$$

The reactions of radicals can be divided into unimolecular (rearrangement and dissociation) and bimolecular, and the latter subdivided into attack on the substrate and radical-destroying processes according as the products do, or do not, include a free radical.

Radical Rearrangement

Reactive radicals can sometimes attain more stable structures by rearrangement. Aromatic nuclei and halogen atoms appear to migrate most frequently, but other atoms (e.g., hydrogen) and groups (e.g., methyl) may also shift. Migration of phenyl is illustrated by the radical β,β,β-triphenylethyl (I) (formed by decarbonation of β,β,β-triphenylpropionaldehyde) which rearranges completely to the radical (II) (11),

$$\underset{\text{(I)}}{Ph_3C\text{—}CH_2\cdot} \rightarrow \underset{\text{(II)}}{Ph_2\dot{C}\text{—}CH_2Ph} \tag{6.27}$$

A number of reactions have been reported by Nesmeyanov and Freidlina (12) in which a chlorine atom migrates in a radical of general structure (III) to give the more stable radical (IV),

$$\underset{\text{(III)}}{Cl_3C\text{—}\dot{C}=} \rightarrow \underset{\text{(IV)}}{Cl_2\dot{C}\text{—}CCl=} \tag{6.28}$$

Radical Dissociation

Radicals may dissociate, characteristically breaking down into a smaller radical and an unsaturated compound, e.g.,

$$Br_2CH\text{—}\dot{C}HBr \rightarrow Br\cdot + BrCH{=}CHBr \tag{6.29}$$

and

$$(CH_3)_3CO\cdot \rightarrow \cdot CH_3 + CH_3COCH_3 \tag{6.30}$$

Acetoxy and acetyl radicals lose carbon dioxide and carbon monoxide respectively,

$$CH_3CO_2\cdot \rightarrow \cdot CH_3 + CO_2 \tag{6.31}$$

$$CH_3CO\cdot \rightarrow \cdot CH_3 + CO \tag{6.7}$$

The decarboxylation of acetoxy radicals (Eq. 6.31) occurs very readily, aided by the high heat of formation of carbon dioxide. In every case dissociation increases in importance as the temperature is raised.

In radiation chemistry, excited radicals formed by the neutralization of a radical-ion may dissociate, in the same way that excited molecules and ions can.

Radical Attack on Substrates

ADDITION: Addition to unsaturated compounds is a characteristic reaction of free radicals,

$$A\cdot + \gt C{=}C\lt \;\rightarrow\; \gt C(A)\text{—}\dot{C}\lt \tag{6.32}$$

This is the reverse of radical dissociation (e.g., Eq. 6.29), and addition may in fact be a reversible reaction. Many examples of addition reactions are known and include radical-induced halogenation, with steps such as

$$Br\cdot + R{-}CH{=}CH_2 \rightarrow R{-}\dot{C}H{-}CH_2Br \qquad (6.33)$$

and the radical-initiated polymerization of unsaturated compounds, where the original radical grows by the stepwise addition of unsaturated molecules, e.g.,

$$-CH_2{-}\dot{C}HR + CH_2{=}CHR \rightarrow -CH_2{-}CHR{-}CH_2{-}\dot{C}HR \text{ etc.} \qquad (6.34)$$

Initiation of polymerization in an unsaturated compound is sometimes used as a diagnostic test for free radicals.

ABSTRACTION: Abstraction reactions are represented by the process,

$$A\cdot + BC \rightarrow AB + C\cdot \qquad (6.35)$$

and are the normal reaction of radicals with saturated organic compounds. Abstraction reactions may also compete with radical-addition in the case of unsaturated compounds. The species abstracted (B in the example above) is generally a univalent atom, either hydrogen or halogen, e.g.,

$$\cdot OH + CH_3OH \rightarrow H_2O + \cdot CH_2OH \qquad (6.36)$$

and

$$H\cdot + CH_3I \rightarrow HI + \cdot CH_3 \qquad (6.37)$$

Generally the radical formed is more stable than the attacking radical. Thus most radicals attack tertiary in preference to secondary or primary hydrogen atoms, though other factors (e.g., polar and energy considerations) will also influence the reaction.

Radical-Destroying Processes

COMBINATION: Combination is the reverse of molecular dissociation to give radicals,

$$R\cdot + S\cdot \rightarrow RS \qquad (6.38)$$

Reactions of this type are favored energetically since they have little or no activation energy and energy is liberated equal to the dissociation energy of the bond formed. Combination of methyl radicals to form ethane for example takes place in the gas phase at almost every radical-radical collision (13),

$$2\cdot CH_3 \rightarrow C_2H_6 \qquad (6.39)$$

The readiness with which radicals combine accounts for their very short lifetimes, even under conditions of low radical concentration.

The energy liberated as a consequence of combination is sufficient, if it is not delocalized or lost, to allow immediate redissociation into the original radicals. In complex molecules it is distributed in a number of internal degrees of freedom and is unlikely to be concentrated in any one bond (so as to cause rupture) before it is lost through collisions with other molecules. Smaller molecules have fewer possibilities for distributing the energy, and diatomic molecules formed by the combination of two free atoms will normally dissociate again unless they can lose energy quickly. In condensed phases the newly formed diatomic molecule can lose energy rapidly to adjacent molecules, but in a gaseous system combination will only give a stable molecule if it takes place on a surface (e.g., a wall of the reaction vessel) or in the presence of a third body which can share the energy liberated,[3] e.g.,

$$O\cdot + O\cdot + M \rightarrow O_2 + M \tag{6.40}$$

Surfaces may therefore affect gas-phase radiolyses in which free atoms are intermediates but will have little effect (in this sense) upon the radiolysis of liquids, where there are ample opportunities for rapid energy loss by collisional processes. It might be pointed out that the energy released by radical combination is less than that liberated by recombination of an ion pair, as the following example shows:

$$H\cdot + \cdot OH \rightarrow H_2O + 116 \text{ kcal/mole } (5.0 \text{ ev/molecule}) \tag{6.41}$$

$$H_2O^+ + e^- \rightarrow H_2O + 291 \text{ kcal/mole } (12.6 \text{ ev/molecule}) \tag{6.42}$$

The energy released by radical combination may be retained by the newly formed molecule long enough to influence its reactions. Alexander and Rosen (14) have suggested that hydrogen peroxide formed by the combination of two hydroxyl radicals in α-particle tracks in water is more reactive towards amino acids than ordinary hydrogen peroxide. They suggest that the enhanced reactivity, which has a relatively long lifetime, is due to the formation of the peroxide in a triplet excited state:

$$2\cdot OH \rightarrow {}^3H_2O_2^* \tag{6.43}$$

In the gas phase, combination of hydrogen atoms with ethyl radicals gives an excited form of ethane which, at low pressures, may dissociate into two methyl radicals before deactivation can occur (15, 16):

$$H\cdot + \cdot C_2H_5 \rightarrow C_2H_6^* \rightarrow 2\cdot CH_3 \tag{6.44}$$

[3] The possibility that the newly formed molecule will lose energy by fluorescence is ignored here since it is not normally significant.

Dissociation of the excited molecule to methyl radicals rather than the original fragments is favored by the lower bond dissociation energy of the carbon-carbon bond (Table 6.2). In other instances molecular dissociation products may result, e.g. (17),

$$\cdot C_2H_5 + I\cdot \rightarrow C_2H_4 + HI \tag{6.45}$$

in a process resembling radical disproportionation (see below).

When two radicals are formed in a liquid by dissociation of a single molecule they may sometimes be prevented from moving apart by the surrounding molecules. In this event they will eventually recombine with one another and, if the original molecule is reformed,[4] there will be no chemical change produced in the system. Recombination of radicals in this way, before they have diffused apart, is known as the Franck-Rabinowitch or cage effect. In Chapter 5 the photodissociation of iodine in various solvents was given as an illustration of the cage effect. A further illustration is provided by the photolysis of azomethane, $CH_3N_2CH_3$, in the vapor phase and in solution (18, 19). Ethane is formed from the azomethane by the sequence of reactions:

$$CH_3N_2CH_3 + h\nu \rightarrow CH_3N_2CH_3^* \tag{6.46}$$

$$CH_3N_2CH_3^* \rightarrow 2\cdot CH_3 + N_2 \tag{6.47}$$

$$2\cdot CH_3 \rightarrow C_2H_6 \tag{6.39}$$

Using a mixture of $CH_3N_2CH_3$ and $CD_3N_2CD_3$ it is possible to estimate the extent to which methyl radicals from the same molecule recombine. Lyon and Levy (18) have carried out such an experiment and have shown that in the vapor phase the proportion of CH_3CD_3 formed is that expected if the methyl radicals separate and then combine with other $\cdot CH_3$ or $\cdot CD_3$ radicals in a purely random fashion. However, when the mixture is photolyzed as a solution in isoöctane a negligible amount of CH_3CD_3 is produced, and it appears that ethane is always formed by combination of methyl radicals from the same azomethane molecule. This is good evidence that caging of the radicals occurs in solution, where they are bounded by close packed solvent molecules, but not in the vapor, where they are free to move apart.

DISPROPORTIONATION: An alternative to the combination of two radicals to give a single stable molecule is transfer of an atom (generally hydrogen) from one radical to the other, giving two stable molecules, one of which is unsaturated:

$$2RH\cdot \rightarrow RH_2 + R \tag{6.48}$$

[4] It need not be since disproportionation can also occur.

Ethyl radicals can react together in this manner to give a molecule each of ethane and ethylene,

$$2 \cdot C_2H_5 \rightarrow C_2H_6 + C_2H_4 \quad (6.49)$$

and the radicals $CH_3\dot{C}HOH$, derived from ethanol by loss of an α-hydrogen atom, to give ethanol and acetaldehyde,

$$2CH_3\dot{C}HOH \rightarrow CH_3CH_2OH + CH_3CHO \quad (6.50)$$

Unlike radicals may also disproportionate, e.g.,

$$\cdot CH_3 + \cdot C_2H_5 \rightarrow CH_4 + C_2H_4 \quad (6.51)$$

Disproportionation is less common than simple radical combination and it is rare with aromatic radicals, which generally dimerize. Often both disproportionation and combination will be found in the same system.

ELECTRON TRANSFER: Just as radicals may be formed by one-electron transfer processes so they may be destroyed in the same way, e.g.,

$$\cdot OH + Fe^{2+} \rightarrow Fe^{3+} + OH^- \quad (6.52)$$

However electron transfer need not always result in radical destruction, for instance in aqueous solutions electron transfer between halide ions and hydroxyl radicals gives halogen atoms, e.g.,

$$\cdot OH + Br^- \rightarrow Br \cdot + OH^- \quad (6.53)$$

"Hot" Radicals

In some situations atoms and radicals may be formed with more kinetic or excitational[5] energy than the average thermal energy of the surrounding molecules; in other words they are "hot" relative to their surroundings.[6]

[5] Electronically excited radicals are "hot" in the sense used here.

[6] A distinction ought, perhaps, to be made here. Hot radicals, in the sense that the term is used in this book, will certainly not exceed thermal energy by more than a few electron volts. Their reactions are essentially those of similar radicals with thermal energies, though the rates of their reactions may be enhanced by the extra energy that they possess. Hot atoms produced by nuclear reactions, for instance the hot tritium atoms produced by the reactions $He^3(n, p)H^3$ and $Li^6(n, \alpha)H^3$, can have very much higher energies in the kilo-electron volt range and can bring about quite different types of reaction. The hot tritium atoms formed in these reactions, for example, can displace other atoms or groups from molecules with which they collide (20), whereas hot hydrogen atoms in our sense, and thermal hydrogen atoms, will only undergo abstraction and addition reactions. The chief difference between the "low-energy" hot hydrogen atoms and thermal hydrogen atoms is that the former

Energetic radicals (distinguished here by italic type) may be formed by the neutralization of molecular or radical ions, i.e., by

$$A^{+} + e^{-} \rightarrow A^{**} \rightarrow R\cdot + S\cdot \tag{6.54}$$

or

$$R\cdot^{+} + e^{-} \rightarrow R\cdot \tag{6.55}$$

respectively. They may also be formed by the dissociation of excited molecules if the excitation energy is greater than the dissociation energy of the bond broken,

$$A^{*} \rightarrow R\cdot + S\cdot \tag{6.56}$$

All three processes can occur in the tracks of ionizing particles.

Exothermic chemical reactions can also produce energetic radicals, an example being the addition of hydrogen atoms to olefins, e.g.,

$$H\cdot + CH_3\text{—}CH\text{=}CH_2 \rightarrow CH_3\text{—}\dot{C}H\text{—}CH_3 + \text{energy} \tag{6.57}$$

Propyl radicals formed by this reaction dissociate to an appreciable extent at room temperature,

$$\cdot C_3H_7 \rightarrow C_2H_4 + \cdot CH_3 \tag{6.58}$$

whereas thermally equilibrated propyl radicals are stable (21).

Energetic radicals formed in a liquid by reactions 6.54 and 6.56 are less likely to be trapped in a solvent cage than similar radicals formed with only thermal energy, and the possibility of reaction between the radicals and the substrate is therefore enhanced. Furthermore the extra energy that the hot radical possesses also favors rapid reaction with the substrate, so that hot radicals generally react in this way rather than with other radicals. However, if the hot radical should escape almost immediate reaction, it will lose energy by collisions with other molecules and will eventually be reduced to thermal energy.

The reactions of hot radicals are likely to be less temperature dependent than those of thermal radicals. For example, hot radicals formed when a frozen material is irradiated at liquid nitrogen temperatures may react with the substrate, though the same radicals formed under these conditions with only thermal energy fail to react because the necessary activation energy is not available.

---

will often react with the first molecule they collide with, and are therefore immune to materials present in the medium in low concentration. Thermal hydrogen atoms, on the other hand, may collide a number of times before they react and will often react preferentially with a reactive solute, even though the concentration of the solute is quite low.

Chain Reactions

Reactions which were grouped earlier under the heading "radical attack on substrates" are characterized by the appearance of a radical among the products. In some situations the newly formed radical may also react with the substrate, and with favorable conditions the sequence of reactions between radical and substrate may be repeated a large number of times before the radical is destroyed; in other words, a chain reaction takes place. The sequence of reactions may be repeated anywhere from two or three to many thousand times and the original radical may give rise to changes involving a very large number of substrate molecules.

Two basic types of chain reaction would be anticipated, corresponding to the two types of radical-substrate reaction, addition and abstraction. Successive addition reactions are typical of radical-induced polymerization, which can be represented by

$$\mathrm{R\cdot + AB \rightarrow R{-}AB\cdot} \tag{6.59}$$

$$\mathrm{R{-}AB\cdot + AB \rightarrow R{-}AB{-}AB\cdot} \tag{6.60}$$

Taking styrene ($PhCH{=}CH_2$) as an example, a typical chain propagating step is

$$\mathrm{{-}CH_2{-}\underset{|}{\overset{Ph}{C}}H\cdot + CH_2{=}\overset{Ph}{\underset{|}{C}}H \rightarrow {-}CH_2{-}\overset{Ph}{C}H{-}CH_2{-}\overset{Ph}{C}H\cdot} \tag{6.61}$$

Chain reactions involving successive abstraction reactions are represented by

$$\begin{array}{l} \mathrm{R\cdot + AB \rightarrow RA + B\cdot} \\ \mathrm{B\cdot + RC \rightarrow BC + R\cdot} \\ \hline \mathrm{AB + RC \rightarrow RA + BC} \end{array} \tag{6.62}$$

Two different abstraction reactions must take place if the products are to be different from the reactants; in the side-chain bromination of toluene these are

$$\mathrm{Br\cdot + PhCH_3 \rightarrow HBr + PhCH_2\cdot} \tag{6.63}$$

and

$$\mathrm{PhCH_2\cdot + Br_2 \rightarrow PhCH_2Br + Br\cdot} \tag{6.64}$$

The repeated sequence of reactions may be more complex than the examples shown above, and it can include radical rearrangement and dissociation as well as addition and abstraction reactions. An interesting reaction between diazomethane and carbon tetrachloride to give pentaerithrytol tetrachloride involves a repeating sequence made up of eight steps (22); the over-all chemical change is

$$4CH_2N_2 + CCl_4 \xrightarrow{h\nu} C(CH_2Cl)_4 + 4N_2 \qquad (6.65)$$

Chain reactions are very sensitive to small quantities of impurities if these are able to react with the radical intermediates. Typically, compounds which inhibit chain reactions are either stable free radicals (e.g., NO, DPPH) or compounds which react to give relatively stable free radicals, such as oxygen and benzoquinone. However, oxygen is an essential reactant in some chain reactions where it forms a peroxy radical ($RO_2\cdot$) able to react with the substrate (as in autoxidation), or else one which breaks down to give a relatively reactive radical.

Before leaving chain reactions it is worthwhile to consider the kinetics of a very simple, radiation-initiated, example. The reaction is broken down into initiation, propagation, and termination steps:

Initiation;	$A \rightsquigarrow R\cdot$	cR_M
Propagation;	$R\cdot + A \rightarrow R\cdot + P$	k_1
Termination;	$2R\cdot \rightarrow$ unreactive products	k_2

The initiation step involves the production of radicals ($R\cdot$) from the substrate (A) by the absorption of ionizing radiation. The rate of formation of radicals by this process is given by the product of the absorbed dose rate R_M (ev/liter sec) and a constant c (moles/ev), related to the G value for the formation of radicals. Propagation is represented as reaction of the radicals with the substrate to give a product (P) and regenerate a radical ($R\cdot$; for simplicity the various radicals involved are not differentiated), the rate constant for the reaction being k_1 (liter/mole sec). Termination is assumed to be combination of two radicals to give unreactive products, which do not include P, with a rate constant k_2 (liter/mole sec). Under steady state conditions the radicals are formed and destroyed at the same rate:

$$d[R\cdot]/dt = 0 = cR_M - k_2[R\cdot]^2$$

and therefore

$$[R\cdot] = (c/k_2)^{1/2}(R_M)^{1/2}$$

The rate of formation of the product P is given by

$$\frac{d[P]}{dt} = k_1[A][R\cdot] = k_1\left(\frac{c}{k_2}\right)^{1/2}[A](R_M)^{1/2}$$

The rate of energy absorption by the system, dE/dt, is equal to the absorbed dose rate R_M, and the G value for the production of P (i.e. the yield per unit energy absorbed) is given by

$$G(\mathrm{P}) = \frac{d[\mathrm{P}]}{dE}$$

From this

$$G(\mathrm{P}) = \frac{d[\mathrm{P}]}{dt} \times \frac{dt}{dE}$$

and

$$G(\mathrm{P}) = k_1 \left(\frac{c}{k_2}\right)^{1/2} [\mathrm{A}](R_M)^{-1/2} \tag{6.66}$$

The important conclusion here is that $G(\mathrm{P})$ is inversely proportional to the square root of the dose rate. Admittedly this is derived for an extremely simple chain reaction, but the conclusion arrived at, essentially that the G value will exhibit a nonlinear dependence on the dose rate, is generally true for radiation-initiated chain reactions; it is in fact a restriction on the use of chain reactions in chemical dosimetry, where their high yields would otherwise be very serviceable. When the reaction mechanism includes more than one chain-terminating step, a nonlinear dose rate dependence will be found whenever one of the competing radical-destroying reactions is second order with respect to radicals.

The dependence of G(product) on a power of the dose rate other than the first leads to an interesting result if the irradiation is intermittent rather than steady. For example, if a disc from which sectors have been cut (Fig. 6.2) is rotated between the radiation source and the sample so that the radiation is cut off from the sample for two thirds of each

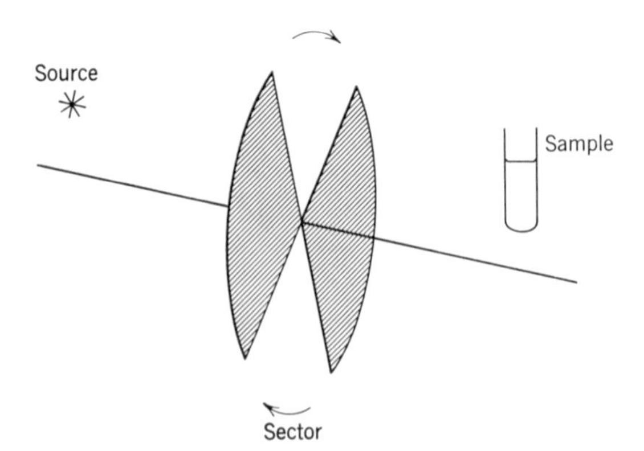

FIGURE 6.2 *Experimental arrangement for intermittent illumination.*

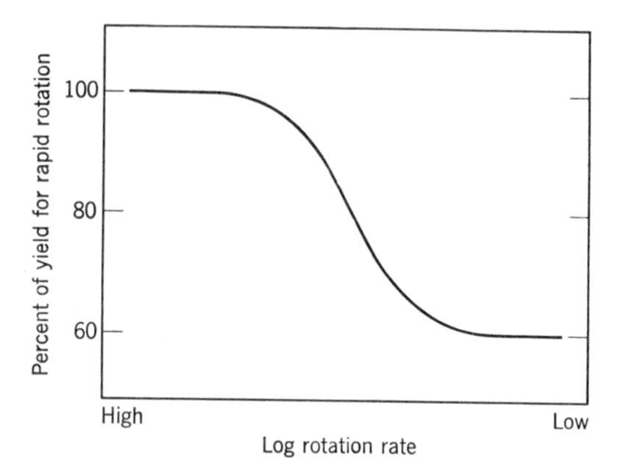

FIGURE 6.3 *Effect of intermittent illumination upon a photo or radiation-induced chain reaction.*

revolution then, when the disc is rotated slowly, the effect is essentially that of full irradiation for one third the time. For the simple chain reaction considered above $G(\mathrm{P})$ will still be given by Eq. 6.66, assuming R_M to be the uninterrupted dose rate. However when the sector is rotating rapidly there will be a range of speeds above which the system does not differentiate between light and dark periods, and the effect is that of continuous irradiation at one third the uninterrupted dose rate, i.e., effectively the dose rate is now $\frac{1}{3}R_M$. The change in effective dose rate means that $G(\mathrm{P})$ will be different at high and low speeds of rotation; a plot of the ratio of the two yields against the rate of rotation will give a curve similar to Fig. 6.3. When the disc has two 60° sectors cut from it, so that the ratio of the light to dark periods is one to two, then from Eq. 6.66,

$$\frac{G(\mathrm{P})_{\mathrm{fast}}}{G(\mathrm{P})_{\mathrm{slow}}} = (3)^{1/2} = 1.7$$

The transition region of the curve occurs when the interval between the radiation pulses is of the same order as the average lifetime of the rate-controlling intermediates (in the present example, the average lifetime of a reaction chain between initiation and termination). Intermittent irradiation experiments can be used to determine these average lifetimes and also the individual rate constants (k_1 and k_2 in present instance).

Experiments with intermittent radiation are common in photochemistry where it is a simple matter to interrupt the illumination, but are less common in radiation chemistry where the experimental difficulties are more formidable. Ghormley (23) has used an aluminum sector to interrupt the beam of electrons from a Van de Graaff accelerator, and found the lifetime of the shortest-lived intermediates in water whose concentration affects the steady state concentration of hydrogen peroxide to be about 10^{-3} sec under the conditions of the experiments. β-radiation may also be stopped with relatively thin metal sectors (e.g., 24). A few experiments have been carried out with γ-rays using massive metal sectors. Thus the lifetimes of the radical chains in γ-irradiated chloral hydrate solutions (25) and in moist aerated chloroform (26) have been shown to be about 0.1 sec and 1 sec respectively. The former value has been confirmed by flowing the chloral hydrate solution past a cobalt-60 source several times in rapid succession, producing the effect of intermittent irradiation (27); varying the flow rate produces similar effects to varying the speed of rotation in the rotating sector experiments.

Radiation from an accelerator may of necessity be pulsed and, if the pulse rate can be varied, can be used directly for experiments of this type. Sutton and Rotblat (28) found that G(ferric) and G(cerous) in aqueous solutions of ferrous sulfate and ceric sulfate respectively, irradiated with 15 Mev electrons from a linear accelerator, were not affected by increasing the pulse rate to an upper limit of 400 pulses per second. Though the reactions here are not chain reactions any increase in radical-radical combination at the expense of radical-solute reaction will alter the observed G values, and it could therefore be concluded that the lifetimes of the radicals involved did not exceed 2.5 millisecond.

Radical Scavenging

Scavenging is the term applied to the deliberate addition to a radical reaction of a compound which will react preferentially with the radicals, at the expense of the normal radical reactions. The object is to identify the radicals taking part in the reaction and to determine what part of the over-all reaction is due to (scavengeable) free radicals. In radiation-induced reactions in liquids the reaction may take place either within spurs or close to the tracks of heavy particles, where the active intermediates are formed, or in the bulk of the medium where reactions are initiated by radicals which have diffused from the track zone. Using moderate scavenger concentrations (e.g., 10^{-6} to $10^{-3}M$ iodine) the scavenging action will be limited to radicals which have diffused into the bulk of the sample and reactions in the track zone will be unaffected, allowing the reactions in these two regions to be differentiated. It should be pointed out that hot radicals often react within one or two collisions and therefore are not scavenged by low concentrations of scavenger. However, if the hot radicals escape reaction and are reduced to thermal energy they will be scavenged in the normal manner.

Substances used as scavengers are either stable free radicals, compounds which eliminate radicals by electron transfer reactions, or compounds which react to give relatively stable free radicals in place of the active radicals originally present. Molecular iodine is probably most widely used (29, 30, 31) and reacts as follows:

$$R\cdot + I_2 \rightarrow RI + I\cdot \tag{6.67}$$

The iodine atoms which are formed are relatively stable and eventually combine, giving molecular iodine. The reaction is a favorable one energetically since D(R—I) is generally greater than D(I—I). Radicals that are scavenged with iodine can be identified by identifying the iodides (RI) formed. This can be accomplished rather elegantly by using radioactive iodine-131 as a scavenger and identifying the radioactive iodides by isotope dilution (32, 33). The quantity of iodine used up gives a measure of the total number of radicals that have reacted with the scavenger. Two practical points deserve mention in connection with the use of iodine as a scavenger. First, hydrogen iodide formed by scavenging of hydrogen atoms is frequently difficult to estimate accurately since, unless special precautions are taken, it reacts with unsaturated radiolysis products and this results in spuriously low estimates of the number of hydrogen atoms formed (31). The second point is that aromatic compounds can enter into complex reactions when irradiated with iodine, so that iodine scavenging experiments with aromatic materials must be interpreted with caution (34). Results obtained with iodine are not entirely unambiguous since iodine (and organic iodides) can react with free electrons:

$$e^- + I_2 \rightarrow I^- + I\cdot \tag{6.68}$$

This may influence the reaction by providing an alternative to the neutralization of positive ions by electrons. The alternative neutralization reaction is

$$A^+ + I^- \rightarrow A^* + I\cdot \tag{6.69}$$

which releases rather less energy than the normal neutralization process and may lead to different products.

Other radical scavengers include the stable free radicals diphenylpicrylhydrazyl (35, 36) and nitric oxide (37), ferric chloride (38, 39, 40), hydrogen iodide (41), and a variety of unsaturated compounds, such as styrene, methylmethacrylate, cyclohexene, etc., (42), including C^{14}-labeled ethylene (43).

Charlesby, Davison, and Lloyd (44) have made a kinetic study of the effect of scavenger concentration and dose rate when anthracene is used as a scavenger in irradiated hexane, cyclohexane, and polysiloxanes. With the hydrocarbon solutions, the rate of anthracene disappearance depends on [anthracene] (dose rate)$^{-1/2}$, as expected if competition exists between a radical-radical reaction and the scavenging radical-anthracene reaction. Anthracene is a relatively inefficient scavenger, allowing the concentration and dose-rate dependence to be observed, but with many scavengers the competing radical-radical reaction is virtually eliminated, and these effects are not seen.

Reaction with Oxygen

Oxygen readily adds to free radicals, and if present will almost invariably play a part in radiation-induced reactions. The combination of oxygen with radicals is easily understood if molecular oxygen is written as a diradical, $\cdot O{-}O\cdot$, in recognition of its triplet ground state; thus,

$$R\cdot + \cdot O{-}O\cdot \rightarrow R{-}O{-}O\cdot \tag{6.70}$$

The product is a relatively stable peroxy radical.

In some cases peroxy radicals are able to abstract hydrogen from the substrate:

$$RO_2\cdot + RH \rightarrow RO_2H + R\cdot \tag{6.71}$$

Reactions 6.70 and 6.71, taken together, constitute a chain reaction of the type responsible for the *autoxidation* (self-oxidation under mild conditions) of a wide variety of organic compounds; everyday examples include the drying of linseed oil based paints, the production of rancidity in fats, and the deterioration of rubber and plastic materials exposed to air and light.

One of the earliest examples of autoxidation to be recognized was the slow, light accelerated, oxidation of benzaldehyde to benzoic acid on exposure to air (45). Later work has shown that the oxidation is a chain reaction that is described by equations 6.70 and 6.71 when R is the group PhCO. The over-all chemical change produced by the chain reaction is the conversion of benzaldehyde to perbenzoic acid,

$$PhCHO + O_2 \rightarrow Ph{-}C\begin{matrix} {/\!\!/}O \\ \diagdown O{-}OH \end{matrix} \tag{6.72}$$

The latter subsequently reacts with another molecule of benzaldehyde giving benzoic acid,

$$PhCO_3H + PhCHO \rightarrow 2PhCOOH \tag{6.73}$$

It might be noted in connection with this oxidation that hydrogen is generally more weakly bound in an aldehyde group than in an unsubstituted saturated hydrocarbon, and this facilitates the hydrogen-abstraction step (Eq. 6.71); D(PhCO—H) is 79 kcal/mole.

Since oxygenated radicals are of very great importance in radiation chemistry some of the reactions attributed to them are given below, though these are not as well established as the reactions of the parent alkyl radicals; the list is by no means complete.

Peroxy radicals ($RO_2\cdot$) are the initial products formed by the addition of oxygen to an organic radical, and they can form hydroperoxides (RO_2H) by hydrogen abstraction (Eq. 6.71) or by reaction with a perhydroxyl radical ($HO_2\cdot$):

$$RO_2\cdot + HO_2\cdot \rightarrow RO_2H + O_2 \tag{6.74}$$

In some cases hydroperoxides can be formed directly by addition of oxygen to an excited molecule. Combination of two peroxy radicals may give an organic peroxide,

$$2RO_2\cdot \rightarrow R—O—O—R + O_2 \tag{6.75}$$

but the products of the reaction are more often two alkoxy radicals ($RO\cdot$),

$$2RO_2\cdot \rightarrow 2RO\cdot + O_2 \tag{6.76}$$

Other reactions which have been suggested whereby a peroxy radical is degraded to an alkoxy radical include

$$RO_2\cdot + R\cdot \rightarrow 2RO\cdot \tag{6.77}$$

$$RO_2\cdot + O_2 \rightarrow RO\cdot + O_3 \tag{6.78}$$

and, at higher temperatures,

$$RO_2\cdot \xrightarrow{RH} RO_2H \rightarrow RO\cdot + \cdot OH \tag{6.79}$$

Alkoxy radicals are more reactive than peroxy radicals and can abstract hydrogen from most organic compounds, resembling hydroxyl radicals in this respect,

$$RO\cdot + RH \rightarrow ROH + R\cdot \tag{6.80}$$

A fairly common, though endothermic, reaction of alkoxy radicals is dissociation into a carbonyl compound and either a hydrogen atom or an alkyl radical, e.g.,

$$CH_3O\cdot \rightarrow HCHO + H\cdot \; - 25 \text{ kcal/mole} \quad (6.81)$$

$$(CH_3)_3CO\cdot \rightarrow CH_3COCH_3 + \cdot CH_3 - 5 \text{ kcal/mole} \quad (6.82)$$

Combination of two alkoxy radicals to give a peroxide appears less probable than disproportionation to give an alcohol and a carbonyl compound:

$$2RCH_2O\cdot \rightarrow RCH_2OH + RCHO \quad (6.83)$$

Similarly, reaction between an alkoxy radical and an alkyl radical is less likely to give an ether (RCH_2OR) than a carbonyl compound and a hydrocarbon,

$$RCH_2O\cdot + R\cdot \rightarrow RCHO + RH \quad (6.84)$$

The reactions of peroxy and alkoxy radicals are also influenced by the other groups attached to the same carbon atom. For instance, radicals in which both halogen (X) and oxygen are attached to the same carbon are often unstable, breaking down with loss of the halogen, e.g.,

$$RCX_2O\cdot \rightarrow R\cdot + COX_2 \quad (6.85)$$

or, in the presence of moisture, giving hydrolysis products (probably RCOOH and HX from $RCX_2O\cdot$). When a hydroxyl group is attached to the same carbon atom as the peroxy group the products obtained in the presence of water generally include hydrogen peroxide and the corresponding carboxylic acid and (or) carbonyl compound.

Metal ions able to undergo one-electron oxidation-reduction reactions can react with alkoxy and peroxy radicals and with hydroperoxides and peroxides (cf. Eq. 6.11 and 6.15–16), and may play an important part if they are present during radical reactions carried out in the presence of oxygen.

Finally it might be remarked that the molecular products from these reactions with oxygen may include chemically unstable hydroperoxides and peroxides which can continue to react slowly long after they have been formed. Radical reactions carried out in the presence of oxygen may therefore show delayed effects.

DETECTION

Several methods based on physical measurements are available for the detection and identification of free radicals. The most important from the point of view of radiation chemistry is electron paramagnetic resonance but others, such as magnetic susceptibility measurements and mass spectroscopy (46), are also useful on occasion. Flash photolysis enables the absorption spectra of momentarily high concentrations of radicals and other transient intermediates to be obtained.

Magnetic Susceptibility

All molecules containing unpaired electrons are paramagnetic, that is, they are drawn from a region of low magnetic field strength into a region of high field strength. With suitable equipment the very small forces exerted on paramagnetic materials by a magnetic field can be measured, though application of this to the detection of free radicals is limited because of the relatively high radical concentration needed to make the measurement possible. As a consequence magnetic susceptibility measurements are restricted to relatively stable radicals; they have been used for example to study the dissociation of substituted hexaphenylethanes into triphenylmethyl-type radicals in solution. The technique has also been used to demonstrate the presence of unpaired electrons in the phosphorescent (triplet) state of fluorescein (47).

Electron Paramagnetic Resonance

Paramagnetic resonance measurements provide the most sensitive method for detecting unpaired electrons and may be used both for stable free radicals and, at low temperatures, for reactive radicals which have been stabilized in frozen media. Further advantages are the possibility of identifying the radicals from their spectra and of estimating their numbers by comparison with a stable paramagnetic substance (e.g., DPPH or a paramagnetic salt). Radicals formed by the irradiation of solids or frozen materials can readily be studied by this technique.

Electron paramagnetic resonance (e.p.r.) or electron spin resonance (e.s.r.) as it is variously called is, like magnetic susceptibility, based upon the magnetic properties associated with an unpaired electron. Measurements are made by placing the paramagnetic material in a uniform magnetic field, which causes the unpaired electron to orientate itself with respect to the field. The orientation will be either parallel or antiparallel to the field, and all unpaired electrons will take up one or other of these two possible states. The two states have slightly different energies and at normal temperatures there will be rather more electrons in the lower-energy state, the number in the lower state increasing as the temperature is lowered. The energy difference between the two states is given by

$$\Delta E = g\beta H \tag{6.86}$$

where H is the strength of the magnetic field (gauss), β is a constant (the Bohr magneton) equal to 0.927×10^{-20} erg/gauss, and g is the spectroscopic splitting factor, a dimensionless number whose value depends upon the environment of the unpaired electron (for a free electron g has the value 2.0023). Simultaneously the sample is subjected to electromagnetic radiation with a frequency such that

$$h\nu = g\beta H \tag{6.87}$$

causing the unpaired electrons to reverse their orientation with respect to the magnetic field. Since there are more electrons in the lower-energy state this results in a net absorption of radiation energy, which with appropriate equipment can be observed as a spectroscopic absorption line.

Substituting numerical values into equation 6.87, taking $g = 2$ and setting the magnetic field strength at a reasonable level (about 3500 gauss), the frequency required is found to be about 10,000 Mc, i.e., is in the microwave region of the electromagnetic spectrum. In practice a wavelength of 3.2 cm (about 9400 Mc) is frequently used as microwave components designed for this wavelength are readily available. The experimental results are obtained in the form of an absorption curve by maintaining the frequency constant and varying the magnetic field by means of small secondary coils, so that the magnetic field varies about the value that corresponds to maximum absorption. A curve of the type obtained by plotting energy absorption against magnetic field strength for a system containing isolated free electrons is shown in Fig. 6.4.

In addition to the external magnetic field, the unpaired electron may experience magnetic fields due to neighboring nuclei which possess nuclear magnetic moments. Nuclei having this property include hydro-

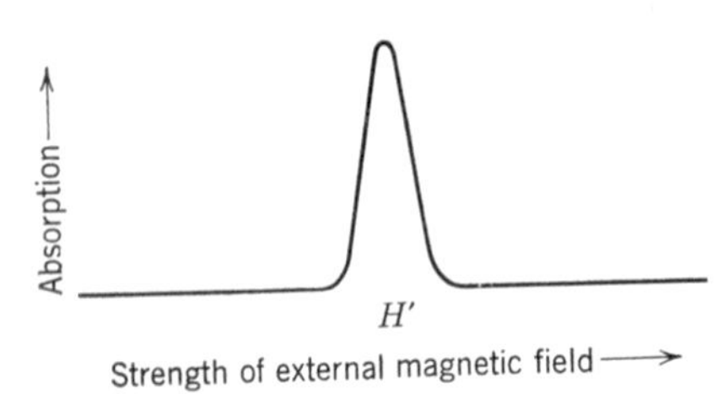

FIGURE 6.4 *E.p.r. absorption spectrum of an isolated electron.*

gen, deuterium, nitrogen-14, and chlorine-35, while carbon-12, oxygen-16, and sulfur-32 are examples of nuclei with zero magnetic moment. In the external magnetic field the nuclear magnetic fields become orientated, the number of different orientations possible for a particular nucleus being given by the expression $(2I + 1)$, where I is the spin of the nucleus (Table 6.3). Nuclear magnetic fields for nuclei close enough to an unpaired electron to affect it can either reinforce the external field or detract from it, and it is the resultant field from these two sources (external and nuclear) that governs the energy absorption. Energy absorption is dependent therefore not only on the external conditions but also on the molecular environment of the unpaired electron.

TABLE 6.3 *Nuclear Spins* (I)

0	$\frac{1}{2}$	1	$\frac{3}{2}$	$\frac{5}{2}$
Helium-4	Hydrogen-1	Deuterium	Chlorine-35	Oxygen-17
Carbon-12	Carbon-13	Nitrogen-14	Chlorine-37	
Oxygen-16	Fluorine-19			
Sulfur-32				

Consider the simplest example of the effect of a nuclear magnetic field, that of an unpaired electron adjacent to a nucleus of spin 1/2 (e.g., hydrogen) and subjected to an external magnetic field H. Then the nuclear magnetic field (a) can, from the expression given above, assume either of two orientations, which can be represented by $+a$ and $-a$. The magnetic field experienced by the electron is therefore $H + a$ or $H - a$ (in the system as a whole, half the electrons present experience the higher field and half the lower field). Thus there will be two values of the external field (H) which satisfy equation 6.87 and each will give maximum energy absorption. The absorption spectrum (Fig. 6.5) does in fact show two peaks arranged symmetrically about the position occupied by the single (isolated free electron) peak in Fig. 6.4. If H' is the value of the external magnetic field for maximum absorption by the isolated electron, then $H' - a$ and $H' + a$ are the values corresponding to the two peaks in Fig. 6.5.

When two nuclei of spin 1/2 are equidistant from the unpaired electron the two nuclear magnetic fields may either reinforce or cancel each other. Four combinations of the external and nuclear fields are possible, $H + a + a$, $H + a - a$, $H - a + a$, and $H - a - a$, but two coincide and the absorption curve (Fig. 6.6) will show three peaks, the center peak having twice the area of the outer peaks. When more than one nuclei with spin 1/2 are equidistant from the odd electron, the number of

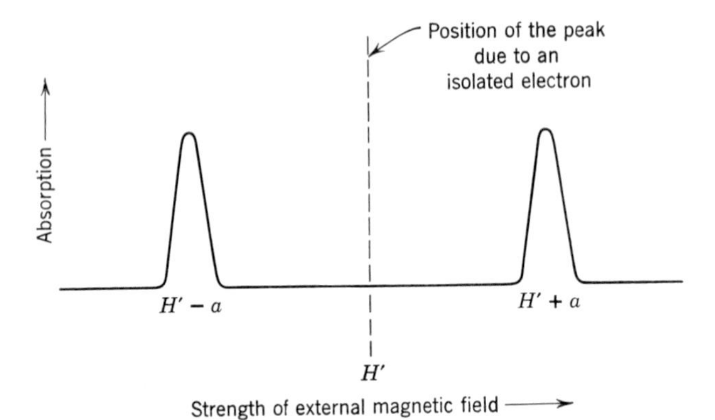

FIGURE 6.5 *E.p.r. absorption spectrum of a hydrogen atom.*

peaks in the spectrum is given by the number of terms in the expansion of $(1 + x)^n$, n being the number of equivalent nuclei. The relative areas of the peaks are given by the numerical coefficients of each term, i.e., 1 : 2 : 1 when $n = 2$ (Fig. 6.6). It must be emphasized however that this only applies when the spins of the nuclei are 1/2 and when they are equidistant from the unpaired electron. To take a practical example, the radical V would be expected to give an e.p.r. spectrum with seven lines with relative intensities 1 : 6 : 15 : 20 : 15 : 6 : 1 (from the expan-

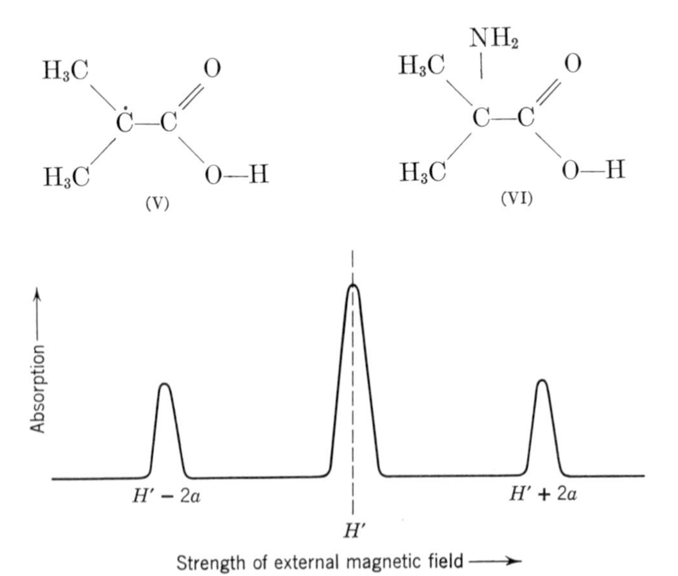

FIGURE 6.6 *E.p.r. absorption spectrum due to 2 equidistant protons.*

sion of $(1 + x)^6$) since there are six hydrogen atoms equidistant from the carbon carrying the odd electron. Carbon and oxygen have zero spin and therefore do not contribute to the nuclear field while the hydrogen of the hydroxyl group is probably too far away to exert much effect. An e.p.r. spectrum with seven peaks in roughly the right ratio has in fact been obtained with irradiated crystalline α-amino isobutyric acid(VI), suggesting that irradiation results in loss of the amino group (48).

More complex spectra are obtained when the nuclei concerned are not equidistant from the unpaired electron. For instance, two hydrogen nuclei at different distances from the electron produce four peaks (Fig. 6.7); the nuclear fields at the electron due to the two protons are not now the same and are represented in Fig. 6.7 as a_1 and a_2. The second proton has thus split into two each of the lines due to the first.

Nuclei with spins greater than 1/2 can give rather more absorption lines. Deuterium has spin 1 and so its nuclear magnetic field can assume three different orientations with respect to the external magnetic field; using the notation above these can be represented as $+a$, O, and $-a$. The spectrum of the deuterium atom therefore consists of three equally intense lines (Fig. 6.8). By listing the various combinations for the magnetic field at the unpaired electron it can be seen that two equidistant deuterium nuclei give a five-line spectrum, the intensities of the lines being in the ratio 1 : 2 : 3 : 2 : 1. Two deuterium nuclei at different distances give nine equally intense lines since none of the lines coincide. The different nuclear spins of deuterium and hydrogen can aid in the interpretation of e.p.r. spectra if deuterium is substituted for selected hydrogen atoms in the compound being studied and the resulting changes in the spectrum are analyzed (49).

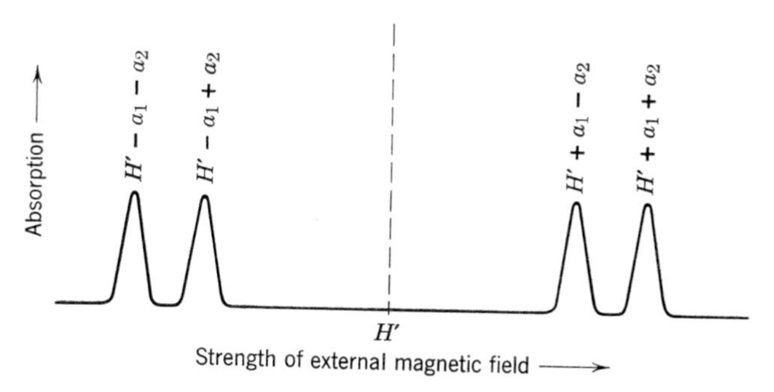

FIGURE 6.7 *E.p.r. absorption spectrum due to 2 nonequidistant protons.*

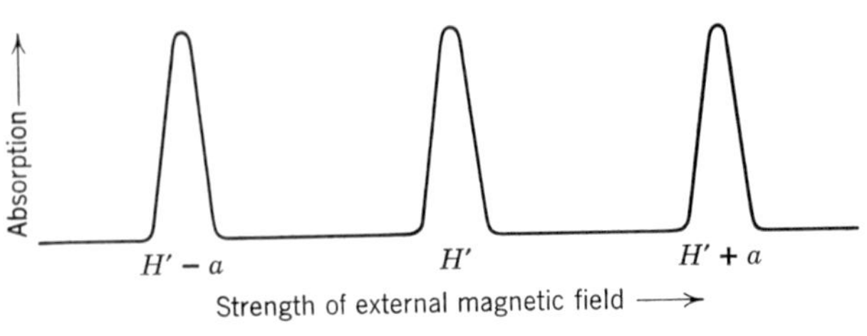

FIGURE 6.8 *E.p.r. absorption spectrum of a deuterium atom.*

Diphenylpicrylhydrazyl (DPPH)(VII) is a stable free radical which is of interest in radiation chemistry as a radical scavenger. The structure of DPPH suggests that it would give a nine line e.p.r. spectrum since the nearest nuclei to the odd electron are two nitrogen nuclei

$$NO_2$$

$$O_2N\text{—}C_6H_2\text{—}\dot{N}\text{—}NPh_2$$

$$NO_2$$

(VII)

(spin = 1). In fact the major features of the DPPH spectrum are five lines with relative intensities of 1 : 2 : 3 : 2 : 1, suggesting that the electron is not localized on one of the nitrogen atoms but is spread over them both, so that both nitrogen nuclei are equivalent as far as the e.p.r. spectrum is concerned.

In radiation chemistry, electron paramagnetic resonance is used to identify the radicals formed on irradiation, by analysis of the fine structure of their spectra. This may be accomplished more readily if the absorption is plotted as a derivative curve, plotting the slope of the normal absorption curve against the magnetic field. An absorption peak is shown by the derivative curve crossing the zero axis; for example, the derivative curve for an isolated free electron would appear as in Fig. 6.9; the normal absorption curve is shown in Fig. 6.4. Actual derivative curves found for the radicals H·, D·, ·OH, and ·OD in irradiated ice are shown in Fig. 8.3.

Flash Photolysis

Flash photolysis is a technique whereby a very high radical concentration is produced momentarily by photolysis, and the absorption spectrum of the reaction mixture determined immediately afterwards or after very short intervals (10^{-5} to 1 sec) (50, 51). The apparatus consists of a reaction vessel (*A* in Fig. 6.10) in the form of a quartz tube with

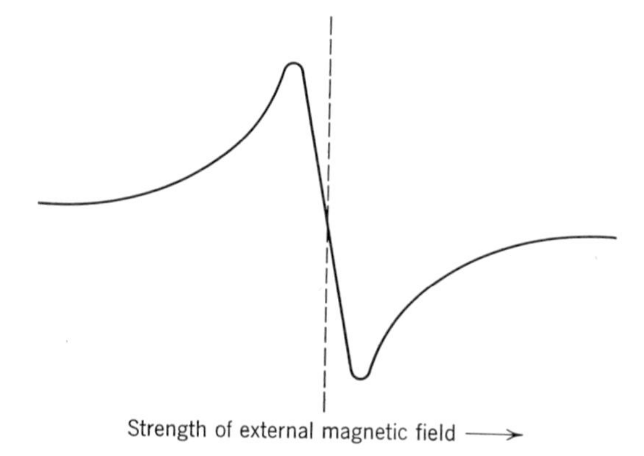

FIGURE 6.9 *Derivative curve for an isolated free electron.*

plane ends and, lying next to it, a quartz discharge lamp (*B*), also in the form of a tube but with tungsten electrodes and filled with about 10 cm pressure of inert gas. The reaction vessel and the lamp are surrounded by a reflector to concentrate the light. A bank of condensers discharge through the lamp and with suitably high potential and capacity give a very intense flash lasting about 100 microseconds (the flash may be sufficiently intense to cause complete dissociation of materials in the reaction tube). A second discharge lamp (*C*) is arranged end-on to the reaction tube and discharged a predetermined interval after the photo-flash. Light from this second lamp travels along the reaction tube and into the spectrograph (*D*) which records the absorption spectrum of the reaction mixture. In practice the experiment is generally repeated a

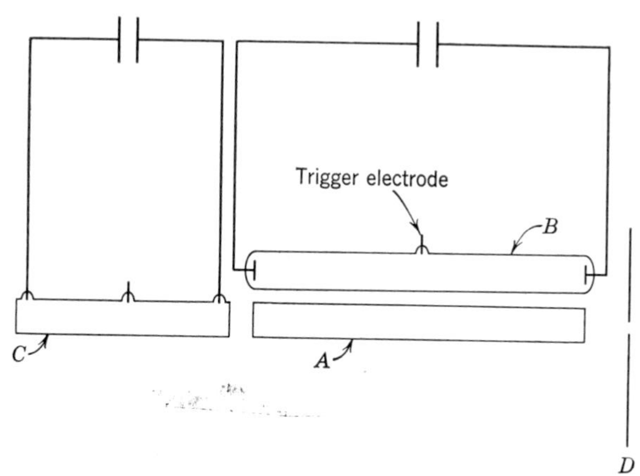

FIGURE 6.10 *Apparatus for flash photolysis.*

number of times, each time increasing the interval between the photo and spectroscopic flashes. In this way the decay of transient intermediates can be followed and their lifetimes estimated.

The material investigated may be either gaseous or in solution. However, the absorbed light is rapidly degraded to thermal energy and in gases at low pressures temperatures of several thousand degrees are generated, so that under these conditions the reaction mixture may contain the products of thermal as well as photolytic dissociation. In solution or in the presence of a relatively large excess of inert gas the temperature rise can be kept to about 10°C.

Flash photolysis has been used to identify free radical intermediates, to study the spectra and chemical reactions of radicals, and, particularly, to study the kinetics of radical reactions.[7] The technique has also been used to investigate nonradical transient intermediates (e.g., triplet excited states). Matheson and Dorfman (52) and McCarthy and MacLachlan (53) have detected radicals produced by ionizing radiation using an essentially similar technique, but replacing the photoflash by an intense pulse of electrons from an accelerator. This technique of pulse radiolysis is being increasingly exploited at the present time (54, 55) both to identify transient radiolysis intermediates and, more particularly, to determine absolute rate constants for their reactions.

SUMMARY OF THE REACTIONS OF FREE RADICALS

FORMATION:

$$RS \rightarrow R\cdot + S\cdot \qquad (6.1)$$

(thermal or photo dissociation)

$$M^{z+} + RO_2H \rightarrow M^{(z+1)+} + RO\cdot + OH^- \qquad \text{etc.} \qquad (6.11)$$

(oxidation-reduction processes)

REACTIONS:

$$AB\cdot \rightarrow BA\cdot$$

(rearrangement)

[7] In the kinetic experiments it is generally more convenient to use a continuous source of light in place of the spectroscopic flash, and to continuously monitor the absorption at a single wavelength which corresponds to an absorption peak of the species being studied. This avoids the necessity for several experiments with different intervals between the photo and spectroscopic flashes, and allows a more accurate measurement of the change in absorption. The modified technique is known as *kinetic spectroscopy*.

$$AB\cdot \rightarrow A\cdot + B$$
(dissociation)

$$R\cdot + \;\; >C{=}C< \;\; \rightarrow \;\; >\overset{R}{\underset{|}{C}}{-}\dot{C}< \qquad (6.32)$$
(addition)

$$A\cdot + BC \rightarrow AB + C\cdot \qquad (6.35)$$
(abstraction)

$$R\cdot + O_2 \rightarrow R{-}O{-}O\cdot \qquad (6.70)$$
(oxygen addition)

DESTRUCTION:

$$R\cdot + S\cdot \rightarrow RS \qquad (6.38)$$
(combination)

$$2RH\cdot \rightarrow RH_2 + R \qquad (6.48)$$
(disproportionation)

$$M^{z+} + R\cdot \rightarrow M^{(z+1)+} + R^- \qquad (6.52)$$
(electron transfer)

REFERENCES

For further reading on free radical chemistry *Free Radicals in Solution* by C. Walling, John Wiley and Sons, New York, 1957, is recommended, and on electron paramagnetic resonance *Free Radicals as Studied by Electron Spin Resonance* by D. J. E. Ingram, Butterworths Scientific Publications, London, 1958. Two other invaluable sources of information about free radicals are *Atomic and Free Radical Reactions* by E. W. R. Steacie, Second edition, Reinhold Publishing Corp., New York, 1954, and *Some Problems in Chemical Kinetics and Reactivity* by N. N. Semenov (translated by M. Boudart), Princeton University Press, Princeton, New Jersey, 1958.

1. M. Gomberg, *Ber.*, **33,** 3150 (1900); *J. Am. Chem. Soc.*, **22,** 757 (1900).
2. H. J. H. Fenton, *J. Chem. Soc.*, **65,** 899 (1894); H. J. H. Fenton and H. Jackson, *ibid.*, **75,** 1 (1899); H. J. H. Fenton and H. O. Jones, *ibid.*, **77,** 69 (1900).
3. G. Stein and J. Weiss, *J. Chem. Soc.*, 3265 (1951); G. R. A. Johnson, G. Stein and J. Weiss, *ibid.*, 3275 (1951).

4. P. Davis, M. G. Evans, and W. C. E. Higginson, *J. Chem. Soc.*, 2563 (1951).
5. C. M. Langkammerer, E. L. Jenner, D. D. Coffman, and B. W. Howk, *J. Am. Chem. Soc.*, **82,** 1395 (1960).
6. C. E. H. Bawn, *Discuss. Faraday Soc.*, **14,** 181 (1953).
7. E. Warhurst, *Quart. Rev.*, **5,** 44 (1951).
8. J. E. Bennett and A. Thomas, *Nature,* **195,** 995 (1962).
9. J. L. Franklin and H. P. Broida, *Ann. Rev. Phys. Chem.*, **10,** 145 (1959).
10. G. A. Russell, *Tetrahedron,* **5,** 101 (1959).
11. D. Y. Curtin and M. J. Hurwitz, *J. Am. Chem. Soc.*, **74,** 5381 (1952).
12. A. N. Nesmeyanov, R. Kh. Freidlina, and L. I. Zakharkin, *Quart. Rev.*, **10,** 330 (1956); A. N. Nesmeyanov, R. Kh. Freidlina, and V. N. Kost, *Tetrahedron,* **1,** 241 (1957).
13. R. Gomer and G. B. Kistiakowsky, *J. Chem. Phys.*, **19,** 85 (1951); G. B. Kistiakowsky and E. K. Roberts, *ibid.*, **21,** 1637 (1953).
14. P. Alexander and D. Rosen, *Nature,* **188,** 574 (1960).
15. B. DeB. Darwent and E. W. R. Steacie, *J. Chem. Phys.*, **16,** 381 (1948).
16. M. R. Berlie and D. J. Le Roy, *Discuss. Faraday Soc.*, **14,** 50 (1953).
17. D. L. Bunbury, R. R. Williams, and W. H. Hamill, *J. Am. Chem. Soc.*, **78,** 6228 (1956).
18. R. K. Lyon and D. H. Levy, *J. Am. Chem. Soc.*, **83,** 4290 (1961).
19. L. Herk, M. Feld, and M. Szwarc, *J. Am. Chem. Soc.*, **83,** 2998 (1961).
20. D. Urch and R. Wolfgang, *J. Am. Chem. Soc.*, **83,** 2982 (1961).
21. B. S. Rabinovitch, S. G. Davis, and C. A. Winkler, *Can. J. Res.*, **B21,** 251 (1943).
22. W. H. Urry and J. R. Eiszner, *J. Am. Chem. Soc.*, **74,** 5822 (1952).
23. J. A. Ghormley, *Radiation Res.*, **5,** 247 (1956).
24. R. F. Platford and J. W. T. Spinks, *Can. J. Chem.*, **37,** 1022 (1959).
25. G. R. Freeman, A. B. Van Cleave, and J. W. T. Spinks, *Can. J. Chem.*, **32,** 322 (1954).
26. R. W. Hummel, A. B. Van Cleave, and J. W. T. Spinks, *Can. J. Chem.*, **32,** 522 (1954).
27. R. G. McIntosh, R. L. Eager, and J. W. T. Spinks, *Science,* **131,** 992 (1960).
28. H. C. Sutton and J. Rotblat, *Nature,* **180,** 1332 (1957).
29. R. W. Fessenden and R. H. Schuler, *J. Am. Chem. Soc.*, **79,** 273 (1957).
30. R. H. Schuler, *J. Phys. Chem.*, **62,** 37 (1958).
31. G. Meshitsuka and M. Burton, *Radiation Res.*, **10,** 499 (1959).
32. R. R. Williams and W. H. Hamill, *J. Am. Chem. Soc.*, **72,** 1857 (1950).
33. L. H. Gevantman and R. R. Williams, *J. Phys. Chem.*, **56,** 569 (1952).
34. A. T. Fellows and R. H. Schuler, *J. Phys. Chem.*, **65,** 1451 (1961).
35. A. Chapiro, J. W. Boag, M. Ebert, and L. H. Gray, *J. Chim. Phys.*, **50,** 468 (1953).
36. L. Bouby and A. Chapiro, *J. Chim. Phys.*, **52,** 645 (1955); L. Bouby, A. Chapiro and E. Chapiro, *ibid.*, **58,** 442 (1961).
37. K. Yang, *J. Phys. Chem.*, **65,** 42 (1961).
38. E. A. Cherniak, E. Collinson, F. S. Dainton, and G. M. Meaburn, *Proc. Chem. Soc.*, **54,** (1958).
39. G. E. Adams, J. H. Baxendale, and R. D. Sedgwick, *J. Phys. Chem.*, **63,** 854 (1959).

40. J. Kumamoto, H. E. De La Mare, and F. F. Rust, *J. Am. Chem. Soc.,* **82,** 1935 (1960).
41. R. H. Schuler, *J. Phys. Chem.,* **61,** 1472 (1957).
42. A. Chapiro, *J. Phys. Chem.,* **63,** 801 (1959).
43. R. A. Holroyd and G. W. Klein, *J. Am. Chem. Soc.,* **84,** 4000 (1962); *Internat. J. Appl. Radiation Isotopes,* **13,** 493 (1962).
44. A. Charlesby and D. G. Lloyd, *Proc. Roy. Soc. (London), Ser. A,* **249,** 51 (1958); A. Charlesby, W. H. T. Davison, and D. G. Lloyd, *J. Phys. Chem.,* **63,** 970 (1959).
45. F. Wöhler and J. Liebig, *Annalen,* **3,** 249 (1832).
46. J. Cuthbert, *Quart. Rev.,* **13,** 215 (1959).
47. G. N. Lewis, M. Calvin, and M. Kasha, *J. Chem. Phys.,* **17,** 804 (1949).
48. H. C. Box and H. G. Freund, *Nucleonics,* **17,** (Jan.), 66 (1959).
49. I. Miyagawa and W. Gordy, *J. Am. Chem. Soc.,* **83,** 1036 (1961).
50. R. G. W. Norrish and B. A. Thrush, *Quart. Rev.,* **10,** 149 (1956).
51. R. G. W. Norrish, *Proc. Chem. Soc.,* **247,** (1958).
52. M. S. Matheson and L. M. Dorfman, *J. Chem. Phys.,* **32,** 1870 (1960).
53. R. L. McCarthy and A. MacLachlan, *Trans. Faraday Soc.,* **56,** 1187 (1960).
54. L. M. Dorfman, *Nucleonis,* **19,** (Oct.), 54 (1961); *Science,* **141,** 493 (1963).
55. M. S. Matheson, *Ann. Rev. Phys. Chem.,* **13,** 77 (1962).

CHAPTER 7

Gases[1]

From the point of view of radiation chemistry, gaseous systems are both simpler and more amenable to diverse experimental investigation than liquids or solids. They are simpler because their lower density greatly reduces the effect of LET, for example α-particles and γ-rays produce practically the same product yields, and because the active species are not confined in the particle tracks where they are formed. Thus the over-all effect of irradiation is to produce these species, which are initially positive ions, electrons, and excited atoms or molecules, distributed more or less homogeneously throughout the gas. This is in marked contrast to the situation in liquids or solids, where the active species are formed close together in spurs and are hindered in moving apart by the close-packed surrounding molecules. Experimentally, gases can be investigated by techniques which often are not applicable to liquids or solids, or else are restricted in application with these condensed systems. Typical experimental techniques are: measurement of the ionization produced in the gas; mass spectrometry, which gives information about

[1] Vapors of compounds which are normally liquid at room temperature and pressure are considered later with the parent liquid.

the ions formed and ion-molecule reactions; and the study of the photochemical or photosensitized decomposition of the gas, which provides information about excited species that may be present, their reactions, and the reactions of free radicals formed from them.

One of the first effects of high-energy radiation to be observed and measured was the production of ionization in air. Similar relatively simple ionization measurements are still valuable and enable the number of ion pairs formed in a gas by irradiation to be determined and also, when the energy absorbed is known, the important quantity W, the mean energy absorbed per ion pair formed. Neither the number of ion pairs produced nor W can be measured directly for liquids or solids. Yields of products formed on irradiation are related to the number of ion pairs formed by the *ion-pair* or *ionic yield*, represented by M/N where M is the number of molecules of product formed and N the number of ion pairs (1). The use of M/N to express yields in gaseous systems was widespread during the earlier years of radiation chemistry, but fell into disuse when the emphasis in the subject shifted from gaseous to condensed systems, since with these N could not readily be determined. In condensed media, the G value has become the standard means of recording radiation yields, and this practice has spread to include gaseous systems (in fact most of the yields given in this Chapter are in the form of G values). However, as Back and his colleagues (2) have recently pointed out, available methods for determining the energy absorbed in a gas, which is necessary if a G value is to be calculated, are far from satisfactory. Consequently they have made the reasonable suggestion that for gases, yields again be expressed in terms of M/N, and they describe a simple radiolysis vessel that may also be used to measure saturation ion currents. Where, or when, reliable values of W are available, ionic yields and G values are readily interconvertible (Eq. 1.1; footnote 4, p. 201).

The early radiation chemistry of gases was strongly influenced by recognition of the close relationship between ionization and product formation. Radiolysis mechanisms at this time were based largely on the formation and neutralization of ions, and the ion-cluster theory (cf. Chapter 1)[2] was advanced to account for ion-pair yields greater than unity. Then, in 1936, in two classical papers on the α-particle induced *para-ortho* hydrogen conversion and the synthesis and decomposition of hydrogen bromide respectively, Eyring, Hirschfelder, and Taylor (4, 5) proposed that excitation, as in photochemistry, was an

[2] A reappraisal of the clustering of ions in irradiated gases has been made by Magee and Funabashi (3).

important first step in radiation-initiated reactions and, furthermore, that both ionization and excitation might lead to free radicals and, in some cases, free-radical chain reactions. Thereafter free-radical mechanisms dominated radiation chemistry. This situation continued until fairly recently, when extensive mass spectrometric investigation of the properties and reactions of ions showed that ions also are of considerable significance in radiolysis reactions. In the following pages the radiolysis of a number of gaseous systems is described and it will be apparent that all three species, ions, excited molecules and atoms, and free radicals are important intermediates.

It should perhaps be mentioned here that electric discharges in gases produce chemical effects similar to those produced by high-energy radiation (cf. 6). Furthermore reactions taking place in the upper atmosphere are often similar to those studied in the radiation chemistry of gaseous systems, though the latter are normally at appreciably greater pressures. As would be anticipated from the composition of the atmosphere the reactions taking place in its upper levels generally involve oxygen and nitrogen, the nitrogen oxides, and, to a lesser extent, water vapor, carbon dioxide, etc.

Values of W *for the Noble Gases*

Working with Po^{210} α-particles,[3] Jesse and Sadauskis (7) found that values of W for the noble gases were very sensitive to traces of impurities. For example W for very pure helium was found to be 41.3 ev/ion pair while for helium containing 0.13% argon W dropped to 29.7 ev/ion pair. Similarly W for pure neon (36.3 ev/ion pair) is reduced to 26.1 ev/ion pair by the addition of 0.12% of argon. The authors attributed these phenomena to the transfer of excitation energy from long-lived (metastable) excited states of helium and neon to argon, followed by ionization of the excited argon, e.g.,

$$He^* + Ar \rightarrow He + Ar^* \tag{7.1}$$

$$Ar^* \rightarrow Ar^+ + e^- \tag{7.2}$$

Thus in the presence of argon the energy associated with excited helium atoms, which normally is dissipated without producing ionization, can

[3] α-particles were, and still are, frequently used in studies on gaseous systems because the radiation energy can be absorbed within a reasonably small volume of gas. However, the yields obtained with different types of radiation and with radiations with differing LET's are generally very nearly the same in gaseous systems. In this chapter we have generally omitted details of the radiation involved and assumed that in gases all radiations produce identical effects.

give rise to ions. Consequently W, the ratio of the energy absorbed to the number of ion pairs formed, is lowered. These systems afford an interesting example of energy transfer in gas-phase radiolysis.

The process represented by equations 7.1 and 7.2 is only possible because the energy of an excited helium atom in its lowest excited state (19.8 v) is greater than the ionization potential of argon (15.8 v), though a favorable energy balance is no guarantee that energy transfer will in fact take place, since the transfer also requires that appropriate energy levels be present in the two reactants. Neon has no effect on W_{He} since the ionization potential of neon (21.6 v) is greater than the energy available from the excited helium atom.

Similar effects have been found with other gas mixtures (8, 9), and in some cases it is necessary to postulate energy transfer from higher electronically excited states than the lowest to account for the results.

Para-ortho *Hydrogen Conversion*

The conversion of *para*-hydrogen to *ortho*-hydrogen under the influence of α-particles was studied by Capron (10) who found it to be a chain reaction with a chain length between 700 and 1100. Eyring, Hirschfelder, and Taylor (4), combining mass spectral, thermal, and kinetic data and treating the reaction theoretically, showed that Capron's results could be accounted for quantitatively by the following mechanism.

INITIATION (the formation of hydrogen atoms):

$$H_2 \rightsquigarrow H_2^+ + e^- \tag{7.3}$$

$$H_2 \rightsquigarrow H_2^* \tag{7.4}$$

$$H_2^* \rightarrow 2H\cdot \tag{7.5}$$

$$H_2^+ + H_2 \rightarrow H_3^+ + H\cdot \tag{7.6}$$

$$H_3^+ + e^- \rightarrow 3H\cdot \tag{7.7}$$

and, to a smaller extent,

$$H_2^+ + e^- \rightarrow 2H\cdot \tag{7.8}$$

CHAIN PROPAGATION:

$$H\cdot + p\text{-}H_2 \rightarrow o\text{-}H_2 + H\cdot \tag{7.9}$$

TERMINATION:

$$H\cdot \rightarrow \tfrac{1}{2}H_2 \text{ (mainly at a surface)} \tag{7.10}$$

It includes steps which have since become familiar as participants in a great many other radiolysis mechanisms, namely ionization (Eq. 7.3), excitation (Eq. 7.4), dissociation of an excited molecule (Eq. 7.5), ion-molecule reaction (Eq. 7.6), ion-neutralization with subsequent dissociation (Eqs. 7.7 and 7.8; cf. ref. 11), and typical free-radical reactions (Eqs. 7.9 and 7.10). Termination probably occurs at the surface of the reaction vessel since the ion-pair yield is independent of the dose rate. If termination were taking place in the gas phase by a three body reaction, i.e.,

$$2H\cdot + M \rightarrow H_2 + M \tag{7.11}$$

the yield would be inversely proportional to the square root of the dose rate.

Hydrogen atoms produced by other means, for example, thermal dissociation of molecular hydrogen at high temperatures or photosensitized dissociation by 2537 Å light in the presence of mercury vapor, can also bring about the conversion of *para* to *ortho* hydrogen. Another gas-phase source of atomic hydrogen is an electric discharge in either hydrogen or hydrogen diluted with an inert carrier gas (e.g., helium). This source has also been adapted to investigate the action of atomic hydrogen in aqueous solutions by bubbling the gases from the discharge through the solution (12, 13).

Hydrogen-Deuterium Mixtures

Very similar to the *para* to *ortho* hydrogen conversion is the exchange reaction between hydrogen and deuterium to give hydrogen deuteride,

$$H_2 + D_2 \rightarrow 2HD \tag{7.12}$$

The α-particle induced exchange was studied by Mund and his collaborators (14) and shown to be a chain reaction with an ion-pair yield[4] of about 1000 at atmospheric pressure and rather less at lower pressures. A free radical mechanism was postulated with the chain propagating steps:

$$H\cdot + D_2 \rightarrow D\cdot + HD \tag{7.13}$$

$$D\cdot + H_2 \rightarrow H\cdot + HD \tag{7.14}$$

The chain reaction is inhibited by traces of oxygen, which reacts with hydrogen atoms:

$$H\cdot + O_2 \rightarrow HO_2\cdot \tag{7.15}$$

[4]Both ion-pair yields and G values will be used in this chapter. They are related by the expression: $G = M/N \times 100/W$ or, roughly, $G = 3M/N$.

By carefully removing both oxygen and other inhibitors (e.g., stopcock grease) Dorfman and Shipko (15) were able to increase the exchange yield considerably and found, for example, an ion-pair yield of about 6×10^4 at 276 mm Hg pressure. Physical processes such as charge transfer can also inhibit the exchange reaction. Thompson and Schaeffer (16, 17) showed that the addition of small amounts of krypton and particularly xenon, both of which have ionization potentials lower than those of possible ionic chain carriers (H^+, H_2^+, H_3^+) markedly reduced the yield of hydrogen deuteride. Moderate amounts (less than 2%) of helium, neon, or argon have little effect on the reaction, for which Thompson and Schaeffer (16) found ion-pair yields of 18,000 at 100 mm Hg pressure. These authors also showed that none of the noble gases has any effect on the thermal or mercury photosensitized exchange reactions, which are known to be free radical in character, and interpreted these results to mean that the high yields obtained in the radiation-initiated process are due to an ionic rather than a free radical chain reaction. The mechanism proposed by Schaeffer and Thompson (17) is

INITIATION:

$$H_2 \rightsquigarrow H_2^+ + e^- \tag{7.3}$$

$$H_2^+ + H_2 \rightarrow H_3^+ + H\cdot \tag{7.6}$$

PROPAGATION:

$$H_3^+ + D_2 \rightarrow HD_2^+ + H_2 \tag{7.16}$$

$$HD_2^+ + H_2 \rightarrow H_2D^+ + HD \tag{7.17}$$

$$H_2D^+ + D_2 \rightarrow HD_2^+ + HD \quad \text{etc.} \tag{7.18}$$

Termination is by neutralization of the positive ions, either by free electrons or at a surface, while inhibition by krypton or xenon involves proton transfer from the chain-propagating positive ions, e.g.,

$$H_3^+ + Xe \rightarrow XeH^+ + H_2 \tag{7.19}$$

Lind (18) has suggested that the very high exchange yields (M/N of the order of 10^4), which are reduced in the presence of krypton and xenon, are due to the ionic chain reaction and the smaller yields (M/N of the order 100 to 1000), found with less pure gases or in the presence of the inhibiting noble gases, are due to a radical chain reaction (Eqs. 7.13 and 7.14), as are the thermal and photosensitized exchange reactions.

Tritium Labeling

Exposure of organic compounds to tritium gas often leads to replacement of part of the hydrogen present in the compound by tritium, so that the procedure can frequently be used to obtain compounds labeled with tritium (19, 20, 21). The tritium is not necessarily uniformly distributed in the labeled compound and the susceptibility of compounds to labeling in this way varies markedly, and not always predictably, with their chemical structure. Incorporation of tritium into a compound can often be accelerated by simultaneous exposure to ultraviolet light, ionizing radiation, or an electric discharge; but a competing process is decomposition of the compound by the tritium β-radiation.

The mechanism of the tritium labeling process is not yet certain but it may involve recoil tritium ions, T^+, or the ion He^3T^+, formed by the β-decay of tritium,

$$T_2 \rightarrow T^+ + He^3 + e^- \qquad (\text{or } He^3T^+ + e^-) \tag{7.20}$$

and ion-molecule reactions, e.g.,

$$T^+ + \text{compound} \rightarrow \text{tritiated products} \tag{7.21}$$

Alternatively tritiation of the compound may be induced by the β-radiation emitted,

$$\text{compound} \xrightarrow{\beta} \begin{array}{c}\text{ions, excited molecules,}\\ \text{and (?) radicals}\end{array} \xrightarrow{T_2} \text{tritiated products} \tag{7.22}$$

(The mechanism is discussed in references 20, 22, and 23, among others.)

Riesz and Wilzbach (20) showed that when *n*-hexane, cyclohexane, and benzene are irradiated by mixing with tritium gas, the radiolysis products are labeled, and they suggested that exposure to tritium offered both a source of radiation and a means (by isotope dilution) of identifying the radiolysis products.

Oxygen

Undoubtedly the earliest recorded reference to a reaction typical of radiation chemistry is that of Homer to the sulfurous smell accompanying lightning. A similar observation was made many years later of air exposed to salts of the then recently discovered element, radium. In both cases the substance chiefly responsible is ozone, whose characteristic odor has more recently come to be associated with high-voltage electrical equipment; it is normally prepared by passing oxygen through a silent electric discharge.

Experimental work on the irradiation of oxygen was first carried out by Lind (24). Lind measured the yield of ozone formed in a slow stream of oxygen exposed to α-radiation and found ion-pair yields of about 0.5, though these were poorly reproducible. Subsequent work by Lind and Bardwell (25) and D'Olieslager (26) showed that in a static system the yield of ozone is very small and that in a flowing system it depends upon the rate of flow and, inversely, on the dose rate; ion-pair yields as high as 2 to 2.5 were obtained by Lind and Bardwell at high flow rates.[5] These observations are explained by the existence of an efficient back reaction which destroys ozone, and which therefore competes with the process producing ozone. The back reaction is in fact a chain reaction with a high ion-pair yield (e.g., 15,000 at 300 mm Hg pressure of pure ozone (28)), though the forward process forming ozone is not. Magee and Burton (29) have suggested a mechanism for the formation of ozone in irradiated oxygen:

$$O_2 \rightsquigarrow O_2^+ + e^- \tag{7.23}$$

$$\rightsquigarrow O_2^* \tag{7.24}$$

$$O_2 + e^- \rightarrow O_2^- \tag{7.25}$$

followed by one or more of the reactions,

$$O_2^+ + O_2^- \rightarrow O + O_3 \tag{7.26}$$

or

$$\rightarrow O_2^* + O_2 \tag{7.27}$$

or

$$\rightarrow 2O + O_2 \tag{7.28}$$

(one or both oxygen atoms will be excited)

and

$$O + O_2 + M \rightarrow O_3 + M \tag{7.29}$$

$$O_2^* \rightarrow 2O \tag{7.30}$$

$$O_2^* + O_2 \rightarrow O + O_3 \tag{7.31}$$

$$O + O_3 \rightarrow 2O_2 \tag{7.32}$$

(in pure oxygen $M = O_2$). The decomposition of ozone becomes a chain reaction if reaction 7.32 is replaced in part by

$$O + O_3 \rightarrow 2O + O_2 \tag{7.33}$$

[5] A summary of radiation-induced yields of ozone for various types of radiation is given by Kircher et al. (27). For gaseous oxygen, ion-pair yields for the formation of ozone are mainly in the range 1 to 3.

The reactions shown also occur in the upper atmosphere where oxygen is dissociated by sunlight,

$$O_2 + h\nu \rightarrow 2O \tag{7.34}$$

Other reactions occurring under these conditions are

$$O_3 + h\nu \rightarrow O + O_2 \tag{7.35}$$

and

$$2O + M \rightarrow O_2 + M \tag{7.36}$$

The presence of atomic oxygen at a height of 106 km has been demonstrated directly by a nightime rocket flight which released nitric oxide at this altitude (30). A silver-gray glow was observed due to reactions in which the nitric oxide catalyzes the recombination of oxygen atoms,

$$NO + O \rightarrow NO_2 + h\nu \tag{7.37}$$

$$NO_2 + O \rightarrow NO + O_2^* \tag{7.38}$$

$$O_2^* \rightarrow O_2 + h\nu \tag{7.39}$$

Ozone is also formed when liquid oxygen or liquid mixtures of oxygen with nitrogen or the noble gases are irradiated (27, 31); $G(O_3) = 6$ for cobalt-60 γ-irradiation of liquid oxygen. This may present a hazard when samples are simultaneously cooled in liquid nitrogen and irradiated if any oxygen (b.p. −183°C) has condensed into the nitrogen (b.p. −196°C). Ozone has a higher boiling point than nitrogen (ozone boils at −112°C) and any formed on irradiation remains as the liquid evaporates. The liquid ozone can cause a dangerous explosion if it comes into contact with organic matter.

Oxygen-Nitrogen Mixtures

When mixtures of oxygen and nitrogen are irradiated, ozone will be formed as described above, but oxides of nitrogen will also be produced. The formation of nitrogen oxides and, in the presence of moisture, nitric acid in this way can create a corrosion and a health problem near nuclear reactors and particle accelerators where air is exposed to high radiation doses. However, the same reaction also presents the possibility of converting atmospheric nitrogen into a commercially useful form (e.g., nitrate fertilizers) and this possibility has been explored in a number of laboratories (32).

The radiolysis of oxygen-nitrogen systems is complex and changes as the concentration of products builds up. However Harteck and Dondes (32, 33) believe that initially the dominant reactions are

$$N_2 \rightsquigarrow 2N \qquad (G \text{ value } 4\text{-}5) \tag{7.40}$$

$$O_2 \rightsquigarrow 2O \qquad (G \text{ value } 8) \tag{7.41}$$

$$N + O_2 \rightarrow O + NO \tag{7.42}$$

$$2NO + O_2 \rightarrow 2NO_2 \tag{7.43}$$

$$N + NO_2 \rightarrow 2NO \tag{7.44}$$

or

$$\rightarrow O + N_2O \tag{7.45}$$

or

$$\rightarrow 2O + N_2 \tag{7.46}$$

$$N + NO \rightarrow O + N_2 \tag{7.47}$$

and, illustrating the many possible ionic reactions,

$$NO + M^+ \rightarrow NO^+ + M \tag{7.48}$$

$$NO^+ + e^- \rightarrow N + O \tag{7.49}$$

or

$$\rightarrow NO + h\nu \tag{7.50}$$

(reactions involving ozone are omitted). Pshezhetsky and Dmitriev (34) have given a rather different group of reactions which they consider predominate:

$$N_2^+ + O_2 \rightarrow NO^+ + NO \tag{7.51}$$

$$(N_2^+)^* + O_2 \rightarrow NO_2^+ + N \tag{7.52}$$

$$N + O_2 \rightarrow O + NO \tag{7.42}$$

$$N + O_2 + M \rightarrow NO_2 + M \tag{7.53}$$

Regardless of the detailed mechanism, an equilibrium is finally reached in dry gas mixtures between the formation and decomposition of the nitrogen oxides. When moisture is present the main product is nitric acid, which is formed until the water vapor is exhausted (35).

Nitrous Oxide

Harteck and Dondes (36; cf. 37) have suggested that the radiation-induced decomposition of nitrous oxide be used as a gas-phase chemical dosimeter. The decomposition products are nitrogen, oxygen, and nitrogen dioxide, and in the range 5×10^4 to 10^7 r the combined yield of nitrogen and oxygen is linear with dose; the dosimeter can be used to measure doses up to almost 10^{10} r by means of calibration curves. In the upper part of the dose range (3×10^7 to 3×10^9 r), sufficient nitrogen dioxide is formed to measure colorimetrically. This may be done without opening the irradiation vessel and offers a convenient alternative to measuring the amount of nitrogen and oxygen formed. Advantages of this dosimeter include the high-dose range which it covers, the stability of both unirradiated and irradiated dosimeter systems, independence of temperature (the dosimeter can be used at temperatures ranging from $-80°C$ to $+200°C$), dose rate, and LET (β and γ radiation and fission products (thermal neutrons + uranium-235 oxide) were tested by Harteck and Dondes). The authors list the main reactions taking place as

$$\left.\begin{array}{l} N_2O \rightsquigarrow N_2O^+ + e^- \\ \text{or} \\ \quad\;\; \rightsquigarrow N_2O^* \end{array}\right\} \rightarrow \begin{array}{l} N_2 + O \quad \text{(about 80\%)} \\ \\ N + NO \;\text{(about 20\%)} \end{array} \tag{7.54}$$

followed by reactions 7.43 to 7.46 and

$$N_2O^+ + NO \rightarrow N_2O + NO^+ \tag{7.55}$$

$$NO^+ + e^- \rightarrow N + O \tag{7.49}$$

or

$$\rightarrow NO + h\nu \tag{7.50}$$

A mechanism based largely upon ionic reactions has been proposed by Burtt and Kircher (38).

With nitrous oxide pressures above 500 mm Hg Harteck and Dondes found the ion-pair yield to be 4.2 ± 0.1 molecules N_2O decomposed per ion pair formed, corresponding to $G(-N_2O) = 12$; the ratio of the products was $N_2 : O_2 : NO_2 = 1 : 0.14 : 0.48$. At a lower pressure (70 mm Hg) Johnson (39) found a very much higher yield, corresponding to $G(-N_2O) = 9.4 \times 10^4$ and obviously the result of a chain reaction. The mechanism of the chain reaction was not elucidated but it was thought to be ionic rather than free-radical since in the same region of pressures photochemical decomposition of nitrous oxide is not a chain reaction; photochemical decomposition presumably proceeds via a radical mechanism. Burtt and Kircher (38) found an ion-pair yield $(-N_2O)$ of 4.85 at both 200 and 555 mm Hg pressure which increased to 6.87 as the pressure was decreased to 50 mm Hg. At lower pressures, therefore, the experimental results appear inconsistent and, for dosimetric purposes, pressures of 500 mm Hg or more should be used; the dosimeter is independent of pressure above 500 mm Hg (36).

Ammonia

Both the synthesis of ammonia from its elements and its decomposition under the influence of radiation have been studied extensively since early work on these systems by Cameron and Ramsay (40) and Usher (41).

The radiation-induced decomposition of ammonia produces nitrogen, hydrogen, and hydrazine (N_2H_4) with $G(-NH_3)$ about 3 to 4; the same products are formed by photochemical decomposition (42) and by subjecting ammonia to an electric discharge (43). The mechanism of the photochemical decomposition is probably as follows, though the reaction producing nitrogen is uncertain:

$$NH_3 + h\nu \rightarrow NH_3^* \tag{7.56}$$

$$NH_3^* + M \rightarrow NH_3 + M \tag{7.57}$$

$$NH_3^* \rightleftharpoons \cdot NH_2 + H\cdot \tag{7.58}$$

$$2\cdot NH_2 + M \rightarrow N_2H_4 + M \tag{7.59}$$

$$2\cdot NH_2 \rightarrow N_2 + 2H_2 \tag{7.60}$$

$$H\cdot \rightarrow \tfrac{1}{2}H_2 \text{ (at wall)} \tag{7.10}$$

Reactions involving hydrazine will occur once this has reached a sufficient concentration; these may be

$$H\cdot + N_2H_4 \rightarrow \cdot NH_2 + NH_3 \tag{7.61}$$

or

$$\cdot NH_2 + N_2H_4 \rightarrow N_2H_3\cdot + NH_3 \tag{7.62}$$

and

$$2N_2H_3\cdot \rightarrow N_2 + 2NH_3 \tag{7.63}$$

In addition to these reactions the radiolysis mechanism (44) will include steps involving ions. The mass spectrum of ammonia (45) suggests that these will probably be mainly NH_3^+ and NH_2^+. Dorfman and Noble (46), also by mass spectrometry, have shown that NH_3^+ undergoes an efficient ion-molecule reaction,

$$NH_3^+ + NH_3 \rightarrow \cdot NH_2 + NH_4^+ \tag{7.64}$$

The NH_2^+ ion probably reacts by charge transfer,

$$NH_2^+ + NH_3 \rightarrow \cdot NH_2 + NH_3^+ \tag{7.65}$$

while the NH_4^+ ions, and possibly some of the other positive ions, are neutralized by electrons, partly in the gas phase and partly at the wall of the irradiation vessel,

$$NH_4^+ + e^- \rightarrow H\cdot + NH_3 \tag{7.66}$$

$$NH_3^+ + e^- \rightarrow NH_3 \qquad \text{(at wall)} \tag{7.67}$$

or

$$\rightarrow \cdot NH_2 + H\cdot \tag{7.68}$$

Essex and his colleagues (47, 48) have irradiated ammonia in the presence of an electric field in order to estimate to what extent ion-recombination in the gas contributes to the over-all reaction. The apparatus used is represented diagrammatically in Fig. 7.1. Two metal disc electrodes are sealed at either end of a glass cylinder containing the gas under examination, and the gas is irradiated with α-particles from a radium preparation placed in a depression in the wall of the cylinder. The cylinder is connected to a trap, which can be cooled in liquid nitrogen to condense out the original gas after irradiation, and to a McLeod gauge where the (noncondensable) product gases can be measured. When irradiations are carried out with a potential applied between the electrodes, some or all of the ions formed are collected on the electrodes and neutralized there rather than in the gas itself, the proportion of ions collected depending on the potential applied. By using a sufficiently high potential all the ions formed can be collected and hence their number determined;

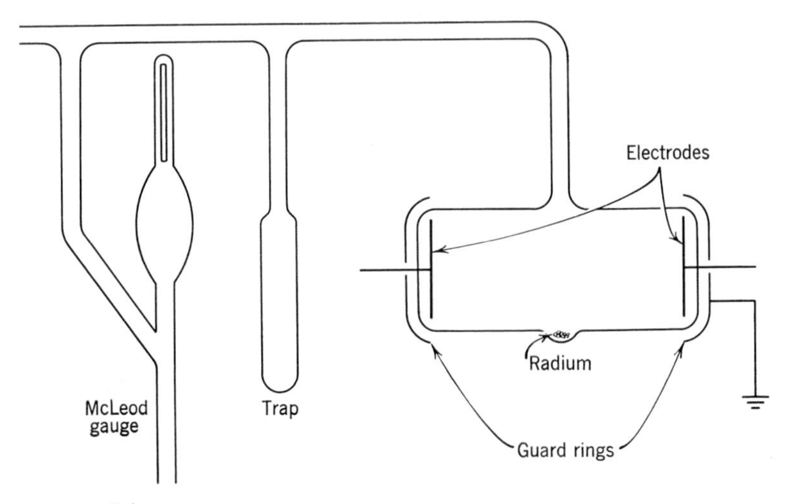

FIGURE 7.1

the current passing between the electrodes under these conditions is known as the *saturation current.* Once the number of ions formed with a given gas and α-particle source is known, ion-pair yields can be determined without, and for various values of, the applied field and hence the effect of the electric field on the radiolysis determined. In the case of ammonia it was estimated that at both 30°C and 100°C the ion-pair yield for the decomposition process is reduced by about 30% by applying a field high enough to produce saturation. This suggests that when gaseous ammonia is irradiated about 30% of the reaction results from an ion-recombination reaction (e.g., 7.68) which does not occur when the ions are neutralized at an electrode. Other gases which have been irradiated in the presence of an electric field by this technique include nitrous oxide, ethane, and azomethane (48). Woodward and Back (49), in similar experiments, have irradiated ethane, propane, and the butanes with γ-radiation. These authors also observed a dose-rate effect in the irradiated gases (in the absence of the electric field) which they attribute to competition between neutralization of the ions in the gas phase and diffusion of the ions to the vessel wall; high dose rates favoring the former process, and low dose rates the latter.

The radiation-induced decomposition of liquid ammonia has also been studied. For cobalt-60 γ-irradiation, Cleaver, Collinson, and Dainton (50) found the yields of nitrogen, hydrogen, and hydrazine formed in the early stages of the irradiation to be: $G(N_2) = 0.22$, $G(H_2) = 0.81$, and $G(N_2H_4) = 0.13$. The mechanism is probably similar to that postulated for gaseous ammonia with the exception that excited ammonia is unimportant in the liquid phase because of the Franck-Rabinowitch effect (recombination of the dissociation products from an excited molecule as in Eq. 7.58 and deactivation of the excited product, Eq. 7.57). The radiolysis of liquid ammonia is of special interest since the liquid has many properties in common with water. Theories concerning the radiolysis of water can therefore be tested to some extent by applying them to the radiolysis of liquid ammonia.

Carbon Dioxide

Gaseous carbon dioxide is practically unaffected by ionizing radiation (51) whereas liquid or solid carbon dioxide decomposes to give carbon monoxide and oxygen with a $G(-CO_2)$ value of about 5 (32, 52). Hirschfelder and Taylor (53) attributed the stability of carbon dioxide in the gas phase (below pressures of about 10 atmospheres) to a back reaction which they postulated to be

$$CO + O_3 \rightarrow CO_2 + O_2 \tag{7.69}$$

However, although this reaction is exothermic, it has an activation energy of over 28 kcal (54) so that it would be very slow at room temperature. Harteck and Dondes (32, 54) proposed instead the following mechanism for the radiolysis of pure carbon dioxide:

$$CO_2 \rightsquigarrow CO + O \; (G \text{ value } 8)^6 \tag{7.70}$$

and, to a minor extent,

$$CO_2 \rightsquigarrow C + 2O \tag{7.71}$$

then,

$$CO + C + M \rightarrow C_2O + M \tag{7.72}$$

$$C_2O + CO + M \rightarrow C_3O_2 + M \tag{7.73}$$

$$O + O_2 + M \rightarrow O_3 + M \tag{7.29}$$

$$C_3O_2 + O \rightarrow C_2O + CO_2 \tag{7.74}$$

$$C_3O_2 + O_3 \rightarrow C_2O + CO_2 + O_2 \tag{7.75}$$

$$CO + O + M \rightarrow CO_2 + M \tag{7.76}$$

The back reaction between carbon monoxide and oxygen atoms or ozone is catalyzed here by C_2O. Part of the C_2O and C_3O_2 diffuse to the walls of the vessel and form polymerization products; as a result a small surplus of oxygen remains after irradiation. In the liquid or solid phase, only reactions 7.70 and 7.71 occur, the oxygen atoms combining in pairs to form molecular oxygen or with carbon atoms to form carbon monoxide,

$$2O \rightarrow O_2 \tag{7.36}$$

$$C + O \rightarrow CO \tag{7.77}$$

Small amounts of nitrogen dioxide inhibit the back reaction to reform carbon dioxide by reacting rapidly with both oxygen and carbon atoms (32, 54), and $G(-CO_2)$ in the gas in this case is about 8[6]. The reactions of the inhibitor are

$$O + NO_2 \rightarrow NO + O_2 \tag{7.78}$$

$$C + NO_2 \rightarrow NO + CO \tag{7.79}$$

and

$$2NO + O_2 \rightarrow 2NO_2 \tag{7.43}$$

[6] A more recent determination of the carbon dioxide yield in the presence of a radical scavenger (nitrogen dioxide or sulfur dioxide) has given a value of $G(CO) = 3.51 \pm 0.23$ for γ-radiation, and the same value, within the limits of the experimental accuracy, for reactor radiation (55). The steady state concentration of carbon monoxide produced by γ-radiation when no scavenger is present is given as less than 0.01% at a dose rate of about 500 rads/min.

Irradiation of carbon monoxide gives carbon dioxide, carbon suboxide polymers $(C_3O_2)_n$, and carbon, which can be accounted for by a mechanism which is consistent with the reactions (7.70 to 7.76) postulated for the radiolysis of carbon dioxide (54, 56),

$$CO \rightsquigarrow C + O \tag{7.80}$$

$$CO + C + M \rightarrow C_2O + M \tag{7.72}$$

$$C_2O + CO + M \rightarrow C_3O_2 + M \tag{7.73}$$

$$C_3O_2 + O \rightarrow C_2O + CO_2 \tag{7.74}$$

$$C \rightarrow \text{graphite} \qquad \text{(at wall)} \tag{7.81}$$

$$C_2O,\ C_3O_2 \rightarrow \text{polymerization products} \qquad \text{(at wall)} \tag{7.82}$$

The radiation-induced decomposition of carbon dioxide is of practical significance in reactor technology since carbon dioxide is used as a heat-transfer agent in a number of power-producing reactors. In a graphite moderated reactor cooled by circulating carbon dioxide the reaction

$$CO_2 + \text{graphite} \rightleftharpoons 2CO \tag{7.83}$$

is also relevant, though apparently not a major problem with present types of reactors (57). Under reactor conditions this reaction appears to be initiated by active intermediates (possibly O or O_3) formed by irradiation of the gas.

Harteck and Dondes (32) have made the interesting suggestion that the atmosphere of the planet Venus, which consists mainly of carbon dioxide with a small proportion of carbon monoxide and a yellowish-white cloudy material, exists in a radiation-induced equilibrium; the small amount of carbon monoxide being in equilibrium with a fine dust of yellowish-white carbon suboxide polymers. Recently, however, water vapor has been identified in the Cytherean atmosphere (58) and this weakens the carbon suboxide theory considerably since water reacts with the suboxide to form malonic acid. There is a strong possibility that the clouds are in fact water.

Hydrogen Bromide

The synthesis and decomposition of hydrogen bromide,

$$H_2 + Br_2 \rightleftharpoons 2HBr \tag{7.84}$$

are reactions which have been studied since the early days of radiation chemistry. Lind (1, 59) observed the combination of hydrogen and bromine under the influence of α-radiation ($M_{HBr}/N = 0.54$) but failed to find any decomposition of gaseous hydrogen bromide, though liquid hydrogen bromide was decomposed with a yield calculated later to be about $M_{-HBr}/N = 2.2$. Later studies, including further work by Lind (60), showed that gaseous hydrogen bromide can be decomposed by radiation and the data for both synthesis and decomposition were used by Eyring, Hirschfelder, and Taylor (5) to test their theory of radiation-induced action. The mechanism proposed by these authors for the synthesis of hydrogen bromide gave results in satisfactory agreement with the experimental results of Lind and Livingston (60); hydrogen was assumed to give hydrogen atoms by the series of reactions given earlier (7.3 to 7.8) and bromine to give bromine atoms by a similar series of reactions and also by steps which are made possible by the greater electron affinity of bromine, i.e.,

$$Br_2 + e^- \rightarrow Br\cdot + Br^- \qquad (7.85)$$

$$(Br^+ + Br_2 \rightarrow Br_3^+) \qquad (7.86)$$

and

$$Br^- + Br_3^+ \rightarrow 4Br\cdot \qquad (7.87)$$

Bromine atoms will not react appreciably with hydrogen or hydrogen bromide at room temperature because of the high energy requirements and the subsequent reactions of the hydrogen and bromine atoms will be

$$H\cdot + Br_2 \rightarrow Br\cdot + HBr \qquad (7.88)$$

$$2Br\cdot + M \rightarrow Br_2 + M \qquad (7.89)$$

The mechanism postulated by Eyring, Hirschfelder, and Taylor (5) for the decomposition of hydrogen bromide was

$$HBr \rightsquigarrow HBr^+ + e^- \qquad (7.90)$$

$$\rightsquigarrow HBr^* \qquad (7.91)$$

$$HBr^* \rightarrow H\cdot + Br\cdot \qquad (7.92)$$

$$HBr + e^- \rightarrow H\cdot + Br^- \qquad (7.93)$$

$$HBr^+ + Br^- \rightarrow H\cdot + 2Br\cdot \qquad (7.94)$$

followed by

$$H\cdot + HBr \rightarrow Br\cdot + H_2 \qquad (7.95)$$

$$2Br\cdot + M \rightarrow Br_2 + M \qquad (7.89)$$

They also considered the possibility of formation of the ion H_2Br^+,

$$HBr^+ + HBr \rightarrow H_2Br^+ + Br\cdot \tag{7.96}$$

and its neutralization,

$$H_2Br^+ + Br^- \rightarrow 2H\cdot + 2Br\cdot \tag{7.97}$$

However, Zubler, Hamill, and Williams (61) consider the two latter reactions unimportant, since with reactions 7.90, 7.93, 7.95, and 7.89 they lead to an ion-pair yield for HBr decomposition of 6.0; the authors find ion-pair yields between 4.0 and 5, and therefore favor reactions 7.93 and 7.94 with a smaller contribution from excited hydrogen bromide (Eq. 7.92).[7]

Zubler, Hamill, and Williams (61) also irradiated mixtures of hydrogen bromide with a much larger amount of a noble gas (argon, krypton, or xenon) and found ion-pair yields, $M_{-\text{HBr}}/N$, between 4.0 and 4.7. These results are explained by the complete transfer of charge from noble gas ions to hydrogen bromide, which in each case has the lower ionization potential of the two gases (cf. Table 5.1), e.g.,

$$Ar^+ + HBr \rightarrow Ar + HBr^+ \tag{7.98}$$

followed by reactions 7.93 to 7.89 in the sequence given above. Where the ion-pair yield is greater than 4.0 some contribution from excited states is inferred, for example via

$$Xe^* + HBr \rightarrow Xe + HBr^* \tag{7.99}$$

and reaction 7.92.

In contrast with the synthesis of hydrogen bromide, which gives low ion-pair yields, the yields for the synthesis of hydrogen chloride are high (e.g., 10^3 to 10^5); indicative of a chain reaction. The difference arises from the greater reactivity of chlorine atoms as compared to bromine atoms. Thus atomic chlorine reacts with hydrogen at room temperature whereas atomic bromine will only react at relatively high temperatures (e.g., 200 to 300°C), and a chlorine-hydrogen chain reaction is possible with the propagation steps,

[7] Nevertheless, the ion-molecule reaction depicted by equation 7.96 has been observed experimentally (62), and it seems possible that it occurs and is followed by the neutralization reaction

$$H_2Br^+ + Br^- \rightarrow H_2 + 2Br\cdot$$

rather than reaction 7.97. The sequence of reactions proposed by Eyring, Hirschfelder, and Taylor then gives an ion-pair yield of 4, neglecting the contribution by excited molecules, which apparently do not all decompose.

$$Cl\cdot + H_2 \rightarrow H\cdot + HCl \quad (7.100)$$

$$H\cdot + Cl_2 \rightarrow Cl\cdot + HCl \quad (7.101)$$

Methane

The radiolysis of methane has been studied extensively and the mechanism is reasonably well understood, though not yet established beyond contention. Information derived from the radiolysis of methane and its mixtures (cf. Table 7.1) is well supported by pertinent data from mass spectroscopy and photochemistry.

TABLE 7.1 *Radiolysis of Mixtures Containing Methane*

(Fast electron or γ-irradiation)

Product	G(product)		Relative yields		
	pure CH_4 (ref. 63)	$CH_4 + NO$ (ref. 63)	$CH_4 + Ar$ (ref. 64)	$CH_4 + Ar + I_2$ (ref. 64)	$CH_4 + I_2$ (ref. 65)
H_2	6.4	3.6	100	100	
C_2H_2			0	1.6	
C_2H_4	0.13	0.64	0.5	14	
C_2H_6	2.1	0.32	45	0.6	
C_3H_6	0	0.03	0.2	0	
C_3H_8	0.26	0.01	7	0	
n-C_4H_{10}	0.13	0	3.5	0	
i-C_4H_{10}	0.06	0			
i-C_5H_{10}	0.05	0			
Liquid polymer, $(CH_2)_n$					
HI					8.5
CH_3I				34	70
C_2H_5I				18	4.5
C_3H_7I				0.5	
C_4H_9I				0.1	
CH_2I_2				9	8.5

In the mass spectrometer the relative abundances of the ions formed from methane are (66): CH_4^+, 48%; CH_3^+, 40%; CH_2^+, 8%; CH^+, 4%; C^+, 1%. These values are for electrons with energies in the range 50-70 ev but they are probably reasonably typical of high-energy radiation also. Other mass-spectrometric experiments with methane, at rather higher pressures, have demonstrated the existence of two rapid ion-molecule reactions involving the major primary ions (64, 67, 68, 69),

$$CH_4^+ + CH_4 \rightarrow CH_5^+ + \cdot CH_3 \quad (7.102)$$

$$CH_3^+ + CH_4 \rightarrow C_2H_5^+ + H_2 \quad (7.103)$$

At very much higher ionization chamber pressures, the secondary ions produced in this way predominate in the mass spectrum of methane. At 0.2 mm Hg, for example, Wexler and Jesse (70) find that CH_5^+ and $C_2H_5^+$ account for about 70% of the ions collected. The parent ion and its dissociation products (i.e., CH_4^+ and CH_3^+, CH_2^+, etc.) make a relatively small contribution, and most of the remaining ions collected contain two or three carbon atoms, though ions with up to seven carbon atoms are detected. The manner in which the ion yields vary with increasing pressure over the range 10^{-6} to 0.2 mm Hg shows, as expected, that ion-molecule reactions are favored by increasing pressure, and also that as the pressure is increased the secondary ions tend to react further, giving C_3 and higher ions by successive ion-molecule reactions. However, neglecting for the moment these secondary ion-molecule reactions, which nevertheless will contribute to methane radiolysis, the main ionic reactions taking place in irradiated methane can be written as

$$CH_4 \rightsquigarrow CH_4^+ + e^- \quad (7.104)$$

$$\rightsquigarrow CH_3^+ + H\cdot + e^- \quad (7.105)$$

$$\rightsquigarrow CH_2^+ + H_2 \text{ (or } 2H\cdot) + e^- \quad (7.106)$$

$$CH_4^+ + CH_4 \rightarrow CH_5^+ + \cdot CH_3 \quad (7.102)$$

$$CH_3^+ + CH_4 \rightarrow C_2H_5^+ + H_2 \quad (7.103)$$

$$CH_2^+ + e^- \rightarrow CH_2 \quad (7.107)$$

$$CH_5^+ + e^- \rightarrow \cdot CH_3 + H_2 \quad (7.108)$$

$$C_2H_5^+ + e^- \rightarrow \cdot C_2H_5 \quad (7.109)$$

or

$$\rightarrow C_2H_4 + H\cdot \quad (7.110)$$

These will be followed by various free radical reactions, including

$$H\cdot + CH_4 \rightarrow \cdot CH_3 + H_2 \quad (7.111)$$

$$2\cdot CH_3 \rightarrow C_2H_6 \quad (7.112)$$

$$2\cdot C_2H_5 \rightarrow C_4H_{10} \quad (7.113)$$

or

$$\rightarrow C_2H_6 + C_2H_4 \quad (7.114)$$

$$\cdot CH_3 + \cdot C_2H_5 \rightarrow C_3H_8 \quad (7.115)$$

or

$$\rightarrow CH_4 + C_2H_4 \quad (7.116)$$

$$2CH_2 \rightarrow C_2H_4 \quad (7.117)$$

$$\cdot CH_2 + CH_4 \rightarrow C_2H_6 \quad (7.118)$$

$$R\cdot + C_2H_4 \rightarrow R{-}CH_2{-}CH_2\cdot \xrightarrow{C_2H_4} \text{polymer} \quad (7.119)$$

where R· is a hydrogen atom or an organic radical. (Third bodies, which may be necessary in some of these neutralization and radical reactions, have been omitted.) Three carbon and higher hydrocarbons may be formed by radical reactions, as shown, or by further ion-molecule reactions, e.g.,

$$C_2H_5^+ + CH_4 \rightarrow C_3H_7^+ + H_2 \quad (7.120)$$

Several authors have attempted to correlate radiation chemical yields with mass spectral data. Dorfman (71) suggested that molecular detachment yields (the yield of product formed directly in molecular form without the agency of scavengeable free radicals) rather than over-all product yields be compared with these data since the over-all yields often change as products build up in the irradiated system. Furthermore the molecular detachment yields, or "molecular" yields, are generally derived from a relatively small number of processes, in contrast to the over-all yields, and there is less temptation to adjust the calculated yields by selecting suitable reactions. Dorfman and Sauer (71) estimated the (experimental) molecular yield of hydrogen from methane ($G_{H_2} = 3.3 \pm 0.2$)[8] from the over-all yield of hydrogen and the contribution "molecular" hydrogen makes to the over-all yield, as determined by scavenger and isotopic techniques. If the reactions taking place in irradiated methane are those already given, molecular hydrogen arises from reactions 7.102 + 7.108, 7.103, and 7.106. Assuming W_{CH_4} to be 27.3 ev/ion pair, then the G value for molecular hydrogen, estimated from the relative ion abundance for CH_4^+, CH_3^+, and CH_2^+ and the reactions cited, is $G_{H_2} = 3.5$, in satisfactory agreement with the experimental value of 3.3 ± 0.2. The process can be taken further and free radical yields (determined by scavenger experiments) (72) and over-all product yields (64) correlated with the mass spectral data. The agreement between calculated and experimental yields is surprisingly good, and probably fortuitous.

[8] The use of subscripts to denote "molecular" yields is described in Chapter 8.

Radical scavengers have been used to demonstrate the presence of free radicals in irradiated methane. Gevantman and Williams (65) and Meisels, Hamill, and Williams (64) used iodine to identify and estimate the radicals formed in pure methane and in mixtures of methane with a noble gas respectively (Table 7.1). Principal radical products detected by the appearance of the corresponding iodide were $H\cdot$, $\cdot CH_3$, $\cdot C_2H_5$, and CH_2. The increase in the yield of ethylene in the presence of scavenger is interesting and is presumably due to the removal of radicals which would otherwise add to ethylene (Eq. 7.119), leading to polymerization. Numerical values given in the Table may not accurately represent the relative proportions of the radicals formed in the irradiated mixture. Hydrogen atoms in particular are often formed with extra energy (i.e., are hot) and tend to react with the substrate (methane) rather than with iodine. If this happens in the present instance, the yields of HI and CH_3I will not give a true measure of the number of hydrogen atoms and methyl radicals produced. Nevertheless the results clearly show that methyl and other radicals are important intermediates. Yang and Manno (63) have suggested that nitric oxide gives a better estimate of radical yields than does iodine since it reacts more efficiently with hydrogen atoms; however, iodine is more convenient for identifying the radicals present. The yields given in columns 3 and 5 of Table 7.1 (excepting the iodides) are believed to be those for the formation of products by nonradical processes, e.g., by ionic reactions and the dissociation of ions and excited molecules into molecular fragments.

Though radiolysis yields from methane can be explained almost completely without assuming any contribution from excited molecules it is probable that these also contribute to the over-all chemical change. Indeed it has been claimed that ions, though undoubtedly formed, play no important part in the formation of products, which can be accounted for satisfactorily solely by reactions involving excited molecules and the free radicals derived from them. It is worthwhile to reflect that these two extreme views (ionization vs. excitation) can be held about a system as thoroughly studied as the radiolysis of methane; very few of the mechanisms given in this book are established beyond the possibility of correction, or even drastic change, at some future date.

The mercury-photosensitized decomposition of methane produces identical products to the radiolysis (73). In this instance the first step is reaction between an excited mercury atom and methane to give a hydrogen atom and a methyl radical (74, 75), which must be responsible for the products formed in the early stages of the reaction,

$$Hg^* + CH_4 \rightarrow Hg + \cdot CH_3 + H\cdot \tag{7.121}$$

As the concentration of initial products builds up, however, these also react with the excited mercury atoms, e.g.,

$$Hg^* + C_2H_6 \rightarrow Hg + \cdot C_2H_5 + H\cdot \tag{7.122}$$

and the concentration of initial products finally reaches a steady state, though the higher hydrocarbon products continue to build up. This is not the case with radiolysis experiments, where all the products continue to build up as the irradiation proceeds. When methane is irradiated with 1236 Å light, the major primary process is elimination of molecular hydrogen (76)

$$CH_4 + h\nu \rightarrow CH_2 + H_2 \tag{7.123}$$

which is accompanied by a smaller amount of breakdown to methyl radicals and hydrogen atoms, as in the mercury photosensitized reaction. It is interesting that detachment of molecular hydrogen does not occur during the photosensitized reaction (hydrogen is practically eliminated as a product when the radical scavenger ethylene is present (75)), and it seems likely that the detachment process requires more energy than is available from the excited mercury atom (113 kcal per mole) (1236 Å photons have an energy of 230 kcal per mole). The higher energy requirement can be met by at least some of the excited molecules produced during radiolysis, so that various excited methane molecules are likely to break down to give both hydrogen atoms and molecular hydrogen under these conditions.

Mains and Newton have irradiated methane in the presence of a fivefold excess of mercury vapor (73). The mercury acts here as an ion scavenger since the ionization potential of mercury (10.43 v) is lower than that of methane (13.0 v):

$$CH_4^+ + Hg \rightarrow Hg^+ + CH_4 \tag{7.124}$$

Subsequently the mercury ion is neutralized and the excited mercury atom formed reacts with methane, as in the mercury sensitized photolysis,

$$Hg^+ + e^- \rightarrow Hg^* \tag{7.125}$$

$$Hg^* + CH_4 \rightarrow Hg + \cdot CH_3 + H\cdot \tag{7.121}$$

The authors found that at 260°C the presence of the mercury did not alter the distribution of products in the radiolysis of methane, and they concluded that ion-molecule reactions contribute little to the radiolysis at this temperature. They noted however that the ion CH_3^+ would not be scavenged by mercury since the ionization potential of the methyl radical is only 10.0 v. However, the authors concluded that the CH_4^+ ion, from which CH_3^+ was presumed to be formed by unimolecular dissociation, would not have a sufficient lifetime to dissociate in their experiments; the estimated lifetime of the ion in the radiolysis experiments was about 10^{-9} sec while the ion collection time in a mass spectrometer is about 10^{-6} sec.

The reverse of the situation when methane is irradiated with excess mercury occurs when the diluting gas is argon or krypton (64). Here charge transfer takes place in the opposite direction:

$$Ar^+ + CH_4 \rightarrow Ar + CH_3^+ + H\cdot \qquad (7.126)$$

$$Kr^+ + CH_4 \rightarrow Kr + CH_4^+ \qquad (7.127)$$

$$(Kr^+)^* + CH_4 \rightarrow Kr + CH_3^+ + H\cdot \qquad (7.128)$$

Charge transfer from argon releases sufficient energy to cause dissociation of the ion CH_4^+ (Eq. 7.126) whereas charge transfer from the krypton ion in its ground state does not (Eq. 7.127), though dissociation is possible if the krypton ion is excited (77). Meisels, Hamill, and Williams (64) attributed differences in the radiolysis of the mixtures methane-argon and methane-krypton to the different results of charge transfer with the two noble gases, as illustrated by reactions 7.126 and 7.127. Melton (78) has suggested that the differences may arise through the formation of the ion CH_2^+ in the mixtures containing argon but not in those containing krypton,

$$Ar^+ + CH_4 \rightarrow Ar + CH_2^+ + H_2 \qquad (7.129)$$

The corresponding charge-transfer reaction with krypton is endothermic and not probable. More recently direct experimental evidence of the abundance of secondary ions in these mixtures has been provided by Cermak and Herman (79). Using a mass spectrometer modified so that only ions produced by secondary reactions were collected, they showed that in methane-argon mixtures the relative abundance was $CH_4^+ : CH_3^+ : CH_2^+ = 2.0 : 79.0 : 19.0$. In methane-krypton mixtures the relative abundance of these ions was 64.5 : 35.0 : 0.5. The results show therefore that with argon the principal charge transfer reaction is 7.126, with a smaller contribution from 7.129. With krypton the principal reaction is 7.127, but there is an important contribution by 7.128. Xenon releases less energy by charge transfer with methane than either argon or krypton. When xenon is the sensitizing gas the major secondary ion is CH_4^+, the ratio of $CH_4^+ : CH_3^+ : CH_2^+$ being 97.0 : 2.5 : 0.5.

The liquid products formed when methane is subjected to large doses of radiation have been examined by Hummel (80), who found that the liquid contains saturated hydrocarbons with carbon contents ranging from C_6 to at least C_{27}. It was suggested that these hydrocarbons, together with molecular hydrogen, result from a series of ion-molecule reactions of the type (cf. ref. 70)

$$CH_3^+ + CH_4 \rightarrow C_2H_5^+ + H_2 \tag{7.103}$$

$$C_2H_5^+ + CH_4 \rightarrow C_3H_7^+ + H_2, \text{ etc.} \tag{7.120}$$

A certain amount of saturated hydrocarbon product will be formed by polymerization reactions, for example, reaction 7.119, which consume unsaturated products produced by irradiation.

When methane is irradiated in the presence of oxygen, oxidation products are formed. With excess oxygen α-particle irradiation eventually converts methane to carbon dioxide and water (81). Irradiation of mixtures containing a smaller proportion of oxygen also produces carbon dioxide and water, but a variety of other gaseous and liquid products are also formed. Products which have been identified include hydrogen, carbon monoxide, formaldehyde, formic acid, alcohols, and peroxides (82), including methyl hydroperoxide (83), CH_3OOH. The irradiation of hydrocarbons in the presence of oxygen shows some similarities to the slow gas-phase combustion of these compounds.

Ethane

The radiolysis of ethane and higher members of the paraffin series is similar to that of methane; hydrogen, dimeric products, and unsaturated compounds are major products, though compounds resulting from carbon-carbon bond fission are also formed. The products obtained from ethane by γ-irradiation are shown in Table 7.2, which also includes yields found in the presence of nitric oxide, a radical scavenger. Yields shown in parentheses were obtained at low doses with very low conversion of ethane to products (e.g., $10^{-3}\%$ conversion); they illustrate the influence which build-up of radiolysis products can have on the observed product yields.

As in the case of methane, mass spectrometric evidence is helpful when postulating a radiolysis mechanism. Ions formed from ethane in the mass spectrometer are, in order of decreasing abundance, $C_2H_4^+$, $C_2H_3^+$, $C_2H_6^+$, $C_2H_5^+$, $C_2H_2^+$, C_2H^+; they are probably formed by the following processes (86):

TABLE 7.2 *Radiolysis of Ethane*

(γ-irradiation; ref. 63. Values in parentheses are for very low conversions and are from ref. 84)

Product	G(product)	
	pure C_2H_6	$C_2H_6 + NO$
H_2	6.8 (8.8)	2.4*
CH_4	0.61 (0.39)	0.34
C_2H_2	0 (~0.2)	0.27
C_2H_4	0.05 (~2)	1.4
C_3H_6	0	0.03
C_3H_8	0.54 (~0.8)	0.14
C_4H_8	0	0.01
n-C_4H_{10}	1.0 (2.5)	0.27
i-C_4H_{10}	0.03	0
i-C_5H_{10}	0.54	0
Liquid polymer		

* Ref. 85.

$$C_2H_6 + e^- \rightarrow C_2H_6^+ + 2e^- \qquad (7.130)$$

$$\rightarrow C_2H_5^+ + H\cdot + 2e^- \qquad (7.131)$$

$$\rightarrow C_2H_4^+ + H_2 + 2e^- \qquad (7.132)$$

$$\rightarrow C_2H_3^+ + H_2 + H\cdot + 2e^- \qquad (7.133)$$

$$\rightarrow C_2H_2^+ + 2H_2 + 2e^- \qquad (7.134)$$

$$\rightarrow C_2H^+ + H_2 + 3H\cdot + 2e^- \qquad (7.135)$$

or

$$\rightarrow C_2H^+ + 5H\cdot + 2e^- \qquad (7.136)$$

On the basis of these processes it is possible to account for the molecular yield of hydrogen from ethane (71, 87); an ion-molecule reaction (68) accounts for the molecular yield of methane,

$$C_2H_3^+ + C_2H_6 \rightarrow C_3H_5^+ + CH_4 \qquad (7.137)$$

Irradiation of ethane mixed with iodine vapor has demonstrated the presence of the radicals $H\cdot$, $\cdot C_2H_5$, $\cdot CH_3$ and, in smaller amounts, n-$C_3H_7\cdot$, n-$C_4H_9\cdot$, and CH_2, by the appearance of the corresponding iodides (65). The radicals will react with ethane and with one another in a similar manner to the radicals formed from methane (Eqs. 7.111

to 7.119). Ethyl radicals will be more important here than in the radiolysis of methane and will be formed by several radical reactions,

$$H\cdot + C_2H_6 \rightarrow \cdot C_2H_5 + H_2 \tag{7.138}$$

$$\cdot CH_3 + C_2H_6 \rightarrow \cdot C_2H_5 + CH_4 \tag{7.139}$$

and, when sufficient ethylene has been formed,

$$H\cdot + C_2H_4 \rightarrow \cdot C_2H_5 \tag{7.140}$$

they may react by reactions 7.113 to 7.116 or by

$$H\cdot + \cdot C_2H_5 \rightarrow C_2H_6^* \tag{7.141}$$

$$C_2H_6^* + M \rightarrow C_2H_6 + M \tag{7.142}$$

$$C_2H_6^* \rightarrow C_2H_4 + H_2 \tag{7.143}$$

or

$$\rightarrow 2\cdot CH_3 \tag{7.144}$$

Ethane excited during the primary processes of energy absorption will probably react as shown in these equations or it may dissociate to give an ethyl radical and a hydrogen atom,

$$C_2H_6^* \rightarrow \cdot C_2H_5 + H\cdot \tag{7.145}$$

Free radicals are also likely products when the positive ions shown above (Eqs. 7.130 to 7.137) are neutralized, though the details of these reactions are not known.

Table 7.2 illustrates the fact that yields of some products, which presumably arise through free radical reactions, are reduced to zero by the presence of a radical scavenger. Yields of other products may be unchanged or merely lowered by the scavenger and these must be formed at least in part by nonradical reactions. Molecular products, for example, are not affected by scavengers or by the build-up of unsaturated radiolysis products, which can also act as radical scavengers. That the "molecular" hydrogen does in fact come from a single molecule of ethane has been demonstrated by irradiating mixtures of C_2H_6, C_2D_6, and a scavenger, when the hydrogen formed consists entirely of H_2 and D_2, apart from a small amount of HD from isotopic impurities (88, 89).[9] It is also clear from the Table that yields of unsaturated products are raised in the presence of a scavenger. When no scavenger is present these

[9] Okabe and McNesby (90) found for ethane irradiated with 1470 Å and 1295 Å light that hydrogen is not only formed from a single molecule, but comes preferentially from a single carbon atom of the molecule.

unsaturated compounds are probably converted to polymer via radical-initiated reactions.

The presence of ethyl radicals in liquid ethane irradiated with fast electrons has been demonstrated by observing the e.p.r. spectrum of the liquid *during irradiation* (91). The only other paramagnetic species detected were methyl radicals, whose concentration was estimated to be 4% of that of the ethyl radical.

Ethylene

The radiolysis products from ethane, ethylene, and acetylene are compared in Table 7.3. Ethylene and acetylene are more sensitive to radiation than the saturated hydrocarbon and are converted to products (mainly polymeric) with moderately high G values. At the same time the yield of hydrogen is less from the unsaturated hydrocarbons than from ethane. Ethylene occupies a position between acetylene and ethane both with respect to the amount of polymer produced and the yield of hydrogen.

TABLE 7.3 *Radiolysis of Ethane, Ethylene, and Acetylene*

Product	G(product)		
	Ethane (γ-irradiation, ref. 63)	Ethylene (Fast electron irradiation, ref. 92)	Acetylene (Tritium β-particle, ref. 93)
—(original gas)		15.5	71.9
H_2	6.8	1.28	
CH_4	0.61	0.12	
C_2H_2	0	1.46	
C_2H_4	0.05	—	
C_2H_6	—	0.27	
C_3H_6	0	0.23	
C_3H_8	0.54	0.11	
Butenes	0	0.40	
Butanes	1.1	0.48	
Pentenes	0.54		
Pentanes		0.06	
Hexanes		0.13	
Polymer		approx. 11*	Benzene 5.1 Cuprene 57*

* Molecules of parent gas converted to polymer per 100 ev energy absorbed.

It might be noted here that since unsaturated hydrocarbons are attacked very readily by free radicals they are effective radical scavengers, and will act in this manner if produced during radiolysis. Because radiolysis products may act as radical scavengers, or otherwise intrude into the radiolysis mechanism, it is always advisable to use as small a radiation dose as possible when determining product yields. This point was not always realized in the past, and radiolysis yields determined after the conversion of more than 1 or 2% (possibly much less; cf. 84, 94, and Table 7.2) of the original material to products should be suspect.

The radiation-induced polymerization of ethylene is of particular interest since ethylene polymerized by other means constitutes the commercially important polymer polyethylene. At atmospheric pressure and room temperature the polymeric material produced by irradiating gaseous ethylene is a liquid. At rather higher pressures (about 21 atm.) γ-irradiation produces a waxy solid with $G(\text{-}C_2H_4)$ about 160, and the yield of polymer is increased still further by increasing the temperature (e.g., $G(\text{-}C_2H_4)$ is about 10^4 at 460°F and 21.3 atm.) though the polymer produced at higher temperatures is liquid (95).

The radiolysis mechanism for ethylene is complex and not yet established, though a considerable amount of data is available about the reactions likely to be concerned. Mass spectrometry shows that the ions formed under the conditions prevailing in the mass spectrometer are, in order of decreasing importance, $C_2H_4^+$, $C_2H_3^+$, $C_2H_2^+$, C_2H^+, and C_2^+, and that many rapid ion-molecule reactions are possible (68, 69, 96, 97), including:

$$C_2H_4^+ + C_2H_4 \rightarrow C_4H_7^+ + H\cdot \tag{7.146}$$

or

$$\rightarrow C_3H_5^+ + \cdot CH_3 \tag{7.147}$$

$$C_2H_3^+ + C_2H_4 \rightarrow C_2H_5^+ + C_2H_2 \tag{7.148}$$

$$C_2H_2^+ + C_2H_4 \rightarrow C_4H_5^+ + H\cdot \tag{7.149}$$

or

$$\rightarrow C_3H_3^+ + \cdot CH_3 \qquad \text{etc.} \tag{7.150}$$

Dorfman and Sauer (71) accounted for the molecular yield of hydrogen from irradiated ethylene on the basis of the two primary ionization processes,

$$C_2H_4 + e^- \rightarrow C_2H_2^+ + H_2 + 2e^- \tag{7.151}$$

and

$$\rightarrow C_2H^+ + H_2 + H\cdot + 2e^- \tag{7.152}$$

and for the molecular yield of acetylene by the ion-molecule reaction 7.148 and charge transfer from the ion $C_2H_2^+$,

$$C_2H_2^+ + C_2H_4 \rightarrow C_2H_4^+ + C_2H_2 \quad (7.153)$$

Reactions of excited ethylene molecules can be studied by photochemical techniques. Sauer and Dorfman (98), for example, found that when ethylene absorbs light of wavelength 1470 Å, the primary processes are

$$C_2H_4^* \rightarrow C_2H_2 + H_2 \quad (7.154)$$

and

$$C_2H_4^{**} \rightarrow C_2H_2 + 2H\cdot \quad (7.155)$$

The observed products, hydrogen, acetylene, ethane, and butane can be explained by these processes and the following free radical reactions:

$$H\cdot + C_2H_4 \rightarrow \cdot C_2H_5 \quad (7.140)$$

$$2\cdot C_2H_5 \rightarrow C_4H_{10} \quad (7.113)$$

or

$$\rightarrow C_2H_6 + C_2H_4 \quad (7.114)$$

On the basis of further experiments the authors concluded that the disseciation of excited molecules also contributes in the radiolysis of ethylone, and that the agreement between the observed (molecular) hydrogen yield and that estimated from the mass spectral pattern is probably fortuitous (99). The mercury photosensitized decomposition of ethylene (100, 101) gives initially only acetylene and hydrogen, so that of the two reactions, 7.154 and 7.155, only the first is effective under these conditions. The rate of the photosensitized decomposition decreases with increasing ethylene concentration, indicating that the excited molecule may be deactivated by

$$C_2H_4^* + C_2H_4 \rightarrow 2C_2H_4 \quad (7.156)$$

When ethylene is irradiated in the presence of 5% of nitric oxide, ethane formation is suppressed but the yields of hydrogen, acetylene, and n-butane are unchanged, suggesting that ethane, but not the other products, arises by a free radical process (102). Ethylene itself is, of course, also a radical scavenger. Irradiation of C_2H_4—C_2D_4 mixtures gives hydrogen composed almost entirely of H_2 and D_2 (99, 103), indicating that the hydrogen is split from a single ethylene molecule by a "molecular" process. The two hydrogen atoms of the molecule may come from the same carbon atom or one may come from each carbon since

H_2, HD, and D_2 are all formed when either CH_2CD_2 or CHDCHD is irradiated (103). The proportions of the three hydrogen isotopes are not the same from the two isomeric ethanes, showing that the elimination process does not involve an intermediate in which all four hydrogen atoms in the molecule are equivalent.

Mixtures of ethylene and argon have been irradiated (92) and it appears that energy absorbed by the argon is transferred very efficiently to the ethylene, either by charge transfer[10] or the transfer of excitation energy,[11]

$$Ar^+ + C_2H_4 \rightarrow Ar + C_2H_4^+ \qquad (7.157)$$

or

$$Ar^* + C_2H_4 \rightarrow Ar + C_2H_4^+ + e^- \qquad (7.158)$$

The relative yields of the products are the same whether energy is absorbed directly by the ethylene or indirectly through argon, suggesting that the mechanism of ethylene radiolysis is the same in both cases. However, the distribution of products changes when sufficient hydrogen is added to the ethylene-argon mixture that ethylene is a minor component. Energy is absorbed mainly by either hydrogen or argon and the only significant products found are acetylene, ethane, *n*-butane and, at high partial pressures of argon and with high ethylene conversion, propane. These four gases account for 70–80% of the ethylene reacting, in contrast with a total of about 30% gaseous products when pure ethylene or ethylene-argon mixtures are irradiated. Lampe (92) postulates that energy absorbed by either hydrogen or argon eventually yields hydrogen atoms which, reacting with ethylene, can give both ethyl and methyl radicals,

$$H\cdot + C_2H_4 \rightarrow \cdot C_2H_5 \qquad (7.140)$$

$$H\cdot + \cdot C_2H_5 \rightarrow C_2H_6^* \qquad (7.141)$$

$$C_2H_6^* \rightarrow 2\cdot CH_3 \qquad (7.144)$$

Radical-radical reactions involving the two organic radicals can then give the products ethane, propane, and *n*-butane. Acetylene is presum-

[10] Cermak and Herman (79), using a modified mass spectrometer, found the relative abundance of secondary ions formed by charge transfer between argon ions and ethylene to be $C_2H_4^+ : C_2H_3^+ : C_2H_2^+ = 3\cdot 0 : 76\cdot 0 : 21\cdot 0$. Charge exchange reactions between noble gas ions and ethylene have also been studied by Franklin and Field (104).

[11] The excitation energies of the lowest excited states of argon are greater than the ionization potential of ethylene.

ably formed via the normal ethylene radiolysis mechanism, upon which these extra reactions are superimposed.

Polymerization of ethylene under the influence of radiation is probably a free radical process represented by

$$R\cdot + CH_2{=}CH_2 \rightarrow R{-}CH_2{-}CH_2\cdot \xrightarrow{C_2H_4} \text{polymer} \qquad (7.119)$$

where $R\cdot$ is a hydrogen atom or an organic radical. When solid ethylene is irradiated at $-196°C$, low molecular weight branched chain polymers are formed by a chain reaction represented (105) by

$$C_nH_{2n}^+ + C_2H_4 \rightarrow C_{n+2}H_{2n+4}^+ \qquad (7.159)$$

and it is possible that this process may also contribute in the gas phase radiolysis. However, in a number of instances where both free radicals and ions can initiate polymerization, it appears that radical polymerization predominates at normal temperatures and the ionic process at low temperatures.

The yield of hydrogen from irradiated ethylene or propylene is independent of the absorbed dose, and it has been suggested (84) that measurement of the hydrogen produced be used as a means of dosimetry in gas-phase systems; $G(H_2)_{\text{ethylene}} = 1.2$ and $G(H_2)_{\text{propylene}} = 1.1$.

Acetylene

Acetylene forms benzene and a polymer, cuprene, upon irradiation, in relative proportions of about one to five (based on the acetylene consumed); little or no gaseous product is formed except where this may be produced by irradiation of the initial products. The polymerization of acetylene, initiated both by radiation and by other means, has been studied extensively but the radiolysis mechanism is still uncertain. The polymer produced is generally referred to as cuprene, though its properties depend on the method of formation. As prepared by irradiation, cuprene is a yellowish powder, insoluble in all common solvents, which neither melts nor sublimes. Little is known of its chemical properties beyond the facts that it is inflammable and will absorb oxygen (up to 25% by weight) when exposed to air.

An interesting feature of the radiolysis of acetylene is the ion-pair yield, $M\text{–}C_2H_2/N$, which under a variety of experimental conditions is remarkably constant at about 20 (106, 107). The yields from polymerization reactions are generally influenced very markedly by any change in the reaction conditions, and the polymerization of acetylene is therefore not a typical chain reaction; the ion-pair yield is reproducible, and largely independent of dose rate, pressure, and temperature; it is not easily changed by inhibitors. The first radiolysis mechanism postulated for acetylene accounted for these facts on the basis of the ion-cluster theory (107, 108). Ions formed in the gas were believed to attract neutral acetylene molecules and hold them as a group of about twenty molecules by polarization forces. Energy released when the cluster is neutralized initiates polymerization of the molecules present to form cuprene,

$$C_2H_2 \rightsquigarrow C_2H_2^+ + e^- \tag{7.160}$$

$$C_2H_2^+ + 19C_2H_2 \rightarrow (19C_2H_2, C_2H_2^+) \tag{7.161}$$

$$(19C_2H_2, C_2H_2^+) + e^- \rightarrow \underset{\text{cuprene}}{C_{40}H_{40}} \tag{7.162}$$

This accounted successfully for the constant ion-pair yield, even in the presence of an inert gas (nitrogen or one of the noble gases) where only part of the ions formed would be produced from acetylene. However, later mechanisms, while maintaining the importance of ions and ionic reactions, have removed the emphasis from cluster formation as an intermediate step, though without offering an alternative explanation of the constancy of the ion-pair yield.

Dorfman (93, 109) has suggested that two independent mechanisms occur in irradiated acetylene, one leading to benzene and the other to cuprene. The benzene precursor is postulated to be an excited acetylene molecule (probably in a triplet state) which for steric reasons is able to give benzene by the sequence of reactions,

$$C_2H_2 \rightsquigarrow C_2H_2^* \tag{7.163}$$

$$C_2H_2^* + C_2H_2 \rightarrow (C_2H_2)_2^* \xrightarrow{C_2H_2} C_6H_6 \tag{7.164}$$

while cuprene is formed by a chain mechanism for which the initiation steps may be

$$C_2H_2 \begin{cases} \rightsquigarrow C_2H_2^+ + e^- \\ \rightsquigarrow C_2H_2'^* \end{cases} \rightarrow \cdot C_2H + H\cdot \tag{7.165}$$

The excited acetylene shown here is presumably in a different excited state to that which leads to benzene. Both radicals, $\cdot C_2H$ and $H\cdot$, add to acetylene to initiate a chain reaction leading to a polymeric cuprene,

$$H\cdot + C_2H_2 \rightarrow CH_2{=}CH\cdot \rightarrow \text{cuprene} \tag{7.166}$$

$$\cdot C_2H + C_2H_2 \rightarrow HC{\equiv}C{-}CH{=}CH\cdot \rightarrow \text{cuprene} \tag{7.167}$$

Reaction 7.166 explains the absence of molecular hydrogen in the radiolysis products from acetylene, even though rupture of a carbon-hydrogen bond does occur, as is shown by isotopic exchange when a mixture of C_2H_2 and C_2D_2 is irradiated (93),

$$C_2H_2 + C_2D_2 \rightarrow 2C_2HD \tag{7.168}$$

Dorfman and Wahl (109) investigated the importance of excitation in the radiolysis of acetylene by irradiating mixtures of acetylene with a preponderance of helium. Under these conditions acetylene radiolysis is initiated by energy transfer to acetylene from an ionized or an excited helium atom, which in both cases leads to ionization of the acetylene,

$$He^+ + C_2H_2 \rightarrow He + C_2H_2^+ \tag{7.169}$$

$$He^* + C_2H_2 \rightarrow He + C_2H_2^+ + e^- \tag{7.170}$$

Excited states of acetylene are not formed and, if an excited state is the necessary precursor of benzene, no benzene should be produced. None was found. Cyclization to benzene is also eliminated when the radiolysis is sensitized by argon, krypton, or xenon. In all the noble gas-sensitized radiolyses, the polymerization yield is apparently unchanged.

Dorfman and Wahl also showed that the fraction of reacted acetylene converted to benzene, which in direct radiolysis at moderate pressures is constant at one fifth, decreases sharply at very low pressures. This is due to deactivation of the transient precursors of benzene at the wall of the irradiation vessel, diffusion to the wall being more rapid at low than at high pressures. From a consideration of the experimental conditions it was shown that the transient intermediates have a lifetime of at least 10^{-4} sec, which is consistent with the postulate that they are molecules excited to a triplet state. Benzene and cuprene are also formed from acetylene by photopolymerization (110) and mercury photosensitization (111). In both cases the yield of benzene falls at low pressures but, unlike the radiation-induced reaction, the yield of cuprene also falls, so that the ratio of benzene to cuprene is constant even at very low pressures. This is nevertheless compatible with the radiolysis mechanism since under these circumstances both benzene and cuprene must be formed via excited molecules (neither excitation process transfers sufficient energy to ionize acetylene).

More recently, Mains, Niki, and Wijnen (112) have obtained evidence that radicals are involved in benzene formation, and that the process cannot be initiated exclusively by excited molecules. Their experiments include the irradiation of equimolar mixtures of C_2H_2 and C_2D_2 and analysis of the mixture of isotopically substituted benzenes formed.

The product was found to contain about 25% of the compounds C_6H_5D, $C_6H_3D_3$, and C_6HD_5, which can only arise by a mechanism involving C—H bond rupture at some stage during the radiolysis. Other experiments showed that benzene formation is completely suppressed by oxygen or iodine. Both experiments suggest a free radical mechanism, and the authors postulate that benzene is formed by a side reaction

$$C_6H_7\cdot \rightarrow C_6H_6 + H\cdot \tag{7.171}$$

of the hydrogen atom-initiated chain polymerization given above (Eq. 7.166). Since the yield of benzene falls with increasing dose rate, this reaction is believed to compete with

$$C_6H_7\cdot + R\cdot \rightarrow \text{products} \tag{7.172}$$

as increasing dose rate raises the radical concentration.

An alternative process which may accompany radical-initiated polymerization of acetylene is polymerization through a series of ion-molecule reactions (cf. 113, 114, 115). Ions formed from acetylene in the mass spectrometer, with their relative abundances (116), are (*a*) (ionization by 75 v electrons), $C_2H_2^+$ (100), C_2H^+ (20.7), C_2^+ (5.7), CH^+ (4.4), C^+ (1), (*b*) (ionization by 5.1 Mev α-particles), $C_2H_2^+$ (100), C_2H^+ (7.3). Feasible ion-molecule reactions include;

$$C_2H_2^+ + C_2H_2 \rightarrow C_4H_4^+ \tag{7.173}$$

or

$$\rightarrow C_4H_3^+ + H\cdot \tag{7.174}$$

$$CH^+ + C_2H_2 \rightarrow C_3H_3^+ \tag{7.175}$$

and these may be followed by chain reactions of the type,

$$C_mH_n^+ + C_2H_2 \rightarrow C_{m+2}H_{n+2}^+ \tag{7.176}$$

Unsaturated hydrocarbons appear rather prolific in the matter of ion-molecule reactions, and other such reactions given in the references cited might equally contribute to the radiolysis mechanism. A second, rather less probable, alternative to free radical polymerization is polymerization via excited molecules alone (cf. 110), e.g.,

$$C_2H_2^* + C_2H_2 \rightarrow C_4H_4^* \xrightarrow{C_2H_2} \text{cuprene} \tag{7.177}$$

When benzene vapor is mixed with acetylene prior to irradiation, the α-particle-induced polymerization is reduced by about a third (117). Benzene will often inhibit the radiation decomposition of other organic liquids, but examples of similar protective action in the gas phase are rare. Rudolph and Melton (118) have shown by means of the α-ray mass spectrometer that a very efficient charge transfer occurs between acetylene and benzene,

$$C_2H_2^+ + C_6H_6 \rightarrow C_6H_6^+ + C_2H_2 \quad (7.178)$$

which will adequately account for the observed decrease in polymer yield. Benzene itself is relatively stable towards radiation decomposition.

Addition to Unsaturated Hydrocarbons

Free radical attack on olefinic and acetylenic systems generally produces either a polymer or an addition compound. Examples of radical-polymerization induced by radiation have already been met when discussing ethylene and acetylene. When these gases are mixed with a second gas and irradiated, a chain reaction may follow giving an addition product. For example, ethyl bromide is formed with an ion-pair yield of the order of 10^5 when a mixture of ethylene and hydrogen bromide is irradiated with γ-radiation (119), the over-all reaction being

$$CH_2{=}CH_2 + HBr \rightarrow CH_3CH_2Br \quad (7.179)$$

The reaction is very similar to the photo-initiated bromination of ethylene, and a similar radical-initiated chain mechanism is proposed with the chain-propagating steps,

$$Br\cdot + CH_2{=}CH_2 \rightleftharpoons \cdot CH_2{-}CH_2Br \quad (7.180)$$

$$\cdot CH_2{-}CH_2Br + HBr \rightarrow Br\cdot + CH_3CH_2Br \quad (7.181)$$

Reaction is initiated by free radicals formed from hydrogen bromide or ethylene in the manner already described. When ethylene is in excess the reaction yield is inversely proportional to the square root of the dose rate.

Addition reactions are not limited to halogens or compounds containing halogen. Lampe (120) has described a radiation-induced alkylation reaction between ethylene and propane which takes place under conditions of relatively high temperature and pressure. The major product is isopentane ($G = 42.8$ at 650°F, 500 psig, 8.5 mole percent ethylene; $G(-C_2H_4) = 93.6$) which is probably formed as follows:

$$C_3H_8 \rightsquigarrow \text{free radicals } (R\cdot) \quad (7.182)$$

$$R\cdot + CH_3CH_2CH_3 \rightarrow CH_3\dot{C}HCH_3 + RH \quad (7.183)$$

$$CH_3\dot{C}HCH_3 + CH_2{=}CH_2 \rightarrow (CH_3)_2CH{-}CH_2{-}CH_2\cdot \quad (7.184)$$

$$(CH_3)_2CHCH_2CH_2\cdot + CH_3CH_2CH_3 \rightarrow CH_3\dot{C}HCH_3 + (CH_3)_2CHCH_2CH_3 \quad (7.185)$$

Reactions 7.184 and 7.185 comprise a chain reaction, and this accounts for the relatively high yield of isopentane. Chain termination is by combination of two of the free radicals involved and, as is to be expected for a chain reaction of this sort, G(isopentane) is inversely proportional to the square root of the dose rate. It is also a function of the temperature and pressure. Isopentane makes up less than half the total radiolysis product and the detailed radiolysis mechanism is obviously very much more complex than shown above.

A similar radiation-induced chain alkylation occurs between propene and isobutane (121). At 55 atmospheres pressure and 350–400°C the chain length is of the order 20 to 100, and it increases with increasing temperature and pressure and is inversely proportional to the square root of the dose rate. A complex mixture of products is obtained and it was noted that under these conditions purely thermal alkylation is negligibly slow.

Radiation-induced addition may also take place with acetylenic compounds. Bartok and Lucchesi (122) have reported the chain alkylation of acetylene by propane to give predominantly 3-methylbut-1-ene with an ion-pair yield between 7 and 12, depending on the dose rate, at 10–15 atm and 250–400°C (mixed reactor radiation):

$$C_2H_2 + CH_3CH_2CH_3 \rightarrow CH_2{=}CH{-}\underset{\displaystyle CH_3}{\overset{|}{C}}H{-}CH_3 \qquad (7.186)$$

A point of interest about this reaction is that there is no thermal counterpart.

REFERENCES

A comprehensive and authoritative account of the radiation chemistry of gases is given by S. C. Lind in *Radiation Chemistry of Gases*, Reinhold Publishing Corp., New York, 1961. W. Mund has given a briefer review in *Actions Chimiques et Biologiques des Radiations* (ed. M. Haissinsky), Masson et Cie, Paris, Vol. 2, 1956.

1. S. C. Lind, *J. Phys. Chem.*, **16,** 564 (1912).
2. R. A. Back, T. W. Woodward, and K. A. McLauchlan, *Can. J. Chem.*, **40,** 1380 (1962).
3. J. L. Magee and K. Funabashi, *Radiation Res.*, **10,** 622 (1959).
4. H. Eyring, J. O. Hirschfelder, and H. S. Taylor, *J. Chem. Phys.*, **4,** 479 (1936).
5. H. Eyring, J. O. Hirschfelder, and H. S. Taylor, *J. Chem. Phys.*, **4,** 570 (1936).
6. G. Glockler and S. C. Lind, *The Electrochemistry of Gases and Other Dielectrics*, John Wiley and Sons, New York, 1939.
7. W. P. Jesse and J. Sadauskis, *Phys. Rev.*, **88,** 417 (1952).

8. G. Bertolini, M. Bettoni, and A. Bisi, *Phys. Rev.*, **92,** 1586 (1953).
9. C. E. Melton, G. S. Hurst, and T. E. Bortner, *Phys. Rev.*, **96,** 643 (1954).
10. P. C. Capron, *Ann. Soc. Sci. Bruxelles,* **55,** 222 (1935).
11. J. L. Magee and M. Burton, *J. Am. Chem. Soc.*, **72,** 1965 (1950).
12. F. E. Littman, E. M. Carr, and A. P. Brady, *Radiation Res.*, **7,** 107 (1957).
13. G. Czapski, J. Jortner, and G. Stein, *J. Phys. Chem.*, **65,** 956, 960, 964 (1961).
14. W. Mund, L. Kaertkemeyer, M. Vanpee, and A. van Tiggelen, *Bull. Soc. Chim. Belges,* **49,** 187 (1940); W. Mund, T. de M. de Hornes, and M. van Meersche, *ibid.*, **56,** 386 (1947); W. Mund and M. van Meersche, *ibid.*, **57,** 88 (1948).
15. L. M. Dorfman and F. J. Shipko, *J. Phys. Chem.*, **59,** 1110 (1955).
16. S. O. Thompson and O. A. Schaeffer, *J. Am. Chem. Soc.*, **80,** 553 (1958).
17. O. A. Schaeffer and S. O. Thompson, *Radiation Res.*, **10,** 671 (1959).
18. S. C. Lind, *Radiation Chemistry of Gases,* Reinhold Publishing Corp., New York, 1961, p. 91.
19. K. E. Wilzbach, *J. Am. Chem. Soc.*, **79,** 1013 (1957).
20. P. Riesz and K. E. Wilzbach, *J. Phys. Chem.*, **62,** 6 (1958).
21. L. M. Dorfman and K. E. Wilzbach, *J. Phys. Chem.*, **63,** 799 (1959).
22. K. Yang and P. L. Gant, *J. Chem. Phys.*, **31,** 1589 (1959).
23. T. H. Pratt and R. Wolfgang, *J. Am. Chem. Soc.*, **83,** 10 (1961).
24. S. C. Lind, *Amer. Chem. J.*, **47,** 397 (1912).
25. S. C. Lind and D. C. Bardwell, *J. Am. Chem. Soc.*, **51,** 2751 (1929).
26. J. D'Olieslager, *Bull. Sci. Acad. roy. Belg.*, **11,** 711 (1925); W. Mund and J. D'Olieslager, *ibid.*, **12,** 309 (1926); W. Mund and J. D'Olieslager, *Bull. Soc. Chim. Belges,* **36,** 399 (1927).
27. J. F. Kircher, J. S. McNulty, J. L. McFarling, and A. Levy, *Radiation Res.*, **13,** 452 (1960).
28. B. Lewis, *J. Phys. Chem.*, **37,** 533 (1933).
29. J. L. Magee and M. Burton, *J. Am. Chem. Soc.*, **73,** 523 (1951).
30. J. Pressman, L. M. Aschenbrand, F. F. Marmo, A. Jursa, and M. Zelikoff, *J. Chem. Phys.*, **25,** 187 (1956).
31. D. W. Brown and L. A. Wall, *J. Phys. Chem.*, **65,** 915 (1961).
32. P. Harteck and S. Dondes, *Proc. Second Intern. Conf. Peaceful Uses Atomic Energy,* United Nations, Geneva, **29,** 415 (1958).
33. P. Harteck and S. Dondes, *J. Chem. Phys.*, **27,** 546 (1957); **28,** 975 (1958); *J. Phys. Chem.*, **63,** 956 (1959).
34. S. Y. Pshezhetsky and M. T. Dmitriev, *Soviet J. At. Energy,* **3,** 350 (1957); *Intern. J. Appl. Radiation Isotopes,* **5,** 67 (1959).
35. A. R. Jones, *Radiation Res.*, **10,** 655 (1959).
36. P. Harteck and S. Dondes, *Nucleonics,* **14,** (Mar.), 66 (1956).
37. R. E. Simpson, *Health Phys.*, **8,** 143 (1962).
38. B. P. Burtt and J. F. Kircher, *Radiation Res.*, **9,** 1 (1958).
39. G. R. A. Johnson, *Proc. Chem. Soc.*, 213 (1960).
40. A. T. Cameron and W. Ramsay, *J. Chem. Soc.*, **93,** 966 (1908).
41. F. L. Usher, *J. Chem. Soc.*, **97,** 389 (1910).
42. C. C. McDonald, A. Kahn, and H. E. Gunning, *J. Chem. Phys.*, **22,** 908 (1954); C. C. McDonald and H. E. Gunning, *ibid.*, **23,** 532 (1955).
43. J. C. Devins and M. Burton, *J. Am. Chem. Soc.*, **76,** 2618 (1954).
44. B. P. Burtt and A. B. Zahlan, *J. Chem. Phys.*, **26,** 846 (1957).

45. M. M. Mann, A. Hustrulid, and J. T. Tate, *Phys. Rev.*, **58**, 340 (1940).
46. L. M. Dorfman and P. C. Noble, *J. Phys. Chem.*, **63**, 980 (1959).
47. H. Essex and D. FitzGerald, *J. Am. Chem. Soc.*, **56**, 65 (1934); C. Smith and H. Essex, *J. Chem. Phys.*, **6**, 188 (1938); M. J. McGuinness and H. Essex, *J. Am. Chem. Soc.*, **64**, 1908 (1942).
48. H. Essex, *J. Phys. Chem.*, **58**, 42 (1954).
49. T. W. Woodward and R. A. Back, *Can. J. Chem.*, **41**, 1463 (1963).
50. D. Cleaver, E. Collinson, and F. S. Dainton, *Trans. Faraday Soc.*, **56**, 1640 (1960).
51. S. C. Lind and D. C. Bardwell, *J. Am. Chem. Soc.*, **47**, 2675 (1925).
52. P. Harteck and S. Dondes, *J. Chem. Phys.*, **26**, 1727 (1957).
53. J. O. Hirschfelder and H. S. Taylor, *J. Chem. Phys.*, **6**, 783 (1938).
54. P. Harteck and S. Dondes, *J. Chem. Phys.*, **23**, 902 (1955).
55. A. R. Anderson, J. V. Best, and D. A. Dominey, *J. Chem. Soc.*, 3498 (1962).
56. A. C. Stewart and H. J. Bowlden, *J. Phys. Chem.*, **64**, 212 (1960).
57. A. R. Anderson, H. W. Davidson, R. Lind, D. R. Stranks, C. Tyzack, and J. Wright, *Proc. Second Intern. Conf. Peaceful Uses Atomic Energy*, United Nations, Geneva, **7**, 335 (1958).
58. M. D. Ross and C. B. Moore (reported by J. Strong), *Sky and Teles.*, **19**, 342 (1960).
59. S. C. Lind, *Le Radium*, **8**, 289 (1911).
60. S. C. Lind and R. Livingston, *J. Am. Chem. Soc.*, **58**, 612 (1936).
61. E. G. Zubler, W. H. Hamill, and R. R. Williams, *J. Chem. Phys.*, **23**, 1263 (1955).
62. D. O. Schissler and D. P. Stevenson, *J. Chem. Phys.*, **24**, 926 (1956).
63. K. Yang and P. J. Manno, *J. Am. Chem. Soc.*, **81**, 3507 (1959).
64. G. G. Meisels, W. H. Hamill and R. R. Williams, *J. Phys. Chem.*, **61**, 1456 (1957).
65. L. H. Gevantman and R. R. Williams, *J. Phys. Chem.*, **56**, 569 (1952).
66. American Petroleum Institute, *Catalog of Mass Spectral Data*, Carnegie Institute of Technology, Pittsburgh, Pa., 1947-1956.
67. V. L. Tal'roze and A. K. Lyubimova, *Dokl. Akad. Nauk SSSR*, **86**, 909 (1952).
68. D. O. Schissler and D. P. Stevenson, *J. Chem. Phys.*, **24**, 926 (1956).
69. F. H. Field, J. L. Franklin, and F. W. Lampe, *J. Am. Chem. Soc.*, **79**, 2419 (1957).
70. S. Wexler and N. Jesse, *J. Am. Chem. Soc.*, **84**, 3425 (1962).
71. L. M. Dorfman and M. C. Sauer, *J. Chem. Phys.*, **32**, 1886 (1960).
72. L. Reinisch, *J. Chim. Phys.*, **57**, 1064 (1960).
73. G. J. Mains and A. S. Newton, *J. Phys. Chem.*, **65**, 212 (1961).
74. K. Morikawa, W. S. Benedict, and H. S. Taylor, *J. Chem. Phys.*, **5**, 212 (1937).
75. R. A. Back and D. van der Auwera, *Can. J. Chem.*, **40**, 2339 (1962).
76. B. H. Mahan and R. Mandal, *J. Chem. Phys.*, **37**, 207 (1962).
77. G. G. Meisels, *J. Chem. Phys*, **31**, 284 (1959).
78. C. E. Melton, *J. Chem. Phys.*, **33**, 647 (1960).
79. V. Cermak and Z. Herman, *Nucleonics*, **19**, (Sept.), 106 (1961).
80. R. W. Hummel, *Nature*, **192**, 1178 (1961).
81. S. C. Lind and D. C. Bardwell, *J. Am. Chem. Soc.*, **48**, 2335 (1926).

82. B. M. Mikhailov, M. E. Kuimova, and V. S. Bogdanov, *Trans. First All Union Conf. Radiation Chemistry, 1957*, Moscow, 1958, p. 234.
83. G. R. A. Johnson and G. A. Salmon, *J. Phys. Chem.*, **65**, 177 (1961).
84. K. Yang and P. L. Gant, *J. Phys. Chem.*, **65**, 1861 (1961).
85. K. Yang, *Can. J. Chem.*, **38**, 1234 (1960).
86. J. A. Hipple, *Phys. Rev.*, **53**, 530 (1938).
87. L. M. Dorfman, *J. Phys. Chem.*, **60**, 826 (1956); **62**, 29 (1958).
88. L. M. Dorfman, *J. Phys. Chem.*, **62**, 29 (1958).
89. L. J. Stief and P. Ausloos, *J. Chem. Phys.*, **36**, 2904 (1962).
90. H. Okabe and J. R. McNesby, *J. Chem. Phys.*, **34**, 668 (1961).
91. R. W. Fessenden and R. H. Schuler, *J. Chem. Phys.*, **33**, 935 (1960).
92. F. W. Lampe, *Radiation Res.*, **10**, 691 (1959).
93. L. M. Dorfman and F. J. Shipko, *J. Am. Chem. Soc.*, **77**, 4723 (1955).
94. R. A. Back, *J. Phys. Chem.*, **64**, 124 (1960).
95. J. C. Hayward and R. H. Bretton, *Chem. Eng. Progr. Symp. Ser.*, **50** (13), 73 (1954).
96. C. E. Melton and P. S. Rudolph, *J. Chem. Phys.*, **32**, 1128 (1960).
97. F. H. Field, *J. Am. Chem. Soc.*, **83**, 1523 (1961).
98. M. C. Sauer and L. M. Dorfman, *J. Chem. Phys.*, **35**, 497 (1961).
99. M. C. Sauer and L. M. Dorfman, *J. Phys. Chem.*, **66**, 322 (1962).
100. A. B. Callear and R. J. Cvetanović, *J. Chem. Phys.*, **24**, 873 (1956).
101. D. J. LeRoy and E. W. R. Steacie, *J. Chem. Phys.*, **9**, 829 (1941).
102. K. Yang and P. J. Manno, *J. Phys. Chem.*, **63**, 752 (1959).
103. P. Ausloos and R. Gorden, *J. Chem. Phys.*, **36**, 5 (1962).
104. J. L. Franklin and F. H. Field, *J. Am. Chem. Soc.*, **83**, 3555 (1961).
105. C. D. Wagner, *J. Phys. Chem.*, **65**, 2276 (1961); **66**, 1158 (1962).
106. W. Mund and W. Koch, *Bull. Soc. Chim. Belges*, **34**, 119, 241 (1925); *J. Phys. Chem.*, **30**, 289 (1926).
107. S. C. Lind, D. C. Bardwell, and J. H. Perry, *J. Am. Chem. Soc.*, **48**, 1556 (1926).
108. W. Mund, C. Velghe, C. de Vos, and M. Vanpee, *Bull. Soc. Chim. Belges*, **48**, 269 (1939).
109. L. M. Dorfman and A. C. Wahl, *Radiation Res.*, **10**, 680 (1959).
110. M. Zelikoff and L. M. Aschenbrand, *J. Chem. Phys.*, **24**, 1034 (1956).
111. S. Shida, Z. Kuri, and T. Furuoya, *J. Chem. Phys.*, **28**, 131 (1958).
112. G. J. Mains, H. Niki, and M. H. J. Wijnen, *J. Phys. Chem.*, **67**, 11 (1963).
113. F. H. Field, J. L. Franklin, and F. W. Lampe, *J. Am. Chem. Soc.*, **79**, 2665 (1957).
114. R. Barker, W. H. Hamill, and R. R. Williams, *J. Phys. Chem.*, **63**, 825 (1959).
115. P. S. Rudolph and C. E. Melton, *J. Phys. Chem.*, **63**, 916 (1959).
116. C. E. Melton and P. S. Rudolph, *J. Chem. Phys.*, **30**, 847 (1959).
117. S. C. Lind and P. S. Rudolph, *J. Chem. Phys.*, **26**, 1768 (1957).
118. P. S. Rudolph and C. E. Melton, *J. Chem. Phys.*, **32**, 586 (1960).
119. D. A. Armstrong and J. W. T. Spinks, *Can. J. Chem.*, **37**, 1210 (1959).
120. F. W. Lampe, *Nucleonics*, **18**, (April), 60 (1960).
121. P. J. Lucchesi and C. E. Heath, *J. Am. Chem. Soc.*, **81**, 4770 (1959).
122. W. Bartok and P. J. Lucchesi, *J. Am. Chem. Soc.*, **81**, 5918 (1959).

CHAPTER 8

Water and Aqueous Solutions

The action of ionizing radiation on water has been the subject of a great deal of experimental and theoretical study. The interest in water arises partly from its relative simplicity and the wide variety of aqueous systems that are available and partly because aqueous systems are of special interest in radiobiology and reactor technology. A great deal of relevant information is also available from other chemical and physical studies on aqueous systems.

Historically, the evolution of gas from aqueous solutions containing radium salts was one of the earliest radiation-induced chemical reactions to be observed and then studied. Early work showed that α-particles decompose water into hydrogen and oxygen and that part of the oxygen remains in solution in the form of hydrogen peroxide. In aerated solutions the yield of hydrogen peroxide is increased by the presence of oxygen. X-rays and γ-rays give much smaller yields of hydrogen peroxide from aerated solutions and produce very little change at all when pure oxygen-free water is irradiated in a closed system. Both oxidation and reduction of dissolved substances were observed, and as far back as 1914 Debierne (1) suggested that free radicals formed from the water might be responsible for the chemical action of radiation. Similar suggestions were made by Risse (2) and later developed by Weiss (3) and by the group working on radiation chemistry in the United States Atomic Energy Project (cf. 4, 5), though in the meantime other, non-radical, mechanisms were also considered (e.g., the activated-water hypothesis (6)). At the present time, free radicals (mainly H·, or an equivalent reducing species such as the solvated electron, and ·OH) are considered the most important intermediates in radiation-induced reactions in water and aqueous solutions, though the radiolysis products hydrogen and hydrogen peroxide can also play a part. The development of these ideas up to 1959 has been described by Hart (7).

Water Vapor

Water vapor is the simplest aqueous system and it has been studied in a similar manner to the other gaseous systems described in Chapter 7. The more important ions formed in the mass spectrometer together with the reactions which have been postulated to explain their formation are listed in Table 8.1. Several of the ions may also be formed in other reactions (8, 9) occurring at higher potentials, but for simplicity these reactions have been omitted.

The relative intensities of the ion peaks (columns 5 and 6 in Table 8.1) were determined by different investigators using ionizing potentials of 50 v (10) and 100 v (11) respectively. The most abundant ions are H_2O^+, H_3O^+, OH^+, and H^+ and these will presumably be the most important ionic intermediates in the radiolysis of water vapor; excited water molecules which will also be formed upon irradiation are not detected by this technique. The intensity of the H_3O^+ peak is found to be proportional to the square of the water vapor pressure in the ion source of the mass spectrometer, and the ion is therefore formed by a secondary (ion-molecule) bimolecular reaction, as shown in the table. Negative ions can be detected by reversing the magnetic field and accelerating potential in the instrument. Such ions are formed in relatively small amounts in water vapor and it is interesting that no H_2O^- is found and only very small amounts of OH^-. From the small negative ion yields it appears that in water vapor most of the electrons formed by ionization neutralize positive ions directly, in preference to reacting with neutral water molecules. This is not necessarily true in liquid water where the electron and other charged species may become hydrated and behave rather differently.

Hydrogen atoms and hydroxyl radicals are produced directly in some of the reactions listed in the table. They may also be formed by neu-

TABLE 8.1 *Principal Ions Formed in Water Vapor in the Mass Spectrometer*

Ion	Appearance potential (v) (ref. 9)	Appearance potential (v) (ref. 10)	Appearance potential (v) (ref. 11)	Relative intensity (at 50 v) (ref. 10)	Relative intensity (at 100 v) (ref. 11)	Formation reaction (refs. 8, 9)
H^-	4.8		5.6		0.6	$H_2O + e^- \rightarrow H^- + \cdot OH$
O^-	7.4		7.5		0.15	$H_2O + e^- \rightarrow O^- + 2H\cdot$ or $\rightarrow O^- + H_2$
H_2O^+	12.61	12.7	13.0	100	100	$H_2O + e^- \rightarrow H_2O^+ + 2e^-$
H_3O^+	12.67	12.7	13.8	20	—	$H_2O^+ + H_2O \rightarrow H_3O^+ + \cdot OH$
OH^+	18.1	18.9	18.7	20	23	$H_2O + e^- \rightarrow OH^+ + H\cdot + 2e^-$
O^+		18.5	18.8	2	2	$H_2O + e^- \rightarrow O^+ + H_2 + 2e^-$
H^+	19.6	18.9	19.5	20	5	$H_2O + e^- \rightarrow H^+ + \cdot OH + 2e^-$
O^+	29.15					$H_2O + e^- \rightarrow O^+ + 2H\cdot + 2e^-$

tralization of the positive ions, probably by reactions of the type shown below:

$$H_2O^+ + e^- \rightarrow H\cdot + \cdot OH \quad (8.1)$$

$$H_3O^+ + e^- \rightarrow 2H\cdot + \cdot OH \quad (8.2)$$

$$H^+ + e^- + H_2O \rightarrow 2H\cdot + \cdot OH \quad (8.3)$$

$$OH^+ + e^- + H_2O \rightarrow H\cdot + 2\cdot OH \quad (8.4)$$

(the first step in both reaction 8.3 and 8.4 could be charge transfer with a neutral water molecule to give the ion H_2O^+.) Hydrogen atoms and hydroxyl radicals will also be formed by the dissociation of excited water molecules,

$$H_2O^* \rightarrow H\cdot + \cdot OH \quad (8.5)$$

so that the over-all result of the absorption of ionizing radiation by water vapor is the production of these two types of reactive radical.

At moderate pressures, the LET of almost all types of radiation in the vapor is low and the radicals will be produced relatively far apart; they will also be able to move about quite freely. Consequently the effect of radiation on water vapor is to produce hydrogen atoms and hydroxyl radicals distributed more or less uniformly throughout the vapor. In the absence of radical scavengers the radicals will react together, either at the surface of the containing vessel or in the presence of a water molecule:

$$H\cdot + \cdot OH \rightarrow H_2O \quad (8.6)$$

$$2H\cdot \rightarrow H_2 \quad (8.7)$$

$$2\cdot OH \rightarrow H_2O_2 \quad (8.8)$$

The molecular products, hydrogen and hydrogen peroxide,[1] will themselves react with the radicals, e.g.,

[1] There is evidence that hydrogen peroxide formed by the combination of two hydroxyl radicals is initially different from ordinary hydrogen peroxide, though it changes to the ordinary form by a relatively slow unimolecular reaction (the lifetime of the unstable form is probably about 10^{-2} sec in liquid water (12)). The evidence is primarily from gas-phase reactions in which hydroxyl radicals are believed to be intermediates (see for example the references cited by Dewhurst, Samuel, and Magee (12)); but it is interesting that Alexander and Rosen (13) have attributed different reactivities towards amino acids in aqueous solution to hydrogen peroxide formed by combination of hydroxyl radicals in α-particle tracks and ordinary hydrogen peroxide. It was suggested that the enhanced reactivity of the newly formed hydrogen peroxide is due to it being in the triplet excited state. However, this interpretation has been challenged by Swallow and Velandia (14) who maintain that in the absence of oxygen the greater decomposition produced by α-rays than

$$H\cdot + H_2O_2 \rightarrow \cdot OH + H_2O \tag{8.9}$$

$$\cdot OH + H_2 \rightarrow H\cdot + H_2O \tag{8.10}$$

and the final result of irradiation is to produce a very small equilibrium concentration of hydrogen and hydrogen peroxide or oxygen in the water vapor.

Firestone (15) has shown that in water vapor irradiated with tritium β-particles, deuterium is a very efficient scavenger for both hydrogen atoms and hydroxyl radicals. The reactions of the scavenger are

$$H\cdot + D_2 \rightarrow D\cdot + HD \tag{8.11}$$

$$\cdot OH + D_2 \rightarrow D\cdot + HOD \tag{8.12}$$

$$2D\cdot \rightarrow D_2 \quad \text{(at a surface or with a third body)} \tag{8.13}$$

Since the numbers of hydrogen atoms and hydroxyl radicals are equal and each is equal to the number of water molecules dissociated, the yield of HD gives the following G values for tritium β-particle irradiation (at temperatures less than 150°C):

$$G(\text{HD}) = G(-\text{D}_2) = G_{\text{H}} = G_{\text{OH}} = G_{-\text{H}_2\text{O}} = 11.7$$

The symbols[2] G_{H}, G_{H_2}, etc. will be used to denote the earliest detectable yields of hydrogen atoms, molecular hydrogen, etc., formed on irradiation; in liquid water these are the yields of the products as they emerge from the spurs or track and diffuse into the bulk of the liquid. The symbols $G(\text{HD})$, $G(H_2O_2)$, etc. still refer to the yields of products found experimentally after the chemical action is over. The value of $W_{\text{H}_2\text{O}}$ is not known but it is probably in the region of 30 ev so that each 100 ev of energy absorbed by water vapor will produce about 3.5 ion pairs. If reactions 8.1 to 8.4 are correct this number of ion pairs will produce about 5 radical pairs. That is, on the assumption that only ions give radicals, G_{H} and G_{OH} should each be about 5. This is well below the figure found by Firestone, even if additional radicals are formed via the ion-molecule reaction giving H_3O^+, and provides good evidence that

---

by x- or γ-rays is due to the production of oxygen and (or) hydrogen peroxide during α-irradiation, so that α-irradiation should in fact be compared with x- or γ-irradiation carried out in the presence of oxygen. If this explanation is accepted there is no need to postulate the production of activated hydrogen peroxide by α-particles.

[2] Several alternative symbols are, or have been, used. Dewhurst and Burton for example (16) employ a subscript W to denote primary chemical yields, e.g., $G_{\text{W}}(\text{H})(= G_{\text{H}})$ while Hart (17) uses a lower case g; e.g., $g(\text{H})$, $g(\text{H}_2)$, etc.

excited molecules as well as ions react in water vapor to give free radicals. The energy actually used in breaking HO—H bonds per 100 ev of energy absorbed is 5.0 × 11.7 ev [since D(HO—H) is 5.0 ev], or about 60 ev, so that the radiation-induced dissociation of water vapor is a relatively efficient process. It is several times more efficient than the same process in liquid water.

Liquid Water

In liquid water the ions and excited molecules will be formed closer together than in water vapor because of the greater density of the medium; the LET in the liquid is of the order of a thousand times greater than in the vapor. The greater density of the medium will also tend to restrict the primary species and the radicals derived from them to the particle tracks, where they will react among themselves to some extent before diffusion distributes them throughout the liquid. Factors which affect the distribution of the primary species in the tracks, such as the LET of the ionizing particles, will be significant in the liquid phase. Two further effects that may be significant in the liquid but not in the vapor are the possibility of solvation[3] of the ions, which may

[3] In aqueous solution ions will become *solvated* if they have a lifetime greater than about 10^{-11} sec. That is, the ion will orientate the surrounding water molecules so that the parts of the molecules which are oppositely charged to the ion are closest to it. A positive ion, for example, attracts the negative oxygen of the water molecules. The solvated (or hydrated) ion will therefore be surrounded by a shell of water molecules, possibly several molecules thick, held more or less loosely by the electrostatic attraction between the ion and the solvent dipoles. Solvation reduces the combined potential energy of the ion and its associated solvent molecules and energy is therefore released. The solvation energy in aqueous solutions is of the order of 1 ev per ion, which may be sufficient to supply the energy requirements of reactions which are endothermic in the gas phase, where solvation does not occur.

In aqueous systems, solvated ions are often distinguished by the subscript "aq," as in H_{aq}^+. However the subscript will only be used in this chapter when it is necessary to emphasize that the ions are solvated, since, apart from events following within 10^{-11} sec of radiation-induced ionization, the ions with which we will be concerned always will be solvated.

The hydrogen ion, H^+, can form a definite hydrate, H_3O^+, the oxonium ion. In aqueous solution (as opposed to the gas phase) and after sufficient time has elapsed for the ions to become solvated the symbols H^+ and H_3O^+ both represent the same thing, namely the solvated hydrogen ion, H_{aq}^+ (i.e., H^+, nH_2O). We will use both H^+ and H_3O^+ to represent the solvated hydrogen ion as proves convenient.

The solvated electron, with which we will be concerned later in this chapter, appears to be an exception to this simple picture of solvation, and is probably better represented as an electron spread over several water molecules.

affect their stability and reactions, and the shorter lifetime of excited states in the liquid medium. The existence of these effects means that the radiolysis of liquid water is rather more complicated than that of water vapor. Nevertheless, a fairly reliable guide to the reactions to be expected in irradiated aqueous solutions is to assume that the species formed from water upon irradiation are hydrogen atoms[4] and hydroxyl radicals (the *radical products*) and molecular hydrogen and hydrogen peroxide (the *molecular products*). Most of the observed chemical changes can be explained qualitatively by invoking only these four intermediates. Detailed quantitative studies under a variety of conditions often require a more sophisticated treatment, and the use of more elaborate models for the primary action of radiation on water. Two important models, the Samuel-Magee and the Lea-Gray-Platzman, are described below.

In liquid water, as in water vapor, ionizing radiation will produce excited and ionized species. Of these, the excited molecules formed directly (the primary excited molecules) are generally ignored, the assumption being that they either return to the ground state directly by a nonradiative process or else dissociate into H· and ·OH radicals which have little extra energy and, confined by a cage of water molecules, recombine without producing any over-all chemical change. Nevertheless, liquid water excited by ultraviolet light does dissociate with a high quantum yield [0.6 for 1850 Å light (18)], giving radicals which can be scavenged by quite low concentrations of inorganic and organic solutes (18, 19). However, although the assumption that the primary excited water molecules contribute little or nothing to the chemical change appears hardly justified, it is none the less true that the value of G_{-H_2O} in liquid water is only about a third of that for water vapor, so that it is quite possible to adequately explain the radiolysis of liquid water without including a contribution from excited molecules.

Excited water molecules may react to give part of the molecular product yield (12, 20), for example by

$$H_2O^* + H_2O^* \text{ (or } H_2O) \rightarrow H_2 + H_2O_2 \tag{8.14}$$

[4] Although in this chapter we have generally assumed that the reducing species formed in liquid water upon irradiation is the hydrogen atom, recent work has shown this assumption to be untrue. It has become apparent that in neutral solutions the major reducing species is the solvated electron, which in acid solutions can react with hydrogen ions to give hydrogen atoms. For simplicity, we have continued to treat the reducing species as the hydrogen atom under all conditions of pH. This is only justified because with most of the solutes to be considered solvated electrons and hydrogen atoms eventually give the same products. However it must be stressed that even where both species react with a solute to give equivalent products, the rates of their reactions with the solute will almost certainly be different.

and Dainton (21, 22) has suggested that reactions involving excited water molecules may enhance the radical yields in both acid and alkaline solution.

The ions formed in liquid water will presumably be the same as those found by mass spectrometry for the vapor. However, the fragment ions H^+ and OH^+ may be effectively caged by the solvent and recombine with $\cdot OH$ and $H\cdot$ respectively to give H_2O^+ before neutralization occurs (12), i.e.,

$$H_2O + e^- \begin{cases} \nearrow H^+ + \cdot OH + 2e^- : H^+ + \cdot OH \searrow \\ \searrow OH^+ + H\cdot + 2e^- : OH^+ + H\cdot \nearrow \end{cases} H_2O^+ \tag{8.15}$$

These rapid reactions would take place before the ions have time to become solvated. Alternatively, if H^+ and OH^+ react as such, H^+ (and H_3O^+) will probably react, if they react at all, with an electron to give a hydrogen atom, though the process may be delayed long enough for the ions to become solvated,[5]

$$H^+ \text{ (or } H_{aq}{}^+) + e^- \text{ (or } e_{aq}{}^-) \rightarrow H\cdot \tag{8.16}$$

The OH^+ ion may react with water as follows (23):

$$OH^+ + H_2O \rightarrow H^+ + 2\ \cdot OH \tag{8.17}$$

possibly via charge transfer, i.e.,

$$OH^+ + H_2O \rightarrow H_2O^+ + \cdot OH \tag{8.18}$$

and

$$H_2O^+ + H_2O \rightarrow H_3O^+ + \cdot OH \tag{8.19}$$

In general, however, positive ions other than H_2O^+ are ignored and the ionization process in liquid water is treated as simply

$$H_2O \rightsquigarrow H_2O^+ + e^- \tag{8.20}$$

The reactions following ionization are still the subject of discussion, and depend to a large degree on the distance traveled by the secondary electron. Samuel and Magee (24) calculated that a 10 ev electron will travel a distance of about 20 Å from the parent ion before being reduced to thermal energy (the process taking about 10^{-13} sec). At this distance the electron will still be within the electrostatic field of the positive ion and it will be drawn back to the ion and will neutralize it. The product

[5] Once solvated, H^+ and H_3O^+ will be identical with the hydrogen ions normally present in water.

of the neutralization is a (secondary) highly excited water molecule which will dissociate into a hydrogen atom and a hydroxyl radical,

$$H_2O^+ + e^- \rightarrow H_2O^{**} \rightarrow H\cdot + \cdot OH \tag{8.21}$$

The radicals will be formed with sufficient energy to escape from the solvent cage.

More recently, Lampe, Field, and Franklin (25) showed that the H_2O^+ ion can react very rapidly with a water molecule (the authors give the lifetime of H_2O^+ in liquid water as about 1.6×10^{-14} sec) and reaction 8.19 may precede neutralization:

$$H_2O^+ + H_2O \rightarrow H_3O^+ + \cdot OH \tag{8.19}$$

However, the over-all reaction is the same as is shown in Eq. 8.21 since neutralization of H_3O^+ gives a hydrogen atom,

$$H_3O^+ + e^- \rightarrow H\cdot + H_2O \tag{8.22}$$

(This differs from neutralization in the vapor phase (Eq. 8.2) since the neighboring molecules will probably rapidly remove part of the energy liberated.)

An alternative model for the primary reactions is due to Lea (26) and Gray (27) who estimated that during thermalization the secondary electron will move an average of about 150 Å from the parent positive ion. Under these circumstances the ion and the electron will react independently with the solvent,[6] the ion giving a hydroxyl radical (Eq. 8.19) near the site of the original ionization and the electron forming a hydrogen atom (Eq. 8.23) at some distance from the particle track,

$$e^- + H_2O \rightarrow H\cdot + OH^- \tag{8.23}$$

Both Magee and Burton (28) and Platzman (29) have pointed out that this reaction is endothermic and can only occur in liquid water where the solvation energy of the hydroxyl ion is available.

Platzman (29) also considered the process of energy loss by a secondary electron and concluded that a 10 ev electron in water would travel an average of at least 50 Å from the positive ion before being reduced to thermal energy. At this distance it would be essentially free of the electrostatic attraction of the parent ion. However, reaction of the thermal electron with water (Eq. 8.23) is relatively slow, requiring at

[6] This applies to electrons which originate as δ-rays even if the Samuel-Magee model is accepted, since these electrons must inevitably be widely separated from their positive ions. However, such electrons cannot represent more than a few percent of the total number produced by ionization.

least 10^{-11} sec, and Platzman concluded that the electron might not undergo this reaction but might survive in a solvated form, e_{aq}^-. The solvated electron reacting in a similar manner to a hydrogen atom.

Both the Samuel-Magee and the Lea-Gray-Platzman model lead to essentially the same products, hydrogen atoms (or some stoichiometrically equivalent species) and hydroxyl radicals, though the initial distribution of the radicals is not the same in the two cases. In the Samuel-Magee model the hydrogen atoms and hydroxyl radicals are formed in pairs close to the track of the ionizing particle (Fig. 8.1*a*; the track of the particle is perpendicular to the plane of the page), whereas, according to the Lea-Gray-Platzman scheme, the hydroxyl radicals will be formed close to the track while the hydrogen atoms will be dispersed around it at a rather greater distance (Fig. 8.1*b*). At the present time it seems that neither model is exclusively correct, and the actual situation appears to include features associated with both.[7]

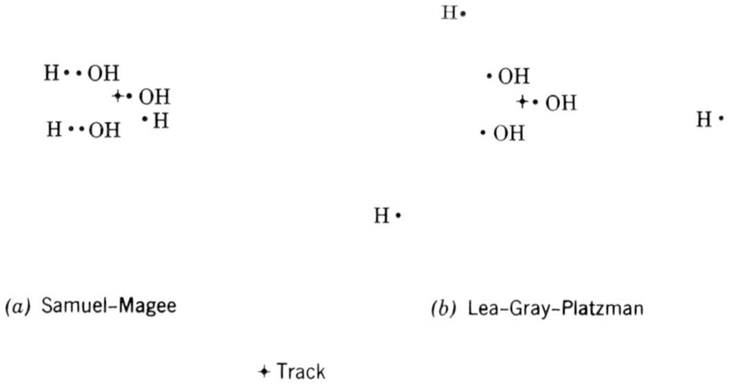

FIGURE 8.1 *Distribution of hydrogen atoms and hydroxyl radicals about the particle track according to the Samuel-Magee and the Lea-Gray-Platzman models (the track is perpendicular to the plane of the paper).*

Regardless of which model is accepted, the radicals will initially be distributed in or near spurs spaced along the track of the ionizing particle in a similar manner to the original ions and excited molecules (Figs. 3.13 and 3.14). When the ionizing particle is a fast electron the spurs initially have a diameter of about 20 Å and contain an average of 2.5 to 5 radical

[7] The models are not limited to water but are also applicable to other liquids. However, the Samuel-Magee model will be relatively more favored in liquids (e.g., organic liquids) (cf. 30) which have lower dielectric constants than water because of the greater extent of the electrostatic field associated with the positive ion. Furthermore, many solvents are unable to react with, or solvate, the free electron, as required if the Lea-Gray-Platzman model is to be feasible.

pairs; they are spaced along the track at relatively large intervals of the order of 5000 Å (24). For α-particles and other high-LET radiation the distance between spurs will only be of the order of 10 Å, and the expanding spurs will overlap from the moment of formation (24). The radicals will thus be concentrated initially in a cylinder of liquid whose axis is the particle track. Other radiations, for example, tritium β-particles, represent intermediate cases.

In the spurs or columnar track zone the initial radical concentration will be high and radical-radical reactions are to be expected. These will include

$$H\cdot + \cdot OH \rightarrow H_2O \tag{8.6}$$

$$2H\cdot \rightarrow H_2 \tag{8.7}$$

and

$$2\ \cdot OH \rightarrow H_2O_2 \tag{8.8}$$

An alternative to reaction 8.7 is

$$2\ e_{aq}^- \rightarrow H_2 + 2OH^- \tag{8.24}$$

(this reaction is apparently not hindered by the like charge on the two ions). The products of these reactions,[8] hydrogen and hydrogen peroxide, are the "molecular products" and their yields at this stage are given by G_{H_2} and $G_{H_2O_2}$. As the spurs or track expand by diffusion the probability of radical-radical reaction diminishes rapidly and some of the original radicals will escape combination and diffuse into the bulk of the liquid. These (H· and ·OH) constitute the "radical products" and their yield is given by G_H and G_{OH}. The relative number of radicals which combine to give the molecular products or escape combination giving the radical products depends on the LET of the radiation; radical-radical combination is most probable where the radical population is high, as in α-particle tracks, but is less favored when the radicals are more dispersed, as in the small isolated spurs characteristic of high-LET radiation. However, it must be remembered that even with high-LET radiation some of the energy will be lost via δ-rays, which will have a lower LET than the primary particle and will boost the yield of radical products. The increase in the yield of molecular products from low-LET radiation at very high

[8] It is possible that at least part of these "molecular products" are formed by some other mechanism, e.g., reactions 8.14 and 8.43. However, the molecular hydrogen yield can be markedly reduced by high concentrations of scavengers capable of reacting with hydrogen atoms (31), suggesting that the major part of the molecular product yield is in fact due to bimolecular radical combination (see also Fig. 8.5 and the related text).

dose rates (e.g., greater than 10^{10} rads/min) (32, 33, 34) is in accord with this picture. Under these circumstances, the number of spurs is so great that expanding spurs from different particles overlap and radicals from these spurs may combine.

An estimate of the upper limit for the radical concentration in irradiated water can be made if the rate constants for the reactions removing radicals and the rate of radical formation are known, and if it is assumed that the radicals are initially homogeneously distributed. The generally accepted rate constants for the reactions (8.6, 8.7, and 8.8) removing radicals assume that reaction occurs at each radical-radical encounter, and are of the order 10^9 to 10^{10} liter/mole sec (35). Taking the lower limit, 10^9 liter/mole sec, a G(radical) value of 10 for water, and the high dose rate of 10^5 rads/sec, the equilibrium radical concentration, $[R\cdot]$ mole/liter, is given by,

$$[R\cdot]^2 \times 10^9 \text{ (liter/mole sec)} = \text{rate of radical production}$$

i.e.,

$$[R\cdot]^2 \times 10^9 \frac{\text{(liter)}}{\text{(mole sec)}} = \frac{10}{100} \frac{\text{(radicals)}}{\text{(ev)}} \times \frac{1}{6.025 \times 10^{23}} \frac{\text{(mole)}}{\text{(molecule or radical)}} \times 10^5 \frac{\text{(rad)}}{\text{(sec)}} \times 6.24 \times 10^{13} \frac{\text{(ev)}}{\text{(g rad)}} \times 10^3 \frac{\text{(g)}}{\text{(liter)}}$$

and

$$[R\cdot] = 10^{-6} \text{ mole/liter} \tag{8.25}$$

In fact, the radicals are not homogeneously distributed, and normally, at lower dose rates and allowing for radical combination in spurs, the radical concentration outside the spurs will be several orders of magnitude lower than estimated here. Therefore, radicals are unlikely to react with one another outside the spurs if any other material with which they can react is present at a concentration greater than about 10^{-6} M, and radical combination in the bulk of the liquid is unlikely except with very carefully purified water. In contrast with the low radical concentration in the bulk of the solution, the initial radical concentration in an average spur containing about 10 radicals and having a radius of 10Å will be about 1 M.

Radical and molecular yields can be estimated experimentally by irradiating suitable aqueous solutions. The principles involved will be described later but a selection of the results is given in Table 8.2. For radiation of a given LET, dilute solutions, and a given pH, the radical and molecular yields are essentially constant, though increasing temperature results in slightly higher radical yields and slightly lower molecular yields (41). The quantity G_{-H_2O} represents water molecules converted to radical and molecular products and not the total number of water molecules originally dissociated, since the latter figure includes molecules which are subsequently reformed by combination of H· and ·OH radicals. The number of water molecules dissociated initially is given by the sum of G_{-H_2O}, G_{H_2}, and $G_{H_2O_2}$. When the solute is present in other than low concentrations, it may intervene in the reactions taking place in the spurs or track and the molecular product yields will be found to fall with increasing solute concentration.

TABLE 8.2 *Radical and Molecular Product Yields in Irradiated Aqueous Solutions*

Radiation	pH	G_{-H_2O}	G_{H_2}	$G_{H_2O_2}$	G_H	G_{OH}	G_{HO_2}	Ref.
γ-rays and fast electrons	7	3.64	0.42	0.71	2.80	2.22	0.02	36
	0.5	4.5	0.40	0.80	3.70	2.90		37
Tritium β-particles (average 5.5 kev)	1	4.1	0.6	1.0	2.9	2.1		38
Polonium α-particles (5.3 Mev)	0.5	3.62	1.57	1.45	0.60	0.50	0.11	39
$B^{10}(n,\alpha)Li^7$ recoil nuclei	0.5	3.55	1.65	1.55	0.25	0.45		40

The results tabulated in Table 8.2 show that to a first approximation G_{-H_2O} is independent of the type of radiation employed and, as expected, that the radical yields are greatest for low-LET radiation and the molecular yields greatest for high-LET radiation. Radical yields and G_{-H_2O} are significantly larger in acid solution than in neutral solution, an effect which has been attributed to the broader initial distribution of hydrogen atoms (or their equivalents) in acid solution (e.g., 42). It has been suggested that this wider distribution may be due to scavenging of the diffusing electrons or hydrogen atoms by hydrogen ions,

$$e^- + H^+ \rightarrow H\cdot \tag{8.26}$$

or

$$H\cdot + H^+ \rightarrow H_2^+ \tag{8.27}$$

An alternative explanation of the effect of acid, due to Dainton and Peterson (21), is described on page 263.

For practical purposes it is often convenient to express the G values given in Table 8.2 in the form

$$(2a + c \text{ or } 2b + d)\ H_2O \rightsquigarrow aH_2 + bH_2O_2 + cH\cdot + d\ \cdot OH \tag{8.28}$$

for a particular type of radiation under a given set of conditions. In earlier studies on water it was customary to express these yields as the yields of two, later three (43), reactions. These were

$$2H_2O \rightsquigarrow H_2 + H_2O_2 \qquad \text{(F, the "forward" reaction)} \tag{8.29}$$

$$H_2O \rightsquigarrow H\cdot + \cdot OH \qquad \text{(R, the "radical" reaction)} \tag{8.30}$$

and, to account for the difference between G_{H_2} and $G_{H_2O_2}$ and between G_H and G_{OH},

$$2H_2O \rightsquigarrow 2H\cdot + H_2O_2 \qquad \text{(E, the "excess" reaction)} \tag{8.31}$$

However, the expression given above (Eq. 8.28) is easier to use and is currently preferred.

The fate of the radical and molecular products in irradiated water depends on the substances present in solution with which they may react. In the absence of such substances and in a closed system (to retain the molecular hydrogen) the radicals will react with the hydrogen and hydrogen peroxide to reform water,

$$H\cdot + H_2O_2 \rightarrow \cdot OH + H_2O \tag{8.9}$$

$$\cdot OH + H_2 \rightarrow H\cdot + H_2O \tag{8.10}$$

Thus the net result of continuous irradiation is to set up a steady state in which the water contains an equilibrium concentration of hydrogen and hydrogen peroxide. The equilibrium concentrations depend on the yields of radical and molecular products. Low-LET radiation, where the radical yield is high and the molecular product yield low, produces a small equilibrium concentration of molecular products. γ-radiation, for example, produces very little change in pure deaerated water irradiated in a closed system. Higher LET radiation, on the other hand, will produce measurable equilibrium concentrations of hydrogen and hydrogen peroxide, and high-LET radiation, such as the recoil nuclei from the $B^{10}(n, \alpha)Li^7$ reaction, will decompose water continuously.

Irradiation of pure deaerated water in a system which is not closed (i.e., where the hydrogen can escape) leads to a build-up of hydrogen peroxide in the solution. This eventually reaches an equilibrium concentration when the rate of formation is balanced by the rate of decomposition by reaction 8.9 and by the sequence of reactions:

$$\cdot OH + H_2O_2 \rightarrow HO_2\cdot + H_2O \tag{8.32}$$

$$2HO_2\cdot \rightarrow H_2O_2 + O_2 \tag{8.33}$$

At this stage radiation effectively decomposes water to hydrogen and oxygen which escape from the system. This is of some practical importance since it represents the situation which exists in "boiling-water" nuclear reactors and in reactors moderated with heavy water. In both instances some allowance must be made for decomposition of the water.

The time scale for the various processes referred to above is given in Table 8.3, which is based on a similar table due to Dewhurst, Samuel and Magee (12, see also 44). In the table the time at which the various processes occur is the time after the passage of an ionizing particle. Though the table refers specifically to liquid water a very similar time scale of events will apply to other liquids. The table is divided into three stages: physical, physiochemical, and chemical, as suggested by Platzman (45) and Kuppermann (46), corresponding with the initial dissipation of energy in the system, the establishment of thermal equilibrium, and the diffusion and chemical reaction which leads to the establishment of chemical equilibrium, respectively. Reactions taking place during the physiochemical and chemical stages have been treated theoretically by the technique of diffusion kinetics, and theoretical results obtained with the aid of electronic computers are in good agreement with experiment, the more so as the radiolysis mechanisms that can be treated in this way become more complex (cf. 46).

Isotope Effect

Molecular and radical yields determined in D_2O differ slightly from those determined in H_2O (cf. 47). The radical yields and the yield of water decomposed are slightly larger for heavy water than for light water (Table 8.4).

The difference has been tentatively attributed to the longer dielectric relaxation time in D_2O than in H_2O which might allow the electron to diffuse further from the track, leading to a broader distribution of D atoms in D_2O than of H atoms in H_2O (49). Some support for this argument is drawn from the radiolysis of liquid ammonia (50). Liquid ammonia has a much smaller relaxation time and dielectric constant than liquid water and shows markedly less radiation decomposition, which is consistent with the return of more secondary electrons to the parent ion and, consequently, more uniform radical distribution and more radical recombination (to reform ammonia) than in water.

TABLE 8.3 *Approximate Time Scale for the Radiolysis of Liquid Water*

	Time (sec)	Events	Reactions	Species present
↑	10^{-18}	Electron with energy in the Mev range traverses a distance of the order of a molecular diameter.		H_2O^+
Physical stage	10^{-17}	α-particle with energy in the Mev range traverses a molecule.		e^-
(Interaction of the primary radiation with the water.)	10^{-16}		$H_2O \rightsquigarrow H_2O^+ + e^-$	H_2O^*
	10^{-15}	Thermal electron (0.025 ev) traverses a molecule. Time between successive ionizations by a Mev energy electron. Time for "vertical" excitation to an electronic excited state.	$H_2O \rightsquigarrow H_2O^*$	(localized in spurs or track zone)
↓↑	10^{-14}	Ion-molecule reactions. Period of molecular vibration. Dissociation of molecules excited to repulsive states.	$H_2O^+ + H_2O \rightarrow H_3O^+ + \cdot OH$ $H_2O^* \rightarrow H\cdot + \cdot OH$ (?; in solvent cage and followed by back reaction?)	$\cdot OH$
Physiochemical stage	10^{-13}	Secondary electrons reduced to thermal energy by this time. Electron capture (Samuel-Magee model). Internal conversion from higher to lowest electronically excited state.	$H_3O^+ + e^- \rightarrow H\cdot + H_2O$	$H\cdot$
(Energy transfer, dissociation, ion-molecule reactions.)	10^{-12}	Radical moves one jump in diffusion.		
	10^{-11}	Relaxation time for the dipole orientation of water.	$e^- \rightarrow e_{aq}^-$ (Platzman) $e^- + H_2O \rightarrow H\cdot + OH_{aq}^-$ (Lea-Gray model)	$H\cdot$ $\cdot OH$ e_{aq}^- H_2O^*(?)

Stage	Time (sec)	Event	Reactions / Species
	10^{-10}	Minimum time for diffusion controlled reactions in the bulk of the liquid.	$H\cdot + \cdot OH \rightarrow H_2O$ $2\cdot OH \rightarrow H_2O_2$ $2H\cdot \rightarrow H_2$ $2e_{aq}^- \rightarrow H_2 + 2OH^-$
	10^{-9}		
	10^{-8}	Radiative lifetime of singlet excited states. Formation of molecular products complete in γ-ray spur.	(in or near spurs and track) $H\cdot$ $\cdot OH$ e_{aq}^- H_2O^*(?) H_2 H_2O_2
	10^{-7}	Formation of molecular products complete in α-particle track.	($\cdot OH + H_2O_2 \rightarrow HO_2\cdot + H_2O$ in tracks of high-LET particles)
	10^{-6}		
Chemical stage (Radical-radical reactions in spurs and track zone followed by diffusion of the radicals and molecular products into the bulk of the liquid.	10^{-5}	Reaction time for radical with solute in molar concentration (5 kcal/mole activation energy).	
Reaction of solute with radicals which are essentially homogeneously distributed in the liquid.)	10^{-4}	Time required for a radical to diffuse the interspur distance in track of Mev energy electron.	
	10^{-3}	Radiative lifetime of triplet excited state.	
	0	Chemical reaction complete.	H_2, H_2O_2, and products of radical reactions with solute.

TABLE 8.4 *Molecular and Radical Yields in Acidified H_2O and D_2O* (ref. 48)

(220 kvp x-rays, 0.8*N* H_2SO_4, 20.5°C)

Product	H_2O	D_2O
G_{-H_2O}	4.46	4.61
G_{H_2}	0.46	0.38
$G_{H_2O_2}$	0.80	0.77
G_H	3.50	3.88
G_{OH}	2.90	3.04
$G(Fe^{3+})_{air}$	15.1	16.2

Oxygenated Water

Oxygen is a very efficient scavenger for hydrogen atoms, combining with them to give the perhydroxyl radical, $HO_2\cdot$,

$$H\cdot + O_2 \rightarrow HO_2\cdot \tag{8.34}$$

This reaction almost invariably occurs in irradiated aqueous solutions if dissolved oxygen has not been carefully removed, although solutes which react very readily with hydrogen atoms can compete with the oxygen so that only a fraction of the hydrogen atoms is converted to perhydroxyl radicals.[9]

The $HO_2\cdot$ radical is not as reactive as the hydrogen atom and, unlike the latter, rarely abstracts hydrogen from organic solutes. It is, however, a strong oxidizing agent and reacts with hydroxyl radicals (which are themselves oxidizing agents) and other $HO_2\cdot$ radicals to give oxygen,

$$HO_2\cdot + \cdot OH \rightarrow O_2 + H_2O \tag{8.35}$$

$$HO_2\cdot + HO_2\cdot \rightarrow O_2 + H_2O_2 \tag{8.33}$$

The yield of hydrogen peroxide in irradiated water is increased when oxygen is present because of reaction 8.33 and because removal of hydrogen atoms by reaction 8.34 prevents the back reaction 8.9.

$$H\cdot + H_2O_2 \rightarrow \cdot OH + H_2O \tag{8.9}$$

The perhydroxyl radical can also be formed by reaction of a hydroxyl radical with hydrogen peroxide,

$$\cdot OH + H_2O_2 \rightarrow HO_2\cdot + H_2O \tag{8.32}$$

[9] Ferradini (51) has estimated the percentage of hydrogen atoms which react with oxygen in various air-saturated solutions containing solutes which readily capture hydrogen atoms.

and it has been suggested that this may occur to some extent in the spurs and track zones where hydrogen peroxide is formed as a molecular product (52, 53). When it is formed under these circumstances, the $HO_2\cdot$ radical can be considered as a primary radical product and as such it is included in Table 8.2. However, the yields of $HO_2\cdot$ are small even in α-particle tracks, where its formation is favored, and very little can be produced by low-LET radiations.

The Reducing Radical

While most of the chemical reactions occurring in irradiated aqueous solutions can be explained superficially by assuming hydrogen atoms and hydroxyl radicals to be the primary reactive species, more detailed analysis of the reactions has led to considerable reservation about the part played by hydrogen atoms as such, and it now appears that in neutral and alkaline solutions (pH > 3) the solvated electron[10] is the major reducing species. A smaller number of hydrogen atoms are probably formed concurrently with the solvated electrons, although this is not certain. Other hydrogen atoms may be formed slowly by the reaction described earlier

$$e_{aq}^- + H_2O \rightarrow H\cdot + OH^- \tag{8.23}$$

though only in the absence of solutes which can react with solvated electrons. In acid solutions, the solvated electrons may be converted to hydrogen atoms by reaction with hydrogen ions

$$e_{aq}^- + H^+ \rightarrow H\cdot \tag{8.16}$$

This reaction is much faster than the previous reaction (8.23), but here again some solutes which react very rapidly with solvated electrons can compete successfully for them, in this case with the hydrogen ions. In many cases both solvated electrons and hydrogen atoms lead to the same final products and, with a few exceptions, we have continued to treat the reducing species as the hydrogen atom under all conditions of pH in the remainder of this chapter. However, it should be emphasized that although the ultimate products may be the same, the rates at which hydrogen atoms and solvated electrons react with a particular solute may be very different. A brief survey is included here of experiments concerned with the nature of the reducing radical.

[10] We have generally used the symbol e_{aq}^- to represent the solvated electron, but H_2O^-, or $(H_2O)^-$, may be preferred as more convenient when balancing chemical equations. Each represents an electron "smeared" over a group of several water molecules.

In 1959, Barr and Allen (54) showed that the hydrogen atom (H′ atom) formed in the radiolysis of neutral aqueous solutions containing hydrogen, oxygen, and hydrogen peroxide by oxidation of hydrogen

$$\cdot OH + H_2 \rightarrow H' + H_2O \tag{8.10}$$

reacts with oxygen much faster than with hydrogen peroxide, whereas in solutions containing only oxygen and hydrogen peroxide, the hydrogen atom formed from water by radiolysis reacts with oxygen and hydrogen peroxide at comparable rates. They concluded that the two types of hydrogen atom were in fact different, and that one was probably atomic hydrogen (H·) and the other a basic or an acidic form of the hydrogen atom, i.e., the solvated electron or the ion H_2^+, respectively. Allen and Schwarz (36) represented the relationship between these species as

$$e_{aq}^- \overset{H^+}{\rightleftharpoons} H\cdot \overset{H^+}{\rightleftharpoons} H_2^+ \tag{8.36}$$

Other work, which is described in part below, indicates that H′ is atomic hydrogen and the species formed in irradiated neutral solutions the solvated electron, so that the fast radiation-induced reduction of hydrogen peroxide in neutral solution is

$$e_{aq}^- + H_2O_2 \rightarrow \cdot OH + OH^- \tag{8.37}$$

and the equally fast reaction of the reducing entity with oxygen

$$e_{aq}^- + O_2 \rightarrow O_2^- \tag{8.38}$$

Atomic hydrogen, formed by reaction 8.10, reacts rapidly with oxygen to give the radical $HO_2\cdot$ but reacts more slowly with hydrogen peroxide

$$H\cdot + H_2O_2 \rightarrow \cdot OH + H_2O \tag{8.9}$$

Evidence for the existence of two reducing entities in irradiated aqueous solutions comes largely from determinations of absolute and relative rate constants for reactions of the reducing species. Often the results obtained in acid solution differ from those obtained in neutral solution. Anderson and Hart (55), for example, concluded that the reducing radical reacts with oxygen and hydrogen peroxide about five times faster in neutral solution than in acid solution, indicating that the reducing species is not the same in the two instances. In some cases (56) the reaction of the reducing species in an irradiated solution has been compared directly with the reaction of hydrogen atoms produced externally in a discharge and introduced into the solution.

Where this has been done, it has been found that the rate constants for the hydrogen atom reactions agree well with the rate constants for reactions of the acid form of the reducing species present in irradiated solutions, suggesting strongly that this is in fact the hydrogen atom. If this is so, the reducing species present in neutral irradiated solutions will be the solvated electron. Where the chemical reactions taking place in irradiated acid and neutral solutions are different, the chemical evidence is consistent with this assignment. Thus in irradiated solutions of chloroacetic acid, hydrogen is a major product from acid solutions but is largely replaced by chloride ion with neutral solutions (57), as seems reasonable if the reducing species present are mainly hydrogen atoms and solvated electrons respectively and the reactions taking place are

$$H\cdot + ClCH_2COOH \rightarrow H_2 + Cl\dot{C}HCOOH \qquad (8.39)$$

and

$$e_{aq}^- + ClCH_2COOH \rightarrow Cl^- + \cdot CH_2COOH \qquad (8.40)$$

Jortner and Rabani (58) have indeed shown that hydrogen atoms produced externally and passed into a neutral chloroacetate solution mainly abstract hydrogen. With aqueous solutions of isopropanol also, the yield of hydrogen falls as the pH of the solution is increased (59), consistent with hydrogen abstraction from the alcohol by hydrogen atoms, where these are present, with solvated electrons taking part in an alternative reaction which does not yield molecular hydrogen. The observation that solvated electrons do not abstract hydrogen represents one of the more important chemical differences in the behavior of solvated electrons and hydrogen atoms, since it has a bearing on the radiolysis of all organic materials containing hydrogen when these are irradiated in deaerated aqueous solution at a pH greater than about 3. Solvated electrons also appear to be stronger reducing agents than hydrogen atoms, reducing, for example, Pb^{2+}, Cd^{2+}, Ni^{2+}, and Cr^{3+} (60). One point must be borne in mind, however; if the solvated electrons do not react with a solute they will eventually give hydrogen atoms (Eq. 8.23), and the products expected of hydrogen atom reaction will be observed.

The strongest evidence that the reducing species in neutral solutions is the solvated electron comes from relative reaction rate determinations made in the presence of chemically inert salts (61, 62). The method depends on the fact that rate constants for reactions between ions of similar charge increase with increasing ionic strength, while rate constants for reactions between ions of opposite charge decrease, and rate constants for reactions between ions and neutral molecules are relatively unaffected. Czapski and Schwarz (61) studied the ratio of the rate constant for the reaction of the reducing radical with H^+, O_2, and NO_2^- to the rate constant for the reaction with hydrogen peroxide as a function of ionic strength. The reactions are, assuming that the reducing species is the solvated electron in the near neutral solutions used, and neglecting water, which is also a product of the reactions,

$$e_{aq}^- + H^+ \xrightarrow{k_1} H\cdot \tag{8.16}$$

$$e_{aq}^- + O_2 \xrightarrow{k_2} O_2^- \tag{8.38}$$

$$e_{aq}^- + NO_2^- \xrightarrow{k_3} NO_2^{2-} \tag{8.41}$$

$$e_{aq}^- + H_2O_2 \xrightarrow{k_4} \cdot OH + OH^- \tag{8.37}$$

and it was found that the ratio k_2/k_4 was unaffected by ionic strength, while k_1/k_4 decreased and k_3/k_4 increased with increasing ionic strength. The results therefore demonstrate that the reducing radical in neutral and slightly acid solutions has a negative charge and, from the slope of the ionic strength curves, it was shown that the charge is minus one. In a similar manner, Collinson and Dainton and their colleagues (62) studied the effect of ionic strength on the relative rate of the reactions between the reducing species and Ag^+ and acrylamide, and concluded that at pH 4 the reducing species has a unit negative charge, while at pH 2 it is uncharged.[11]

Estimates of the relative numbers of hydrogen atoms and solvated electrons present in irradiated solutions can be made by using solutes which scavenge one or other of the two species. Rabani and Stein (64), for example, have used a variety of scavengers including mixtures of acetone and isopropanol, ferricyanide and formate, and bicarbonate and methanol, where the first component scavenges solvated electrons and the second hydrogen atoms. Baxendale, Thomas, and Woodward (65) used oxygen and (or) hydrogen peroxide to measure the total yield of reducing species, and acetic acid to determine hydrogen atoms (from the yield of hydrogen). A selection of results are collected in Table 8.5 and, as far as they go, show the expected dependence on pH, i.e., that hydrogen atoms predominate in acid solutions (below about pH 2) and solvated electrons in neutral and alkaline solutions. The relative amounts of the two species produced by irradiation of neutral solutions is open to some doubt. Several groups, using both organic (57, 59, 64, 67, 68) and inorganic (60) scavengers, find G_H to be about 0.5 to 0.6, whereas groups studying the radiolysis of the oxygenated hydrogen peroxide

[11] Similar experiments intended to establish the charge, if any, on the oxidizing radical produced in water radiolysis showed this to be uncharged (63), supporting the general conclusion that this is the $\cdot OH$ radical.

system (57, 66) conclude that there are essentially no hydrogen atoms formed in neutral solution. A possible explanation of these divergent results has been put forward by Hayon (69), who suggests that in de-aerated solutions about 20% of the reducing radicals are hydrogen atoms formed by

$$H_2O^* \rightarrow H\cdot + \cdot OH \qquad (8.5)$$

but that when oxygen is present it quenches the excited water molecules, leading to electron transfer

$$H_2O^* + O_2 \rightarrow H_2O^+ + O_2^- \qquad (8.42)$$

TABLE 8.5 *Variation with pH of the Radical and Molecular Product Yields in X- and γ-Ray Irradiated Water*

<table>
<tr><th>pH</th><th>G_{H_2}</th><th>$G_{H_2O_2}$</th><th>G_H</th><th>$G_{e_{aq}^-}$</th><th>G_{OH}</th><th>Ref.</th></tr>
<tr><td>0.5</td><td>0.40</td><td>0.80</td><td colspan="2">3.70</td><td>2.90</td><td>37</td></tr>
<tr><td>2 to 4</td><td>0.5</td><td></td><td>0.55</td><td>2.65</td><td></td><td>64</td></tr>
<tr><td>5</td><td>0.55</td><td>0.8</td><td>1.9</td><td>0.9</td><td>2.2</td><td>65</td></tr>
<tr><td>7</td><td>0.42</td><td>0.71</td><td colspan="2">2.80</td><td>2.22</td><td>36</td></tr>
<tr><td></td><td></td><td></td><td>0.6</td><td>2.3</td><td></td><td>59</td></tr>
<tr><td></td><td></td><td></td><td>0</td><td>2.85</td><td></td><td>66</td></tr>
<tr><td>8</td><td>0.6</td><td>0.65</td><td>0.9</td><td>1.7</td><td>2.5</td><td>65</td></tr>
<tr><td>13</td><td>0.7</td><td>0</td><td>0.15</td><td>2.5</td><td>4.1</td><td>65</td></tr>
<tr><td></td><td>0.45</td><td>0.6</td><td colspan="2">3.5</td><td>3.2</td><td>21, 22</td></tr>
</table>

The O_2^- ion is equivalent to $e_{aq}^- + O_2$, so the over-all result is that in the absence of oxygen both solvated electrons and hydrogen atoms are observed, but when oxygen is present only solvated electrons and the product formed from them (O_2^-) are seen. Hayon has also concluded, from an examination of the effect of scavenger concentration upon the molecular yield of hydrogen, that molecular hydrogen is produced by two mechanisms, the greater part resulting from combination of solvated electrons (Eq. 8.24), but about 25% resulting from the combination of hydrogen atoms (Eq. 8.7) which are produced in this form in the spurs where combination occurs (70). This again supports the contention that both solvated electrons and hydrogen atoms are primary chemical products in irradiated water.

Additional evidence for the existence of hydrogen atoms in irradiated neutral solutions has been obtained by Lifshitz (71), who measured the isotopic composition of hydrogen evolved from irradiated solutions of formate in mixtures of light and heavy water. The isotopic composition of the "molecular" hydrogen and that formed by hydrogen abstraction by hydrogen atoms is different, and Lifshitz showed that the latter reaction did contribute to the total hydrogen yield to an extent corresponding to a G_H of about 0.6. The experiments also indicated that the hydrogen atoms were formed by a process involving more than one water molecule, i.e., reaction 8.16 rather than reaction 8.5.

Weiss (72) has suggested that both the solvated electron, which by analogy with the behavior of electrons in ionic crystals he calls a "polaron" with the symbol $(H_2O)^-$, and the solvated positive ion (cf. footnote 11), the positive polaron $(H_2O)^+$, have a sufficiently long lifetime in liquid water (at least 10^{-11} to 10^{-10} sec) to enter into chemical reactions with dissolved substances if the concentration of the solute is sufficiently high and the relevant activation energies are sufficiently low. The solvated electron, or negative polaron, reacts as already described. The positive polaron, it is suggested, may dimerize to hydrogen peroxide, like the hydroxyl radical,

$$2(H_2O)^+ \rightarrow H_2O_2 + 2H^+ \tag{8.43}$$

or react with solutes, e.g. (73),

$$(H_2O)^+ + CH_3COOH \rightarrow CH_3COO\cdot + H^+ + H_2O \tag{8.44}$$

In the absence of other reaction, the positive polaron eventually dissociates to give a hydroxyl radical.

Quite recently, Hart and Boag (74) have observed in deaerated water irradiated with a high intensity electron pulse a broad transient absorption band near 7000 Å which they attribute to the solvated electron. The absorption spectrum is similar to that of the solvated electron in liquid ammonia, which is well established, and is reduced in intensity by small concentrations of electron scavengers such as oxygen, carbon dioxide, and nitrous oxide. The absorption band was observed with irradiated neutral and alkaline solutions but was weak, if present at all, with acid solutions. Hart and his colleagues (75) have also followed the decay of the absorption band (actually at 5780 Å) when a number of solutes were present, and thereby determined rate constants for a number of reactions of the solvated electron. Some of their results are given in Table 8.6 together with rate constants for the corresponding reactions of hydrogen atoms.

pH Effects

The preceding sections have shown that pH may markedly influence the reactions occurring in irradiated water. This is true to an even

TABLE 8.6 *Rate Constants for Solvated Electron and Hydrogen Atom Reactions*

(References are given in parentheses)

Reaction	Rate Constant (liter/mole sec)	
	R = e_{aq}^- (ref. 75) (21–23°C)	R = H·*
R + e_{aq}^-	approx. 10^{10}	
R + H·		6×10^9 (35)
R + H^+	2.36×10^{10}	2.6×10^3 (76)
R + H_2O	less than 4×10^4 sec^{-1}	
R + O_2	1.88×10^{10}	10^9 (77)
R + H_2O_2	1.23×10^{10}	6×10^8 (55)
R + Cu^{2+}	3.3×10^{10}	10^8 (77)

* The rate constants shown for hydrogen atom reactions represent an arbitrary selection from the literature, which should be consulted for a full discussion of their reliability.

greater extent in the case of irradiated aqueous solutions. In some solutions pH will determine the structure of the solute, but in all solutions changes in pH may alter the nature and reactivity of the primary radicals. Some of these changes have been mentioned already but for convenience all the pH-dependent reactions of the primary radicals with which we will be concerned are collected here. Those already mentioned are:

(i) Conversion of a solvated electron to a hydrogen atom in acid solutions,

$$e_{aq}^- + H^+ \rightleftharpoons H\cdot \tag{8.45}$$

(ii) The relatively slow (56,76) association of a hydrogen atom and a hydrogen ion in acid solutions (78, 79),

$$H_2^+ \rightleftharpoons H\cdot + H^+ \quad (pK_a \nless 2.7) \tag{8.27}$$

Other pH-dependent equilibria are:

(iii) Dissociation of the hydroxyl radical in alkaline solutions (80),

$$\cdot OH \rightleftharpoons H^+ + O^- \quad (pK_a \text{ about } 10) \tag{8.46}$$

(iv) Dissociation of the perhydroxyl radical in neutral or alkaline solutions (81),

$$HO_2\cdot \rightleftharpoons H^+ + O_2^- \quad (pK_a \text{ probably } 2) \tag{8.47}$$

The O_2^- ion formed by this reaction can act as a reducing agent (82), e.g.,

$$Fe^{3+} + O_2^- \rightarrow Fe^{2+} + O_2 \tag{8.48}$$

(v) Conversion of a hydrogen atom to a solvated electron in alkaline solutions,

$$H\cdot + OH^- \rightleftharpoons e_{aq}^- \tag{8.49}$$

This reaction is implied by the equilibrium between solvated electrons and hydrogen atoms shown in equation 8.36. Experimental evidence in support of it has been provided by Jortner and Rabani (58), who generated atomic hydrogen in the gas phase by means of a high frequency electrodeless discharge and passed the gas into aqueous solutions of monochloroacetic acid. In neutral or near neutral solutions (pH 4 to 10) the main reaction is hydrogen abstraction by hydrogen atoms,

$$H\cdot + ClCH_2COO^- \rightarrow H_2 + Cl\dot{C}HCOO^- \tag{8.39}$$

but in alkaline solutions (pH above 11) chloride ion is the major product. The production of chloride can be accounted for by the formation of solvated electrons (Eq. 8.47) and their reaction (cf. 83),

$$e_{aq}^- + ClCH_2COO^- \rightarrow Cl^- + \cdot CH_2COO^- \tag{8.40}$$

At low chloroacetate concentrations ($0.01M$) and a pH of about 12.5, practically all the hydrogen atoms react as solvated electrons, though at higher concentrations less chloride is formed and competition apparently occurs between reactions 8.49 and 8.39.

Evidence has also been obtained that the conversion of hydrogen atoms to solvated electrons is significant when alkaline aqueous solutions are irradiated. Thus Allan, Robinson, and Scholes (84) irradiated aqueous solutions of organic alcohols (RH; 10^{-1} or $10^{-2}M$) in the presence of hydroxyl ion (10^{-6} to $10^{-1}M$) and acetone ($10^{-4}M$), which scavenges solvated electrons without producing molecular hydrogen, and showed that the yield of hydrogen falls as the proportion of hydroxyl ion to alcohol is increased. This observation is readily explained if hydroxyl ions and alcohol compete for hydrogen atoms

$$H\cdot + OH^- \rightarrow e_{aq}^- \tag{8.49}$$

$$H\cdot + RH \rightarrow H_2 + R\cdot \tag{8.50}$$

since the solvated electrons produced react with the acetone and do not form any hydrogen. The experiment also offers some support for the belief that both solvated electrons and hydrogen atoms are produced initially in irradiated neutral and alkaline solutions.

(vi) At pH below about 3 and above about 11, the yields of reducing and hydroxyl radicals increase without any corresponding decrease in the yields of molecular hydrogen and hydrogen peroxide (Fig. 8.2). Dainton and Peterson (21) have interpreted the increase in radical yield in acid solutions as due to attack upon the acid by an intermediate that would otherwise revert to water. The latter reaction is first order with respect to the concentration of the intermediate, suggesting that the intermediate is either an excited water molecule, possibly in a triplet state, or an isolated radical pair ($H\cdot + \cdot OH$) trapped in a solvent cage, so that the reaction with acid is either

$$H_2O^* + H^+ \rightarrow H_2^+ + \cdot OH \tag{8.51}$$

or

$$(H\cdot + \cdot OH) + H^+ \rightarrow H_2^+ + \cdot OH \tag{8.52}$$

Similar reactions of the intermediate with hydroxyl ions are postulated by Dainton and Watt (22) to account for the increase in radical yield at high pH

$$H_2O^* + OH^- \rightarrow e_{aq}^- + \cdot OH \tag{8.53}$$

or

$$(H\cdot + \cdot OH) + OH^- \rightarrow e_{aq}^- + \cdot OH \tag{8.54}$$

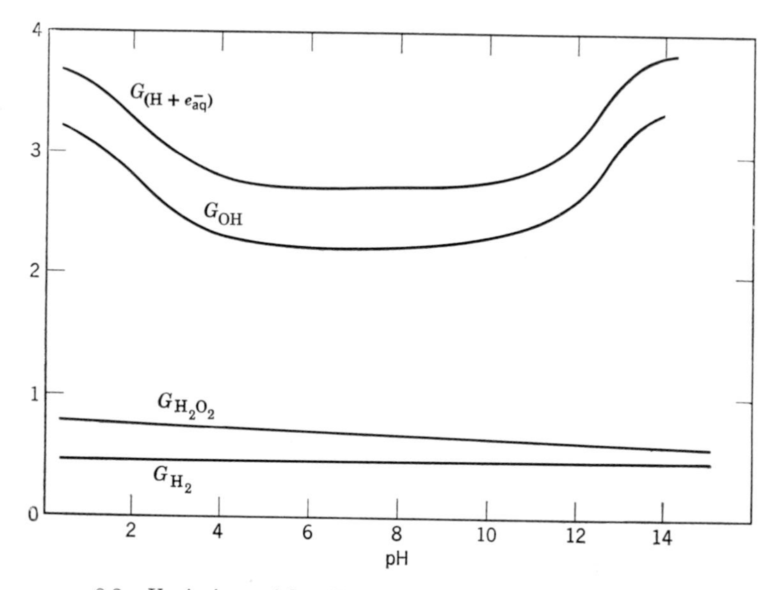

FIGURE 8.2 *Variation with pH of primary yields in γ-irradiated water (ref. 22).*

Solutes may also react with the intermediate, competing with the reactions shown in solutions of low and high pH respectively, though in many cases the result will be to convert the intermediate to water. With oxygen, for example, the reaction sequence might be

$$H_2O^* \text{ or } (H\cdot + \cdot OH) + O_2 \rightarrow (HO_2\cdot + \cdot OH) \quad (8.55)$$

$$(HO_2\cdot + \cdot OH) \rightarrow H_2O + O_2 \quad (8.56)$$

Effectively, therefore, the solute quenches the excited molecule or catalyzes the conversion of the radical pair to water.

Ice

The ions and free radicals produced in water by irradiation have such short lifetimes that they cannot be observed directly. However, in ice at low temperatures some of these species do reach concentrations high enough to make physical observation possible.

The primary effects of radiation on ice are probably similar to those produced in liquid water, though the rigid structure of the solid will affect subsequent chemical reactions. The efficiency with which water is decomposed for example is considerably lower in the solid state, and it falls as the temperature during irradiation is made lower. Thus G_{-H_2O} falls from 4.5 in neutral water at 20°C to 3.4 in ice at −10°C, 1.0 at −78°C, and 0.5 at −200°C (42, 85).

Radicals trapped in irradiated ice can be detected and identified by means of their electron paramagnetic resonance (e.p.r.) spectra. Additional information can often be obtained by following the spectrum as the frozen sample gradually warms up. For example, irradiation of pure ice at −269°C produces hydrogen atoms which are stable at this temperature and can be identified by their e.p.r. spectrum. As the temperature is raised the hydrogen atoms begin to disappear and are completely gone at −196°C (86). However, pure ice irradiated at −196°C (liquid nitrogen temperature) does show absorption characteristic for the hydroxyl radical (e.g., Fig. 8.3) which in turn disappears in the temperature range −170°C to −140°C (87) (an optical absorption peak at 2800 Å disappears in the same temperature range). Hydrogen atoms are stable in ice containing sulfuric, phosphoric, or perchloric acid up to about −180°C (88). The stabilization depends upon the structure of the acid and is not found with all acids; hydrochloric acid, for instance, is not effective. The rate at which hydrogen atoms disappear from the frozen acid solutions has been measured and shown to be second order with respect to the atoms, suggesting that they combine to form molecular hydrogen (88). Hydrogen peroxide has also been identified in melted irradiated ice.

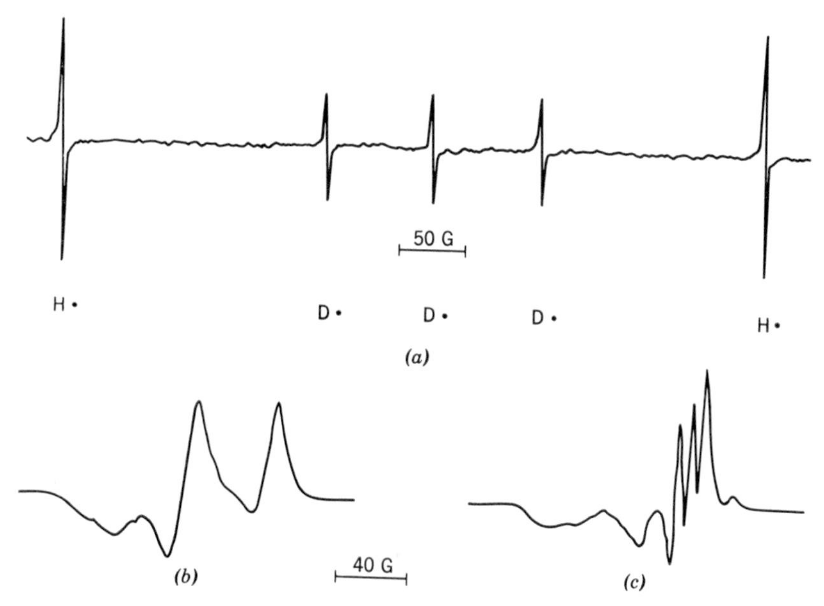

FIGURE 8.3 *Electron paramagnetic resonance spectrum of ice irradiated with tritium β-particles at −196°C (87). (a) acid H_2O-D_2O ice, H· doublet and D· triplet, (b) H_2O ice, ·OH doublet, (c) D_2O ice, ·OD triplet.*

Radiation-induced chemical reactions can take place in frozen solutions. Ghormley and Stewart (85) showed that hydrogen peroxide can be decomposed when ice containing dissolved hydrogen and hydrogen peroxide is irradiated at low temperatures. The amount of decomposition is increased when the irradiation is carried out at temperatures at which the hydroxyl radical is believed to be mobile (i.e., above about −50°C). Under these conditions both H· and ·OH are able to diffuse through the solid and the mechanism is probably similar to that occurring in the liquid phase.

Irradiated ice also exhibits fluorescence and thermoluminescence, both of which are influenced by substances present in solution (89).

AQUEOUS SOLUTIONS

In the following pages a rather arbitrary selection of inorganic and organic systems are described which, it is felt, will illustrate the main features of the reactions induced by radiation in dilute aqueous solutions. Very often the initial products from these reactions will themselves react with the primary radicals, particularly if the irradiation is prolonged. This experimental complication has been ignored in the following account.

When dilute aqueous solutions are irradiated practically all the energy absorbed is deposited in water molecules and the observed chemical changes are brought about *indirectly* via the molecular and, particularly, the radical products. *Direct* action due to energy deposited directly in the solute is generally unimportant in dilute solutions (i.e., at solute concentrations below about $0.1M$). At higher solute concentrations direct action may be significant (cf. 90), and there is some evidence that excited water molecules may transfer energy directly to the solute (91, 92).

Solutes which Alter the Proportions of Radical Products

These substances will not be dealt with fully but deserve mention since, under favorable circumstances, they offer the possibility of increasing the number of either hydrogen atoms or hydroxyl radicals reacting with the solute.

Chemical effects due to hydroxyl radicals may be enhanced by the addition of hydrogen peroxide, which acts as a scavenger for hydrogen atoms (and solvated electrons) and at the same time produces more hydroxyl radicals (93).

$$H\cdot + H_2O_2 \rightarrow \cdot OH + H_2O \tag{8.9}$$

An alternative scavenger for solvated electrons is nitrous oxide (21, 94, 95)

$$e_{aq}^- + N_2O \rightarrow (N_2O^-) \rightarrow O^- + N_2 \tag{8.57}$$

(the ion O^- may react as such, particularly at high pH, or react with H^+ or H_2O to give an $\cdot OH$ radical).

The reverse process, an increase in the number of hydrogen atoms at the expense of hydroxyl radicals, is accomplished by the presence of hydrogen,[12]

$$\cdot OH + H_2 \rightarrow H\cdot + H_2O \tag{8.10}$$

or carbon monoxide,

$$\cdot OH + CO \rightarrow H\cdot + CO_2 \tag{8.58}$$

The reaction with carbon monoxide is about 17 times faster than that with hydrogen (96).

[12] Dainton and Peterson (21) find that the "hydrogen atom" formed in reaction 8.10 can apparently react rapidly with nitrous oxide, suggesting that it may be a solvated electron rather than a hydrogen atom.

Halide Ions

Halide ions can enter into rapid electron transfer reactions with hydroxyl radicals, e.g.,

$$\cdot OH + Cl^- \rightarrow Cl\cdot + OH^- \tag{8.59}$$

The reaction is facilitated by the presence of acid (97), in the case of chloride ions at least, and can then be written

$$\cdot OH + Cl^- + H^+ \rightarrow Cl\cdot + H_2O \tag{8.60}$$

This particular reaction is of practical interest since it is responsible for the decreased sensitivity towards organic impurities of the Fricke (ferrous sulfate) dosimeter in the presence of sodium chloride.

Bromide and iodide ions are even more readily oxidized by hydroxyl radicals than are chloride ions. When present in low concentrations (10^{-6} to $10^{-2}M$) in acid or neutral deaerated water, bromide, and iodide ions enable the molecular yield of hydrogen to be measured directly (98, 99), i.e.,

$$G(H_2) = G_{H_2}$$

This is possible because both hydroxyl radicals and hydrogen atoms are scavenged before they can enter into reactions which influence the yield of hydrogen. The scavenging reactions are

$$\cdot OH + Br^- \rightarrow Br\cdot + OH^- \tag{8.61}$$

and

$$H\cdot + Br\cdot \rightarrow H^+ + Br^- \tag{8.62}$$

or, equivalent,

$$2Br\cdot \rightarrow Br_2 \tag{8.63}$$

$$H\cdot + Br_2 \rightarrow H^+ + Br^- + Br\cdot \tag{8.64}$$

In acid, oxygen-free solutions of bromide,

$$G(H_2O_2) = G(H_2) = G_{H_2} = G_{H_2O_2} - \tfrac{1}{2}G_H + \tfrac{1}{2}G_{OH}$$

but in neutral and alkaline solutions the hydrogen peroxide is rapidly converted to oxygen.

In the presence of air or oxygen (100), the reactions taking place in acid or neutral bromide solution are reaction 8.61 and

$$H\cdot + O_2 \rightarrow HO_2\cdot \tag{8.34}$$

$$Br\cdot + HO_2\cdot \rightarrow H^+ + Br^- + O_2 \tag{8.65}$$

and, since more hydrogen atoms are formed than hydroxyl radicals, the excess hydroperoxyl radicals react

$$2HO_2\cdot \rightarrow H_2O_2 + O_2 \tag{8.33}$$

From these reactions it can be seen that the yield of hydrogen peroxide is given by

$$G(H_2O_2) = G_{H_2O_2} + \tfrac{1}{2}G_H - \tfrac{1}{2}G_{OH}$$

or, since the material balance requires that

$$G_{-H_2O} = G_H + 2G_{H_2} = G_{OH} + 2G_{H_2O_2}$$

by

$$G(H_2O_2) = 2G_{H_2O_2} - G_{H_2}$$

In neutral solutions these results only apply to the initial yield of hydrogen peroxide. Once this product has built up in the solution, another reaction, either 8.9 or 8.37, competes with reaction 8.34 for the available hydrogen atoms:

$$H\cdot + H_2O_2 \rightarrow \cdot OH + H_2O \tag{8.9}$$

$$e_{aq}^- + H_2O_2 \rightarrow \cdot OH + OH^- \tag{8.37}$$

However, by choice of suitable conditions it is possible to estimate both G_{H_2} and $G_{H_2O_2}$ by irradiating a bromide solution. The solution might, for example, be irradiated in the absence of air and the hydrogen yield measured and then irradiated in the presence of air and the hydrogen peroxide yield determined.

Ferrous Sulfate

The radiation-induced oxidation of ferrous sulfate solutions is one of the most thoroughly studied reactions in radiation chemistry. It is also the basis for the widely used Fricke dosimeter (cf. Chapter 4) and, since the mechanism is well established, is used to derive information about the primary radical and molecular yields in irradiated water.

The oxidation is invariably studied in acid solution (generally 0.8N or 0.1N sulfuric acid) and either in the presence or the complete absence of air. When air (oxygen) is present, as in the Fricke dosimeter solution, the reactions taking place are

$$\cdot OH + Fe^{2+} \rightarrow Fe^{3+} + OH^- \tag{8.66}$$

$$H_2O_2 + Fe^{2+} \rightarrow Fe^{3+} + \cdot OH + OH^- \tag{8.67}$$

$$H\cdot + O_2 \rightarrow HO_2. \tag{8.34}$$

$$HO_2\cdot + Fe^{2+} \rightarrow Fe^{3+} + HO_2^- \tag{8.68}$$

$$HO_2^- + H^+ \rightarrow H_2O_2 \tag{8.69}$$

Reaction 8.67 is the process which occurs in the Fenton reagent (Chapter 6).

The yield of ferric ion is related to the molecular and radical yields by the following expression:

$$G(Fe^{3+})_{air} = 2G_{H_2O_2} + 3G_H + G_{OH}$$

Factors which alter the molecular and radical yields will therefore alter the yield of ferric ion. One such factor is the LET of the incident radiation. As the LET is increased, G_H and G_{OH} fall while $G_{H_2O_2}$ increases (Table 8.2), and if typical numerical values are substituted in the expression above it is found that $G(Fe^{3+})_{air}$ falls with increasing LET (some G values for various types of radiation are given in Table 4.7). At the very high dose rates attainable with linear electron accelerators the yield of ferric ion falls for the same reason, i.e., increased radical-radical reaction to give molecular products at the expense of radical-solute reaction (32).

Organic impurities can increase the yield of ferric ion in aerated solutions (101) by the sequence of reactions:

$$\cdot OH + RH \rightarrow R\cdot + H_2O \tag{8.70}$$

$$R\cdot + O_2 \rightarrow RO_2\cdot \tag{8.71}$$

$$RO_2\cdot + H^+ + Fe^{2+} \rightarrow Fe^{3+} + RO_2H \tag{8.72}$$

$$RO_2H + Fe^{2+} \rightarrow Fe^{3+} + RO\cdot + OH^- \tag{8.73}$$

$$RO\cdot + H^+ + Fe^{2+} \rightarrow Fe^{3+} + ROH \tag{8.74}$$

Thus each hydroxyl radical brings about the oxidation of three ferrous ions instead of only one, and the yield of ferric ion is spuriously high. Deliberate addition of organic compounds sometimes leads to even higher yields of ferric ion than would be predicted from reactions 8.70 to 8.74. For example, $G(Fe^{3+})_{air}$ values up to 75 in the presence of ethanol (101) and about 250 in solutions containing formic acid (102) have been reported. In these examples a chain reaction must be taking place and reaction 8.74 is probably replaced by

$$RO\cdot + RH \rightarrow R\cdot + ROH \tag{8.75}$$

(The chain is made up of reactions 8.71 to 8.73 and reaction 8.75.) In the presence of chloride the hydroxyl radicals are replaced by chlorine atoms (Eq. 8.60), which may react with either the ferrous ions or the organic impurity, i.e.,

$$Cl\cdot + Fe^{2+} \rightarrow Fe^{3+} + Cl^- \tag{8.76}$$

or

$$Cl\cdot + RH \rightarrow R\cdot + HCl \tag{8.77}$$

In practice the first reaction predominates, and the over-all result of adding chloride is that each hydroxyl radical again oxidizes one ferrous ion and the yield of ferric ion is not affected by the impurity.

A prerequisite for oxidation by reactions 8.66 to 8.69 is the presence of oxygen, which is consumed during the oxidation process. For air-saturated solutions the dissolved oxygen is exhausted when a dose of about 50,000 rads has been absorbed and at higher doses the yield of ferric ion drops. A plot of the ferric ion formed against the absorbed dose has the form shown in Fig. 8.4; the break in the plot corresponds to exhaustion of the oxygen originally present. Curves of this general shape are typical of many other radiation-induced reactions in aqueous solution where the yield of products is dependent on the presence of oxygen. The break in the curve is often quite sharp, showing that oxygen is effective down to very low concentrations.

In the absence of oxygen, reaction 8.34 is replaced (103) by

$$H\cdot + H^+ + Fe^{2+} \rightarrow Fe^{3+} + H_2 \qquad (8.78)$$

and reactions 8.68 and 8.69 do not occur. Reaction 8.78 is unusual since hydrogen atoms are acting as oxidizing agents instead of their more usual role of reducing agents. Weiss (78, 79) has suggested that they might first add a hydrogen ion to give the radical-ion H_2^+, which acts as an oxidizing agent because it can readily accept electrons to form molecular hydrogen, i.e.,

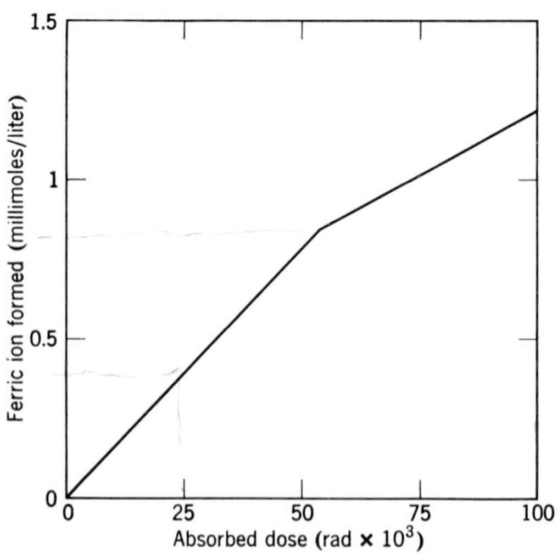

FIGURE 8.4 *Radiation-induced oxidation of air-saturated ferrous sulfate solutions.*

$$H\cdot + H^+ \rightarrow H_2^+ \quad (8.27)$$

$$H_2^+ + Fe^{2+} \rightarrow Fe^{3+} + H_2 \quad (8.79)$$

Alternative explanations are that the hydrogen atom reacts with a polarized water molecule in the solvation shell of the ferrous ion (104),

$$H\cdot + Fe^{2+}(H_2O) \rightarrow Fe^{3+}OH^- + H_2 \quad (8.80)$$

or adds to the ferrous ion to form an intermediate hydride complex which then reacts with a hydrogen ion (105),

$$H\cdot + Fe^{2+} \rightleftharpoons (FeH)^{2+} \quad (8.81)$$

$$(FeH)^{2+} + H^+ \rightarrow Fe^{3+} + H_2 \quad (8.82)$$

Whatever form this reaction takes, G(ferric) in the absence of oxygen (e.g., in evacuated samples) is given by

$$G(Fe^{3+})_{vacuum} = 2G_{H_2O_2} + G_H + G_{OH}$$

After long irradiation, the ferric ion formed competes with the ferrous ion for hydrogen atoms and hydroperoxyl radicals

$$H\cdot + Fe^{3+} \rightarrow Fe^{2+} + H^+ \quad (8.83)$$

$$HO_2\cdot + Fe^{3+} \rightarrow Fe^{2+} + H^+ + O_2 \quad (8.84)$$

and eventually a steady state concentration of ferric ion is reached where the rates of oxidation and reduction are equal.

Dainton (48, 106) has pointed out an interesting feature of the reactions in irradiated ferrous ion solutions. This is that the reaction between hydrogen peroxide and ferrous ions,

$$H_2O_2 + Fe^{2+} \rightarrow Fe^{3+} + \cdot OH + OH^- \quad (8.67)$$

is much slower than the other reactions occurring. A practical consequence of this is that for short irradiations and very low ferrous ion concentrations ($10^{-5}M$, or lower) reaction 8.67 can be neglected if the ferric ion formed is measured immediately after the irradiation. Under these particular circumstances, the presence of oxygen does not affect the yield and

$$G(Fe^{3+})_{air} = G(Fe^{3+})_{vacuum} = G_H + G_{OH}$$

If the irradiated solution is allowed to stand, the hydrogen peroxide formed will of course oxidize ferrous ions, giving the normal ferric ion yield.

Ferrous Sulfate–Cupric Sulfate

Solutions containing both ferrous sulfate and cupric sulfate in $0.01N$ sulfuric acid have been proposed for use in dosimetry by Hart (52, 107, 108). They have the advantage of being independent of oxygen so that the range of the dosimeter is considerably extended. The mechanism is

$$\cdot OH + Fe^{2+} \rightarrow Fe^{3+} + OH^- \tag{8.66}$$

$$H_2O_2 + Fe^{2+} \rightarrow Fe^{3+} + \cdot OH + OH^- \tag{8.67}$$

$$H\cdot + O_2 \rightarrow HO_2\cdot \tag{8.34}$$

$$HO_2\cdot + Cu^{2+} \rightarrow Cu^+ + H^+ + O_2 \tag{8.85}$$

$$Cu^+ + Fe^{3+} \rightarrow Cu^{2+} + Fe^{2+} \tag{8.86}$$

The yield of ferric ion in the presence of excess cupric ion is given by

$$G(Fe^{3+})^{Cu^{2+}} = 2G_{H_2O_2} - G_H + G_{OH} \quad (-G_{HO_2})$$

This is consistent with an increase in the yield of ferric ion with increasing LET, as has been observed with this system. Oxygen enters into the sequence of reactions shown, but it is not consumed.

When oxygen is not present, reaction 8.34 is replaced by

$$H\cdot + Cu^{2+} \rightarrow Cu^+ + H^+ \tag{8.87}$$

This does not alter $G(Fe^{3+})^{Cu^{2+}}$. Even when oxygen is originally absent a small amount is formed on irradiation by reaction 8.85, the necessary $HO_2\cdot$ radicals being formed by the interaction of hydroxyl radicals and molecular hydrogen peroxide in the spurs and track zones,

$$\cdot OH + H_2O_2 \rightarrow HO_2\cdot + H_2O \tag{8.32}$$

The deaerated ferrous-cupric system therefore offers a means of measuring G_{HO_2} since

$$G(O_2)^{Fe^{2+},Cu^{2+}} = G_{HO_2}$$

To be consistent, G_{HO_2} should be included in the expression for $G(Fe^{3+})^{Cu^{2+}}$ (it is shown in parentheses), however with low-LET radiation (e.g., x- and γ-rays) it is quite small and can ordinarily be neglected.

Ceric Sulfate

Solutions of ceric sulfate in sulfuric acid are also used in chemical dosimetry, the significant chemical reaction in this case being the reduction of ceric ions to cerous ions. The reduction is independent of the presence of oxygen and G(cerous) increases with increasing LET. The mechanism is as follows:

$$H\cdot + O_2 \rightarrow HO_2\cdot \quad (8.34)$$

$$HO_2\cdot + Ce^{4+} \rightarrow Ce^{3+} + H^+ + O_2 \quad (8.88)$$

$$H_2O_2 + Ce^{4+} \rightarrow Ce^{3+} + HO_2\cdot + H^+ \quad (8.89)$$

$$\cdot OH + Ce^{3+} \rightarrow Ce^{4+} + OH^- \quad (8.90)$$

Oxygen is not consumed during the reaction but in its absence reactions 8.34 and 8.88 are replaced by

$$H\cdot + Ce^{4+} \rightarrow Ce^{3+} + H^+ \quad (8.91)$$

In both cases one hydrogen atom leads to the reduction of one ceric ion and the absence of oxygen does not lead to any change in G(cerous). In both aerated and deaerated solution G(cerous) is given by

$$G(Ce^{3+}) = 2G_{H_2O_2} + G_H - G_{OH}$$

($HO_2\cdot$ is neglected as a primary product). The mechanism is consistent with an increase in G(cerous) with increasing LET.

In deaerated solutions

$$G(O_2) = G_{H_2O_2}$$

Ceric Sulfate-Thallous Sulfate

The yield of cerous ion from air-saturated solutions of ceric sulfate in dilute sulfuric acid is increased by the addition of thallous sulfate (109). With this reagent cerous ions are no longer oxidized by hydroxyl radicals and reaction 8.90 is replaced by the sequence

$$\cdot OH + Tl^+ \rightarrow Tl^{2+} + OH^- \quad (8.92)$$

$$Tl^{2+} + Ce^{4+} \rightarrow Tl^{3+} + Ce^{3+} \quad (8.93)$$

Thus,

$$G(Ce^{3+})^{Tl^+} = 2G_{H_2O_2} + G_H + G_{OH}$$

Determination of Molecular and Radical Yields

Molecular and radical yields can be determined from the extent of the radiation-induced changes produced in aqueous sytems if the detailed radiolysis mechanism is known. Good examples are the four systems based on ferrous or ceric ions described above. Assuming that H_2, H_2O_2,

H·, and ·OH are the only primary products, the molecular and radical yields can be calculated from results obtained with the systems; aerated ferrous sulfate, deaerated ferrous sulfate, and ceric sulfate. The values determined experimentally are $G(Fe^{3+})_{air}$, $G(Fe^{3+})_{vacuum}$, and $G(Ce^{3+})$ respectively, and the pertinent equations are

$$G(Fe^{3+})_{air} = 2G_{H_2O_2} + 3G_H + G_{OH}$$

$$G(Fe^{3+})_{vacuum} = 2G_{H_2O_2} + G_H + G_{OH}$$

$$G(Ce^{3+}) = 2G_{H_2O_2} + G_H - G_{OH}$$

The radical yields are therefore given by

$$2G_H = G(Fe^{3+})_{air} - G(Fe^{3+})_{vacuum}$$

$$2G_{OH} = G(Fe^{3+})_{vacuum} - G(Ce^{3+})$$

$G_{H_2O_2}$ can then be found by substitution, and G_{H_2} and G_{-H_2O} from the material balance equation,

$$G_{-H_2O} = 2G_{H_2} + G_H = 2G_{H_2O_2} + G_{OH}$$

For cobalt-60 γ-radiation and solutions made up in 0.8*N* sulfuric acid the values of $G(Fe^{3+})_{air}$, $G(Fe^{3+})_{vacuum}$, and $G(Ce^{3+})$ are 15.6, 8.2, and 2.4 respectively. Substitution of these numerical values in the equations given above gives, for 0.8*N* sulfuric acid,

$$G_{-H_2O} = 4.5$$

$$G_{H_2O_2} = 0.8$$

$$G_{H_2} = 0.4$$

$$G_H = 3.7$$

$$G_{OH} = 2.9$$

Various other combinations of experimental results from the ferrous, ferrous-cupric, ceric, and ceric-thallous systems can be used to obtain the same results. The values found for the molecular and radical yields will be slightly different from those shown if solutions with different acidities are used.

Many other systems can be used to determine molecular and radical yields provided only that the radiolysis mechanism is known. Table 8.7, based on a table compiled by Hart (7), lists a selection of such systems. The results obtained from them are in substantial agreement with each other.

TABLE 8.7 *Systems for Measuring Molecular and Radical Yields in Aqueous Solutions*

	System	Simplified yield equation
1	Deuterium (deaerated, i.e., no O_2 present)	$G(HD) = G_H$
2	Hydrogen + oxygen	$G(H_2O_2 = G_{H_2O_2} + \frac{1}{2}G_H + \frac{1}{2}G_{OH}$
3	Bromide (deaerated)	$G(H_2) = G_{H_2}$
4	Bromide + oxygen	$G(H_2O_2) = G_{H_2O_2} + \frac{1}{2}G_H - \frac{1}{2}G_{OH}$
5	Ferrous sulfate (deaerated)	$\begin{cases} G(Fe^{3+}) = 2G_{H_2O_2} + G_H + G_{OH} \\ G(H_2) = G_{H_2} + G_H \end{cases}$
	very low ferrous ion concentration and rapid analysis (48)	$G(Fe^{3+}) = G_H + G_{OH}$
6	Ferrous sulfate + oxygen	$\begin{cases} G(Fe^{3+}) = 2G_{H_2O_2} + 3G_H + G_{OH} \\ G(H_2) = G_{H_2} \end{cases}$
	very low ferrous ion concentration and rapid analysis (48)	$G(Fe^{3+}) = G_H + G_{OH}$
7	Ferrous sulfate + cupric sulfate (deaerated or + oxygen)	$G(Fe^{3+}) = 2G_{H_2O_2} - G_H + G_{OH} - G_{HO_2}$ $= 2G_{H_2} - 4G_{HO_2}$
	(deaerated)	$G(O_2) = G_{HO_2}$
8	Ceric sulfate (deaerated or + oxygen)	$G(Ce^{3+}) = 2G_{H_2O_2} + G_H - G_{OH}$
	(deaerated)	$G(O_2) = G_{H_2O_2}$

TABLE 8.7 *(Continued)*

	System	Simplified yield equation
9	Ceric sulfate + thallous sulfate + oxygen	$G(Ce^{3+}) = 2G_{H_2O_2} + G_H + G_{OH}$
10	Ferric sulfate + formic acid (deaerated)	$G(Fe^{2+}) = G_H + G_{OH}$ (rows 10–12)
11	Ferric sulfate + methanol (deaerated)	
12	Ferric sulfate + cupric sulfate + formic acid + oxygen	
13	Formic acid + oxygen	$G(H_2O_2) = G_{H_2O_2} + \frac{1}{2}G_H + \frac{1}{2}G_{OH}$ $G(CO_2) = G_{OH}$ $G(H_2) = G_{H_2}$ $G(\text{-}O_2) = \frac{1}{2}G_H + \frac{1}{2}G_{OH}$
14	Boiling water	$G(H_2) = G_{H_2}$

15 Stoichiometric equations; (a) assuming that only H_2, H_2O_2, $H\cdot$, and $\cdot OH$ are formed,

$$G_{-H_2O} = 2G_{H_2} + G_H = 2G_{H_2O_2} + G_{OH}$$

(b) including $HO_2\cdot$,

$$2G_{H_2} + G_H = 2G_{H_2O_2} + G_{OH} + 3G_{HO_2}$$

and

$$G_{-H_2O} = 2G_{H_2} + G_H - G_{HO_2} = 2G_{H_2O_2} + G_{OH} + 2G_{HO_2}$$

Effect of Solute Concentration on the Molecular Yields

Dilute solutions (generally 10^{-5} to $10^{-3}M$) are normally used when making determinations of molecular yields, since more concentrated solutions may give erroneous results due to interference with the spur and track reactions forming the molecular products, particularly with high-LET radiation (110).

Although, at the low concentrations normally used, solute concentration does not greatly affect the molecular yields, careful examination does show that solutes which react with hydroxyl radicals (e.g., Br^-, Cl^-) gradually lower the molecular yield of hydrogen peroxide as their concentration is increased (111), while solutes which react with hydrogen atoms or solvated electrons (e.g., O_2, H_2O_2, KNO_2, $CuSO_4$) reduce the molecular yield of hydrogen (112, 113). Sworski (111) showed that an approximately linear relationship exists between the molecular hydrogen peroxide yield produced by γ-rays and the cube root of the solute concentration. The relationship takes the form

$$G_{H_2O_2} = (G_{H_2O_2})_0 - b[S]^{1/3} \tag{8.94}$$

where $(G_{H_2O_2})_0$ is $G_{H_2O_2}$ at infinite dilution, i.e., in the absence of solute, and b is a constant that varies slightly with different solutes; [S] is the solute concentration. A similar relationship holds for G_{H_2}. The cube-root relationship found for γ-rays is fortuitous and only approximate, the exponent varying with the range of concentrations being considered. Furthermore, the value of the exponent depends upon the LET of the radiation — being smaller at higher LET (114); thus Burton and Kurien (115) give values of 0.33, 0.26, and 0.15 for cobalt-60 γ-rays, 50 kvp x-rays, and 3.4 Mev α-rays respectively.

A second relationship involving the yields of molecular products and the solute concentration was discovered by Schwarz (112), who plotted the ratios $G_{H_2}/(G_{H_2})_0$ and $G_{H_2O_2}/(G_{H_2O_2})_0$ against the logarithm of the solute concentration and obtained a curve of the shape shown in Fig. 8.5. The interesting feature of this plot is that the shape of the curve is the same for both hydrogen and hydrogen peroxide yield and for a wide variety of solutes. Furthermore, the curves can all be brought into coincidence by multiplying the concentration by an arbitrary factor appropriate to the particular product and solute. In the case of the hydrogen yields, Schwarz was able to show that these factors were in the same ratio as the rate constants for reaction of hydrogen atoms with the solute, wherever the rate constants were known, suggesting strongly that the molecular hydrogen is formed via hydrogen atoms. It also suggests that

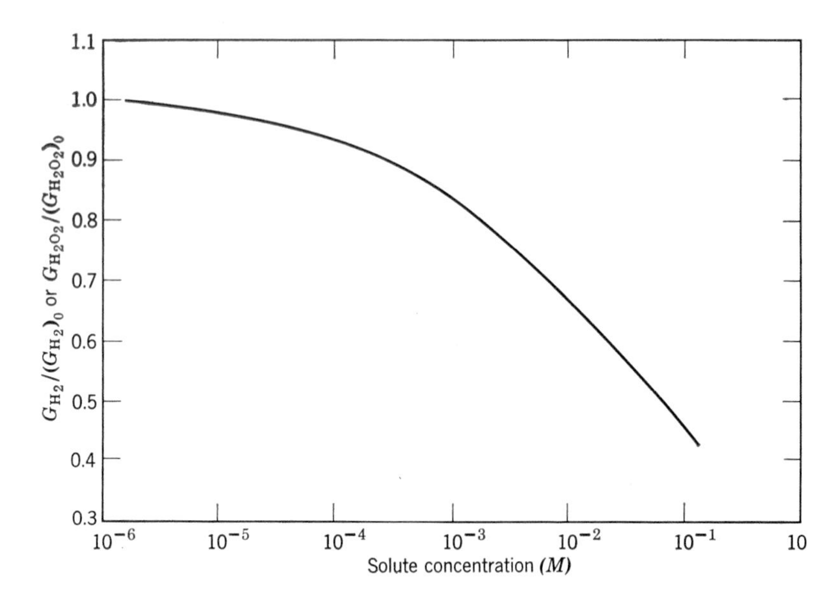

FIGURE 8.5 *The effect of solute concentration on the molecular yields of hydrogen and hydrogen peroxide.*

the molecular hydrogen peroxide is formed via a radical reaction since the hydrogen peroxide yield varies with solute concentration in the same way as the hydrogen yield.

The concentration effect in γ-irradiated solutions has been accounted for by approximate mathematical treatments based on the radical-diffusion model for the radiolysis of water (35, 112, 114). This assumes that hydrogen atoms (or solvated electrons) and hydroxyl radicals are produced in localized regions (spurs) in the irradiated medium, that the molecular products are formed by combination of these species as they diffuse from the spurs, and that the combination reactions compete with reactions between the radicals and the solute. For the purposes of calculation it was assumed that only one radical is formed, R· (which represents H·, e_{aq}^-, and ·OH), so that formation of molecular products is represented by

$$2R\cdot \xrightarrow{k_1} R_2 \tag{8.95}$$

and the radical-solute reactions by

$$R\cdot + S \xrightarrow{k_2} RS \tag{8.96}$$

where k_1 and k_2 are the rate constants for these reactions respectively. If the radicals and solute were homogeneously distributed in the medium, normal chemical kinetics would be applicable and the rate equation would be

$$d[R]/dt = -k_1[R]^2 - k_2[R][S] \tag{8.97}$$

However under radiolysis conditions the radicals are not initially homogeneously distributed, and the changing radical concentration in the region of each spur must be considered. This is done by including a diffusion term, so that the rate equation becomes

$$\delta[R]/\delta t = D\nabla^2[R] - k_1[R]^2 - k_2[R][S] \tag{8.98}$$

where D is the diffusion constant for the radicals and ∇^2 is a Laplacian operator. Calculations based on this one radical–one solute model are in quite good agreement with the experimental results, indicating that the model is probably substantially correct. Later studies of the diffusion kinetics of irradiated aqueous solutions (46, 116, 117) have taken more complex models, which include hydrogen atoms and hydroxyl radicals separately, reactive intermediates, and more than one solute, and have eliminated some of the approximations necessary for the earlier calculations. Although choice of values for the various diffusion and rate constants and for the initial number and distribution of radicals in the spurs is still somewhat arbitrary, the success of the calculations in describing qualitatively and semiquantitatively the relationship between solute concentration and molecular yields, and isotope, LET, and dose-rate effects is strong evidence in favor of the radical-diffusion model for the radiolysis of water.

Relative Rate Constants

The fact that free radicals are very reactive entities leads to competition for them when the solution contains more than one substance with which they can react. If the solution contains two such substances, A and B, the ratio of the number of radicals reacting with A (R_A) to the number reacting with B (R_B) is

$$\frac{R_A}{R_B} = \frac{[A]k_{RA}}{[B]k_{RB}}$$

where [A] and [B] are the concentrations of A and B in the solution and k_{RA} and k_{RB} are the bimolecular rate constants for the reaction between radical R· and A and between R· and B respectively. Since the ratio R_A/R_B can be determined by experiment and the concentrations of the two reactants are known, the ratio of the two rate constants can be obtained. In radiation chemistry, B is generally a standard substance (e.g., ferrous ion or formic acid) for which the radiolysis reactions are established. A number of relative rate constants relevant to the radiation-induced oxidation of ferrous sulfate are given by Dainton (44), and others for the reactions of hydrogen atoms and hydroxyl radicals in acid solution are given by Swallow (118). A more extensive survey of the relative rates of reaction of hydrogen atoms and hydroxyl radicals in aqueous solutions has been made by Ferradini (51). It should be mentioned that the determination of relative rate constants is not limited to radiation chemistry, but in fact is often more readily made using other sources of radicals.

Techniques such as intermittent irradiation with either ultraviolet light (76) or ionizing radiation (119), and pulse radiolysis (120), analogous to flash photolysis, enable absolute values for rate constants such as k_{RA} and k_{RB} to be measured. These absolute values can then be used to calculate other absolute rate constants using the rate constant ratios determined as described above.

Formic Acid

A disadvantage of the cationic systems in estimating molecular and radical yields is that they must be used in quite strongly acid solution and consequently are restricted to a rather limited range of pH. This restriction can be overcome by choosing solutes such as formic acid, which can be used over a wide range of pH (121).

The reactions which occur in irradiated formic acid solutions in the presence of oxygen are

$$\cdot OH + HCOOH \rightarrow \cdot COOH + H_2O \tag{8.99}$$

$$\cdot COOH + O_2 \rightarrow HO_2\cdot + CO_2 \tag{8.100}$$

$$H\cdot + O_2 \rightarrow HO_2\cdot \tag{8.34}$$

$$2HO_2\cdot \rightarrow H_2O_2 + O_2 \tag{8.33}$$

Thus the molecular and radical yields can be calculated from the measured values of $G(H_2)$, $G(H_2O_2)$, $G(CO_2)$, and $G(-O_2)$ (121, 122, 123, 124) and

$$G_{H_2} = G(H_2)$$

$$G_{H_2O_2} = G(H_2O_2) - G(-O_2)$$

$$G_H = 2G(-O_2) - G(CO_2)$$

$$G_{OH} = G(CO_2)$$

Hart (121) carried out measurements in the pH range from 0.32 to 11.58 and found that above pH 3, $G_{H_2O_2}$ and G_{H_2} are nearly equal, while below pH 3 the molecular yield of hydrogen peroxide is rather greater than that of hydrogen. The decrease in G_{H_2} in acid solution is accompanied by an increase in G_H and it has been suggested that these effects are due either to the formation of the radical-ion H_2^+ (121) or to the scavenging of solvated electrons in acid solutions (44), or to a reaction involving excited water molecules (21).

The radiolysis of aqueous formic acid solutions is more complex when oxygen is not present. Fricke and Hart (93, 125) showed that below pH 3 and for concentrations less than 5 mM, hydrogen and carbon dioxide are formed in equimolar amounts with a G value of about 4. The mechanism is believed to be

$$H\cdot + HCOOH \rightarrow \cdot COOH + H_2 \tag{8.101}$$

$$\cdot OH + HCOOH \rightarrow \cdot COOH + H_2O \tag{8.99}$$

$$H_2O_2 + \cdot COOH \rightarrow \cdot OH + CO_2 + H_2O \tag{8.102}$$

$$2\cdot COOH \rightarrow HCOOH + CO_2 \tag{8.103}$$

Reactions 8.99 and 8.102 together constitute a chain reaction, and the radiolysis of formic acid solutions containing hydrogen peroxide does proceed in this way, though if oxygen is present, the chain reaction is inhibited by reaction 8.100 (126). The intermediate organic radical appears to be $\cdot COOH$ rather than $HCOO\cdot$ since irradiation of DCOOH in H_2O (127) and of HCOOD in D_2O (128) gives hydrogen composed largely of HD. At higher pH the yields of hydrogen and carbon dioxide fall. Above pH 7 only hydrogen is evolved and oxalic acid is the major organic product, the over-all reaction being

$$2HCOOH \rightarrow H_2 + (COOH)_2 \tag{8.104}$$

Under these conditions the intermediate radical will be $\cdot COO^-$ rather than $\cdot COOH$ and reaction 8.103 is replaced by (129)

$$2\cdot COO^- \rightarrow (COO^-)_2 \tag{8.105}$$

These are also the conditions when deaerated sodium formate solutions are used in chemical dosimetry (130, 131), where the reducible organic products (mainly oxalic acid) are titrated with permanganate.

Garrison and his colleagues (132, 133) found that irradiation of dilute oxygen-free solutions of formic acid with cyclotron-produced helium ions produces glyoxal and glyoxylic acid in addition to smaller amounts of other organic acids and formaldehyde. They proposed that hydrogen atoms add reversibly to formic acid to give the radical $H\dot{C}(OH)_2$, which under the conditions of high radical concentration dimerizes to glyoxal or combines with $\cdot COOH$ to give glyoxylic acid,

$$H\cdot + HCOOH \rightleftharpoons H\dot{C}(OH)_2 \quad (8.106)$$

$$2H\dot{C}(OH)_2 \rightarrow OHC{-}CHO + 2H_2O \quad (8.107)$$

$$H\dot{C}(OH)_2 + \cdot COOH \rightarrow OHC{-}COOH + H_2O \quad (8.108)$$

When the radical concentration is lower, as in γ-induced reactions, and in more dilute formic acid solutions, the competing reaction between hydrogen atoms and formic acid to give molecular hydrogen (Eq. 8.101) is assumed to occur.

Formaldehyde, which appears in the cyclotron irradiation of dilute formic acid solutions, is also formed by γ-irradiation but at rather higher formic acid concentrations (122). The aldehyde can be accounted for by assuming that at high formic acid concentrations the radical $H\dot{C}(OH)_2$ is also formed by γ-irradiation, and that a competing process for the removal of this entity is

$$H\dot{C}(OH)_2 + HCOOH \rightarrow \cdot COOH + HCHO + H_2O \quad (8.109)$$

An alternative explanation is that at high concentrations formic acid competes with water for the capture of electrons. Formaldehyde might then arise by

$$e^- + HCOOH \rightarrow HCO\cdot + OH^- \quad (8.110)$$

$$HCO\cdot + HCOOH \rightarrow \cdot COOH + HCHO \quad (8.111)$$

For very concentrated formic acid solutions, in the range from molar to essentially pure formic acid, the yield of carbon dioxide increases and $G(CO_2)$ values as high as 12 can be obtained (134). Hart has postulated a chain reaction under these conditions comprised of

$$\cdot COOH + HCOOH \rightarrow HCO\cdot + CO_2 + H_2O \quad (8.112)$$

and

$$HCO\cdot + HCOOH \rightarrow \cdot COOH + HCHO \quad (8.111)$$

The formaldehyde builds up to a very low steady state concentration and may possibly be removed by

$$\cdot COOH + HCHO \rightarrow \cdot CH_2OH + CO_2 \quad (8.113)$$

$$\cdot CH_2OH + HCOOH \rightarrow \cdot COOH + CH_3OH \quad (8.114)$$

although methanol has not yet been identified as a product.

Carbon monoxide is also formed at formic acid concentrations greater than about $10^{-2}M$ (134, 135). It was suggested that at low formic acid concentrations this might be due to water subexcitation electrons exciting the acid, which then dissociates

$$HCOOH^* \rightarrow HCO\cdot + \cdot OH \tag{8.115}$$

$$HCO\cdot \rightarrow CO + H\cdot \tag{8.116}$$

At high acid concentrations the carbon monoxide was thought to be the result of direct action.

Acetic Acid

Dilute oxygen-free acetic acid solutions give hydrogen, hydrogen peroxide, and succinic acid when irradiated with helium ions or deuterons (136). These products are quite different from those formed when the pure acid is irradiated. In aqueous solution both hydrogen atoms and hydroxyl radicals abstract hydrogen from the methyl group of acetic acid to give the radical $\cdot CH_2COOH$, which dimerizes to succinic acid;

$$H\cdot + CH_3COOH \rightarrow \cdot CH_2COOH + H_2 \tag{8.117}$$

$$\cdot OH + CH_3COOH \rightarrow \cdot CH_2COOH + H_2O \tag{8.118}$$

$$2\cdot CH_2COOH \rightarrow (CH_2COOH)_2 \tag{8.119}$$

Higher carboxylic acids are produced when the irradiation is prolonged (137). These include tricarballylic acid, $HOOC{-}CH(CH_2COOH)_2$, malic acid, and citric acid. They presumably arise in secondary reactions involving the succinic acid.

When relatively concentrated acetic acid solutions ($1M$ or higher) are irradiated with heavy particle radiation or x-rays, appreciable amounts of carbon dioxide and methane and rather smaller amounts of carbon monoxide, ethane, acetaldehyde, and biacetyl are formed (73, 136). Hayon and Weiss (73) accounted for these products on the basis of reactions between negative and positive polarons, $(H_2O)^-$ and $(H_2O)^+$ respectively, and acetic acid;

$$(H_2O)^- + CH_3COOH \rightarrow (CH_3COOH)^- + H_2O \tag{8.120}$$

$$(CH_3COOH)^- \rightarrow CH_3CO^- + \cdot OH \tag{8.121}$$

$$(CH_3COOH)^- \rightarrow CH_3COO^- + H\cdot \tag{8.122}$$

$$(CH_3COOH)^- \rightarrow CH_3CO\cdot + OH^- \tag{8.123}$$

Carbonyl compounds and probably carbon monoxide would be anticipated from the reactions of the $CH_3CO\cdot$ radical. The positive polaron might react,

$$(H_2O)^+ + CH_3COOH \rightarrow CH_3COO\cdot + H^+ + H_2O \qquad (8.44)$$

and this would probably be followed by

$$CH_3COO\cdot \rightarrow \cdot CH_3 + CO_2 \qquad (8.124)$$

$$\cdot CH_3 + CH_3COOH \rightarrow \cdot CH_2COOH + CH_4 \qquad (8.125)$$

$$2\cdot CH_3 \rightarrow C_2H_6 \qquad (8.126)$$

Under favorable conditions of pH and acetic acid concentration, reactions 8.120 and 8.44 would compete with reactions 8.117 and 8.118, respectively. When the polaron reactions are not so favored, the polarons would presumably break down to give hydrogen atoms or hydroxyl radicals and these would then react in the normal manner.

Succinic acid formation is suppressed when oxygen is present and carbon dioxide, formaldehyde, glycollic acid, glyoxylic acid, and oxalic acid are produced (138), apparently via the peroxy radical $\cdot O_2CH_2COOH$ formed by the addition of oxygen to $\cdot CH_2COOH$.

Ethanol

Irradiation of deaerated ethanol solutions with x- or γ-radiation produces hydrogen, acetaldehyde, butane-2,3-diol, and hydrogen peroxide (the molecular product yield from the water) which originate in the following reactions (139):

$$H\cdot + CH_3CH_2OH \rightarrow CH_3\dot{C}HOH + H_2 \qquad (8.127)$$

$$\cdot OH + CH_3CH_2OH \rightarrow CH_3\dot{C}HOH + H_2O \qquad (8.128)$$

$$H\cdot + CH_3\dot{C}HOH \rightarrow CH_3CH_2OH \qquad (8.129)$$

$$\cdot OH + CH_3\dot{C}HOH \rightarrow CH_3CHO + H_2O \qquad (8.130)$$

$$2CH_3\dot{C}HOH \rightarrow CH_3\text{—}CHOH\text{—}CHOH\text{—}CH_3 \qquad (8.131)$$

or

$$\rightarrow CH_3CH_2OH + CH_3CHO \qquad (8.132)$$

Hydrogen abstraction is shown from a CH group rather than from the OH group since the yield of D_2 obtained by irradiating a solution of CH_3CH_2OD in D_2O (pD 2.2) is no greater than the molecular yield of

D_2 from irradiated D_2O, so that hydrogen resulting from hydrogen abstraction must be predominantly HD (128). The hydrogen yield is greater ($G = 4.2$) in the pH range 1.2 to 4 than above pH 4.5 ($G = 2.5$ at pH 7), and the acetaldehyde yield falls from $G = 2$ in the lower pH range to $G = 0.2$ at pH 7; the glycol yield is not greatly influenced by changes in pH. The authors attribute these results to the formation of H_2^+ in solutions of low pH. Thus, at low pH, reaction 8.129 may be replaced by

$$H_2^+ + CH_3\dot{C}HOH \rightarrow CH_3CHO + H_2 + H^+ \qquad (8.133)$$

and reaction 8.127 by the stoichiometrically equivalent,

$$H_2^+ + CH_3CH_2OH \rightarrow CH_3\dot{C}HOH + H_2 + H^+ \qquad (8.134)$$

When oxygen is present, butanediol is not formed but the yield of acetaldehyde is increased. Both hydrogen and the intermediate organic radical add oxygen to form peroxy radicals and these then react together,

$$H\cdot + O_2 \rightarrow HO_2\cdot \qquad (8.34)$$

$$CH_3\dot{C}HOH + O_2 \rightarrow CH_3C(O_2\cdot)HOH \qquad (8.135)$$

$$HO_2\cdot + CH_3C(O_2\cdot)HOH \rightarrow CH_3CHO + H_2O_2 + O_2 \qquad (8.136)$$

Typical yields for deaerated and oxygen-saturated ethanol solutions are given in Table 8.8. The yields in oxygen-saturated solutions are

TABLE 8.8 *Radiolysis of Aqueous Ethanol Solutions*

(Ref. 139; 200 kvp x-rays, $3.4 \times 10^{-2}M$ ethanol, pH 1.2)

Product	Deaerated solution	Oxygen-saturated solution
H_2	$G = 4.2$	$G =$ approx. 0.6
H_2O_2	approx. 0.6	4.15
CH_3CHO	1.90	2.6
glycol	1.65	0

relatively constant over the pH range 1 to 11 except for an increase in $G(H_2O_2)$ and a slight increase in the yield of acetaldehyde in strongly acid solutions, and the system has been used to estimate radical yields in irradiated water (140, 141), when

$$G(H_2O_2) = G_{H_2O_2} + \tfrac{1}{2}G_H + \tfrac{1}{2}G_{OH}$$

and

$$G(CH_3CHO) = G_{OH}$$

Allan, Hayon, and Weiss (142) showed that the same products are formed when deaerated ethanol solutions are irradiated at room temperature or are frozen and irradiated at temperatures down to −196°C, though the yields are lower at the lower irradiation temperatures. At −196°C, for example, a 0.1 molar solution (pH 1.2) gave the following yields: $G(H_2) = 0.40$, $G(H_2O_2) = 0.05$, $G(CH_3CHO) = 0.27$.

Glucose

Upon irradiation in aqueous solution, carbohydrates undergo a complex series of reactions, including oxidation, degradation, and polymerization. The over-all picture is often complicated further by reactions involving the initial products.

Grant and Ward have postulated the following mechanism for the radiolysis of D-glucose solutions irradiated *in vacuo* (143):

CHO
|
H—C—OH
|
$(CHOH)_3$
|
CH_2OH
D-glucose

$\xrightarrow[(-H)]{H\cdot \text{ or } \cdot OH}$

·CO
|
H—C—OH
|
$(CHOH)_3$
|
CH_2OH

+

CHO
|
·C—OH
|
$(CHOH)_3$
|
CH_2OH

·OH →

COOH
|
H—C—OH
|
$(CHOH)_3$
|
CH_2OH
D-gluconic acid

→ Polymer

·OH →

CHO
|
CO
|
$(CHOH)_3$
|
CH_2OH
D-glucosone

→ Polymer

D-gluconic acid is the major product, but D-arabinose (apparently formed from the gluconic acid) and D-glucosone (2-oxo-D-*arabino*-aldohexose) are also formed. Polymeric materials are produced, apparently by radical combination reactions that are suppressed in the presence of oxygen by the formation of peroxy radicals (144).

In the presence of oxygen, the radiolysis reactions are represented by Phillips, Mattok, and Moody (145, 146) as

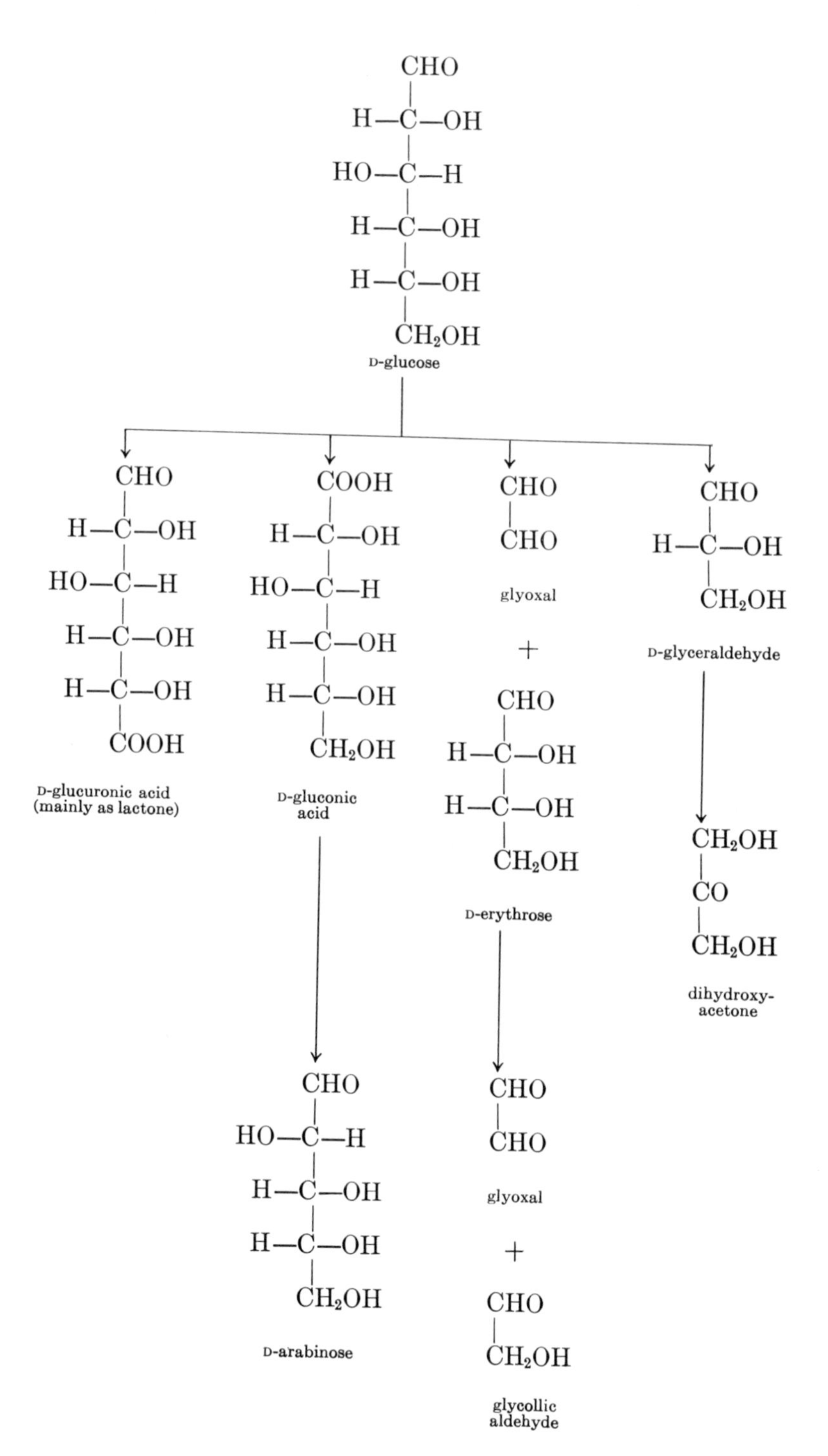
D-glucose
D-glucuronic acid
(mainly as lactone)
D-gluconic
acid
glyoxal
D-erythrose
D-glyceraldehyde
dihydroxy-
acetone
D-arabinose
glyoxal
glycollic
aldehyde

The major products produced by electron or γ-irradiation are glyoxal ($G = 1.8$), D-glucuronic acid ($G = 0.9$), D-arabinose, D-gluconic acid ($G = 0.4$), and dihydroxyacetone; smaller amounts of D-erythrose, D-xylose, saccharic acid, and formaldehyde are also formed. Phillips and his colleagues used paper chromatography and radioactive tracers to identify and estimate the products, and these were classed as primary or secondary by considering their rate of formation with respect to energy input. In aerated solutions the over-all yield of acid products, expressed in terms of G(monobasic acid), is 1.2 to 1.3, compared with a yield of 0.4 for deaerated solutions.

The products formed from glucose and other carbohydrates in aqueous solution suggest that primary alcohol groups are rather more vulnerable towards radiation-induced reactions than secondary alcohol groups. Also vulnerable are aldehyde groups, which will normally be in the cyclic semi-acetal form —CHOH—O—CH(—)(—). Attack at either of these terminal groups (—CH_2OH or —CHO) in the presence of oxygen leads to oxidation products (—CHO or —COOH), whereas attack at a secondary alcohol group (—CHOH—) gives either a keto-group (—CO—) or leads to fission of the carbon chain.

The mechanism whereby alcohol groups (primary or secondary) are oxidized to carbonyl groups is probably similar to that already given for the oxidation of ethanol in the presence of oxygen, i.e.,

$$H\cdot + O_2 \rightarrow HO_2\cdot \tag{8.34}$$

$$\cdot OH + {>}CHOH \rightarrow {>}\dot{C}OH + H_2O \tag{8.137}$$

$$ {>}\dot{C}OH + O_2 \rightarrow {>}C(O_2\cdot)OH \quad \text{(I)} \tag{8.138}$$

$$ {>}C(O_2\cdot)OH + HO_2\cdot \rightarrow {>}C{=}O + H_2O_2 + O_2 \tag{8.139}$$

The same peroxy intermediate (I) will probably be formed when fission of the carbon chain occurs. If, as seems likely, the two carbon atoms which break apart form aldehyde groups, the reaction can be represented by

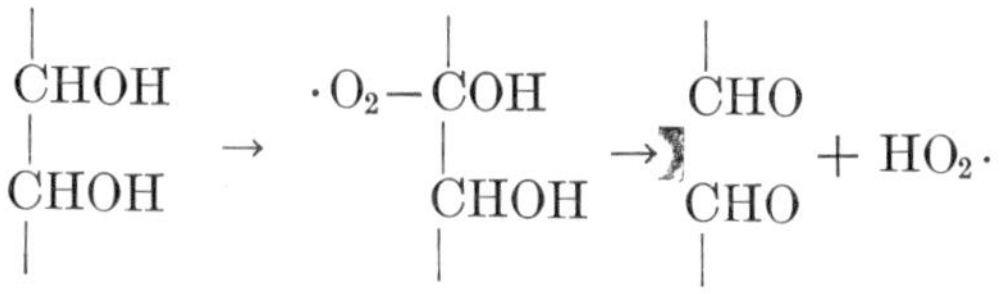

$$\begin{array}{c} | \\ \text{CHOH} \\ | \\ \text{CHOH} \\ | \end{array} \rightarrow \begin{array}{c} | \\ \cdot O_2-\text{COH} \\ | \\ \text{CHOH} \\ | \end{array} \rightarrow \left\{ \begin{array}{c} | \\ \text{CHO} \\ \\ \text{CHO} \\ | \end{array} \right. + HO_2\cdot \qquad (8.140)$$

However, the mechanism of the chain fission is not known and the inclusion of the $HO_2\cdot$ radical is purely speculative.

The vulnerability of primary alcohol groups to free radical attack is illustrated by the action of Fenton's reagent (a mixture of ferrous ions and hydrogen peroxide which generates hydroxyl radicals) upon mannitol:

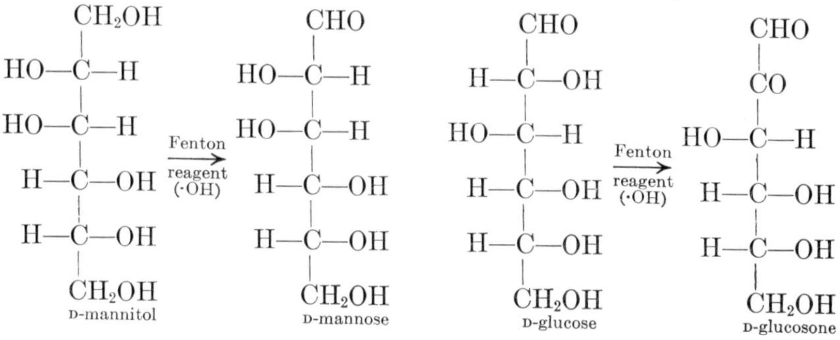

$$\underset{\text{D-mannitol}}{\begin{array}{c} CH_2OH \\ | \\ HO-C-H \\ | \\ HO-C-H \\ | \\ H-C-OH \\ | \\ H-C-OH \\ | \\ CH_2OH \end{array}} \xrightarrow[\text{reagent }(\cdot OH)]{\text{Fenton}} \underset{\text{D-mannose}}{\begin{array}{c} CHO \\ | \\ HO-C-H \\ | \\ HO-C-H \\ | \\ H-C-OH \\ | \\ H-C-OH \\ | \\ CH_2OH \end{array}} \qquad \underset{\text{D-glucose}}{\begin{array}{c} CHO \\ | \\ H-C-OH \\ | \\ HO-C-H \\ | \\ H-C-OH \\ | \\ H-C-OH \\ | \\ CH_2OH \end{array}} \xrightarrow[\text{reagent }(\cdot OH)]{\text{Fenton}} \underset{\text{D-glucosone}}{\begin{array}{c} CHO \\ | \\ CO \\ | \\ HO-C-H \\ | \\ H-C-OH \\ | \\ H-C-OH \\ | \\ CH_2OH \end{array}}$$

D-Mannose is formed in high yield (147). The oxidation of D-mannitol to D-mannose is a particularly favorable example since oxidation of either $-CH_2OH$ group gives the same product. This oxidation also occurs in relatively good yield (G(mannose) $= 2.25$) when aerated aqueous solutions of D-mannitol are irradiated with electrons and γ-rays (148); hydrogen peroxide is also formed ($G = 3.0$). The action of Fenton's reagent on aldoses is not as simple. Glucose, for example, gives a variety of products which are apparently derived from D-glucosone (149). With carbohydrates, however, reactions produced by Fenton's reagent are not necessarily those of radiation-produced hydroxyl radicals. The metal ions present in the Fenton reagent may complex with the sugar so that the complex rather than the free sugar, is oxidized.

Accompanying the chemical changes produced in glucose solutions by irradiation is a change in the optical activity of the solution. The decrease in optical activity is a linear function of the absorbed dose, and it offers a convenient means of dosimetry independent of dose rate over a wide range and applicable to high doses (up to 10^8 or 10^9 r) (150). The particular advantage claimed for this dosimeter is the simplicity and speed with which the dose can be determined following irradiation.

Sucrose solutions can also be used but are not as satisfactory as glucose solutions.

Glycine

Radiation-induced reactions in amino-acid solutions have been studied extensively as a step toward elucidating the changes which radiation produces in proteins and biological systems. Glycine and alanine as the simplest members of the amino acid series have been investigated most frequently and it is apparent that even for these relatively simple molecules the radiolysis mechanism is complex. Both oxygen and pH affect the radiolysis.

Table 8.9 lists the products obtained by irradiating aerated and deaerated solutions of glycine with x-rays. In the absence of oxygen, the mechanism is probably (153),

$$H\cdot + NH_2CH_2COOH \rightarrow NH_2\dot{C}HCOOH + H_2 \quad (8.141)$$

or

$$\rightarrow \cdot CH_2COOH + NH_3 \quad (8.142)$$

$$\cdot OH + NH_2CH_2COOH \rightarrow NH_2\dot{C}HCOOH + H_2O \quad (8.143)$$

$$\cdot CH_2COOH + NH_2CH_2COOH \rightarrow NH_2\dot{C}HCOOH + CH_3COOH \quad (8.144)$$

$$NH_2\dot{C}HCOOH + H_2O_2 \rightarrow \cdot OH + HN{=}CHCOOH + H_2O \quad (8.145)$$

$$2NH_2\dot{C}HCOOH \rightarrow NH_2CH_2COOH + HN{=}CHCOOH \quad (8.146)$$

$$HN{=}CHCOOH + H_2O \rightarrow OHCCOOH + NH_3 \quad (8.147)$$

or

$$\rightarrow HCHO + NH_3 + CO_2 \quad (8.148)$$

Most of the imino-acetic acid ($HN{=}CHCOOH$) hydrolyses to give glyoxylic acid (Eq. 8.147), but part gives formaldehyde and carbon dioxide (Eq. 8.148).

Direct action may be important when $1M$ aqueous glycine solutions are irradiated since an appreciable part [7.5% for x-rays (152)] of the energy absorbed is absorbed directly by the amino acid. When glycine is irradiated in the solid state the principal products isolated after dissolution in water are methylamine and carbon dioxide, and it is possible that direct action in the solution produces the same result, i.e.,

$$NH_2CH_2COOH \dashrightarrow CH_3NH_2 + CO_2 \quad (8.149)$$

Consistent with this proposal is the essentially constant yield of methylamine when glycine solutions are irradiated with α-particles and x-rays (154), though the relative yields of the other products are quite different,

TABLE 8.9 *Radiolysis of Aqueous Glycine Solutions*

(1*M* unbuffered solutions, pH 6, irradiated with x-rays)

Product	*G*(product)	
	Oxygen-saturated solutions (ref. 151)	Deaerated solutions (ref. 152)
H_2		2.02
H_2O_2	3.6	<0.01
NH_3	4.3	3.97
CO_2		0.90
HCHO	1.1	0.53
HCOOH		0.085
CH_3NH_2	0.16	0.19
CH_3COOH		1.20
OHCCOOH	3.4	2.10
$HOOCCH_2CH(NH_2)COOH$		0.25*
$HOOCCH(NH_2)CH(NH_2)COOH$		0.08*

* Ref. 153.

as would be expected if they are produced indirectly. Garrison and Weeks (153, 155) have suggested that, in deaerated solutions, glycine may be excited directly or by subexcitation electrons, the excited glycine molecule subsequently dissociating

$$NH_2CH_2COOH^* \rightarrow \cdot NH_2 + \cdot CH_2COOH \qquad (8.150)$$

$$\cdot NH_2 + NH_2CH_2COOH \rightarrow NH_2\dot{C}HCOOH + NH_3 \qquad (8.151)$$

The organic radicals then enter into the sequence of reactions given above.

When oxygen is present the mechanism is modified by the formation of peroxy radicals (153) and becomes

$$H\cdot + O_2 \rightarrow HO_2\cdot \qquad (8.34)$$

$$2HO_2\cdot \rightarrow H_2O_2 + O_2 \qquad (8.33)$$

$$\cdot OH + NH_2CH_2COOH \rightarrow NH_2\dot{C}HCOOH + H_2O \qquad (8.143)$$

$$NH_2\dot{C}HCOOH + O_2 \rightarrow HO_2\cdot + HN{=}CHCOOH \qquad (8.152)$$

$$HN{=}CHCOOH + H_2O \rightarrow OHCCOOH + NH_3 \qquad (8.147)$$

or

$$\rightarrow HCHO + NH_3 + CO_2 \qquad (8.148)$$

Hydroxyl radicals produced by Fenton's reagent react with glycine in the same way (156). Garrison and Weeks (155) found the yield of ammonia on radiolysis to be rather greater than the maximum calculable from this mechanism and postulated that direct action was also taking place in the presence of oxygen. Excited glycine molecules were postulated, as in deaerated solutions, but in the presence of oxygen these were assumed to react with hydrogen peroxide,

$$NH_2CH_2COOH^* + H_2O_2 \rightarrow \cdot OH + NH_2\dot{C}HCOOH + H_2O \quad (8.153)$$

The radicals formed were assumed to react in the normal manner.

The results described above apply to glycine solutions which contain no buffer to alter the pH of the solution (pH about 6). Quite different product yields may be found with solutions of other pH because of the amphoteric nature of both glycine and the intermediates involved in the radiolysis (157).

Cysteine

The thiol group is particularly susceptible to attack by free radicals, and it is this which is attacked when cysteine, $HSCH_2CH(NH_2)COOH$, is irradiated in aqueous solution. This is in marked contrast to the radiolysis of most amino acids since the reaction usually centers on the amino group. Radiolysis of cysteine solutions produces cystine, $HOOCCH(NH_2)CH_2S{-}SCH_2CH(NH_2)COOH$, both in the presence and absence of oxygen, but the mechanism is uncertain. When oxygen is absent the reactions taking place probably include the following (RSH = cysteine):

$$H\cdot + RSH \rightarrow RS\cdot + H_2 \quad (8.154)$$

$$\cdot OH + RSH \rightarrow RS\cdot + H_2O \quad (8.155)$$

$$2RS\cdot \rightarrow RS{-}SR \quad (8.156)$$

though the yield of cystine is higher than these reactions alone would allow for; G(cystine) is about 9 in the absence of oxygen. When oxygen is present, the yield of cystine increases very considerably and G values up to 70 have been reported (158); under these conditions the reaction must be a chain reaction, possibly

$$HO_2\cdot + RSH \rightarrow RS\cdot + H_2O_2 \quad (8.157)$$

$$RS\cdot + O_2 \rightarrow RSO_2\cdot \quad (8.158)$$

$$RSO_2\cdot + RSH \rightarrow RS{-}SR + HO_2\cdot \quad (8.159)$$

The role of hydrogen atoms in the radiolysis has been investigated by passing a stream of hydrogen diluted with helium through an electric discharge and bubbling the emergent gases through cysteine solutions (159). The main product in both acid and neutral solutions (oxygen was not present) is cystine. In alkaline solutions hydrogen sulfide is the major product and the yield of cystine falls to zero with increasing pH. The thiol group will be ionized when the solution is alkaline and reaction 8.154 may be replaced by

$$H\cdot + RS^- \rightarrow R\cdot + SH^- \qquad (8.160)$$

or

$$\rightarrow RH + S^- \qquad (8.161)$$

followed by conversion of the anion to H_2S. In another type of experiment, hydrogen abstraction by hydrogen atoms has been investigated for this system. Riesz and Burr (128) irradiated an oxygen-free, near neutral (pD 5.9), solution of the deuterium substituted cysteine, $DSCH_2CH(ND_2)COOD$, in D_2O and showed that the yield of D_2 was substantially greater than the yield when the cysteine was not present, and was much larger than the HD yield. In a similar experiment with deuterated glycine, ND_2CH_2COOD, in D_2O, HD and not D_2 was the main product of hydrogen abstraction. These results indicate that hydrogen and deuterium atoms do not abstract hydrogen from the $—NH_2$ (or $—NH_3^+$) group of amino acids but do abstract hydrogen from the —SH group of compounds such as cysteine where, for the experiment reported, about 90% of the abstraction was from the —SD group. A further interesting point that emerged from these experiments was that only about 25% of the D· atoms formed abstract hydrogen or deuterium, the remainder (which are probably solvated electrons rather than D· atoms) react with the solute by some other process.

In some cases compounds such as thiols which are very readily attacked by free radicals will protect other solutes from radical attack by preferentially reacting with the radicals. For example, Dale and Russell (160) found that cysteine and glutathione protect catalase against radiation-inactivation in aqueous solution. Protection by addition of a compound that is preferentially destroyed is referred to as "sacrificial" protection.

Chloroform

Chloroform, like most other aliphatic halogen compounds, breaks down upon irradiation in aqueous solution with the liberation of a halogen acid (hydrochloric acid in the case of chloroform). The ease with which hydrochloric acid can be determined by a variety of standard analytical procedures has prompted the suggestion that air-saturated aqueous chloroform solutions be used as a chemical dosimeter. Aqueous chloroform solutions (but not moist chloroform itself) have the advantage over many other systems containing organic halogen compounds in that the acid yield is independent of the dose rate, which is an essential prerequisite if the absorbed dose is to be measured rather than merely detected. Other products from chloroform, both in aerated and deaerated solution, are hydrogen peroxide and carbon dioxide (Table 8.10).

TABLE 8.10 *Radiolysis of Aqueous Chloroform Solutions*

(Ref. 161; saturated, 0.07M, solutions; 150 kvp x-rays)

Product	G(product)	
	Aerated solutions	Deaerated solutions
HCl	26.6	6.3
H_2O_2	2.04	1.22
CO_2	8.4	0.4

In deaerated solutions the first steps in the radiolysis mechanism are probably

$$H\cdot (\text{or } e_{aq}^-) + CHCl_3 \rightarrow \cdot CHCl_2 + HCl \quad (8.162)$$

$$\cdot OH + CHCl_3 \rightarrow \cdot CCl_3 + H_2O \quad (8.163)$$

$$Cl\cdot + CHCl_3 \rightarrow \cdot CCl_3 + HCl \quad (8.164)$$

The solutions will contain free hydrochloric acid, if not immediately, then certainly after the irradiation has been in progress for a short time, and some charge transfer between hydroxyl radicals and chloride ions to give chlorine atoms would be anticipated. The subsequent steps are uncertain, but they may include

$$\cdot OH + \cdot CCl_3 + H_2O \rightarrow CO_2 + 3HCl \quad (8.165)$$

$$H\cdot + \cdot CCl_3 \rightarrow CHCl_3 \quad (8.166)$$

$$2\cdot CCl_3 \rightarrow C_2Cl_6 \quad (8.167)$$

and similar reactions involving the $\cdot CHCl_2$ radical. When oxygen is present the mechanism will probably include

$$\cdot CCl_3 + O_2 \rightarrow \cdot OCl + COCl_2 \tag{8.168}$$

$$\cdot OCl + CHCl_3 \rightarrow Cl\cdot + COCl_2 + HCl \tag{8.169}$$

$$COCl_2 + H_2O \rightarrow CO_2 + 2HCl \tag{8.170}$$

Taken in conjunction with reaction 8.164, these steps constitute a chain reaction, though the radiolysis of chloroform is not a typical chain reaction since the acid yield is independent of the dose rate. Thus chain termination cannot be by combination of two radicals capable of propagating the chain and it probably results from the formation of a stable, unreactive radical. This might be a higher, polychloro, organic radical which would eventually disappear by combination with a similar unreactive radical (161).

TABLE 8.11 *Acid Yields from Organic Halogen Compounds Irradiated in Aqueous Solution*

(Ref. 162; $0.1M$ or $0.1N$ (acid) solutions, pH 3.5–5, irradiated with Co^{60} γ-radiation)

Compound	G(total acid) or, in parentheses, G(halide ion)		
	Air-saturated (1020 rads/min)	Air-saturated (17 rads/min)	Nitrogen-saturated (17 rads/min)
Br_3CCOOH	23	21	
	(41)	(39)	(14)
Br_3CCH_2OH	36.5	104	
	(31)	(89)	(18)
$Br_3CCH(OH)_2$	80	440	27.5
	(69)	(360)	(20.5)
$Br_2CHCH(OH)_2$	24.5	51.5	
	(21)	(35)	(16)
$Cl_3CCH(OH)_2$	43	112	19.5
$F_3CCH(OH)_2$	6.7	7.1	

Acid yields obtained by irradiating aerated aqueous solutions of several other aliphatic halogen compounds are shown in Table 8.11. In general the yields are greatest from compounds in which the carbon-halogen bonds would be expected to have the lowest bond dissociation energies. In several cases the acid yields are much larger than that from chloroform and clearly must arise from a chain reaction; in every such instance the acid yield is dose-rate dependent, suggesting a radical-radical termination reaction between reactive, chain-propagating, radicals. The chain reactions are dependent upon the presence of oxygen and a plot of acid produced against absorbed dose for these compounds is similar to that shown in Fig. 8.4 for ferrous sulfate solutions; the acid yield falls abruptly when the dissolved oxygen is used up. Radiolysis mechanisms for these compounds are more complex than for chloroform since radical attack may be on either of the two carbon atoms present. This is demonstrated by the formation of acid products other than halogen acid as shown in Table 8.11 (total acid yields were determined by titration with sodium hydroxide solution while bromide yields were determined by titration with silver nitrate solution).

The mean lifetime of the radiation-induced reaction chains in chloral hydrate solutions has been estimated by the rotating sector technique to be about 0.1 sec in γ-irradiated $1M$ solutions (163). A similar estimation using Sr^{90}-Y^{90} β-rays under roughly comparable conditions gave a mean lifetime of 0.5 sec (164).

Benzene

Table 8.12 lists the yields of major products formed from benzene on irradiation in acid or neutral aqueous solution in the presence or absence of air. Polymeric products[13] are also formed, particularly in deaerated solutions.

TABLE 8.12 *Radiolysis of Aqueous Benzene Solutions*

(Ref. 165; saturated solutions irradiated with Co^{60} γ-radiation. Acid solutions contained $0.8N$ H_2SO_4)

Product	G(product)			
	Deaerated solutions		Aerated solutions	
	(acid)	(neutral)	(acid)	(neutral)
H_2	0.39	0.42	0.39	0.42
H_2O_2	0.57	0	2.84	2.88
phenol	0.35	0.36	2.64	2.64
biphenyl	0.96	1.22	0	0

[13] The polymer has not been identified unequivocally but, with most of the authors cited, we have assumed it to be largely biphenyl.

The results in the absence of oxygen can be accounted for on the basis of a rather simple mechanism (165) ($Ph = C_6H_5$):

$$H\cdot + PhH \rightarrow PhH_2\cdot \rightarrow \text{polymer} \tag{8.171}$$

$$\cdot OH + PhH \rightarrow Ph\cdot + H_2O \tag{8.172}$$

$$\cdot OH + Ph\cdot \rightarrow PhOH \tag{8.173}$$

$$2Ph\cdot \rightarrow Ph\text{-}Ph \quad \text{(biphenyl)} \tag{8.174}$$

Phung and Burton showed clearly that hydrogen atoms add to benzene rather than abstract hydrogen from it, though the latter is the usual reaction of hydrogen atoms with saturated compounds. In neutral solutions, the "molecular" yield of hydrogen peroxide is destroyed by the reaction

$$H\cdot + H_2O_2 \rightarrow \cdot OH + H_2O \tag{8.9}$$

In order to explain the pH dependence of $G(H_2O_2)$, the authors speculate that in acid solution the ion H_2^+ is formed and is less reactive towards hydrogen peroxide than the hydrogen atom is, i.e., that reaction 8.175 is slower than reaction 8.9.

$$H_2^+ + H_2O_2 \rightarrow \cdot OH + H^+ + H_2O \tag{8.175}$$

The radical-ion H_2^+ is assumed to react with benzene just as hydrogen atoms do,

$$H_2^+ + PhH \rightarrow PhH_2\cdot + H^+ \tag{8.176}$$

It should be mentioned that an explanation of the pH dependence of $G(H_2O_2)$ can also be advanced on the assumption that the reducing species in neutral solution is the solvated electron and in acid solution the hydrogen atom.

In aerated solutions, biphenyl is not formed and the yields of hydrogen peroxide and phenol are increased. Phung and Burton (165) suggest that the mechanism is

$$\cdot OH + PhH \rightarrow Ph\cdot + H_2O \tag{8.172}$$

$$Ph\cdot + O_2 \rightarrow PhO_2\cdot \tag{8.177}$$

$$PhO_2\cdot + H_2O \rightarrow HO_2\cdot + PhOH \tag{8.178}$$

$$H\cdot + O_2 \rightarrow HO_2\cdot \tag{8.34}$$

$$2HO_2\cdot \rightarrow H_2O_2 + O_2 \tag{8.33}$$

They also include the step,

$$PhO_2\cdot + PhH \rightarrow \cdot OH + \text{oxygenated product} \tag{8.179}$$

which yields a short chain reaction, to account for the rather high consumption of oxygen; $G(-O_2) = 5.33$. A dialdehyde is also formed upon irradiation of aerated benzene solutions, but not in sufficient yield [G(aldehyde) is about 0.2] to account for the oxygen uptake (166). The aldehyde is probably mucondialdehyde (III) for which Daniels, Scholes and Weiss (166) suggest the following origin:

$$\xrightarrow{\cdot OH} \quad (H,\ OH,\ H)\ \text{(II)} \quad \xrightarrow{O_2} \quad (H,\ OH,\ O_2\cdot,\ H) \quad \longrightarrow$$

$$(H,\ OH,\ O_2H,\ H) \quad \xrightarrow{-H_2O} \quad OHC{-}CH{=}CH{-}CH{=}CH{-}CHO$$

(III)

The intermediate (II) could also be involved in the formation of phenol:

$$Ph(H)OH + O_2 \rightarrow HO_2\cdot + PhOH \qquad (8.180)$$

and, in the absence of oxygen

$$2Ph(H)OH \rightarrow PhOH + Ph(H_2)OH \qquad (8.181)$$

Evidence that Ph(H)OH (II) is an intermediate in the radiolysis of benzene solutions has been obtained by Dorfman, Bühler, and Taub (120) by a technique similar to flash spectroscopy employing a pulse of electrons in place of the photoflash. A transient species was observed in aqueous benzene solutions which could reasonably be identified with II.

At higher temperatures (about 200°C) the yield of phenol from oxygenated benzene solutions is increased to 10 to 15 times the yield at room temperature (91, 167), and the process is obviously a chain reaction.

Other Solutes

Table 8.13 lists data for a number of other compounds which have been irradiated in aqueous solution. The table is very far from complete and is intended merely to illustrate the diversity of aqueous systems which have been investigated. Only major products are given, and for detailed information the reader is referred to the references and to the current literature. The G values generally refer to x- or γ-irradiation.

TABLE 8.13 *Radiolysis of Aqueous Solutions*

Solute	Oxygen present	Products (*G* values are given in parentheses)	Ref.
Inorganic			
Arsenite	Yes	Arsenate and, in acid solution, H_2O_2	168
Nitrate	No	Nitrite	90
Phosphite	No	Phosphate	169
	Yes	Phosphate (*G* up to about 30)	
Hydrazine	No	Ammonia (about 5.2), H_2 (2.5), N_2 (2.5)	16
	Yes	(pH < 8) H_2, H_2O_2, N_2	170
Organic (aliphatic)			
Ethylene	No	(pH 1.2) H_2O_2 (0.4), aldehyde (CH_3CHO + $CH_3CH_2CH_2CHO$)(0.24), polymer	171
	Yes	(pH 1.2; 1:1 ethylene-oxygen mixture) H_2O_2 (2.4), aldehyde (HCHO + CH_3CHO) (2.4), $HOCH_2CHO$ (2.4), RO_2H (0.4)	
Propene ($CH_3CH{=}CH_2$)	Yes	(pH 1.2) $CH_3CH(O_2H)CH_2OH$ (2.6), H_2O_2 (1.9), HCHO (about 0.4), CH_3CHO (about 0.4), HCOOH (about 0.4), CH_3CH_2CHO (about 0.2)	172 173
Acetylene	Yes	(pH 1.2; 1:1 acetylene-oxygen mixture) H_2O_2 (2.6), OHC—CHO (14)	174
Oxalic acid	No	(pH < 2) G(−oxalic acid) = 4.9, CO_2 (7.8), H_2 (0.46). Suggested for use as a chemical dosimeter for high doses, e.g., 1.6 to 160 × 10^6 rads, measuring loss of acid.	175
	Yes	(pH < 2) G(−oxalic acid) = 2.9, CO_2 (5.6), H_2O_2 (4.0), H_2 (0.46)	
Glycollic acid ($HOCH_2COOH$)	No	CO_2 (0.5), HCOOH (0.5), glyoxylic acid (1.5), tartaric acid (2.1)	73 176
	Yes	CO_2 (1.9), HCOOH (1.6), glyoxylic acid (2.75), tartaric acid (0.04)	
Glyoxylic acid (OHCCOOH)	No	Oxalic acid, dimer, trimer	177
	Yes	Oxalic acid	
Lactic acid ($CH_3CHOHCOOH$)	Yes	(pH 1.2) H_2O_2 (4.2), $CH_3COCOOH$ (3.5), some CH_3CHO	178
D-Fructose	Yes	H_2O_2 (2.0), D-glucosone, glycollaldehyde, D-glyceraldehyde, glycerosone, etc.	179
Sucrose	Yes	H_2O_2 (2.0), D-glycose, D-fructose, D-glucosone, D-gluconic acid, etc.	180

TABLE 8.13 *(continued)*

Solute	Oxygen present	Products (*G* values are given in parentheses)	Ref.
Diethylamine	Yes	(*a* and *b*)(pH 2.8) H_2O_2 (2.58), CH_3CHO (about 0.77), ethylamine (about 0.8), oxime (0)	(*a*) 181 (*b*) 182
	Yes	(*b*) (pH 11) H_2O_2 (3.16), CH_3CHO (3.16), oxime (0.36)	
Acrylonitrile ($CH_2{=}CHCN$)	No	Polyacrylonitrile, repeating unit —(CH_2—CH(CN))—	183
Phenylalanine ($PhCH_2CH(NH_2)COOH$)	Yes	Phenylpyruvic acid, products formed by hydroxylation of the phenyl ring	184 185
Choline chloride ($[(CH_3)_3NCH_2CH_2OH]^+Cl^-$)		$G(-\text{choline chloride}) = 2$ to 4.5	186
Thiourea (H_2NCSNH_2)	Yes	Sulfur (*G* up to 10^4 at low dose rates)	187
Organic (aromatic)			
Toluene	Yes	Benzoic acid, HCOOH	188
Chlorobenzene	Yes	*o*-, *m*-, and *p*-chlorophenol	189
Phenol	Yes	*o*- and *p*-dihydroxybenzene, *o*-benzoquinone	190
Benzyl alcohol ($PhCH_2OH$)	Yes	H_2O_2 (3), PhCHO (1.6), phenols (1.2) (roughly equal attack on side chain and ring)	191
Benzoic acid (PhCOOH)	Yes	CO_2 (0.73), *o*-(0.74), *m*-(0.42), and *p*-hydroxybenzoic acid (0.33)	192

Summary of the Reactions of $H\cdot$, $\cdot OH$, $HO_2\cdot$, and e_{aq}^-, in Aqueous Solutions

HYDROGEN ATOMS:

$$H\cdot + \cdot OH \rightarrow H_2O \tag{8.6}$$

$$H\cdot + H\cdot \rightarrow H_2 \tag{8.7}$$

$$H\cdot + H_2O_2 \rightarrow \cdot OH + H_2O \tag{8.9}$$

$$H\cdot + H^+ \rightleftharpoons H_2^+ \tag{8.27}$$

$H\cdot + OH^- \rightleftharpoons e_{aq}^-$ (8.49)

$H\cdot + O_2 \rightarrow HO_2\cdot$ (8.34)

$H\cdot + Br\cdot \rightarrow H^+ + Br^-$ (8.62)

$H\cdot + Br_2 \rightarrow H^+ + Br^- + Br\cdot$ (8.64)

$H\cdot + H^+ + Fe^{2+} \rightarrow Fe^{3+} + H_2$ (8.78–82)

$H\cdot + Fe^{3+} \rightarrow Fe^{2+} + H^+$ (8.83)

$H\cdot + Cu^{2+} \rightarrow Cu^+ + H^+$ (8.87)

$H\cdot + Ce^{4+} \rightarrow Ce^{3+} + H^+$ (8.91)

$H\cdot + HCOOH \rightarrow \cdot COOH + H_2$ (8.101)

$H\cdot + HCOOH \rightleftharpoons H\dot{C}(OH)_2$ (8.106)

$H\cdot + CH_3COOH \rightarrow \cdot CH_2COOH + H_2$ (8.117)

$H\cdot + ClCH_2COOH \rightarrow Cl\dot{C}HCOOH + H_2$ (8.39)

$H\cdot + CH_3CH_2OH \rightarrow CH_3\dot{C}HOH + H_2$ (8.127)

$H\cdot + CH_3\dot{C}HOH \rightarrow CH_3CH_2OH$ (8.129)

$H\cdot + NH_2CH_2COOH \rightarrow NH_2\dot{C}HCOOH + H_2$ (8.141)

$H\cdot + NH_2CH_2COOH \rightarrow \cdot CH_2COOH + NH_3$ (8.142)

$H\cdot + HSCH_2CH(NH_2)COOH \rightarrow \cdot SCH_2CH(NH_2)COOH + H_2$ (8.154)

$H\cdot + CHCl_3 \rightarrow \cdot CHCl_2 + HCl$ (8.162)

$H\cdot$ + PhH (benzene) $\rightarrow PhH_2\cdot$ (8.171)

HYDROXYL RADICALS:

$\cdot OH \rightleftharpoons H^+ + O^-$ (8.46)

$\cdot OH + H\cdot \rightarrow H_2O$ (8.6)

$\cdot OH + \cdot OH \rightarrow H_2O_2$ (8.8)

$\cdot OH + HO_2\cdot \rightarrow O_2 + H_2O$ (8.35)

$\cdot OH + H_2 \rightarrow H\cdot + H_2O$ (8.10)

$\cdot OH + H_2O_2 \rightarrow HO_2\cdot + H_2O$ (8.32)

$$\cdot OH + CO \rightarrow H\cdot + CO_2 \quad (8.58)$$

$$\cdot OH + Cl^- \rightarrow Cl\cdot + OH^- \quad (8.59)$$

$$\cdot OH + Cl^- + H^+ \rightarrow Cl\cdot + H_2O \quad (8.60)$$

$$\cdot OH + Br^- \rightarrow Br\cdot + OH^- \quad (8.61)$$

$$\cdot OH + Fe^{2+} \rightarrow Fe^{3+} + OH^- \quad (8.66)$$

$$\cdot OH + Ce^{3+} \rightarrow Ce^{4+} + OH^- \quad (8.90)$$

$$\cdot OH + Tl^+ \rightarrow Tl^{2+} + OH^- \quad (8.92)$$

$$\cdot OH + HCOOH \rightarrow \cdot COOH + H_2O \quad (8.99)$$

$$\cdot OH + CH_3COOH \rightarrow \cdot CH_2COOH + H_2O \quad (8.118)$$

$$\cdot OH + CH_3CH_2OH \rightarrow CH_3\dot{C}HOH + H_2O \quad (8.128)$$

$$\cdot OH + CH_3\dot{C}HOH \rightarrow CH_3CHO + H_2O \quad (8.130)$$

$$\cdot OH + NH_2CH_2COOH \rightarrow NH_2\dot{C}HCOOH + H_2O \quad (8.143)$$

$$\cdot OH + HSCH_2CH(NH_2)COOH \rightarrow \cdot SCH_2CH(NH_2)COOH + H_2O \quad (8.155)$$

$$\cdot OH + CHCl_3 \rightarrow \cdot CCl_3 + H_2O \quad (8.163)$$

$$\cdot OH + \cdot CCl_3 + H_2O \rightarrow CO_2 + 3HCl \quad (8.165)$$

$$\cdot OH + PhH \text{ (benzene)} \rightarrow Ph\cdot + H_2O \quad (8.172)$$

or $\rightarrow Ph(H)OH$

$$\cdot OH + Ph\cdot \rightarrow PhOH \quad (8.173)$$

PERHYDROXYL RADICALS:

$$HO_2\cdot \rightleftharpoons H^+ + O_2^- \quad (8.47)$$

$$HO_2\cdot + HO_2\cdot \rightarrow H_2O_2 + O_2 \quad (8.33)$$

$$HO_2\cdot + \cdot OH \rightarrow O_2 + H_2O \quad (8.35)$$

$$HO_2\cdot + Br\cdot \rightarrow H^+ + Br^- + O_2 \quad (8.65)$$

$$HO_2\cdot + Fe^{2+} \rightarrow Fe^{3+} + HO_2^- \quad (8.68)$$

$$HO_2\cdot + Fe^{3+} \rightarrow Fe^{2+} + H^+ + O_2 \quad (8.84)$$

$$HO_2\cdot + Cu^{2+} \rightarrow Cu^+ + H^+ + O_2 \quad (8.85)$$

$$HO_2\cdot + Ce^{4+} \rightarrow Ce^{3+} + H^+ + O_2 \quad (8.88)$$

$$HO_2\cdot + CH_3C(O_2\cdot)HOH \rightarrow CH_3CHO + H_2O_2 + O_2 \quad (8.136)$$

SOLVATED ELECTRONS:

$$e_{aq}^- + H_2O \rightarrow H\cdot + OH^- \quad (8.23)$$

$$e_{aq}^- + e_{aq}^- \rightarrow H_2 + 2OH^- \quad (8.24)$$

$$e_{aq}^- + H^+ \rightleftharpoons H\cdot \quad (8.45)$$

$$e_{aq}^- + H_2O_2 \rightarrow \cdot OH + OH^- \quad (8.37)$$

$$e_{aq}^- + O_2 \rightarrow O_2^- \quad (O_2^- + H^+ \rightleftharpoons HO_2\cdot) \quad (8.38)$$

$$e_{aq}^- + ClCH_2COO^- \rightarrow \cdot CH_2COO^- + Cl^- \quad (8.40)$$

$$e_{aq}^- + NO_2^- \rightarrow NO_2^{2-} \quad (8.41)$$

$$e_{aq}^- + N_2O \rightarrow O^- + N_2 \quad (O^- + H^+ \rightleftharpoons \cdot OH) \quad (8.57)$$

REFERENCES

Authoritative reviews of the radiation chemistry of aqueous solutions have been published by A. O. Allen, *The Radiation Chemistry of Water and Aqueous Solutions,* Van Nostrand, Princeton, New Jersey, 1961, by E. J. Hart and R. L. Platzman in *Mechanisms in Radiobiology* (eds. M. Errera and A. Forssberg), Academic Press Inc., New York, 1961, Vol. 1, and by M. Lefort in *Actions Chimiques et Biologiques des Radiations,* (ed. M. Haissinsky) Masson et Cie, Paris, Vol. 1, 1955. Aqueous solutions of a variety of complex substances of biological interest are discussed by A. J. Swallow in *Radiation Chemistry of Organic Compounds,* Pergamon Press, Oxford, 1960.

1. A. Debierne, *Ann. Physique (Paris),* **2,** 97 (1914).
2. O. Risse, *Strahlentherapie,* **34,** 578 (1929).
3. J. Weiss, *Nature,* **153,** 748 (1944).
4. A. O. Allen, *J. Phys. Colloid Chem.,* **52,** 479 (1948).
5. M. Burton, *Ann. Rev. Phys. Chem.,* **1,** 113 (1950).
6. H. Fricke, *Cold Spring Harbor Symp.,* **2,** 241 (1934); **3,** 55 (1935).
7. E. J. Hart, *J. Chem. Educ.,* **36,** 266 (1959).
8. K. J. Laidler, *J. Chem. Phys.,* **22,** 1740 (1954).
9. M. Cottin, *J. Chim. Phys.,* **56,** 1024 (1959).
10. H. D. Smyth and D. W. Mueller, *Phys. Rev.,* **43,** 116 (1933).
11. M. M. Mann, A. Hustrulid, and J. T. Tate, *Phys. Rev.,* **58,** 340 (1940).
12. H. A. Dewhurst, A. H. Samuel, and J. L. Magee, *Radiation Res.,* **1,** 62 (1954).
13. P. Alexander and D. Rosen, *Nature,* **188,** 574 (1960); *Radiation Res.,* **15,** 475 (1961).
14. A. J. Swallow and J. A. Velandia, *Nature,* **195,** 798 (1962).

15. R. F. Firestone, *J. Am. Chem. Soc.*, **79,** 5593 (1957).
16. H. A. Dewhurst and M. Burton, *J. Am. Chem. Soc.*, **77,** 5781 (1955).
17. E. J. Hart, *J. Chem. Educ.*, **34,** 586 (1957).
18. J. Barrett and J. H. Baxendale, *Trans. Faraday Soc.*, **56,** 37 (1960).
19. J. H. Baxendale, *Radiation Res.*, **17,** 312 (1962).
20. P. Kelly, T. Rigg, and J. Weiss, *Nature,* **173,** 1130 (1954).
21. F. S. Dainton and D. B. Peterson, *Proc. Roy. Soc. (London), Ser. A* **267,** 443 (1962).
22. F. S. Dainton and W. S. Watt, *Nature,* **195,** 1294 (1962).
23. F. S. Dainton, *Brit. J. Radiol.*, **31,** 645 (1958).
24. A. H. Samuel and J. L. Magee, *J. Chem. Phys.*, **21,** 1080 (1953).
25. F. W. Lampe, F. H. Field, and J. L. Franklin, *J. Am. Chem. Soc.*, **79,** 6132 (1957).
26. D. E. Lea in *Actions of Radiations on Living Cells,* Cambridge University Press, Cambridge, 1946.
27. L. H. Gray, *J. Chim. Phys.*, **48,** 172 (1951).
28. J. L. Magee and M. Burton, *J. Am. Chem. Soc.*, **73,** 523 (1951).
29. R. L. Platzman in *Basic Mechanisms in Radiobiology, Nat. Res. Council Publication 305,* Washington, D.C., 1953.
30. M. Burton in *Actions Chimiques et Biologiques des Radiations,* (ed. M. Haissinsky) Masson et Cie, Paris, Vol. 3, 1958.
31. R. G. Sowden, *J. Am. Chem. Soc.*, **79,** 1263 (1957).
32. J. Rotblat and H. C. Sutton, *Proc. Roy. Soc. (London), Ser. A* **255,** 490 (1960).
33. A. R. Anderson and E. J. Hart, *J. Phys. Chem.*, **66,** 70 (1962).
34. J. K. Thomas and E. J. Hart, *Radiation Res.*, **17,** 408 (1962).
35. H. Fricke, *Ann. N.Y. Acad. Sci.*, **59,** 567 (1955).
36. A. O. Allen and H. A. Schwarz, *Proc. Second Intern. Conf. Peaceful Uses Atomic Energy,* United Nations, Geneva, **29,** 30 (1958).
37. C. J. Hochanadel and S. C. Lind, *Ann. Rev. Phys. Chem.*, **7,** 83 (1956).
38. E. Collinson, F. S. Dainton, and J. Kroh, *Nature,* **187,** 475 (1960).
39. M. Lefort and X. Tarrago, *J. Phys. Chem.*, **63,** 833 (1959).
40. M. Lefort, *Ann. Rev. Phys. Chem.*, **9,** 123 (1958).
41. C. J. Hochanadel and J. A. Ghormley, *Radiation Res.*, **16,** 653 (1962).
42. C. J. Hochanadel in *Comparative Effects of Radiation,* (eds. M. Burton, J. S. Kirby-Smith, and J. L. Magee) John Wiley and Sons, New York, 1960, Chapter 8.
43. A. O. Allen, *Radiation Res.*, **1,** 85 (1954).
44. F. S. Dainton, *Radiation Res. Suppl. 1,* 1 (1959).
45. R. L. Platzman in *Radiation Biology and Medicine* (ed. W. D. Claus), Addison-Wesley, Reading, Mass., 1958.
46. A. Kupperman, *J. Chem. Educ.*, **36,** 279 (1959), and in *Actions Chimiques et Biologiques des Radiations,* (ed. M. Haissinsky) Masson et Cie, Paris, Vol. 5, 1961.
47. J. Jortner and G. Stein, *Intern. J. Appl. Radiation Isotopes,* **7,** 198 (1960).
48. K. Coatsworth, E. Collinson, and F. S. Dainton, *Trans. Faraday Soc.*, **56,** 1008 (1960).
49. D. A. Armstrong, E. Collinson, and F. S. Dainton, *Trans. Faraday Soc.*, **55,** 1375 (1959).

50. D. Cleaver, E. Collinson, and F. S. Dainton, *Trans. Faraday Soc.,* **56,** 1640 (1960).
51. C. Ferradini in *Advances in Inorganic Chemistry and Radiochemistry,* (eds. H. J. Emeléus and A. G. Sharpe) Academic Press Inc., New York, Vol. 3, 1961.
52. E. J. Hart, *Radiation Res.,* **2,** 33 (1955).
53. D. M. Donaldson and N. Miller, *Trans. Faraday Soc.,* **52,** 652 (1956).
54. N. F. Barr and A. O. Allen, *J. Phys. Chem.,* **63,** 928 (1959).
55. A. R. Anderson and E. J. Hart, *J. Phys. Chem.,* **65,** 804 (1961).
56. G. Czapski, J. Jortner, and G. Stein, *J. Phys. Chem.,* **65,** 964 (1961); J. Jortner and J. Rabani, *J. Phys. Chem.,* **66,** 2078 (1962).
57. E. Hayon and A. O. Allen, *J. Phys. Chem.,* **65,** 2181 (1961).
58. J. Jortner and J. Rabani, *J. Am. Chem. Soc.,* **83,** 4868 (1961); *J. Phys. Chem.,* **66,** 2081 (1962).
59. J. T. Allan and G. Scholes, *Nature,* **187,** 218 (1960).
60. J. H. Baxendale and R. S. Dixon, *Proc. Chem. Soc.,* 148 (1963).
61. G. Czapski and H. A. Schwarz, *J. Phys. Chem.,* **66,** 471 (1962).
62. E. Collinson, F. S. Dainton, D. R. Smith, and S. Tazuké, *Proc. Chem. Soc.,* 140 (1962).
63. A. Hummel and A. O. Allen, *Radiation Res.,* **17,** 302 (1962).
64. J. Rabani and G. Stein, *J. Chem. Phys.,* **37,** 1865 (1962).
65. J. H. Baxendale, J. K. Thomas, and T. Woodward, reported by M. S. Matheson, *Ann. Rev. Phys. Chem.,* **13,** 77 (1962).
66. G. Czapski and A. O. Allen, *J. Phys. Chem.,* **66,** 262 (1962).
67. P. Kelly and M. Smith, *J. Chem. Soc.,* 1487 (1961).
68. J. Rabani, *J. Am. Chem. Soc.,* **84,** 868 (1962).
69. E. Hayon, *Nature,* **196,** 533 (1962).
70. E. Hayon, *Nature,* **194,** 737 (1962).
71. C. Lifshitz, *Can. J. Chem.,* **40,** 1903 (1962).
72. J. Weiss, *Nature,* **186,** 751 (1960).
73. E. Hayon and J. Weiss, *J. Chem. Soc.,* 5091 (1960).
74. E. J. Hart and J. W. Boag, *J. Am. Chem. Soc.,* **84,** 4090 (1962); J. W. Boag and E. J. Hart, *Nature,* **197,** 45 (1963).
75. S. Gordon, E. J. Hart, M. S. Matheson, J. Rabani, and J. K. Thomas, *J. Am. Chem. Soc.,* **85,** 1375 (1963).
76. F. S. Dainton and S. A. Sills, *Proc. Chem. Soc.,* 223 (1962).
77. P. Riesz and E. J. Hart, *J. Phys. Chem.,* **63,** 858 (1959).
78. J. Weiss, *Nature,* **165,** 728 (1950).
79. T. Rigg, G. Stein, and J. Weiss, *Proc. Roy. Soc. (London), Ser. A* **211,** 375 (1952).
80. E. J. Hart, S. Gordon, and D. A. Hutchison, *J. Am. Chem. Soc.,* **74,** 5548 (1952); *J. Chim. Phys.,* **52,** 570 (1955).
81. M. G. Evans, N. S. Hush, and N. Uri, *Quart. Rev.,* **6,** 186 (1952).
82. W. G. Barb, J. H. Baxendale, P. George, and K. R. Hargrave, *Trans. Faraday Soc.,* **47,** 462, 591 (1951).
83. E. Hayon and J. Weiss, *Proc. Second Intern. Conf. Peaceful Uses Atomic Energy,* United Nations, Geneva, **29,** 80 (1958).
84. J. T. Allan, M. G. Robinson, and G. Scholes, *Proc. Chem. Soc.,* 381 (1962).
85. J. A. Ghormley and A. C. Stewart, *J. Am. Chem. Soc.,* **78,** 2934 (1956).

86. L. H. Piette, R. C. Rempel, H. E. Weaver, and J. M. Flournoy, *J. Chem. Phys.,* **30,** 1623 (1959).
87. J. Kroh, B. C. Green, and J. W. T. Spinks, *Can. J. Chem.,* **40,** 413 (1962).
88. R. Livingston, H. Zeldes, and E. H. Taylor, *Discuss. Faraday Soc.,* **19,** 166 (1955).
89. J. A. Ghormley, *J. Chem. Phys.,* **24,** 1111 (1956).
90. H. A. Mahlman and G. K. Schweitzer, *J. Inorg. Nucl. Chem.,* **5,** 213 (1958).
91. M. A. Proskurnin and Y. M. Kolotyrkin, *Proc. Second Intern. Conf. Peaceful Uses Atomic Energy,* United Nations, Geneva, **29,** 52 (1958).
92. V. A. Sharpatyi, V. D. Orekhov, and M. A. Proskurnin, *Dokl. Akad. Nauk SSSR,* **122,** 852 (1958); **124,** 1279 (1959).
93. E. J. Hart, *J. Am. Chem. Soc.,* **73,** 68 (1951).
94. F. S. Dainton and D. B. Peterson, *Nature,* **186,** 878 (1960).
95. J. Jortner, M. Ottolenghi, and G. Stein, *J. Phys. Chem.,* **66,** 2037 (1962).
96. F. S. Dainton and T. J. Hardwick, *Trans. Faraday Soc.,* **53,** 333 (1957).
97. A. O. Allen, *The Radiation Chemistry of Water and Aqueous Solutions,* Van Nostrand, Princeton, New Jersey, 1961, p. 63.
98. E. R. Johnson and A. O. Allen, *J. Am. Chem. Soc.,* **74,** 4147 (1952).
99. C. J. Hochanadel, *J. Phys. Chem.,* **56,** 587 (1952).
100. H. A. Schwarz, J. M. Caffrey, and G. Scholes, *J. Am. Chem. Soc.,* **81,** 1801 (1959).
101. H. A. Dewhurst, *J. Chem. Phys.,* **19,** 1329 (1951); *Trans. Faraday Soc.,* **48,** 905 (1952).
102. E. J. Hart, *J. Am. Chem. Soc.,* **74,** 4174 (1952).
103. T. W. Davis, S. Gordon, and E. J. Hart, *J. Am. Chem. Soc.,* **80,** 4487 (1958).
104. N. Uri, *Chem. Rev.,* **50,** 375 (1952).
105. G. Czapski, J. Jortner, and G. Stein, *J. Phys. Chem.,* **65,** 960 (1961).
106. F. S. Dainton and H. C. Sutton, *Trans. Faraday Soc.,* **49,** 1011 (1953).
107. E. J. Hart and P. D. Walsh, *Radiation Res.,* **1,** 342 (1954).
108. E. J. Hart, W. J. Ramler, and S. R. Rocklin, *Radiation Res.,* **4,** 378 (1956).
109. T. J. Sworski, *Radiation Res.,* **4,** 483 (1956).
110. C. B. Senvar and E. J. Hart, *Proc. Second Intern. Conf. Peaceful Uses Atomic Energy,* United Nations, Geneva, **29,** 19 (1958).
111. T. J. Sworski, *J. Am. Chem. Soc.,* **76,** 4687 (1954); *Radiation Res.,* **2,** 26 (1955).
112. H. A. Schwarz, *J. Am. Chem. Soc.,* **77,** 4960 (1955).
113. J. A. Ghormley and C. J. Hochanadel, *Radiation Res.,* **3,** 227 (1955).
114. J. L. Magee, *J. Chim. Phys.,* **52,** 528 (1955); A. K. Ganguly and J. L. Magee, *J. Chem. Phys.,* **25,** 129 (1956).
115. M. Burton and K. C. Kurien, *J. Phys. Chem.,* **63,** 899 (1959).
116. A. Kuppermann, *Nucleonics,* **19,** (Oct.), 38 (1961); in *Actions Chimiques et Biologiques des Radiations,* (ed. M. Haissinsky) Masson et Cie, Paris, Vol. 5, p. 85 (1961).
117. A. Kuppermann and G. G. Belford, *J. Chem. Phys.,* **36,** 1412 (1962).
118. A. J. Swallow, *Radiation Chemistry of Organic Compounds,* Pergamon Press, Oxford, 1960, pp. 55, 56.
119. H. A. Schwarz, *J. Phys. Chem.,* **66,** 255 (1962).
120. L. M. Dorfman, R. E. Bühler, and I. A. Taub, *J. Chem. Phys.,* **36,** 549, 3051 (1962).

121. E. J. Hart, *J. Am. Chem. Soc.*, **76,** 4198 (1954).
122. E. J. Hart, *J. Am. Chem. Soc.*, **76,** 4312 (1954).
123. E. J. Hart, *Radiation Res.*, **1,** 53 (1954).
124. A. R. Anderson and E. J. Hart, *Radiation Res.*, **14,** 689 (1961).
125. H. Fricke, E. J. Hart, and H. P. Smith, *J. Chem. Phys.*, **6,** 229 (1938).
126. E. J. Hart, *J. Am. Chem. Soc.*, **73,** 68 (1951).
127. E. J. Hart, *J. Phys. Chem.*, **56,** 594 (1952).
128. P. Riesz and B. E. Burr, *Radiation Res.*, **16,** 661 (1962).
129. E. J. Hart, *J. Am. Chem. Soc.*, **83,** 567 (1961).
130. T. J. Hardwick and W. S. Guentner, *J. Phys. Chem.*, **63,** 896 (1959).
131. T. J. Hardwick, *Radiation Res.*, **12,** 5 (1960).
132. W. M. Garrison, W. Bennett, and M. Jayko, *J. Chem. Phys.*, **24,** 631 (1956).
133. W. M. Garrison, W. Bennett, and S. Cole, *Radiation Res.*, **9,** 647 (1958).
134. D. Smithies and E. J. Hart, *J. Am. Chem. Soc.*, **82,** 4775 (1960).
135. G. E. Adams and E. J. Hart, *J. Am. Chem. Soc.*, **84,** 3994 (1962).
136. W. M. Garrison, W. Bennett, S. Cole, H. R. Haymond, and B. M. Weeks, *J. Am. Chem. Soc.*, **77,** 2720 (1955).
137. W. M. Garrison, H. R. Haymond, D. C. Morrison, B. M. Weeks, and J Gile-Melchert, *J. Am. Chem. Soc.*, **75,** 2459 (1953).
138. W. M. Garrison, H. R. Haymond, W. Bennett, and S. Cole, *J. Chem. Phys.*, **25,** 1282 (1956) ; *Radiation Res.*, **10,** 273 (1959).
139. G. G. Jayson, G. Scholes, and J. Weiss, *J. Chem. Soc.*, 1358 (1957).
140. H. A. Schwarz, J. M. Caffrey, and G. Scholes, *J. Am. Chem. Soc.*, **81,** 1801 (1959).
141. A. Hummel and A. O. Allen, *Radiation Res.*, **17,** 302 (1962).
142. J. T. Allan, E. M. Hayon, and J. Weiss, *J. Chem. Soc.*, 3913 (1959).
143. P. M. Grant and R. B. Ward, *J. Chem. Soc.*, 2871 (1959).
144. S. A. Barker, P. M. Grant, M. Stacey, and R. B. Ward, *J. Chem. Soc.*, 2648 (1959).
145. G. O. Phillips, G. L. Mattok, and G. J. Moody, *Proc. Second Intern. Conf. Peaceful Uses Atomic Energy*, United Nations, Geneva, **29,** 92 (1958); *J. Chem. Soc.*, 3522 (1958).
146. G. O. Phillips and G. J. Moody, *Intern. J. Appl. Radiation Isotopes*, **6,** 78 (1959).
147. H. J. H. Fenton and H. Jackson, *J. Chem. Soc.*, **75,** 1 (1899).
148. G. O. Phillips, *J. Chem. Soc.*, 297 (1963).
149. A. Th. Küchlin, *Rec. Trav. Chim.*, **51,** 887 (1932).
150. S. V. Starodubtsev, Sh. A. Ablyaev, and V. V. Generalova, *Soviet. J. At. Energy*, **8,** 264 (1960).
151. C. R. Maxwell, D. C. Peterson, and W. C. White, *Radiation Res.*, **2,** 431 (1955).
152. C. R. Maxwell, D. C. Peterson, and N. E. Sharpless, *Radiation Res.*, **1,** 530 (1954).
153. B. M. Weeks and W. M. Garrison, *Radiation Res.*, **9,** 291 (1958).
154. C. R. Maxwell and D. C. Peterson, *J. Phys. Chem.*, **63,** 935 (1959).
155. W. M. Garrison and B. M. Weeks, *J. Chem. Phys.*, **25,** 585 (1956).
156. C. R. Maxwell and D. C. Peterson, *J. Am. Chem. Soc.*, **79,** 5110 (1957).
157. G. Stein and J. Weiss, *J. Chem. Soc.*, 3256 (1949).

158. A. J. Swallow, *J. Chem. Soc.*, 1334 (1952).
159. F. E. Littman, E. M. Carr, and A. P. Brady, *Radiation Res.*, **7**, 107 (1957).
160. W. M. Dale and C. Russell, *Biochem. J.*, **62**, 50 (1956).
161. J. Teply, *Collection Czech. Chem. Commun.*, **25**, 24 (1960).
162. R. J. Woods and J. W. T. Spinks, *Can. J. Chem.*, **38**, 77 (1960).
163. G. R. Freeman, A. B. Van Cleave, and J. W. T. Spinks, *Can. J. Chem.*, **32**, 322 (1954).
164. R. F. Platford and J. W. T. Spinks, *Can. J. Chem.*, **37**, 1022 (1959).
165. P. V. Phung and M. Burton, *Radiation Res.*, **7**, 199 (1957).
166. M. Daniels, G. Scholes, and J. Weiss, *J. Chem. Soc.*, 832 (1956).
167. M. A. Proskurnin, E. V. Barelko, and L. I. Kartasheva, *Dokl. Akad. Nauk SSSR.*, **121**, 671 (1958).
168. M. Daniels and J. Weiss, *J. Chem. Soc.*, 2467 (1958).
169. M. Cottin, *J. Chim. Phys.*, **53**, 917 (1956).
170. M. Lefort and M. Haissinsky, *J. Chim. Phys.*, **53**, 527 (1956).
171. P. G. Clay, G. R. A. Johnson, and J. Weiss, *J. Chem. Soc.*, 2175 (1958).
172. P. G. Clay, J. Weiss, and J. Whiston, *Proc. Chem. Soc.*, 125 (1959).
173. G. Scholes and J. Weiss, *Nature*, **185**, 305 (1960).
174. P. G. Clay, G. R. A. Johnson and J. Weiss, *J. Phys. Chem.*, **63**, 862 (1959).
175. I. Draganic, *J. Chim. Phys.*, **56**, 9, 16, 18 (1959); *Nucleonics*, **21**, (Feb.), 33 (1963).
176. P. M. Grant and R. B. Ward, *J. Chem. Soc.*, 2654, 2659 (1959).
177. S. A. Barker, P. M. Grant, M. Stacey, and R. B. Ward, *Nature*, **183**, 376 (1959).
178. G. R. A. Johnson, G. Scholes and J. Weiss, *J. Chem. Soc.*, 3091 (1953).
179. G. O. Phillips and G. J. Moody, *J. Chem. Soc.*, 754 (1960).
180. G. O. Phillips and G. J. Moody, *J. Chem. Soc.*, 762 (1960).
181. M. E. Jayko and W. M. Garrison, *J. Chem. Phys.*, **25**, 1084 (1956).
182. G. G. Jayson, G. Scholes, and J. Weiss, *J. Chem. Soc.*, 2594 (1955).
183. F. S. Dainton, *J. Phys. Colloid Chem.*, **52**, 490 (1948).
184. J. Nosworthy and C. B. Allsopp, *J. Colloid Sci.*, **11**, 565 (1956).
185. C. Vermeil and M. Lefort, *Compt. Rend.*, **244**, 889 (1957).
186. R. M. Lemmon, P. K. Gordon, M. A. Parsons, and F. Mazzetti, *J. Am. Chem. Soc.*, **80**, 2730 (1958).
187. W. M. Dale and J. V. Davies, *Radiation Res.*, **7**, 35 (1957).
188. A. Kailan, *Monatsh. Chem.*, **40**, 445 (1920).
189. G. R. A. Johnson, G. Stein, and J. Weiss, *J. Chem. Soc.*, 3275 (1951).
190. G. Stein and J. Weiss, *J. Chem. Soc.*, 3265 (1951).
191. N. Bach, *Proc. Intern. Conf. Peaceful Uses Atomic Energy*, United Nations, New York, **7**, 538 (1956).
192. A. M. Downes, *Australian J. Chem.*, **11**, 154 (1958).

CHAPTER 9

Aliphatic Compounds[1]

A wide variety of organic compounds have been irradiated. In this and the two succeeding chapters we have attempted only to present some examples illustrating current work. Several gaseous hydrocarbons have already been mentioned (Chapter 7) and aqueous solutions of organic compounds have been included in Chapter 8.

It might be pointed out here that many of the radiolysis mechanisms given in this chapter are, to some degree, speculative or incomplete; certainly none should be regarded as unalterable. Until recently emphasis has been almost entirely upon the free radicals formed upon irradiation, and mechanisms have been based on the reactions of these species alone. It now seems clear, however, that reactions of the primary ions and excited molecules should not be neglected. Nevertheless, and in spite of the reservation that such mechanisms are likely to be incomplete, radical reactions do provide a useful basis for interpreting the action of radiation on many organic systems.

[1] Unless the contrary is stated it should be assumed that the organic compound is free of air or oxygen.

The primary processes in the radiolysis of organic compounds can, in most cases, be represented by (1, 2):

$$\text{(excitation)} \qquad A \rightsquigarrow A^* \tag{9.1}$$

$$\text{(ionization)} \qquad A \rightsquigarrow A^+ + e^- \tag{9.2}$$

$$\text{(ion dissociation)} \qquad A^+ \rightarrow R\cdot^+ + S\cdot \tag{9.3}$$

$$A^+ \rightarrow M^+ + N \tag{9.4}$$

$$\text{(neutralization)} \qquad A^+ + e^- \rightarrow A^{**} \tag{9.5}$$

$$\text{(dissociation)} \qquad A^* \text{ and } A^{**} \rightarrow R\cdot + S\cdot \tag{9.6}$$

$$A^* \text{ and } A^{**} \rightarrow M + N \tag{9.7}$$

where R· and S· are free radicals and M and N are molecular products. Excited molecules and ions are initially distributed along the track of the ionizing particle in small groups or spurs, which may overlap neighboring spurs as the active species (at this stage mainly free radicals) diffuse apart. Whether or not the expanding spurs overlap before these species have reacted depends upon the spacing of the spurs along the particle track and hence upon the LET of the ionizing particle. Electrons ejected in the ionization step are normally slowed down and return to neutralize the parent ion within 10^{-13} sec (3), producing a highly excited molecule (A**). Neutralization of the parent ion in this fashion corresponds to the Samuel-Magee model for the radiolysis of water (3) which, in the case of organic liquids, is favored over the alternative Lea-Gray-Platzman model (see Chapter 8) since these liquids have lower dielectric constants and, generally, lower electron affinities than water. The highly excited molecule formed by ion-recombination will most likely rapidly dissociate into free radicals, though molecular products can also be formed in this way. Primary excited molecules (A*) may also dissociate into radical or molecular products, though it has generally been assumed that these will be formed with less extra energy than products from the dissociation of the secondary excited molecules (A**). A radical pair formed by dissociation of a primary excited molecule may therefore be unable to escape from its solvent cage before the radicals react together, reforming the parent molecule (Franck-Rabinowitch effect).[2] Such radical recombination, or caging, is particularly likely if the radicals are both bulky. Molecular dissociation products are not subject to caging since they will not react together should they collide. The intermediate

[2] The radical reaction need not reform the parent molecule, since disproportionation may occur to give new products.

positive ions may also dissociate to either radical or molecular products (Eqs. 9.3 and 9.4) before neutralization occurs. Other reactions involving ions or excited molecules are possible and have been discussed in Chapter 5; ion-molecule reactions are one of the more important omissions from the simple scheme shown above.

The radiolysis of organic liquids differs from the radiolysis of water since generally some of the radicals formed can react with the solvent, whereas hydrogen atoms and hydroxyl radicals do not react with water but only between themselves or with dissolved substances. Radicals formed in an organic liquid will in fact react predominantly with the liquid if this reaction is at all facile. Hydrogen atoms, for example, rarely combine to form molecular hydrogen in organic systems but instead abstract hydrogen or halogen from the solvent, or add to it. Track effects may be unimportant in the radiolysis of organic compounds because of such radical-solvent reactions; for instance, product yields may be independent of LET. This is not invariably true and some organic materials (e.g., alcohols) behave in the same way as water, giving product yields which are dependent upon LET.

In organic media, as in aqueous solutions, it is often possible to distinguish between "radical" and "molecular" products.[3] Radical products are those which are formed via scavengeable free radicals and which are eliminated by the presence of an efficient radical scavenger. The term may also be applied to the scavengeable free radicals themselves. Molecular products are those not affected by scavenger, and hence formed by unimolecular or other nonradical processes or by radical reactions which are inaccessible to scavenger (e.g., radical reactions occurring within a spur). In many radiolysis reactions a product may be formed partly by a radical and partly by a molecular mechanism. For instance, a particular radical-molecule reaction may give both types of product depending on whether the individual radicals react as hot radicals (molecular product) or are reduced to thermal energies before reacting (radical product). Radical-radical reactions can give products which are classed as molecular if the reaction occurs within a spur or solvent cage, and as radical products if the radicals diffuse into the bulk of the medium and react there. Molecular products may also be formed by processes which involve ions or excited states instead of free radicals.

Photochemical and mass-spectrometric data are valuable aids in elucidating radiolysis mechanisms. Photochemical data are perhaps

[3] Radical and molecular yields of product will be distinguished from over-all product yields by the use of subscripts, as for aqueous solutions. For example, the radical and molecular yields of hydrogen would be G_{H} and $G_{\mathrm{H_2}}$ respectively.

rather less useful in the case of liquid materials than for gaseous systems, since in the liquid there is a greater possibility of the excited states being quenched before any chemical change occurs, or of radical dissociation products being caged and recombining with, again, no over-all chemical effect. Mass spectrometric data can also be applied with more confidence to gaseous systems, which approach more closely to the conditions in the mass spectrometer; but, used with caution, such information appears pertinent to liquid systems also.

Finally, it may be remarked that since ionizing radiation produces free radicals in all organic materials, any reaction which normally proceeds by way of radical intermediates can be expected to occur under the influence of radiation. This opens up a wide field of radiation chemistry which is barely touched upon in this chapter, where we have confined our attention mainly to pure compounds. It should be pointed out, however, that ionizing radiation is rarely the most economic means of producing free radicals in a reaction mixture and it is likely to be less specific than chemical or photochemical methods.

SATURATED HYDROCARBONS[4]

The radiolysis of saturated aliphatic hydrocarbons (alkanes) offers an opportunity to correlate radiolysis products with the length of the carbon chain in the absence of reactive chemical groups. Upon irradiation both carbon-carbon and carbon-hydrogen bonds are broken and it is found, making a rather rough generalization, that all carbon-carbon and all carbon-hydrogen bonds are equally likely to rupture. Furthermore, carbon-carbon and carbon-hydrogen bond scission are of comparable importance. This tendency towards random splitting of the chemical bonds present in the hydrocarbons can be illustrated by reference to the radiolysis products and to the radicals detected by scavenger experiments. Methane, for example, becomes less important a product as the proportion of terminal methyl groups present falls (i.e., as the chain length increases in straight-chain alkanes), whereas the yield of hydrogen shows much less variation, consistent with the relatively constant proportion of carbon-hydrogen bonds in these hydrocarbons (Table 9.1; ref. 7).

Radiolysis of the alkanes produces other products beside hydrogen and methane. These include low molecular-weight saturated hydrocarbons with the same or fewer carbon atoms than the parent alkane, intermediate molecular-weight hydrocarbons with a number of carbon

[4] Unsaturated hydrocarbons are considered in Chapter 11.

TABLE 9.1 *Yields of Hydrogen and Methane from Saturated Hydrocarbons*

Hydrocarbon	Structure	$G(H_2)$	$G(CH_4)$
Vapor phase (α-irradiation; ref. 4)			
Propane	$CH_3—CH_2—CH_3$	8.2	0.37
Butane	$CH_3—(CH_2)_2—CH_3$	9.0	1.2
Pentane	$CH_3—(CH_2)_3—CH_3$	7.3	0.81
Hexane	$CH_3—(CH_2)_4—CH_3$	5.6	0.78
Isobutane	$(CH_3)_2CH—CH_3$	7.4	2.7
Neopentane	$(CH_3)_4C$	2.0	2.0
Liquid phase (800 kvp electron irradiation; refs. 5, 6)			
Cyclohexane*	$(CH_2)_6$	5.55–5.85	0.09–0.021
Pentane	$CH_3—(CH_2)_3—CH_3$	4.2	0.4
Hexane	$CH_3—(CH_2)_4—CH_3$	5.0	0.15
Heptane	$CH_3—(CH_2)_5—CH_3$	4.7	0.09
Octane	$CH_3—(CH_2)_6—CH_3$	4.8	0.08
Nonane	$CH_3—(CH_2)_7—CH_3$	5.0	0.07
Decane	$CH_3—(CH_2)_8—CH_3$	5.2	0.06
Dodecane	$CH_3—(CH_2)_{10}—CH_3$	4.9	0.05
Hexadecane	$CH_3—(CH_2)_{14}—CH_3$	4.8	0.04
2-Methylpentane	$(CH_3)_2CH—CH_2—CH_2—CH_3$	4.0	0.5
2,2-Dimethylbutane	$(CH_3)_3C—CH_2—CH_3$	2.0	1.2

* See Table 9.3.

atoms intermediate between those of the parent and its dimer, dimeric products with twice as many carbon atoms as the parent, and unsaturated hydrocarbons with a range of molecular weights; G(-alkane) is generally between 6 and 10. With straight-chain alkanes, products with fewer carbon atoms than the parent tend to become less important as the chain length is increased — the higher alkanes giving mainly products with more carbon atoms than the parent. The effect of radiation on these compounds is therefore to increase the average molecular weight of the hydrocarbon, and this is shown by changes in the physical properties of the material. The most obvious change is the formation of an insoluble gel in liquid hydrocarbons and an increase in the melting point of solid hydrocarbons when these are exposed to rather large amounts of radiation. This is illustrated particularly well by the cross-linking of polymers such as polyethylene (cf. Chapter 11). The unsaturated products formed from alkanes are efficient radical scavengers and, as their concentration builds up, may markedly influence the later stages of the radiolysis.

Closer examination of the yields of products from irradiated alkanes shows that the hydrogen and methane yields are only approximately proportional to the proportions of C—H and C—CH_3 bonds in the compounds irradiated, and that bond scission is by no means completely random. It appears, for example, that tertiary carbon-carbon bonds are more readily broken than secondary or primary carbon-carbon bonds since neopentane and 2,2-dimethylbutane, which both contain tertiary C—CH_3 bonds, give a particularly high proportion of methane. This is a fairly general observation, and normally tertiary carbon-carbon bonds ($\equiv$C—R) break in preference to secondary (=CH—R) and secondary in preference to primary (—CH_2—R), in line with the lower bond dissociation energies in the series primary > secondary > tertiary. In the present examples R is —CH_2— or —CH_3, but the bond dissociation energies change in the same manner, decreasing in the series primary, secondary, tertiary, when R is some other group or atom; for example, a hydrogen or halogen atom. Preferential (but not exclusive) breaking of tertiary and secondary bonds is also inferred from the mass spectra of hydrocarbons and, in radiolysis, is confirmed when the radical intermediates are identified by means of scavenger experiments. As would be expected, branched-chain alkanes give higher yields of radiolysis products resulting from carbon-carbon bond fission than do straight-chain alkanes.

Electron paramagnetic resonance data for frozen alkanes irradiated at low temperatures are also consistent with this pattern; straight-chain alkanes give spectra characteristic of the loss of a hydrogen atom, with little evidence of carbon-carbon bond breaking, while branched-chain alkanes give more complex spectra suggestive of carbon-carbon bond fission (8).

Hexane

Table 9.2 lists the radiolysis products formed from hexane; data are included for both liquid and vapor, and for the vapor in the presence of a radical scavenger (propylene). The yields were determined after conversion of 5% of the hexane to products, but they are in substantial agreement with initial yields determined by Futrell (10) and Back and Miller (4). The product yields are not influenced by the LET of the radiation (electrons, deuterons, and helium ions give very similar yields (11)), though they may be affected by changes in the dose rate. Dewhurst and Winslow (12) found higher yields of the C_8 to C_{10} group of products at high dose rates, though Hardwick (13) was unable to substantiate this effect.

TABLE 9.2 *Radiolysis of Hexane*

(800 kvp electrons; ref. 9)

Product	G(product)		
	Liquid hexane	Vapor*	Vapor + 10% propylene*
H_2	5.0	5.0	2.1
CH_4	0.12	0.5	0.48
C_2H_2		0.3	0.20
C_2H_4	0.30	1.1	1.3
C_2H_6	0.30	1.0	0.80
C_3H_6	0.13	0.3	
C_3H_8	0.42	2.3	3.0
C_4H_8	0.03	0.06	0.12
C_4H_{10}	0.50	2.2	1.2
i-C_4H_{10}	0	0.50	0.70
C_5H_{12}	0.30	0.60	0.60
trans-C_6H_{12}	1.2	0.10	
i-C_6H_{14}	0	0.30	0.40
C_7	0.15	0.50	0.40
C_8	0.53	1.10	0.48
C_9	0.45	0.47	1.30
C_{10}	0.43	0.14	0.10
C_{11}	0.02	0.10	
C_{12}	2.0	0.40	0.18

* Vapor phase yields were calculated relative to $G(H_2) = 5\cdot0$ for pure hexane.

In the presence of scavenger, the hydrogen yield from hexane vapor is reduced by about 60% and the yield from liquid hexane by about 40% (14), the remaining hydrogen being formed by "molecular" processes. Yields of butane and higher hydrocarbons (C_7 to C_{12} but excepting C_9) from hexane vapor are also reduced in the presence of propylene, while in the liquid phase iodine and oxygen almost completely eliminate the C_7 to C_{12} group of products (14). The enhanced yields of propane and C_9-hydrocarbons when propylene is present can be attributed to reactions involving the scavenger; Futrell (10) found that the yield of propane from hexane vapor was not changed when ethylene or oxygen was added as a radical scavenger. Yields of low molecular weight products (C_1 to C_3) and of pentane from the vapor are little affected by scavenger and these products probably arise via nonradical reactions. Upon prolonged irradiation, hexane is subject to a form of self-scavenging due to the formation of unsaturated radiolysis products. Hardwick (13), for instance, found that the yield of hydrogen from liquid hexane falls continuously during irradiation from an initial value of $G(H_2) = 5.28$.[5] This is almost certainly due to scavenging by hexene and other unsaturated products of hydrogen atoms which would otherwise abstract hydrogen from the solvent, i.e.,

$$H\cdot + C_6H_{12} \rightarrow \cdot C_6H_{13} \rightarrow \text{products} \quad (9.8)$$

occurs instead of

$$H\cdot + C_6H_{14} \rightarrow \cdot C_6H_{13} + H_2 \quad (9.9)$$

Scavenger experiments with iodine have been carried out to identify the radicals formed in irradiated hexane (14). Radicals detected, with the G value for the corresponding iodide in parentheses, were: methyl (about 0.10), ethyl (0.40), propyl (0.70), butyl (0.30), hexyl (0.70), and *s*-hexyl (1-methylpentyl) (2.60). In a separate series of experiments, Meshitsuka and Burton (16) identified hydrogen iodide as a product and estimated $G(HI)$ to be about 2.5. Hydrogen iodide is formed by scavenging of thermal hydrogen atoms, but it has proved a difficult product to estimate accurately owing to its rapid addition to unsaturated radiolysis products.

The radiolysis mechanism for hexane is complex, but Futrell (10) has suggested a number of feasible ion-molecule reactions of the hydride-ion-transfer type. Thirteen of the primary ions identified in the mass spectrometer, ranging from CH_3^+ to $C_5H_{11}^+$, were considered able to react in this way; the reaction being represented by

$$R^+ + C_6H_{14} \rightarrow C_6H_{13}^+ + RH \quad (9.10)$$

In several cases the neutral product retains sufficient energy to dissociate,

$$C_2H_3^+ + C_6H_{14} \rightarrow C_2H_4^* + C_6H_{13}^+ \quad (9.11)$$

$$C_2H_4^* \rightarrow C_2H_2 + H_2 \quad (9.12)$$

The ion-molecule reactions are assumed to convert essentially all the primary ions to $C_6H_{13}^+$, which is then neutralized and breaks down,

$$C_6H_{13}^+ + e^- \rightarrow C_6H_{13}^{**} \rightarrow C_6H_{12} + H\cdot \quad (9.13)$$

The only organic radicals formed in significant quantities are ethyl, propyl, and hexyl, but by combination and disproportionation these can give rise to many of the products found experimentally. Using the mass spectral ion-abundance pattern to represent the initial distribution of ions and assuming reasonable ion-formation reactions, ion-molecule

[5] It was estimated (15) that the unsaturated products formed by the absorption of 1 Mrad in hexane reduce the measured value of $G(H_2)$ by 2%.

reactions (as indicated above), and inter-radical reactions, G values could be calculated for the radiolysis products from hexane vapor. The calculated G values were remarkably close to those found experimentally. Other types of ion-molecule reaction may also contribute to the over-all mechanism. Williams (17) for example, basing his conclusions on the energetics of ion reactions in liquid hydrocarbons, has suggested that dimeric products might be formed by ion-molecule reactions. For liquid hexane the reaction would be represented by

$$C_6H_{14}^+ + C_6H_{14} \rightarrow C_{12}H_{26}^+ + H_2 \quad (9.14)$$

though this may be made up of more than one step.

A different approach to the radiolysis mechanism has been adopted by Hardwick (13), who has emphasized the role of free radical reactions and concluded that ion-molecule reactions play little or no part in the radiolysis of liquid hexane. Hardwick represents the radical-forming reactions, which occur as a result of ion-recombination and the dissociation of primary and secondary excited molecules, as

$$C_6H_{14} \rightsquigarrow \cdot C_6H_{13} + H\cdot \quad (9.15)$$

$$\rightsquigarrow \cdot C_5H_{11} + \cdot CH_3 \quad (9.16)$$

$$\rightsquigarrow \cdot C_4H_9 + \cdot C_2H_5 \quad (9.17)$$

$$\rightsquigarrow 2\cdot C_3H_7 \quad (9.18)$$

A "molecular" dissociation is also included in the initial group of reactions,

$$C_6H_{14} \rightsquigarrow H_2 + \text{hexene, or other product} \quad (9.19)$$

though this too may involve (hot) radical intermediates. Hydrogen atoms produced in reaction 9.15 will have a range of energies and may either lose energy by successive collisions, until they react with the solvent (hexane) or an added scavenger, or, if they are formed with sufficient energy to react on first collision (i.e., are hot), react immediately with an adjacent solvent molecule. If the latter course is followed, the reactions

$$C_6H_{14} \rightarrow \cdot C_6H_{13} + H\cdot \quad (9.15)$$

and

$$H\cdot + C_6H_{14} \rightarrow \cdot C_6H_{13} + H_2 \quad (9.9)$$

($H\cdot$ represents a hot hydrogen atom) occur with neighboring molecules in the same solvent cage. Under these circumstances the two organic radicals formed will react together either by disproportionation, giving a molecule each of hexane and hexene, or by combination to give a C_{12} hydrocarbon,

$$2 \cdot C_6H_{13} \rightarrow C_6H_{14} + C_6H_{12} \tag{9.20}$$

or

$$\rightarrow C_{12}H_{26} \tag{9.21}$$

It should be noted that several isomeric structures are possible for the hexyl radicals, so that isomeric hexenes and dodecanes can be produced by these reactions. Reactions taking place within a solvent cage will not be affected by moderate concentrations of scavenger and the products from such reactions would be classified as "molecular" products. In the present instance this is true not only of the reaction sequence 9.15 + 9.9 but also of reactions 9.16 to 9.18 if the radicals formed react together before they can escape from the solvent cage. However, these reactions will only be observed if disproportionation occurs, since combination will reform the original molecule. Once the radicals have diffused out of the solvent cage they may react together or with the solvent, or they may be removed by reaction with a radical scavenger. Hydrogen atoms which are reduced to thermal energies react either by abstracting hydrogen from the solvent (Eq. 9.9) or by adding to one of the unsaturated products (Eq. 9.8), rather than by combining with another radical.

Dewhurst (9) has compared the yields of radiolysis products from hexane vapor and liquid hexane. A higher proportion of products resulting from carbon-carbon bond fission was found in the vapor phase, which in this respect resembles the mass spectral behavior, while in the liquid a higher proportion of the products result from carbon-hydrogen bond cleavage. Furthermore, two products — isobutane and isohexane — are only formed in the vapor phase. These appear to be produced by molecular rather than radical processes since the yields are not affected by scavenger, and it was suggested that they might be formed via excited molecules which are quenched in the liquid. *trans*-Hexene is an important product in the liquid phase but only a minor product from the vapor; it may be formed by a disproportionation reaction (Eq. 9.20) occurring in the spurs.

In the presence of oxygen, the radiolysis products from hexane include carbon monoxide and carbon dioxide and probably peroxides and water (10). Hexanone-2 and hexanone-3 have also been identified by gas-phase chromatography (14), though under the conditions used (a column temperature of 150°C) they may have been formed by breakdown of some less stable oxygenated intermediates. Oxygen also acts as a radical scavenger and practically eliminates the higher products

(C_7 and above). At higher temperatures the radiation-induced reaction between hexane and oxygen becomes a chain reaction with G(-hexane) values between 1000 and 20,000 at temperatures in the range 150°C to 235°C (18). A complex mixture of products is formed though major products, are, in order of decreasing abundance, epoxides, 2,5-dimethyltetrahydrofuran, acetone, and methanol. Above 235°C a thermal chain-decomposition predominates, masking the radiation-induced reaction, and giving mainly dissociation products (CO, CO_2, H_2O). The lower-temperature reaction initiated by radiation is influenced by temperature, pressure, and dose rate.

Cyclohexane

Many studies have been made of the radiolysis of cyclohexane and of mixtures containing it. Cyclic alkanes have the advantage that all the hydrogen atoms are equivalent and loss of any one of them gives the same product, thereby limiting the number of radiolysis reactions that need be considered. Cyclohexane is of particular interest since it is related structurally to benzene.

The more important products formed when pure liquid cyclohexane is irradiated are hydrogen, cyclohexene, and bicyclohexyl (Table 9.3), and the main features of the radiolysis can be explained by a relatively simple sequence of reactions (19):

$$\text{c-C}_6\text{H}_{12} \rightsquigarrow \text{c-C}_6\text{H}_{11}\cdot + \text{H}\cdot \quad \text{(about 85\%)} \qquad (9.22)$$

$$\rightsquigarrow \text{c-C}_6\text{H}_{10} + \text{H}_2 \quad \text{(about 15\%)} \qquad (9.23)$$

$$\text{H}\cdot + \text{c-C}_6\text{H}_{12} \rightarrow \text{c-C}_6\text{H}_{11}\cdot + \text{H}_2 \qquad (9.24)$$

$$2\text{c-C}_6\text{H}_{11}\cdot \rightarrow \text{C}_{12}\text{H}_{22} \qquad (9.25)$$

or

$$\rightarrow \text{c-C}_6\text{H}_{12} + \text{c-C}_6\text{H}_{10} \qquad (9.26)$$

with a small contribution from reactions which result in carbon-carbon bond scission in the cyclohexane ring. The predominance of carbon-hydrogen bond scission is consistent with mass-spectral evidence that the parent cyclohexane ion, $C_6H_{12}^+$, is highly stable. At high doses, polymeric products (C_{18}, C_{24}, etc.) are formed, apparently by reaction of cyclohexyl radicals with cyclohexene formed earlier in the irradiation (24).

The hydrogen yield from liquid cyclohexane is independent of the LET of the ionizing radiation (25) and of temperature (26), and it has

TABLE 9.3 *Radiolysis of Cyclohexane*

(References are given in parentheses)

Product	G(product)		
	Vapor (α-radiation; 108°C; ref. 20)	Liquid (γ-radiation)	Liquid + iodine (0.02 or 0.04M; γ-radiation; ref. 22)
H_2	8.0	5.55 (21) 5.85 (22)	3.90
CH_4		0.09–0.021 (23)	
C_2H_2	0.65	0.011 (23)	
C_2H_4	2.48	0.21–0.14 (23)	
C_2H_6	0.28	0.025 (23)	
C_3H_6	0.78		
C_3H_8	0.95		
C_4H_8	0.30		
C_4H_{10}	0.04		
methylcyclopentane		approx. 0.3 (19)	
hexene (linear)		approx. 0.2 (19)	
cyclohexene	0.77	3.27 (21)	1.9
bicyclohexyl, ⬡–⬡	(total C_{12} 0.69)	1.95 (21)	0.3 (19)
cyclohexyl-hexene-1	—	0.27 (21)	
HI	—	—	2.0
hexyl iodide	—	—	0.3
cyclohexyl iodide	—	—	3.7

been suggested that determination of this product be used as a means of chemical dosimetry (5, 27). However, Hardwick and his colleagues (28) find that the yield of hydrogen is not constant but decreases continuously as the irradiation progresses — as the radiolysis products build up in the liquid. Over-all yields of products other than hydrogen are also independent of LET (11), though there is a small variation in the intermediate radical yields (estimated by scavenger experiments) between fast electron, 18 Mev deuteron, and 33 Mev helium ion irradiation; the radical yields were lower by 10% and 30% respectively for the two heavy particle radiations (29). Product yields are apparently dependent upon the dose rate (11; cf. 30); yields of cyclohexene and bicyclohexyl increase at high dose rates (of the order of 10^{20} ev/g/sec) while at lower dose rates unsaturated, polymeric, materials may be formed (31). Dyne and Fletcher (32), however, have claimed that dose rate and LET effects are only observed in cyclohexane in the presence of a radical scavenger (which can be an unsaturated radiolysis product, e.g., cyclohexene) and that initially the radiolysis of cyclohexane is independent of both dose rate and LET.

Radical scavengers reduce the yield of hydrogen and cyclohexene from cyclohexane (cf., Table 9.3) but do not eliminate them completely, showing that these products are formed by both "radical" and "molecular" processes. Hydrogen production is also reduced in the presence of benzene, but this will be discussed separately (Chapter 10). Unsaturated products formed during irradiation act as scavengers and reduce the yield of hydrogen. Thus, added cyclohexene reduces $G(H_2)$ to 2.9, though it is without effect upon the yield of bicyclohexyl (19) since cyclohexyl radicals, which are the precursors of bicyclohexyl, are produced both by the normal hydrogen atom reaction (Eq. 9.24) and by the cyclohexene scavenging reaction,

$$H\cdot + \text{c-}C_6H_{10} \rightarrow \text{c-}C_6H_{11}\cdot \tag{9.27}$$

A number of liquid mixtures containing cyclohexane have been irradiated by Forrestal and Hamill (22) (cf., Table 9.3, column 4) who showed that the hydrogen yield can be divided into three components; one due to reactions of thermal hydrogen atoms (H·), one to reactions of hot, high-velocity, hydrogen atoms ($H\cdot$), and the third corresponding to hydrogen formed by molecular processes. The decrease in the yield of hydrogen from cyclohexane when small amounts of iodine are present ($\Delta G(H_2) = -2\cdot0$) is equal to the yield of hydrogen iodide formed, and is attributed to scavenging of thermal hydrogen atoms (Eq. 9.28); $G(\text{H}\cdot)$ is therefore 2·0. Hot hydrogen atoms will not be scavenged at the low iodine concentrations used, but an estimate of their yield can be made from the difference between G(cyclohexyl iodide) and G(HI); this will be appreciated if reaction 9.22 is broken down into two parts and the reactions of thermal and hot hydrogen atoms are considered separately:

$$\text{c-}C_6H_{12} \rightsquigarrow \text{c-}C_6H_{11}\cdot + \text{H}\cdot \tag{9.22a}$$

or

$$\rightsquigarrow \text{c-}C_6H_{11}\cdot + H\cdot \tag{9.22b}$$

$$\text{H}\cdot + I_2 \rightarrow I\cdot + HI \tag{9.28}$$

$$H\cdot + \text{c-}C_6H_{12} \rightarrow \text{c-}C_6H_{11}\cdot + H_2 \tag{9.29}$$

$$\text{c-}C_6H_{11}\cdot + I_2 \rightarrow \text{c-}C_6H_{11}I + I\cdot \tag{9.30}$$

Thus,

$$G(\mathrm{HI}) = G(\mathrm{H}\cdot)$$

$$G(\text{c-C}_6\mathrm{H}_{11}\mathrm{I}) = 2G(H\cdot) + G(\mathrm{H}\cdot)$$

and

$$G(H\cdot) = \tfrac{1}{2}[G(\text{c-C}_6\mathrm{H}_{11}\mathrm{I}) - G(\mathrm{HI})]$$

By substituting the numerical values given in Table 9.3, $G(H\cdot) = 0.85$. The remaining hydrogen is that formed by molecular processes (e.g., Eq. 9.23) and $G_{\mathrm{H}_2} = 5.85 - 2.85 = 3.0$. Forrestal and Hamill concluded that primary excited cyclohexane molecules — those not formed from ionic precursors — dissociate to give either a thermal or a hot hydrogen atom,

$$\text{c-C}_6\mathrm{H}_{12}^* \longrightarrow \text{c-C}_6\mathrm{H}_{11}\cdot + \mathrm{H}\cdot \text{ (or } H\cdot) \tag{9.31}$$

and $G(\text{c-C}_6\mathrm{H}_{12}^*) = 2.85$, while excited molecules formed by ion recombination dissociate to give molecular products,

$$\text{c-C}_6\mathrm{H}_{12}^+ + e^- \longrightarrow \text{c-C}_6\mathrm{H}_{12}^{**} \longrightarrow \mathrm{H}_2 + \text{unsaturated products} \tag{9.32}$$

and $G(\text{c-C}_6\mathrm{H}_{12}^{**}) = 3.0$. An additional excited species with the ability to increase the yield of hydrogen in the presence of small amounts of hydrogen iodide (22, 33) was also proposed. However, subsequent work (34) showed that the effect of hydrogen iodide could be attributed to dissociative electron attachment

$$e^- + \mathrm{HI} \longrightarrow \mathrm{H}\cdot + \mathrm{I}^- \tag{9.33}$$

and its consequences.

The production of hydrogen by "molecular" processes has been investigated by isotopic tracer techniques. Nevitt and Remsberg (35) irradiated mixtures of $\text{c-C}_6\mathrm{H}_{12}$ and $\text{c-C}_6\mathrm{D}_{12}$ and concluded from the isotopic composition of the hydrogen produced that not more than 25% of the hydrogen was formed by direct (unimolecular) detachment,

$$\text{c-C}_6\mathrm{H}_{12} \rightsquigarrow \mathrm{H}_2 + \text{c-C}_6\mathrm{H}_{10}, \text{ or other unsaturate} \tag{9.23}$$

On the basis of scavenger experiments these authors attributed about 40% of the hydrogen yield to reactions of hydrogen atoms and suggested that the remainder (35 to 60% after allowing for direct detachment) might be formed in part by ion-molecule reactions such as

$$\text{c-C}_6\mathrm{H}_{12}^+ + \text{c-C}_6\mathrm{H}_{12} \longrightarrow \text{c-C}_6\mathrm{H}_{13}^+ + \text{c-C}_6\mathrm{H}_{11}\cdot \tag{9.34}$$

$$\text{c-C}_6\mathrm{H}_{13}^+ + e^- \longrightarrow \text{c-C}_6\mathrm{H}_{11}\cdot + \mathrm{H}_2 \tag{9.35}$$

However, ion-molecule reactions involving cyclohexane do not appear to have been observed in the mass spectrometer. Dyne and Jenkinson (36) have also irradiated mixtures of c-C_6H_{12} and c-C_6D_{12} and have estimated the hydrogen formed by unimolecular processes at between 10 and 20% of the total yield of hydrogen — the remainder being formed by bimolecular processes. It was also found that both iodine and benzene reduce the unimolecular and the bimolecular yields of hydrogen in approximately the same proportion as the total yield of hydrogen (37). Dyne and Jenkinson argued from this observation that both unimolecular and bimolecular reactions have the same precursor, an excited state of cyclohexane, which is quenched by both iodine and benzene — the additives acting as quenching agents and not as radical scavengers. This conclusion is at variance with the mechanism postulated by Forrestal and Hamill and outlined above, and despite a good deal of effort the radiolysis mechanism for cyclohexane cannot yet be considered established.

Freeman (38), by kinetic analysis of irradiated cyclohexane systems, has concluded that the radiolysis mechanism involves at least two distinct activated species, one of which is deactivated in the presence of benzene. Yields of the two species are $G = 3.0$ and 2.4 for the benzene-deactivated and the benzene-immune species respectively. These are similar to the molecular and radical yields of hydrogen estimated by Forrestal and Hamill, in whose mechanism c-$C_6H_{12}^{**}$ and c-$C_6H_{12}^{*}$ would presumably correspond with the benzene-deactivated and the benzene-immune species.

Radiolysis of cyclohexane in the vapor phase (20) (Table 9.3) gives results significantly different from those obtained in liquid-phase irradiations. In the vapor yields of products resulting from carbon-carbon bond scission are enhanced, as Dewhurst (9) found for the radiolysis of *n*-hexane in the vapor phase. The difference may be due to cage effects in the liquid, which are absent in the vapor, or to reactions of ions or excited states in the vapor which are prevented in the liquid by rapid energy loss from the active species.

In the presence of oxygen, irradiation of cyclohexane produces both cyclohexanol ($G = 3.7$) and cyclohexanone ($G = 3.5$) (19), but the yield of cyclohexene is reduced (to $G = 0.7$) and negligible amounts of dimer are formed. No peroxides were detected by Dewhurst (19) but Bach (39) found cyclohexyl hydroperoxide, c-$C_6H_{11}OOH$ ($G = 1.0$), and a peroxide, R_1OOR_2 ($G = 0.2$), but no hydrogen peroxide. The major products formed in the presence of oxygen can be accounted for (19) by reactions 9.22 and 9.23 and

$$H\cdot + c\text{-}C_6H_{12} \rightarrow c\text{-}C_6H_{11}\cdot + H_2 \quad (9.24)$$

$$c\text{-}C_6H_{11}\cdot + O_2 \rightarrow c\text{-}C_6H_{11}O_2\cdot \quad (9.36)$$

$$2c\text{-}C_6H_{11}O_2\cdot \rightarrow c\text{-}C_6H_{11}OH + c\text{-}C_6H_{10}O + O_2 \quad (9.37)$$

Part of the intermediate peroxy-radicals may be converted into hydroperoxide or peroxide. Hydrogen atoms presumably react directly with cyclohexane even when oxygen is present, rather than adding oxygen to form perhydroxyl radicals ($HO_2\cdot$), since hydrogen peroxide is not formed. Dobson and Hughes (40) have made the interesting observation that radical scavengers reduce the yield of cyclohexanone from oxygenated cyclohexane, though only to a limiting value ($G = 0.46$), which is independent of the scavenger used. They suggest that the limiting yield of cyclohexanone is due to a "molecular" process involving an excited cyclohexane molecule and oxygen:

$$c\text{-}C_6H_{12}^* + O_2 \rightarrow c\text{-}C_6H_{10}O + H_2O \quad (9.38)$$

Consistent with this mechanism, they find that the yield of cyclohexanol is always less than the yield of cyclohexanone by an amount equal to the molecular yield of ketone. This is to be expected if the radical process forming cyclohexanone is represented by the disproportionation reaction 9.37, which gives equal amounts of ketone and alcohol.

DETERMINATION OF RATE CONSTANTS

A radiolysis method for determining relative rate constants for the reaction of hydrogen atoms with organic liquids has been developed by Hardwick (15). The experimental technique consists of measuring the change in hydrogen yield as a function of solute concentration when a solution of the liquid (the solute) in a saturated hydrocarbon is irradiated. Concentrations of solute up to about 2% are used. The solvent is normally n-hexane, and the method is based on the assumption that with relatively low doses of radiation the processes influencing hydrogen production can be represented as follows (RH is the saturated hydrocarbon solvent, and S the solute);

$$RH \rightsquigarrow H_2 + \text{products} \quad (\text{yield } G_1) \quad (9.39)$$

$$RH \rightsquigarrow H\cdot + R\cdot \quad (\text{yield } G_2) \quad (9.40)$$

$$H\cdot + RH \xrightarrow{k_3} H_2 + R\cdot \quad (9.41)$$

$$H\cdot + S \xrightarrow{k_4} HS \quad (9.42)$$

$$H\cdot + S \xrightarrow{k_5'} H_2 + R'\cdot \quad (9.43)$$

(the rate constants are given as k_3, k_4, and k_5 to preserve the notation of the original papers). The first reaction represents the formation of "molecular" hydrogen from the solvent, and by definition this process is not affected by small concentrations of solute; the actual mechanism of the "molecular" process is not important. The second reaction (9.40) gives thermal hydrogen atoms, which react either by hydrogen abstraction from the solvent or solute (Eqs. 9.41 and 9.43) or by addition to the solute (Eq. 9.42). Assuming a steady-state with respect to hydrogen atoms, the following kinetic expression can be derived:

$$\frac{1}{G_{\mathrm{H_2(O)}} - G_{\mathrm{H_2(S)}}} = \frac{1}{\Delta G_{\mathrm{H_2}}} = \frac{k_3}{k_4}\frac{[\mathrm{RH}]}{[\mathrm{S}]}\frac{1}{G_2} + \frac{1}{G_2}\left(\frac{k_5}{k_4} + 1\right) \qquad (9.44)$$

where $G_{\mathrm{H_2(O)}}$ ($= G_1 + G_2$) is the hydrogen yield from the pure solvent, $G_{\mathrm{H_2(S)}}$ the hydrogen yield from a solution of concentration [S], and $\Delta G_{\mathrm{H_2}}$ the difference between these two quantities. A plot of $1/\Delta G_{\mathrm{H_2}}$ against [RH]/[S] gives a straight line of slope $(k_3/k_4)(1/G_2)$ and intercept $(1/G_2)(k_5/k_4 + 1)$. G_2 can be determined by taking a solute which reacts with hydrogen atoms by addition alone, for example a vinyl monomer, when k_5 is zero and the intercept is $1/G_2$. Then, knowing G_2 and, from the conditions of the experiment, [RH] and [S], and measuring $\Delta G_{\mathrm{H_2}}$ the ratios k_3/k_4 and k_5/k_4 can be determined. Furthermore, if an absolute value of k_3 is available, absolute values of k_4 and k_5 can be obtained.

A selection from the many rate constants determined by Hardwick (15, 41) is given in Table 9.4. The values are based on a k_3 for hexane in the liquid phase of 4.9×10^6 liter/mole sec at 23°C. G_1 and G_2 for hexane are 2.12 and 3.16 respectively. Hardwick also correlates the measured rate constants with chemical structure and concludes, for example, that the relative rates of hydrogen abstraction by hydrogen atoms from primary ($\mathrm{RCH_2}$—H), secondary ($\mathrm{R_2CH}$—H) and tertiary ($\mathrm{R_3C}$—H) groups are 1, 4.4, and 31 respectively.

HALIDES

Aliphatic halides, with the exception of the fluorides, are among the organic compounds most sensitive to radiation. In these compounds the carbon-halogen bonds are weaker than either carbon-carbon or carbon-hydrogen bonds and the main effect of radiation is to break a carbon-halogen bond to give an organic free radical and a halogen atom. The high electron affinity of the halogens permits electron attachment reactions such as

TABLE 9.4 *Rate Constants for Reactions of Hydrogen Atoms with Organic Liquids* (refs. 15, 41)

Compound (S)	Hydrogen addition k_4 ($\times 10^8$ liter/mole sec)	Hydrogen abstraction k_5 ($\times 10^8$ liter/mole sec)
Hexane	0	0.049
Cyclohexene	4.9	1.12
1-Hexene	7.9	2.4
2-Methyl pentene-1	11.7	3.7
2-Methyl pentene-2	6.6	1.2
Tetramethyl ethylene	5.5	<0.1
Benzene	1.8	<0.1
Toluene	2.9	<0.1
Mesitylene	5.5	<0.1
Ethyl benzene	3.5	1.1
Isopropyl benzene	3.8	0.2
t-Butyl benzene	0.1	<0.1
Biphenyl	13.5	~ 0
o and *m* Terphenyl	20	~ 0
p-Terphenyl	37	~ 0
Anthracene	31	~ 0
Diphenylpicrylhydrazyl (DPPH)	105	
Acetic acid	6.1	1.5
Methyl acetate	0.69	<0.05
Acetone	3.2	1.6
Benzoic acid	29	8.3
Benzophenone	27.7	<1.0
	(Halogen atom abstraction)	
Alkyl chloride	1.4	0.96
Alkyl bromide	12.4	3.3
Methyl iodide	60	7.2
n-Butyl bromide	12.4	3.3
s-Butyl bromide	16.5	6.4
t-Butyl bromide	15.1	<0.5
Methylene dichloride	14.9	4.0
Chloroform	16.1	2.2
Carbon tetrachloride	17.5	

$$RX + e^- \rightarrow R\cdot + X^- \tag{9.45}$$

and

$$\rightarrow R^+ + X^- + e^- \tag{9.46}$$

where X^- is a halogen ion, in addition to the more usual reactions listed at the beginning of this chapter. Fluorides form a class apart since carbon-fluorine bonds are generally stronger than the other bonds in the molecule, and irradiation leads most frequently to scission of carbon-carbon bonds.

The halogen atoms show a marked diminution in reactivity in the series $F\cdot > Cl\cdot \gg Br\cdot > I\cdot$ which is paralleled in the halogen-substituted radicals. In the substituted methyl radicals, for instance, reactivity decreases in the series $\cdot CF_3 \gg \cdot CCl_3 > \cdot CBr_3$ (cf. Table 5.1). The reactivity or, conversely, the stability of the first-formed radicals has considerable influence upon the subsequent course of the radiolysis. Chlorine atoms, for example, can abstract hydrogen from organic molecules; bromine atoms do so less readily and iodine atoms not at all.[6] Thus the initial radiolysis products from chloro-compounds tend to include hydrogen chloride, whereas iodo-compounds tend to give iodine, and bromides give on occasion both hydrogen bromide and bromine.

Methyl Iodide

Irradiation of organic iodides liberates iodine, which can react with the free radical intermediates in the radiolysis to reform similar iodides. When it is the original iodide which is reformed in this way, radiation will produce less chemical change than might be expected, though an appreciable number of molecules may have dissociated and then reformed the parent compound. This is illustrated by the relatively low yields of radiolysis products from methyl and ethyl iodides (Table 9.5), although irradiation of these iodides in the presence of radioactive iodine shows that for both compounds the exchange yield — G(radioactive iodide) — is about 6 (46, 47, 48). The tracer experiments also show that most of the organic radicals formed when methyl and ethyl iodides are irradiated are methyl radicals and ethyl radicals respectively.

[6] Although iodine atoms will not abstract hydrogen from an organic molecule, iodine may displace hydrogen under some circumstances. Willard and his colleagues (42) showed that hot iodine atoms formed by the nuclear reaction $I^{127}(n, \gamma)I^{128}$ will displace hydrogen from methane,

$$I\cdot + CH_4 \rightarrow CH_3I + H\cdot$$

Iodine also replaces hydrogen in methane when a mixture of iodine and methane is irradiated with 1849 Å ultraviolet light (43, 44),

$$I_2^* + CH_4 \rightarrow CH_3I + HI$$

TABLE 9.5 *Radiolysis of Methyl Iodide and Ethyl Iodide*

(Co^{60} γ-irradiation of the pure deaerated liquids; ref. 45)

Product	G(product)	
	Methyl iodide	Ethyl iodide
H_2	0.060	0.23
CH_4	0.77	0.01
C_2H_2		0.09
C_2H_4	0.081	2.20
C_2H_6	1.11	1.92
C_4H_{10}		0.33
I_2	1.26	2.12
HI	approx. 0.01	0.33

The effect of radiation on methyl iodide can be represented as causing fission of the carbon-iodine bond to give methyl radicals and iodine atoms,

$$CH_3I \rightsquigarrow \cdot CH_3 + I\cdot \tag{9.47}$$

which interact to give the three major products, methyl iodide, ethane, and iodine. However, closer study of the radiolysis and related reactions and of the effect of added substances has enabled this simple mechanism to be expanded into one considerably more detailed (45).

The mass spectrum and ion-molecule reactions of methyl iodide have been studied by Hamill and his colleagues (45, 49). Major primary ions and their relative abundances are CH_3I^+ (100), I^+ (53), CH_3^+ (28), CH_2I^+ (14), and CI^+ (5). The corresponding neutral fragments formed are, for the ions I^+, CH_3^+, CH_2I^+, and CI^+, $\cdot CH_3$, $I\cdot$, $H\cdot$, and $H\cdot + H_2$ respectively. Ion-molecule reactions proposed include

$$CH_3I^+ + CH_3I \rightarrow C_2H_6I^+ + I\cdot \tag{9.48}$$

$$CH_3^+ + CH_3I \rightarrow C_2H_6I^+ \tag{9.49}$$

$$CH_2I^+ + CH_3I \rightarrow I_2^+ + \cdot C_2H_5 \tag{9.50}$$

$$I^+ + CH_3I \xrightarrow{?} I_2^+ + \cdot CH_3 \tag{9.51}$$

(the ion $C_2H_6I^+$ has the structure $CH_3ICH_3^+$). Other mass spectrometric observations (50) have shown that the reaction

$$e^- + CH_3I \rightarrow \cdot CH_3 + I^- \tag{9.52}$$

has a very low threshold energy and can reasonably be expected to occur in irradiated methyl iodide. The more important ion-neutralization reactions are therefore likely to be

$$C_2H_6I^+ + I^- \rightarrow 2\cdot CH_3 + 2I\cdot \tag{9.53}$$

and

$$I_2^+ + I^- \rightarrow 3I\cdot \tag{9.54}$$

The over-all effect of these ionic processes is to produce methyl radicals and iodine atoms (which may also be formed by the dissociation of excited methyl iodide molecules) with smaller numbers of hydrogen atoms and ethyl radicals. Reactions between methyl radicals and iodine atoms in irradiated methyl iodide are represented by Gillis, Williams, and Hamill (45) as

$$(2\cdot CH_3 + 2I\cdot) \rightarrow CH_3I + (\cdot CH_3 + I\cdot) \rightarrow 2CH_3I \tag{9.55}$$

or

$$\rightarrow C_2H_6 + 2I\cdot \tag{9.56}$$

The radicals are enclosed in parentheses to emphasize that they will be formed to a large extent in small groups in spurs, though these need not necessarily contain two radical pairs. Radicals which escape into the bulk of the medium will eventually react in a similar manner, though they may also react with the products of the radiolysis (e.g., iodine) or with added radical scavengers. Methane arises by the reaction

$$H\cdot + CH_3I \rightarrow (\cdot CH_3 + HI) \rightarrow CH_4 + I\cdot \tag{9.57}$$

which occurs largely within the spurs, and ethylene by reaction between ethyl radicals and iodine atoms,

$$\cdot C_2H_5 + I\cdot \rightarrow C_2H_4 + HI \tag{9.58}$$

Hydrogen is formed by dissociation of some of the parent CH_3I^+ ions to give CI^+, H_2, and $H\cdot$. As would be anticipated on the basis of these reactions, added iodine reduces the yields of methane and ethane but has less effect upon the yield of hydrogen (47).

Sturm and Schwarz (51) studied the effect of LET on the radiolysis of methyl iodide and found that the yields of ethane and methane, and of the minor products hydrogen, ethylene, and acetylene, increased with LET in a manner analogous to the increase in molecular product yields in the radiolysis of water. This supports the mechanism of Gillis, Hamill, and Williams (45) in which these products are formed by diffusion-controlled reactions of radicals in spurs. The yield of acetylene is particularly dependent upon LET, and Sturm and Schwarz conclude that it is a secondary track product, analogous to $HO_2\cdot$ in water radiolysis.

Higher alkyl iodides decompose upon irradiation in a similar manner to methyl iodide, though additional reactions leading to unsaturated products are possible. Hamill and his colleagues (45) have proposed that ethylene arises in irradiated ethyl iodide by a reaction (Eq. 9.58) between ethyl radicals and iodine atoms which competes with the addition reaction

$$\cdot C_2H_5 + I\cdot \rightarrow C_2H_5I \tag{9.59}$$

Ethane is produced by an efficient reaction between ethyl radicals and hydrogen iodide,

$$\cdot C_2H_5 + HI \rightarrow C_2H_6 + I\cdot \tag{9.60}$$

Other authors (48, 52, 53) have suggested that hydrogen iodide is eliminated from alkyl iodides by unimolecular dissociation of excited molecules, e.g.,

$$C_2H_5I^* \rightarrow C_2H_4 + HI \tag{9.61}$$

rather than by the bimolecular reaction described by equation 9.58. It is interesting in connection with the elimination of hydrogen iodide that Luebbe and Willard (53) detected appreciable quantities of ethyl radicals in frozen ethyl iodide glass irradiated with γ-radiation, but none when the glass was exposed to ultraviolet radiation, though both ultraviolet and γ-irradiation produce ethylene and hydrogen iodide in liquid ethyl iodide. Symons and Townsend (54) also failed to detect any radicals by electron paramagnetic resonance in an ethyl iodide-ethanol glass exposed to ultraviolet light, although subsequent examination of the glass showed that hydrogen iodide had been formed by the photolysis, presumably by reaction 9.61. An essential requirement for the elimination of hydrogen iodide to give an unsaturated product is the presence of hydrogen on the carbon atom adjacent to the iodine-substituted carbon atom. In both radiolysis and photolysis it is found that the yield of iodine increases as the number of hydrogen atoms attached to the β-carbon atom is increased — the iodine presumably arising via hydrogen iodide elimination (48, 55).

Reactions involving hot radicals, which have frequently been included in mechanisms proposed for the radiolysis of alkyl iodides (47, 52, 56), are unnecessary if the mechanism suggested by Gillis, Williams, and Hamill (45) is accepted.

Butyl Bromides and Chlorides

The butyl bromides and chlorides illustrate radiation-induced rearrangements, which appear particularly important with the alkyl halides as a class, although not all members undergo reactions of this type. Table 9.6 lists the major products found when the isomeric butyl bromides and butyl chlorides are irradiated; bromine and chlorine could not be detected among the products and only small amounts of hydrogen bromide (G less than 0.2) were formed from the bromides.

TABLE 9.6 *Radiolysis of Butyl Bromides and Chlorides*

Product	G(product)			
	Normal $CH_3(CH_2)_3X$	Secondary $CH_3CH_2CHXCH_3$	Iso $(CH_3)_2CHCH_2X$	Tertiary $(CH_3)_3CX$
Bromides ($X = Br$; *ref. 57*)				
H_2	Very small	Very small	Appreciable	Appreciable
Butane	3.4	6.2	0	0
Isobutene	0	0	6.2	9.0
n-butyl bromide	—	0.9	0	0
s-butyl bromide	0.2	—	0	0
Isobutyl bromide	0	0	—	1.8
t-butyl bromide	0	0	4.5	—
Dibromobutanes*	1.2	2.2	2.0	3.0
Chlorides ($X = Cl$; *ref. 58*)				
H_2	1.4	1.0	0.9	0.6
HCl	1.0	1.1	—	0.2
Butane	6.9	5.6	0	0
Isobutane	0	0	6.9	3.7
n-butyl chloride	—	0	0	0
s-butyl chloride†	60	—	0	0
Isobutyl chloride†	0	0	—	1.6
t-butyl chloride	0	0	24	—
Dichlorobutanes*	1.5	1.0	2.2	1.5

* The original references give the product distribution among the isomeric dihalogen compounds.

† *s*-butyl chloride and isobutyl chloride were not identified separately, but the authors' assignments (58) appear reasonable.

The straight-chain halides (normal and secondary) apparently react similarly, as do the branched-chain compounds (iso and tertiary), though the two groups differ from one another. Butane is the major hydrocarbon product from both the straight-chain bromides and chlorides, while isobutene is formed from the branched-chain bromides and isobutane from the branched-chain chlorides. Isomerization is most important with *n*-butyl chloride, which is converted to *s*-butyl chloride in yields indicative of a chain reaction, and with isobutyl chloride which gives high yields of *t*-butyl chloride. The tertiary halides also show some isomerization to the iso-compounds. Though both bromides and chlorides show evidence of isomerization the yields of rearranged product are greatest with the chlorides.

Isomerization of the butyl halides can take place without any rearrangement of the carbon skeleton, the isomerizations being represented by

$$\mathrm{C{-}C{-}C{-}\overset{*}{C}} \rightarrow \mathrm{C{-}C{-}\overset{*}{C}{-}C} \tag{9.62}$$

and

$$\begin{matrix}\mathrm{C} & & \\ & \diagdown & \\ & & \mathrm{C{-}\overset{*}{C}} \\ & \diagup & \\ \mathrm{C} & & \end{matrix} \rightleftharpoons \begin{matrix}\mathrm{C} & & \\ & \diagdown & \\ & & \mathrm{\overset{*}{C}{-}C} \\ & \diagup & \\ \mathrm{C} & & \end{matrix} \tag{9.63}$$

the reverse of reaction 9.63 taking place rather less readily than the forward reaction. This is consistent with the proposal that the first step in the rearrangement is rupture of the carbon-halogen bond and that this is followed by rearrangement of the radical produced (the asterisks in equations 9.62 and 9.63 representing both the site of the halogen substituents and the free electron of the radicals undergoing rearrangement). The radical rearrangements are plausible since, with the exception of the reverse of reaction 9.63 (to form an iso-compound), a more stable radical is produced in each case. Dismukes and Wilcox (58) have included a radical rearrangement in the mechanism postulated for the radiation-induced isomerization of *n*-butyl chloride. The initial dissociation

$$n\text{-}\mathrm{C_4H_9Cl} \rightsquigarrow n\text{-}\mathrm{C_4H_9\cdot} + \mathrm{Cl\cdot} \tag{9.64}$$

being followed by a chain reaction with the chain-propagating steps,

$$n\text{-}\mathrm{C_4H_9\cdot} \longrightarrow s\text{-}\mathrm{C_4H_9\cdot} \tag{9.65}$$

$$s\text{-}\mathrm{C_4H_9\cdot} + n\text{-}\mathrm{C_4H_9Cl} \longrightarrow s\text{-}\mathrm{C_4H_9Cl} + n\text{-}\mathrm{C_4H_9\cdot} \tag{9.66}$$

(n-$\mathrm{C_4H_9\cdot} = \mathrm{CH_3CH_2CH_2CH_2\cdot}$; s-$\mathrm{C_4H_9\cdot} = \mathrm{CH_3CH_2\dot{C}HCH_3}$). Similar mechanisms can be drawn up for the other isomerizations observed.

Wiley and his colleagues (59) have studied the radiation-induced isomerization of *n*-propyl chloride to isopropyl chloride, which is also a chain reaction, and have proposed the following mechanism for the chain-propagating stage:

$$CH_3\dot{C}HCH_2Cl \rightarrow CH_3CHClCH_2\cdot \qquad (9.67)$$

$$CH_3CHClCH_2\cdot + CH_3CH_2CH_2Cl \rightarrow CH_3CHClCH_3 + CH_3\dot{C}HCH_2Cl \qquad (9.68)$$

Isomerization is brought about here by migration of a chlorine atom in the intermediate chloroisopropyl radical. The yield of isopropyl chloride is enhanced in the presence of hydrogen chloride; G(isopropyl chloride) rising from 56 to 80 on adding 1 to 2mM of gaseous hydrogen chloride. Benson and Willard (60) have suggested that in the presence of hydrogen chloride the chain propagating steps are

$$Cl\cdot + CH_3CH_2CH_2Cl \rightarrow CH_3\dot{C}HCH_2Cl + HCl \qquad (9.69)$$

$$CH_3\dot{C}HCH_2Cl \rightarrow CH_3CHClCH_2\cdot \qquad (9.67)$$

$$CH_3CHClCH_2\cdot + HCl \rightarrow CH_3CHClCH_3 + Cl\cdot \qquad (9.70)$$

The two latter reactions may be slightly endothermic, though not sufficiently so to preclude this mechanism at room temperature. The latter authors also showed that a similar hydrogen chloride-catalyzed chain isomerization occurs during the photolysis of *n*-propyl chloride with light of wavelength of less than 2200 Å (60). This supports the contention that the mechanism of the chain reaction in the presence of hydrogen chloride involves radicals rather than ions.

Carbon Tetrachloride

Carbon tetrachloride presents one of the simplest examples of radiolysis since the reactions of the free radicals derived from it are quite restricted. Only two products are found when pure carbon tetrachloride is irradiated, chlorine ($G = 0.66$ (61)) and hexachloroethane, and they can be accounted for by the following radical reactions:

$$CCl_4 \rightsquigarrow \cdot CCl_3 + Cl\cdot \qquad (9.71)$$

$$\cdot CCl_3 + Cl\cdot \rightarrow CCl_4 \qquad (9.72)$$

$$\cdot CCl_3 + Cl_2 \rightarrow CCl_4 + Cl\cdot \qquad (9.73)$$

$$2\cdot CCl_3 \rightarrow C_2Cl_6 \qquad (9.74)$$

$$2Cl\cdot \rightarrow Cl_2 \qquad (9.75)$$

Once a small amount of chlorine has accumulated it will act as a scavenger for the $\cdot CCl_3$ radicals which escape from the spurs, and the observed yields will be those for the "molecular" products (C_2Cl_6 and an equivalent amount of chlorine).

The primary dissociation reaction (Eq. 9.71) may take place directly through the dissociation of excited molecules or indirectly through ionic intermediates. The latter are likely to be the ions observed in the mass spectrometer, namely (with their relative abundances) (62); CCl_3^+ (100), Cl^+ (27), CCl^+ (22.5), and CCl_2^+ (22). Negative ions are also formed, either by

$$CCl_4 + e^- \rightarrow CCl_3^+ + Cl^- + e^- \quad (9.76)$$

or

$$\rightarrow \cdot CCl_3 + Cl^- \quad (9.77)$$

so that the main neutralization reaction will probably be

$$CCl_3^+ + Cl^- \rightarrow \cdot CCl_3 + Cl\cdot \quad (9.78)$$

A certain amount of molecular chlorine might be anticipated from the processes giving the ions CCl^+ and CCl_2^+.

An estimate of the number of $\cdot CCl_3$ radicals which escape from the spurs can be made by adding radioactive chlorine and measuring the amount incorporated into the carbon tetrachloride by reaction 9.73. A relatively high yield ($G = 3.5$) was found for this exchange by Schulte (63) using cobalt-60 γ-radiation, indicating a radical yield ($\cdot CCl_3 + Cl\cdot$) of about 7. However, Pearson and Garner (64) consider that these yields may be high due to organic impurity in the irradiated mixture. Dainton and his colleagues (65) have used ferrocene as a radical scavenger with this system, finding G(-ferrocene) = 2.34. If chlorine atoms are the only radicals scavenged by ferrocene $G_{Cl} = 2.34$; however, this was not established and the authors conclude that 2.34 represents a minimum value for $G_{Cl} + G_{CCl_3\cdot}$. Diphenylpicrylhydrazyl (DPPH) was also used as a radical scavenger (66) though this compound is removed, in part, by excited carbon tetrachloride molecules, so that the action of the scavenger is represented by

$$CCl_4 \rightsquigarrow \text{excited molecules } (S^*) \text{ and radicals } (R\cdot) \quad (9.79)$$

$$S^* + DPPH \rightarrow R\cdot + \text{products} \quad (9.80)$$

$$R\cdot + DPPH \rightarrow \text{products} \quad (9.81)$$

The yields of excited molecules reacting with the scavenger and of radicals could be estimated separately, and were found to be G(excited states) = 10.0 ± 2.0 and $G_{Cl} + G_{CCl_3} = 2.9 \pm 0.3$. The combined yield agrees with radical yields of about 20 estimated by Chapiro and his colleagues (cf. 67) using DPPH.

When carbon tetrachloride is irradiated in the presence of oxygen, carbonyl chloride, and possibly other products, are formed in addition to chlorine and hexachloroethane; under these conditions $G(Cl_2) = 3.6$ and $G(COCl_2) = 12.1$ (68). The mechanism probably includes reactions 9.71 and 9.75 and

$$\cdot CCl_3 + O_2 \rightarrow CCl_3O_2\cdot \tag{9.82}$$

$$CCl_3O_2\cdot \rightarrow \cdot OCl + COCl_2 \qquad (\text{or } \cdot COCl + Cl_2O) \tag{9.83}$$

$$\cdot OCl + CCl_4 \rightarrow \cdot CCl_3 + Cl_2O \tag{9.84}$$

In contrast with the chloroform-oxygen system, no peroxides have been detected in irradiated carbon tetrachloride-oxygen mixtures, possibly because the absence of hydrogen precludes stabilization of the intermediate $CCl_3O_2\cdot$ radical by hydrogen abstraction to form the relatively stable hydroperoxide, CCl_3O_2H.

Chloroform

The radiolysis of chloroform is markedly influenced by traces of oxygen or moisture and published results are not entirely consistent. Table 9.7 lists the products found by Ottolenghi and Stein (69) for chloroform from which oxygen and moisture were rigorously excluded; the G values vary somewhat with absorbed dose and those shown are for a dose of 5.9×10^{19} ev/ml. Traces of oxygen and water were found to induce a chain reaction giving a multitude of products.

TABLE 9.7 *Radiolysis of Chloroform* (ref. 69)

Product	G value
HCl	5.6
CH_2Cl_2	0.9
$Cl_2C{=}CCl_2$	0.15
$CHCl_2{-}CH_2Cl$	0.57
$CHCl_2{-}CHCl_2$	1.1
$CHCl_2{-}CCl_3$	1.2
$CCl_3{-}CCl_3$	3.1

Ottolenghi and Stein have proposed a radical mechanism which accounts for the observed radiolysis products and, within the experimental accuracy, for their relative proportions. The reactions are

$$CHCl_3 \rightsquigarrow \cdot CHCl_2 + Cl\cdot \tag{9.85}$$

$$\cdot CHCl_2 + CHCl_3 \rightarrow \cdot CCl_3 + CH_2Cl_2 \tag{9.86}$$

or

$$\rightarrow CHCl_2{-}CHCl_2 + Cl\cdot \tag{9.87}$$

$$Cl\cdot + CHCl_3 \rightarrow \cdot CCl_3 + HCl \tag{9.88}$$

$$\cdot CHCl_2 + \cdot CCl_3 \rightarrow CHCl_2{-}CCl_3 \tag{9.89}$$

or

$$\rightarrow Cl_2C{=}CCl_2 + HCl \tag{9.90}$$

$$2\cdot CHCl_2 \rightarrow CHCl_2{-}CHCl_2 \tag{9.91}$$

$$2\cdot CCl_3 \rightarrow CCl_3{-}CCl_3 \tag{9.74}$$

1,1,2-trichloroethane is a secondary product formed by

$$\cdot CHCl_2 + CH_2Cl_2 \rightarrow CHCl_2{-}CH_2Cl + Cl\cdot \tag{9.92}$$

Tetrachloroethylene is the only unsaturated product and this may be formed either by reaction 9.90 or, more probably, by a molecular elimination process:

$$CHCl_3 \rightsquigarrow :CCl_2 + HCl \tag{9.93}$$

$$:CCl_2 + CHCl_3 \rightarrow Cl_2C{=}CCl_2 + HCl \tag{9.94}$$

These reactions (Eqs. 9.85 to 9.94) do not constitute a chain reaction and do not form chlorine or carbon tetrachloride, which were found to be absent from the products.

In the presence of oxygen, chloroform takes part in a radiation-initiated chain reaction to give a peroxide (probably CCl_3OOH) in relatively high yield; yields of hydrochloric acid found after hydrolysis of the radiolysis products are often of the order of several hundred, though the yields are strongly influenced by impurities, temperature, and dose rate (70). Other products formed include carbonyl chloride, hydrogen chloride, chlorine, and hexachloroethane. The mechanism of the chain reaction is not known, though it might conceivably be

$$\cdot CCl_3 + O_2 \rightarrow CCl_3O_2\cdot \tag{9.82}$$

$$CCl_3O_2\cdot + CHCl_3 \rightarrow \cdot CCl_3 + CCl_3OOH \tag{9.95}$$

When both oxygen and moisture are present, the acid yields are rather lower (70), though two-phase chloroform-water systems saturated with air or oxygen have been employed as chemical dosimeters (71; see also Chapter 4). Most of the radiolysis products are hydrolyzed by water to give hydrochloric acid, which can be detected or measured by a variety of standard techniques, e.g.,

$$CCl_3OOH + H_2O \rightarrow 3HCl + CO_2 + \tfrac{1}{2}O_2 \qquad (9.96)$$

$$COCl_2 + H_2O \rightarrow 2HCl + CO_2 \qquad (9.97)$$

Aqueous, single-phase, solutions of chloroform do not decompose by a chain reaction; such solutions are considered in Chapter 8.

Mixtures Containing Polyhalogen Compounds

A variety of free-radical chain reactions are known which involve polyhalogen compounds and unsaturated or oxygenated compounds. These can be initiated by any process which produces moderately reactive free radicals in the mixture, including exposure to ionizing radiation. Since the reactions are chain reactions, product yields may be high. Many polyhalogen compounds can be used ($CHCl_3$, Cl_3CBr, CBr_4, etc.) but for simplicity most of the examples given here involve carbon tetrachloride. Polyfluoro compounds which do not contain any other halogen are exceptions and do not react in this manner.

Carbon tetrachloride and alcohols will react together forming hydrogen chloride, chloroform, and a carbonyl compound,

$$CCl_4 + R_1R_2CHOH \rightarrow CHCl_3 + R_1R_2CO + HCl \qquad (9.98)$$

The reaction can be initiated by ionizing radiation and the yields depend upon such conditions as the proportions of the reactants, the presence or absence of oxygen, temperature, and dose rate. Under standard conditions (air-saturated 1:1 mixtures of halide and alcohol irradiated with γ-radiation) Hannerz (72) found the following yields of hydrochloric acid from mixtures of carbon tetrachloride with various alcohols:

Alcohol	Ethyl	Ethyl (air-free)	*n*-Butyl	*s*-Butyl	Isobutyl	*t*-Butyl
$G(HCl)$	620	370	390	1250	530	17

In the absence of oxygen, equivalent amounts of hydrochloric acid and carbonyl compound are formed and the mechanism is probably

$$CCl_4 \text{ and } R_1R_2CHOH \rightsquigarrow \text{radicals} \rightarrow \cdot CCl_3 \text{ and } R_1R_2\dot{C}OH \qquad (9.99)$$

followed by the chain reaction

$$\cdot CCl_3 + R_1R_2CHOH \rightarrow R_1R_2\dot{C}OH + CHCl_3 \quad (9.100)$$

$$R_1R_2\dot{C}OH + CCl_4 \rightarrow \cdot CCl_3 + R_1R_2CO + HCl \quad (9.101)$$

When oxygen is present and the products are identified after extraction with water, roughly twice as much hydrochloric acid is formed as carbonyl compound. This is almost certainly due to the formation of peroxy radicals from all or part of the intermediate organic radicals, and it is significant that peroxides (probably hydroperoxides) can be identified in mixtures irradiated in the presence of oxygen. One way in which the extra hydrochloric acid might arise would be by hydrolysis of the hydroperoxide CCl_3OOH, formed by

$$\cdot CCl_3 + O_2 \rightarrow CCl_3O_2\cdot \quad (9.82)$$

$$CCl_3O_2\cdot + R_1R_2CHOH \rightarrow R_1R_2\dot{C}OH + CCl_3OOH \quad (9.102)$$

It is interesting that the highest yields of acid are obtained from alcohols which, by loss of an α-hydrogen atom, would be expected to give the most stable radical; radical stability increases in the series *n*-butyl < isobutyl < *s*-butyl. The radical derived from isopropyl alcohol is probably rather more stable than that from *s*-butyl alcohol, and isopropyl alcohol gave the highest yield of acid ($G = 1810$) of all the alcohols tested. Tertiary butyl alcohol, which lacks an α-hydrogen atom, gave a low yield of acid. Under the standard conditions diethyl ether gave a high yield of acid ($G = 350$) while acetone and ethyl acetate gave relatively low yields ($G = 18$ and 33 respectively). Mixtures of carbon tetrachloride and an alcohol might be used as chemical dosimeters but, though very sensitive to radiation (doses of a few rads can be detected), they suffer from several disadvantages including poor stability towards heat and light and high susceptibility to traces of impurity. Spurný (73) has suggested that mixtures of ethanol and carbon tetrachloride be used in dosimetry while Clark and Bierstedt (74) have investigated a number of systems containing a halide (carbon tetrachloride or chloroform), ethanol, and a dye.

Solutions of straight-chain aliphatic aldehydes in carbon tetrachloride react in a similar manner to alcohols when irradiated in the absence of oxygen (75). The products in this case are chloroform and the appropriate acid chloride, and the chain-propagating steps are

$$\cdot CCl_3 + RCHO \rightarrow RCO\cdot + CHCl_3 \quad (9.103)$$

$$RCO\cdot + CCl_4 \rightarrow \cdot CCl_3 + RCOCl \quad (9.104)$$

The yields are dose-rate dependent.

Addition reactions between carbon tetrachloride and olefins are represented by the sequence of reactions

$$\cdot \mathrm{CCl_3} + \underset{|}{\overset{|}{\mathrm{C}}}{=}\underset{|}{\overset{|}{\mathrm{C}}} \rightarrow \cdot\underset{|}{\overset{|}{\mathrm{C}}}{-}\underset{|}{\overset{|}{\mathrm{C}}}{-}\mathrm{CCl_3} \tag{9.105}$$

$$\cdot\underset{|}{\overset{|}{\mathrm{C}}}{-}\underset{|}{\overset{|}{\mathrm{C}}}{-}\mathrm{CCl_3} + \mathrm{CCl_4} \rightarrow \cdot \mathrm{CCl_3} + \mathrm{Cl}{-}\underset{|}{\overset{|}{\mathrm{C}}}{-}\underset{|}{\overset{|}{\mathrm{C}}}{-}\mathrm{CCl_3} \tag{9.106}$$

where the fragments formed by splitting a carbon-chlorine bond add across the double bond. A large number of similar addition reactions are known (76). When the olefin is not symmetrical about the double bond, two addition products can be formed, depending on which end of the bond the trichloromethyl radical attacks. Often, however, only one of the possible products is obtained. In some cases the intermediate organic radical formed by the first reaction is not sufficiently reactive to abstract halogen from the polyhalogen compound, and the second step in the sequence (Eq. 9.106) cannot take place. Under these circumstances the intermediate radical may react with further molecules of olefin to produce a polymer, e.g.,

$$\cdot\underset{|}{\overset{|}{\mathrm{C}}}{-}\underset{|}{\overset{|}{\mathrm{C}}}{-}\mathrm{CCl_3} + \underset{|}{\overset{|}{\mathrm{C}}}{=}\underset{|}{\overset{|}{\mathrm{C}}} \rightarrow \cdot\underset{|}{\overset{|}{\mathrm{C}}}{-}\underset{|}{\overset{|}{\mathrm{C}}}{-}\underset{|}{\overset{|}{\mathrm{C}}}{-}\underset{|}{\overset{|}{\mathrm{C}}}{-}\mathrm{CCl_3} \quad \text{etc.} \tag{9.107}$$

Here the halogen compound serves merely to initiate polymerization and takes no part in the chain reaction; in systems irradiated with ionizing radiation, radicals formed from the olefin will also initiate polymerization. Polymerization is more probable than addition when the carbon-halogen bonds in the polyhalogen compound are relatively strong, while addition is favored by weak carbon-halogen bonds (or at least one weak one, as in $Cl_3C{-}Br$). It is of course possible for both polymerization and addition to occur in the same mixture.

Since other methods of introducing radicals are available and are often more convenient, relatively few radiation-induced addition reactions between polyhalogen compounds and olefins have been studied. Heiba and Anderson (77), however, examined the γ-initiated addition of bromotrichloromethane to alkenes. This compound has a relatively weak carbon-bromine bond and the fragments $Br\cdot$ and $\cdot CCl_3$ were found to add across the double bond of 1-alkenes,

$$\mathrm{BrCCl_3} + \mathrm{R{-}CH{=}CH_2} \rightarrow \mathrm{R{-}CHBr{-}CH_2{-}CCl_3} \tag{9.108}$$

When other groups are substituted for the hydrogen in the alkene, different addition products may also be formed. Stein and his colleagues (69, 78) have suggested that deaerated solutions of biallyl, $CH_2{=}CH{-}CH_2{-}CH_2{-}CH{=}CH_2$, in dry chloroform be used in chemical dosimetry. Upon irradiation the chloroform adds to the biallyl and the absorbed dose is a function of the reduction in unsaturation in the mixture.

Other types of compound can also add to alkenes by way of radiation-induced free radical reactions. Compounds added in this manner include alkanes (cf. Chapter 7), aldehydes (79), mercaptans (RSH), which add as RS· and H· (80), and phosphines (R_1R_2PH), which add as $R_1R_2P\cdot$ and H· or possibly, if R_2 is hydrogen, as R_1P: and 2H· (81).

Halides in Dosimetry

The use of pure chloroform and of aqueous solutions of organic halides in chemical dosimetry has already been described (Chapters 4 and 8). Other halides, such as the chlorine substituted ethylenes, can be used in a similar manner to chloroform, and mixtures of halogen compounds with alcohols may be used as described in the previous section. There is one further point that might be made with respect to such halide systems and that is that by using hydrogen-free materials the system can be made insensitive to fast neutrons. Aerated tetrachloroethylene, either alone or overlayered with water, is insensitive to fast neutrons, and when exposed to both fast neutrons and γ-radiation will only register the absorbed dose due to the γ-radiation (82, 83). A saturated aqueous solution of trichloroethylene (tetrachloroethylene is insoluble) will respond to both the fast neutrons and the γ-radiation, and by using both systems the absorbed dose due to the neutrons and the γ-radiation can be estimated separately. Both dosimeters are sensitive to slow neutrons and would have to be protected from these by suitable shielding.

Fluorides

Relatively little work has been carried out on the radiolysis of organic fluorides. In these compounds the carbon-fluorine bonds are strong and carbon-carbon bond scission generally occurs. Radical attack on the fluorides leads to hydrogen abstraction in preference to fluorine abstraction, in contrast to the fairly ready halogen abstraction reactions found with the other halides.

One of the more frequently investigated fluorides is the polymer Teflon, perfluropolyethylene—$(CF_2)_n$—. Teflon is relatively resistant to radiation in the absence of oxygen but rapidly deteriorates when oxygen is present, becoming extremely brittle (84). A number of radiolysis products have been identified (85) including, in the absence of oxygen, CF_4, C_2F_6, C_3F_8, and higher fluorocarbons, and SiF_4 (from the glass container) and, when oxygen is present during the irradiation, CF_4 and C_2F_6 (in rather smaller amounts than are formed in the absence of oxygen), SiF_4, and a high proportion of COF_2. Golden (85) has suggested that these products are formed by random splitting of carbon-carbon bonds, and to a smaller extent carbon-fluorine bonds, to give radicals which in the absence of oxygen combine to give the observed products or else remain as relatively stable free radicals in the solid, i.e.,

$$—CF_2—CF_2—CF_2— \rightsquigarrow —CF_2—CF_2\cdot + \cdot CF_2— \qquad (9.109)$$

or, less often

$$—CF_2—CF_2—CF_2— \rightsquigarrow —CF_2—\dot{C}F—CF_2— + F\cdot \qquad (9.110)$$

Oxygen will add to the organic radicals to give peroxy radicals, which can react together to form alkoxy radicals,

$$—CF_2—CF_2\cdot + O_2 \rightarrow —CF_2—CF_2O_2\cdot \qquad (9.111)$$

$$2\,—CF_2—CF_2O_2\cdot \rightarrow 2\,—CF_2—CF_2O\cdot + O_2 \qquad (9.112)$$

Dissociation of the alkoxy radicals produces carbonyl fluoride and a new organic radical, smaller than the original radical by one $—CF_2—$ group,

$$—CF_2—CF_2O\cdot \rightarrow —CF_2\cdot + COF_2 \qquad (9.113)$$

A similar sequence of reactions can be envisaged for the secondary radicals:

$$—CF_2—\dot{C}F—CF_2 \xrightarrow{O_2} —CF_2—C(O\cdot)F—CF_2— \qquad (9.114)$$

$$—CF_2—C(O\cdot)F—CF_2— \rightarrow —CF_2\cdot + OFC—CF_2— \qquad (9.115)$$

or

$$\rightarrow —CF_2\cdot + COF_2 + CF_2{=}CF— \qquad (9.116)$$

By repetition of these reactions an entire polymer molecule may be rapidly degraded once a free radical center has been formed in some part of it. This is analogous to the photochemical degradation of perfluorohalides in the presence of oxygen (86).

ALCOHOLS AND ETHERS

Alcohols are the organic analogues of water and their behavior upon irradiation is similar in several respects to that of water. The products obtained by irradiating pure alcohols include hydrogen, hydrocarbons, water, carbon monoxide, glycols, and aldehydes, or ketones. Primary alcohols are oxidized to aldehydes, secondary alcohols to a mixture of aldehydes and ketones, and tertiary alcohols to ketones alone. In the absence of oxygen, glycols are invariably formed, and are predominantly α-glycols, $R_1R_2C(OH)—C(OH)R_1R_2$, consistent with the postulate that a common radiation-induced reaction of alcohols (R_1R_2CHOH) is loss of an α-hydrogen atom to give the radical $R_1R_2\dot{C}OH$. The yield of hydrogen is greatest with the straight-chain alcohols and decreases with increased branching, while hydrocarbon yields are greatest with branched-chain alcohols. As the length of the carbon chain is increased the products tend to include smaller amounts of those characteristic of the alcohol group and more of those resulting from bond breaking in the hydrocarbon chain, suggesting that reaction is partly through random bond breaking in the molecule as a whole and partly through preferential reaction involving the functional group.

The radiolysis of the ethers is rather similar to that of the alcohols, though less has been published about them.

Methanol

Representative values of the radiolysis yields from deaerated methanol are given in Table 9.8; however, few authors agree. The table illustrates two features in which the radiolysis of methanol resembles that of water, namely the pronounced effect of LET and the effect of pH. It also demonstrates, through the effect of radical scavengers, that "radical" and "molecular" processes can be distinguished with methanol as with water.

Plausible radiolysis mechanisms can be postulated for methanol which are similar to the Samuel-Magee and Lea-Gray-Platzman models proposed to account for the radiolysis of water (cf. Chapter 8). The mass spectrometer provides evidence of the ions that are most likely to be concerned. The more important ions and their relative abundances (91) are: CH_2OH^+ (100), CH_3OH^+ (68), and CHO^+ (52). These are formed by the reactions

TABLE 9.8 *Radiolysis of Methanol*

Radiation	Solute	$G(H_2)$	$G(CO)$	$G(CH_4)$	$G(HCHO)$	$G(C_2H_6O_2)$	Ref.
$B^{10}(n,\alpha)Li^7$ recoil nuclei	$0.2M$ methyl borate	5.14	0.92	0.67	3.45	1.40	87
Co^{60} γ-rays	none	5.40*	0.15	0.80	2.15	3.7	88
"	"	5.39	0.11	0.54	1.84	3.63	89
"	$0.04M$ iodine†	2.02	0.14	0.19	0.36	0.09	89
"	$>0.01N$ H_2SO_4	6.05	0.12	0.60	2.55	3.8	88
"	$0.01N$ CH_3ONa	5.50	0.11	0.87	2.05	3.9	88
"	$Fe_2(SO_4)_3 + 0.1N$ H_2SO_4 + 3% water‡	5.55	0.16	0.39	8.5		90

* Unchanged by the addition of 3% water.

† G(-iodine) = 1.78.

‡ $G(Fe^{3+}) = 6.5$.

$$CH_3OH + e^- \rightarrow CH_3OH^+ + 2e^- \quad (9.117)$$

$$\rightarrow CH_2OH^+ + H\cdot + 2e^- \quad (9.118)$$

$$\rightarrow CHO^+ + H_2 + H\cdot + 2e^- \quad (9.119)$$

Under normal radiolysis conditions the ions can take part in ion-molecule reactions, if these are feasible. In methanol, probable ion-molecule reactions are (92)

$$CH_3OH^+ + CH_3OH \rightarrow CH_3OH_2^+ + \cdot CH_2OH \text{ (or } CH_3O\cdot) \quad (9.120)$$

$$CH_2OH^+ + CH_3OH \rightarrow CH_3OH_2^+ + HCHO \quad (9.121)$$

$$CHO^+ + CH_3OH \rightarrow CH_3OH_2^+ + CO \quad (9.122)$$

or

$$\rightarrow CH_2OH^+ + HCHO \quad (9.123)$$

or

$$\rightarrow CH_3^+ + CO + H_2O \quad (9.124)$$

$$CH_3^+ + CH_3OH \rightarrow CH_2OH^+ + CH_4 \quad (9.125)$$

Reactions 9.123 and 9.125 are examples of hydride-ion transfer, a form of ion-molecule reaction less common than proton transfer, of which the remaining ion-molecule reactions are representative.

Assuming a Samuel-Magee type mechanism, the original positive ions, or positive ions formed by rapid ion-molecule reactions, will be neutralized by return of the ejected electron, e.g.,

$$CH_3OH_2^+ + e^- \rightarrow CH_3OH + H\cdot \quad (9.126)$$

or

$$\rightarrow CH_3O\cdot + H_2 \quad (9.127)$$

or

$$\rightarrow \cdot CH_3 + H_2O \quad (9.128)$$

The over-all result of these, or similar, ionic reactions is the production of radicals and molecular products. The radicals usually considered to be present are $H\cdot$, $\cdot CH_2OH$ and, to a lesser extent, $\cdot CH_3$; the inclusion of methoxy radicals ($CH_3O\cdot$) in the scheme above is purely speculative since they have not been identified in this system. Products are formed in part by the reactions of scavengeable radicals and in part by "molecular" processes. The latter may be ionic reactions, as shown above, hot hydrogen atom reactions, or radical reactions in spurs or in the tracks of densely ionizing particles. In pure methanol probable radical reactions are

$$H\cdot + CH_3OH \rightarrow \cdot CH_2OH + H_2 \tag{9.129}$$

$$\cdot CH_3 + CH_3OH \rightarrow \cdot CH_2OH + CH_4 \tag{9.130}$$

$$2\cdot CH_2OH \rightarrow (CH_2OH)_2 \tag{9.131}$$

and, possibly

$$CH_3O\cdot + CH_3OH \rightarrow \cdot CH_2OH + CH_3OH \tag{9.132}$$

$$2CH_3O\cdot \rightarrow CH_3OH + HCHO \tag{9.133}$$

An alternative description of the primary steps, which corresponds more closely to the Lea-Gray-Platzman model for water, has been postulated by Hayon and Weiss (93). The description is similar to that proposed by these authors for the radiolysis of aqueous solutions (cf. page 260) and assumes that the initial ionic species are positive and negative polarons, $(CH_3OH)^+$ and $(CH_3OH)^-$ respectively. The polarons may react with solutes or, failing this, dissociate,

$$(CH_3OH)^+ \rightarrow \cdot CH_2OH + H^+ \tag{9.134}$$

$$(CH_3OH)^- \rightarrow CH_3O^- + H\cdot \tag{9.135}$$

and (or) be neutralized,

$$(CH_3OH)^- + H^+ \rightarrow CH_3OH + H\cdot \tag{9.136}$$

$$CH_3O^- + H^+ \rightarrow CH_3OH \tag{9.137}$$

The products from the ionic dissociation and neutralization reactions are the radicals $H\cdot$ and $\cdot CH_2OH$, as for the first sequence of reactions (Eqs. 9.117 to 9.128).

Radical scavenging experiments were carried out by Baxendale (88, 90) with pure methanol and methanol acidified with sulfuric acid. Yields found for acidified methanol in the presence of ferric sulfate are shown in Table 9.8. This scavenger almost completely suppresses the formation of glycol, but it increases the yield of formaldehyde by an equivalent amount, and is believed to react with $\cdot CH_2OH$ radicals,

$$Fe^{3+} + \cdot CH_2OH \rightarrow Fe^{2+} + HCHO + H^+ \tag{9.138}$$

The yield of ferrous ion provides a measure of the total radical yield since hydrogen atoms and methyl radicals both react with methanol to give $\cdot CH_2OH$. Ferric chloride and benzoquinone were also used as scavengers in both neutral and acid methanol, enabling radical and molecular yields to be estimated for these media (Table 9.9). At sufficiently high ferric chloride concentrations, all the hydrogen atoms react with the scavenger directly,

$$H\cdot + Fe^{3+} \rightarrow H^+ + Fe^{2+} \tag{9.139}$$

and $G(H_2)$ is then a measure of the hydrogen formed by molecular processes. Aromatic hydrocarbons (benzene, biphenyl, naphthalene, and anthracene) were found by Baxendale and Mellows (88) to reduce the yield of hydrogen but to be without effect on the yield of formaldehyde, and their action was attributed to scavenging of hydrogen atoms. Two forms of "hydrogen atom" were distinguished, one the normal hydrogen atom ($H\cdot$) and the other believed to be an electron, presumably solvated with methanol. Biphenyl, naphthalene, and anthracene are able to scavenge both hydrogen atoms and electrons (the latter forming negative ions, e.g., $C_{14}H_{10}^-$) whereas benzene scavenges only the hydrogen atoms. Carbon monoxide yields are not affected by any of the scavengers used and this may well be formed by an ion-molecule reaction, as suggested by equation 9.122.

TABLE 9.9 *Radical and Molecular Yields for Methanol*

(Ref. 90. Values in parentheses were estimated from more recent data by Baxendale and Mellows (88) and are based on the radiolysis mechanism proposed by these authors.)

Product	G(product)	
	Pure MeOH (neutral)	97% MeOH* + 0.1N H_2SO_4
$H\cdot$	2.4 (3.85)	3.8 (4.45)
$\cdot CH_3$	1.0 (0.60)	0.2 (0.40)
$\cdot CH_2OH$	2.7 (1.25)	2.5 (0.85)
$\cdot OH$	(0.60)	(0.60)
H_2	1.7 (1.55)	1.8 (1.55)
CH_4	0.2 (0.20)	0.2 (0.20)
CO	0.15 (0.12)	0.16 (0.12)
HCHO	2.05 (2.15)	2.2 (2.55)
$C_2H_6O_2$	0.2 (0.65)	0.2 (0.65)

* 97% methanol + about 3% water.

Meshitsuka and Burton (89) examined the effect of iodine upon methanol radiolysis and interpreted the results in terms of the initial production of ionized molecules and two types of excited molecules, one in a singlet excited state and one in a triplet excited state. Changes in product yields in the presence of iodine (Table 9.8) were attributed to both radical scavenging and electron capture by iodine (to give I^-). Electron capture will interfere with the ion-neutralization processes; for example, reactions 9.126–128 might be replaced by

$$CH_3OH_2^+ + I^- \rightarrow CH_3OH + HI \qquad (9.140)$$

Product yields from irradiated methanol are not altered by the presence of alkali, but the yields of hydrogen and formaldehyde are increased and the yield of methane decreased in the presence of acid (Table 9.8); the changes are independent of the acid concentration above about $0.01N$ acid. The effect of acid has been explained by Baxendale and Mellows (88) as due to rapid scavenging of electrons by methyl-oxonium ions, $CH_3OH_2^+$ (i.e., $CH_3OH + H^+$),

$$CH_3OH_2^+ + e^- \rightarrow CH_3OH + H\cdot \qquad \text{(fast)} \qquad (9.126)$$

In acid solutions all electrons are assumed to react in this manner, while in neutral solutions some may react in other ways:

$$CH_2OH^+ + e^- \rightarrow \cdot CH_2OH \qquad (9.141)$$

$$CH_3OH + e^- \rightarrow CH_3O^- + H\cdot \qquad \text{(relatively slow)} \qquad (9.142)$$

or

$$\rightarrow \cdot CH_3 + OH^- \qquad (9.143)$$

The first alternative will compete with proton transfer (reaction 9.121) and the authors conclude that it must take place rapidly within spurs; the relatively high concentrations of acid necessary to produce an effect are cited as evidence in support of this. The remaining reactions (Eqs. 9.142 and 9.143) occur outside the spurs and the electrons involved can be scavenged (e.g., by aromatic hydrocarbons) before the reaction takes place.

The effect of LET upon the product yields from methanol is illustrated by the first three horizontal groups of figures in Table 9.8; a more exact comparison is made in ref. 87 where γ-ray yields in methanol containing $0.2M$ methyl borate are given. It is clear that yields of products which are derived by molecular processes (i.e., formaldehyde and carbon monoxide) are increased with the higher LET radiation, while products which are formed mainly by radical processes (methane[7] and ethylene glycol) are produced in lower yield. Hydrogen is formed by both molecular and radical processes and is less affected by changes in LET; no

[7] Methane is formed largely by a process involving free radicals, but the effect of LET upon methane yields may be questioned since reported values for these yields are ambiguous.

change in the hydrogen yield with LET would be expected if the only fate of hydrogen atoms is to abstract hydrogen from a molecule of methanol (Eq. 9.129).

Methanol vapor has been irradiated by Baxendale and Sedgwick (94), with the results shown in Table 9.10. Compared to the radiolysis of the

TABLE 9.10 *Radiolysis of Methanol Vapor*

(Ref. 94. The results are for γ-irradiation and are based on a value of $G(N_2) = 9.68$ for the nitrous oxide dosimeter.)

Product	G(product)		
	Pure MeOH* (liquid)	Pure MeOH (vapor)	MeOH + ~2% C_6H_6 (vapor)
H_2	5.40	10.4	4.6
CH_4	0.80	0.26	0.29
CO	0.15	0.84	1.00
HCHO	2.15	5.6	3.7
$C_2H_6O_2$	3.7	3.1	

* Ref. 88.

liquid, more methanol is decomposed and the yields of hydrogen and formaldehyde are markedly increased, though the yields of these two products are reduced by the presence of benzene in the vapor. The mechanism postulated by Baxendale and Sedgwick for the radiolysis of the vapor is similar to that proposed for the radiolysis of liquid methanol, except for the step involving neutralization of the ion $CH_3OH_2^+$. These authors suggest that neutralization of this ion gives an excited molecule which, in the vapor, dissociates to hydrogen and formaldehyde

$$CH_3OH_2^+ + e^- \rightarrow CH_3OH^* + H\cdot \tag{9.144}$$

$$CH_3OH^* \rightarrow HCHO + H_2 \tag{9.145}$$

The latter reaction has already been identified in the photolysis of methanol vapor (95). In liquid methanol the excited molecule is presumably quenched without appreciable dissociation. Quenching may also occur in the vapor if benzene is present, thereby reducing the yields of hydrogen and formaldehyde, though the benzene can further reduce the hydrogen yield by scavenging hydrogen atoms.

In the presence of oxygen the major products formed from methanol are (93) formaldehyde ($G = 4.28$), hydrogen peroxide ($G = 2.89$), and hydrogen ($G = 1.41$); ethylene glycol is not formed. The yields given are for air-saturated methanol irradiated with γ-radiation. When the methanol is saturated with oxygen slightly lower yields are found due to the formation of another product (presumably formic acid) which is dependent upon the concentration of oxygen in the methanol. Lichtin, Rosenberg, and Immamura (96) have confirmed the formation of formic acid ($G = 1.8$) from aerated methanol, but find *no* hydrogen peroxide when the methanol is carefully dried before irradiation. However, hydrogen peroxide is formed when the methanol contains water; the hydrogen peroxide yield becoming constant ($G = 2.8$) when the concentration of water is greater than about $0.3M$. These authors also find a greater yield of formaldehyde ($G = 10 \pm 1$) than Hayon and Weiss (93), which they attribute to the absence of benzene from their methanol; the higher formaldehyde yield suggests that in the presence of oxygen this product may be formed by a short chain reaction. The absence of glycol when the irradiation is carried out in the presence of oxygen indicates that $\cdot CH_2OH$ radicals are efficiently scavenged by oxygen.

Ethanol

The radiolysis of ethanol is similar in its main features to the radiolysis of methanol, though a rather larger number of minor products are produced (Table 9.11). Major products are accounted for if the primary processes lead to loss of an α-hydrogen atom,

$$CH_3CH_2OH \rightsquigarrow CH_3\dot{C}HOH + H\cdot \qquad (9.146)$$

and the radicals formed react:

$$H\cdot + CH_3CH_2OH \rightarrow CH_3\dot{C}HOH + H_2 \qquad (9.147)$$

$$2CH_3\dot{C}HOH \rightarrow CH_3CH(OH)CH(OH)CH_3 \qquad (9.148)$$

or

$$\rightarrow CH_3CH_2OH + CH_3CHO \qquad (9.149)$$

Peroxy radicals will be produced if oxygen is present; these can react together to form hydrogen peroxide and acetaldehyde,

$$HO_2\cdot + CH_3CH(O_2\cdot)OH \rightarrow H_2O_2 + CH_3CHO + O_2 \qquad (9.150)$$

The assumption that α-hydrogen atoms are lost rather than β-hydrogen atoms, i.e., that the intermediate organic radicals are $CH_3\dot{C}HOH$ rather than $\cdot CH_2CH_2OH$, is supported by results obtained by irradiating partially deuterated ethanols (99). Substitution of deuterium for the hydrogen in the —CH_2— group lowers $G(H_2 + D_2)$ from the value found

TABLE 9.11 *Radiolysis of Ethanol*

Product	G(product)		
	Vapor (α-radiation; 108°C; ref. 97)	Liquid (γ-radiation; 20°C; ref. 98)	Air-saturated liquid (γ-radiation; 20°C; ref. 98)
H_2	8.9	4.87	1.73
H_2O	5.4		
H_2O_2			4.62
CH_4	1.66	0.58	trace
C_2H_2	0.03	trace	trace
C_2H_4	0.72	trace	trace
C_2H_6	0.23	trace	trace
CO	1.1	0.26	trace
HCHO	0.9		
CH_3CHO	4.5	3.14	6.40
C_3H_7OH	0.6		
C_4H_9OH	0.19		
1,2-propanediol	0.15		
2,3-butanediol	1.2	1.67	about 0.3

for ethanol (3.66) to that found for fully deuterated ethanol, CD_3CD_2OD (2.98), showing that the formation of hydrogen is controlled by splitting of a carbon-hydrogen bond in this group. Substitution of hydrogen in the CH_3 or OH group by deuterium does not alter the hydrogen yield, which remains at the value found for ethanol. Hydrogen formed from CH_3CD_2OH and CH_3CH_2OD contains about 40% deuterium while hydrogen from CD_3CH_2OH contains only 4%, so that hydrogen atoms from both methylene and hydroxyl groups appear finally as product hydrogen. This does not necessarily mean that hydrogen atoms lost from the methylene group subsequently abstract hydrogen from the hydroxyl group,

$$H\cdot + CH_3CH_2OH \rightarrow CH_3CH_2O\cdot + H_2 \qquad (9.151)$$

since isotopic mixing could also be achieved through ion-molecule reactions. Further support for the assumption of α-hydrogen loss comes from electron paramagnetic resonance studies on frozen, irradiated ethanol. The studies suggest that $CH_3\dot{C}HOH$ is the predominant organic radical formed (100). This conclusion is also supported by experiments by Taub and Dorfman (101) in which ethanol was subjected to a single very intense pulse of electrons, and the ultraviolet absorption spectrum of the transient species produced recorded. The same spectrum was obtained with both deaerated ethanol and deaerated aqueous ethanol and was attributed to the radical $CH_3\dot{C}HOH$. The experiments also gave absolute rate constants for the dimerization of this radical in ethanol and in water.

Ramaradhya and Freeman (97) have examined the vapor phase radiolysis of ethanol and find appreciably greater product yields than in the liquid (Table 9.11); they have suggested a comprehensive, multistage, mechanism for the radiolysis.

Ethers

Ethers are decomposed by radiation to about the same extent as alcohols, in contrast to their stability toward many chemical reagents which react with alcohols. The main products obtained upon irradiating diethyl ether with helium ions (102) are hydrogen ($G = 3.62$), ethylene ($G = 1.07$), and ethane ($G = 0.62$), with smaller amounts of acetylene, carbon monoxide, methane, and other alkanes and alkenes. Alcohols, carbonyl compounds, and polymeric materials are also important products with most ethers, and the products formed in greatest yield apparently result from rupture of a carbon-oxygen bond. The radiolysis of diethyl ether has not been studied sufficiently for a mechanism to be proposed although the mass spectrum of this compound, where the most important ions are (102) CH_2OH^+ (100), $C_2H_5^+$ (62), and $C_2H_5OCH_2^+$ (41), suggests a possible mechanism for the formation of ethylene and organic radicals, i.e.,

$$C_2H_5OC_2H_5 + e^- \rightarrow CH_2OH^+ + C_2H_4 + \cdot CH_3 + 2e^- \quad (9.152)$$

$$\rightarrow C_2H_5^+ + C_2H_5O\cdot + 2e^- \qquad \text{etc.} \quad (9.153)$$

Irradiation of diethyl ether in the presence of oxygen produces relatively large amounts of carbonyl compounds (G about 30) and peroxides (G about 15) (reported by N. A. Bach (103)). It was suggested that these products arise by a chain reaction consisting, in part, of

$$C_2H_5OC_2H_5 \rightsquigarrow CH_3\dot{C}HOC_2H_5 + H\cdot \quad (9.154)$$

$$CH_3\dot{C}HOC_2H_5 + O_2 \rightarrow CH_3CH(O_2\cdot)OC_2H_5 \quad (9.155)$$

$$CH_3CH(O_2\cdot)OC_2H_5 + C_2H_5OC_2H_5 \rightarrow CH_3\dot{C}HOC_2H_5 + CH_3CH(O_2H)OC_2H_5 \quad (9.156)$$

followed by decay of the hydroperoxide to give carbonyl products. The first step in this mechanism (Eq. 9.154) is supported by electron paramagnetic resonance measurements made upon frozen, irradiated diethyl ether (100), which show an e.p.r. spectrum similar to that given by irradiated ethanol glass. In each case loss of an α-hydrogen atom is indicated, giving from diethyl ether the radical $CH_3\dot{C}HOC_2H_5$.

Newton (104) has investigated the radiolysis of deaerated di-isopropyl ether and has discussed the radiolysis mechanism in some detail, while Bach (103) has described the irradiation of this ether in the presence of oxygen.

ACIDS, ESTERS, AND CARBONYL COMPOUNDS

Relatively little work has been published on the radiolysis of these compounds. The lower members of the carboxylic acid series tend to decarboxylate upon irradiation, giving mainly carbon dioxide and various hydrocarbons; water may also be a significant product. Esters largely breakdown at the functional group and hydrogen, carbon monoxide, and carbon dioxide are major products, while ketones tend to break at a C—CO bond.

Acetic Acid

The radiolysis of aqueous solutions of acetic acid has been described in Chapter 8, the main products formed under these conditions being hydrogen, succinic acid, and higher polybasic carboxylic acids. When the pure acid is irradiated a quite different series of products is formed (Table 9.12), and succinic and the polybasic acids do not appear. In addition to the products shown in Table 9.12, Newton (105) identified acetaldehyde, acetone, and methyl acetate among the liquid products; other nongaseous products must also be formed.

The radiolysis mechanism for acetic acid is uncertain, though the primary stages are likely to lead to breakdown of the molecule into radicals, e.g.,

$$CH_3COOH \rightsquigarrow CH_3COO\cdot + H\cdot \tag{9.157}$$

$$\rightsquigarrow CH_3CO\cdot + \cdot OH \tag{9.158}$$

$$\rightsquigarrow \cdot CH_3 + \cdot COOH \tag{9.159}$$

and this may be followed by further dissociation of the primary radicals,

$$CH_3COO\cdot \rightarrow \cdot CH_3 + CO_2 \tag{9.160}$$

$$CH_3CO\cdot \rightarrow \cdot CH_3 + CO \tag{9.161}$$

$$\cdot COOH \rightarrow H\cdot + CO_2 \tag{9.162}$$

TABLE 9.12 *Radiolysis of Acetic Acid*

Product	G(product)			
	Pure acid (α-radiation; ref. 105)	Pure acid (γ-radiation; ref. 106)	Acid + 0.01M I_2 (γ-radiation; ref. 106)	Acid + O_2 (γ and x-rays; ref. 39)
H_2	0.52	0.35		0
H_2O	2.15			
CH_4	1.38	3.34	0.69	0
C_2H_6	0.85	0.62	0.65	
CO	0.38	0.73	0.44	0
CO_2	4.04	6.0	6.2	2.4
HCHO		0*		1.1
CH_3COCH_3		0.45*		0.45
$H_2O_2 + CH_3CO_3H$		0*		0.36
$(CH_3CO)_2O_2$		0*		0.78
CH_3O_2H		0*		1.1

* Ref. 39.

Yields of carbon dioxide and carbon monoxide are almost unchanged by the presence of radical scavengers (106, 107), suggesting that if they are formed by reactions 9.160 and 9.161 the parent radicals must dissociate rapidly before scavenging can occur. The yield of ethane is also unaffected by radical scavengers.

Burr (108) has irradiated deuterated and tritiated acetic acids and from the isotopic composition of the hydrogen and methane formed, and the rate of production of hydrogen, shown that methane arises almost entirely by the process,

$$\cdot CH_3 + CH_3COOH \rightarrow CH_4 + \cdot CH_2COOH \tag{9.163}$$

and that hydrogen most probably arises by a similar process,

$$H\cdot + CH_3COOH \rightarrow H_2 + \cdot CH_2COOH \tag{9.164}$$

Methane might also be formed in part by dissociation of an excited molecule,

$$CH_3COOH^* \rightarrow CH_4 + CO_2 \tag{9.165}$$

This process contributes about 10% of the methane produced when acetic acid vapor is decomposed photochemically (109). Burr concludes that such direct dissociation could not account for more than 15% of the methane formed by irradiation, though scavenger experiments (106, 107) suggest that about 20% of the methane is produced by "molecular" processes. The difference between the estimates may be indicative of hot methyl radical reactions or of radical reactions within spurs, which produce methane but are inaccessible to scavengers.

Johnsen (106) has noted that with higher carboxylic acids, unbranched acids containing an odd number of carbon atoms give rather lower yields of carbon dioxide than acids with even numbers of carbon atoms, though in general the carbon dioxide yield decreases with increasing chain length. Branched-chain acids give higher yields of carbon dioxide than the straight-chain isomer, particularly when the carboxyl group is attached at the point of branching. Thus isobutyric acid, $(CH_3)_2CHCOOH$, gives an exceptionally high yield of carbon dioxide ($G = 14.4$), which is considerably greater than the yield from the straight-chain isomer, *n*-butyric acid ($G = 5.0$).

Methyl Acetate

Radiolysis products from methyl acetate, a fairly typical ester, are given in Table 9.13. Hummel (111) obtained similar results and also identified and estimated formaldehyde ($G = 0.42$) and sixteen liquid products, of which the more abundant were methanol ($G = 0.80$) and acetic acid ($G = 0.50$). Ausloos and Trumbore (110) were able to identify the methyl group from which products originate and to gain other information about the radiolysis process by irradiating the deuterium substituted ester, CH_3COOCD_3.

Although a complete radiolysis mechanism is not available for methyl acetate, the radiolysis results can be explained on the basis of known

TABLE 9.13 *Radiolysis of Methyl Acetate*

(γ-radiation; ref. 110)

Product	G(product)			
	Vapor (27°C)	Vapor + iodine (65°C)	Liquid (27°C)	Liquid + 0.01*M* iodine (27°C)
H_2	2.14	0.54	0.76	0.57
CH_4	1.76	0.05	2.03	0.50
C_2H_6	0.43	0.04	0.34	0.27
CO	2.68	2.00	1.64	1.51
CO_2	1.10	1.0	0.95	0.90
CH_3OCH_3	0.034	0	0.15	0.14

free-radical reactions and the assumption that, to a greater or lesser extent, every bond in the molecule except the C=O bond is liable to break. The primary stages can then be represented by

$$CH_3COOCH_3 \rightsquigarrow CH_3CO\cdot + \cdot OCH_3 \rightarrow \cdot CH_3 + CO + \cdot OCH_3 \quad (9.166)$$

$$\rightsquigarrow \cdot CH_3 + CH_3COO\cdot \text{ (or } \cdot COOCH_3) \rightarrow 2\cdot CH_3 + CO_2 \quad (9.167)$$

$$\rightsquigarrow H\cdot + \cdot CH_2COOCH_3 \text{ (or } CH_3COOCH_2\cdot) \quad (9.168)$$

The first two reactions will almost certainly take place with the intermediate formation of $CH_3CO\cdot$ and $CH_3COO\cdot$ (or $\cdot COOCH_3$) respectively. Both reactions have been observed in the photolysis and mercury photosensitized decomposition of methyl acetate (112), where the first (Eq. 9.166) predominates. However, in these photochemical reactions, the radical $CH_3CO\cdot$ is sufficiently stable to react to a large extent without dissociation, and is the precursor of such products as biacetyl, acetaldehyde, and acetone. These products are only formed in small amounts upon irradiation, suggesting that here the acetyl radical is formed with sufficient energy to dissociate almost immediately, as implied by equation 9.166.

The primary stages will be followed by a variety of radical reactions including, in all probability, the following:

$$\cdot CH_3 + CH_3COOCH_3 \rightarrow CH_4 + \cdot CH_2COOCH_3 \text{ (or } CH_3COOCH_2\cdot) \quad (9.169)$$

$$H\cdot + CH_3COOCH_3 \rightarrow H_2 + \cdot CH_2COOCH_3 \text{ (or } CH_3COOCH_2\cdot) \quad (9.170)$$

$$\cdot CH_3 + \cdot OCH_3 \rightarrow CH_3OCH_3 \quad (9.171)$$

or

$$\rightarrow CH_4 + HCHO \quad (9.172)$$

$$H\cdot + \cdot OCH_3 \rightarrow H_2 + HCHO \quad (9.173)$$

$$2\cdot OCH_3 \rightarrow CH_3OH + HCHO \quad (9.174)$$

$$2\cdot CH_3 \rightarrow C_2H_6 \quad (9.175)$$

though this can only be a partial list.

By carrying out scavenger experiments in both liquid and vapor phases it is possible to distinguish between the formation of "molecular" products by radical reactions in a spur and by unimolecular dissociation of an excited molecule. In the radiolysis of methyl acetate, for example, ethane may be formed by one or both of the molecular processes:

$$2 \cdot CH_3 \rightarrow C_2H_6 \tag{9.175}$$

$$CH_3COOCH_3^* \rightarrow C_2H_6 + CO_2 \tag{9.176}$$

In the liquid phase the yield of ethane is not greatly reduced by added scavenger (Table 9.13) and it might be formed by either reaction. However, in the vapor phase, where spur formation and radical caging are not significant effects, the ethane yield is markedly reduced by scavenger, suggesting that ethane is formed by the radical reaction. In the liquid phase this reaction must occur in spurs, or within a solvent cage where a pair of methyl radicals are formed together (e.g., by reaction 9.167). The limited reduction in carbon dioxide yield in the presence of scavenger excludes the possibility that the scavenger quenches an excited state (which would otherwise dissociate, giving ethane and carbon dioxide, as in equation 9.176), or acts as an electron trap, interfering with an ion-neutralization process that leads to both ethane and carbon dioxide.

Scavenging experiments with methyl acetate (Table 9.13) also show that methane is formed almost entirely by radical reactions, though in the liquid these are not entirely accessible to scavenger. Hydrogen is apparently formed in part by unimolecular dissociation or, more probably, by hydrogen abstraction by hot hydrogen atoms, which are not scavenged by iodine. Dimethyl ether, CH_3OCH_3, may be formed in a similar manner to ethane by caging of the radicals formed in reaction 9.166.

Acetone

Ausloos and Paulson (113) have identified the major gaseous radiolysis products from acetone as hydrogen, methane, ethane, and carbon monoxide (Table 9.14). Minor gaseous products (G less than 0.02) were acetylene, ethylene, methyl acetylene, propane, and propene.[8] The main products can be accounted for on the basis of known radical reactions if it is assumed that the primary steps are

$$CH_3COCH_3 \rightsquigarrow CH_3CO\cdot + \cdot CH_3 \rightarrow 2\cdot CH_3 + CO \tag{9.177}$$

$$\rightsquigarrow H\cdot + \cdot CH_2COCH_3 \tag{9.178}$$

Acetyl radicals are presumably intermediates in the first of these reactions, though products derived from them are not found, and they are probably formed with sufficient energy to dissociate rapidly to a methyl

[8] In a more recent study by Barker (114), sixteen products were identified and estimated; the main results are in substantial agreement with the earlier ones given in this section.

radical and carbon monoxide. This is substantiated by the slight effect which scavengers (Table 9.14) or reduction in temperature (27° to −80°C) have upon the yield of carbon monoxide; normally the dissociation of acetyl radicals is reduced by lowering the reaction temperature.

TABLE 9.14 *Radiolysis of Acetone* (27°C; ref. 113)

Product	*G*(product)	
	Liquid	Liquid + $0.02M I_2$
H_2	0.88	0.66
CH_4	2.62	0.33
C_2H_6	0.48	0.36
CO	0.835	0.70

The effect of scavenger on the methane yield indicates that at least 85% of the methane is formed by hydrogen abstraction by methyl radicals,

$$\cdot CH_3 + CH_3COCH_3 \rightarrow CH_4 + \cdot CH_2COCH_3 \qquad (9.179)$$

The remaining methane may be formed by hot methyl radicals, reacting in the same way, or by an ion-molecule reaction, e.g.,

$$CH_3COCH_3^+ + CH_3COCH_3 \rightarrow CH_3COCH_4^+ + \cdot CH_2COCH_3 \qquad (9.180)$$

$$CH_3COCH_4^+ + e^- \rightarrow CH_3CO\cdot + CH_4 \qquad (9.181)$$

Scavengers cause a relatively small decrease in the hydrogen yield, and it is possible that hydrogen atoms formed in reaction 9.178 are hot and react with the solvent before they can be scavenged,

$$H\cdot + CH_3COCH_3 \rightarrow H_2 + \cdot CH_2COCH_3 \qquad (9.182)$$

However, thermal hydrogen atoms appear rather to add to acetone (115)

$$H\cdot + CH_3COCH_3 \rightarrow CH_3\dot{C}HOHCH_3 \qquad (9.183)$$

than abstract hydrogen from it, and it is quite possible that some process other than reaction 9.182 is responsible for the molecular hydrogen yield. Ethane is also largely independent of scavenger and is probably formed by combination of methyl radicals in spurs or solvent cages (possibly by combination of the methyl radicals formed in reaction 9.177).

Barker (116) has shown that the yields of gaseous products and of methylethyl ketone (formed by reaction 9.184) are dependent upon both LET and dose rate; relative yields of ethane and methylethyl ketone being increased by increasing LET or dose rate, while the yield of methane is decreased. At high LET, radical-radical reactions between radicals formed in neighboring spurs on the same particle track are enhanced, and at high dose rates, radical-radical reactions between radicals formed in spurs on different tracks are increased.

$$\cdot CH_3 + \cdot CH_2COCH_3 \rightarrow CH_3CH_2COCH_3 \qquad (9.184)$$

Thus, at high LET or high dose rate the reactions forming ethane (Eq. 9.175) and methylethyl ketone (Eq. 9.184) compete more strongly with the radical-solvent reaction (Eq. 9.179) giving methane. The dose rate effect becomes significant at a lower dose rate (of the order of 10^7 rads/min) than does a similar effect in water (occurring at dose rates greater than about 10^9 rads/min) because of the relative inefficiency of the radical-solvent reaction forming methane.

Ausloos (113, 117) has also studied the vapor phase radiolysis of acetone and CD_3COCD_3, concluding that in this phase the methane and hydrogen formed in the presence of scavengers are produced by molecular detachment processes, e.g.,

$$CH_3COCH_3 \rightsquigarrow CH_4 + CH_2{=}CO \qquad (9.185)$$

$$\rightsquigarrow H_2 + CHCOCH_3 \qquad (9.186)$$

Acetic acid and acetonylacetone, $(CH_3COCH_2)_2$, were reported to be important products in the radiolysis of acetone vapor; they may be produced by the reactions

$$CH_2{=}CO + H_2O \rightarrow CH_3COOH \qquad (9.187)$$

$$2 \cdot CH_2COCH_3 \rightarrow (CH_3COCH_2)_2 \qquad (9.188)$$

Both the photochemical and the thermal decomposition of acetone vapor have been investigated very thoroughly; they are classic examples of free radical reactions.

MISCELLANEOUS COMPOUNDS

Choline Chloride

Crystalline choline chloride is abnormally sensitive to radiation, breaking down to trimethylamine hydrochloride and acetaldehyde with *G* values as high as 55,000 (118); the *G* values are dependent upon dose rate and temperature and the type of radiation.

$$[(CH_3)_3NCH_2CH_2OH]^+ Cl^- \rightsquigarrow (CH_3)_3NH^+ Cl^- + CH_3CHO \qquad (9.189)$$

The decomposition is obviously a chain reaction and it appears unique among chain decomposition reactions in being limited to the solid, crystalline, state; aqueous or alcoholic solutions of choline chloride decompose with G values less than 5 (119). A number of compounds chemically similar to choline chloride have been irradiated (119) but only choline bromide, $[(CH_3)_3NCH_2CH_2OH]^+ Br^-$, approaches the sensitivity of the chloride, and this decomposes with yields about one third or one quarter those for choline chloride. The radiation decomposition of choline chloride increases with increasing temperature in the region 18° to 50°C, but the material is much more stable towards radiation at 150°C than it is at room temperature (120). It appears that the chain-decomposition is retarded by a phase transition which occurs in the crystals at about 75°C (121). Thus the high yields in the decomposition reaction are evidently closely related to the crystal structure in solid choline chloride.

Lemmon and Lindblom (119) have shown that substitution of deuterium for hydrogen in choline chloride only lowers the radiation sensitivity appreciably when hydrogen in the hydroxyl-substituted methylene group is replaced. Hydrogen abstraction from this group is therefore a likely step in the decomposition. Subsequently Lindblom, Lemmon, and Calvin (118) proposed, on the basis of data from kinetic and electron paramagnetic resonance studies, a chain mechanism with the chain-propagating step,

$$CH_3\dot{C}HOH + (CH_3)_3\overset{+}{N}CH_2CH_2OH \rightarrow (CH_3)_3NH^+ + CH_3CHO + CH_3\dot{C}HOH \quad (9.190)$$

Organic Solids

A large number of organic solids have been irradiated and the radicals trapped in the solid detected, and in many cases identified, by electron paramagnetic resonance techniques. Materials investigated in this way include compounds which are solid under normal conditions and also liquids and vapors which are frozen before irradiation. Solids examined include a wide variety of biologically interesting compounds, such as amino acids, proteins, carbohydrates, etc., (cf. 122) which are more frequently irradiated in aqueous solution than in the pure state. Information derived in this manner is a valuable adjunct to other chemical and physical evidence of the radiolysis processes.

REFERENCES

A comprehensive review of the radiation chemistry of aliphatic compounds, including all work published up to the middle of 1958, has been given by A. J. Swallow in *Radiation Chemistry of Organic Compounds*, Pergamon Press, London, 1960. A shorter review has been published by M. Burton in *Actions Chimiques et Biologiques des Radiations*, (ed. M. Haissinsky) Masson et Cie, Paris, Vol. 3, 1958, and a useful collection of data in tabular form by B. M. Tolbert and M. H. Krinks in *Radiation Research, Supplement 2*, 1960, p. 586.

1. M. Burton in *Symposium on Radiobiology: The Basic Aspects of Radiation Effects on Living Systems* (ed. J. J. Nickson) John Wiley and Sons, Inc. New York, 1952, Chapter 8; *J. Chem. Educ.*, **36,** 273 (1959).
2. M. Burton, J. L. Magee, and A. H. Samuel, *J. Chem. Phys.*, **20,** 760 (1952).
3. A. H. Samuel and J. L. Magee, *J. Chem. Phys.*, **21,** 1080 (1953).
4. R. A. Back and N. Miller, *Trans. Faraday Soc.*, **55,** 911 (1959).
5. H. A. Dewhurst, *J. Phys. Chem.*, **61,** 1466 (1957).
6. H. A. Dewhurst, *J. Am. Chem. Soc.*, **80,** 5607 (1958).
7. T. J. Hardwick, *J. Phys. Chem.*, **66,** 1611 (1962).
8. M. S. Matheson, *Nucleonics*, **19,** (Oct.), 57 (1961).
9. H. A. Dewhurst, *J. Am. Chem. Soc.*, **83,** 1050 (1961).
10. J. H. Futrell, *J. Am. Chem. Soc.*, **81,** 5921 (1959).
11. H. A. Dewhurst and R. H. Schuler, *J. Am. Chem. Soc.*, **81,** 3210 (1959).
12. H. A. Dewhurst and E. H. Winslow, *J. Chem. Phys.*, **26,** 969 (1957).
13. T. J. Hardwick, *J. Phys. Chem.*, **64,** 1623 (1960).
14. H. A. Dewhurst, *J. Phys. Chem.*, **62,** 15 (1958).
15. T. J. Hardwick, *J. Phys. Chem.*, **65,** 101 (1961).
16. G. Meshitsuka and M. Burton, *Radiation Res.*, **10,** 499 (1959).
17. T. Ff. Williams, *Trans. Faraday Soc.*, **57,** 755 (1961).
18. P. J. Lucchesi and W. Bartok, *J. Am. Chem. Soc.*, **82,** 4528 (1960).
19. H. A. Dewhurst, *J. Phys. Chem.*, **63,** 813 (1959).
20. J. M. Ramaradhya and G. R. Freeman, *J. Chem. Phys.*, **34,** 1726 (1961).
21. P. J. Dyne and J. A. Stone, *Can. J. Chem.*, **39,** 2381 (1961).
22. L. J. Forrestal and W. H. Hamill, *J. Am. Chem. Soc.*, **83,** 1535 (1961).
23. M. Burton in *Actions Chimiques et Biologiques des Radiations,* (ed. M. Haissinsky) Masson et Cie, Paris, Vol. 3, 1958. Table 2, p. 19.
24. R. Barker and M. R. H. Hill, *Nature*, **194,** 277 (1962).
25. R. H. Schuler and A. O. Allen, *J. Am. Chem. Soc.*, **77,** 507 (1955).
26. M. Hamashima, M. P. Reddy, and M. Burton, *J. Phys. Chem.*, **62,** 246 (1958).
27. J. Prévé and G. Gaudemaris, *Compt, Rend.*, **250,** 3470 (1960).
28. W. S. Guentner, T. J. Hardwick, and R. P. Nejak, *J. Chem. Phys.*, **30,** 601 (1959).
29. R. H. Schuler, *J. Phys. Chem.*, **63,** 925 (1959).
30. G. A. Muccini and R. H. Schuler, *J. Phys. Chem.*, **64,** 1436 (1960).
31. A. C. Nixon and R. E. Thorpe, *J. Chem. Phys.*, **28,** 1004 (1958).
32. P. J. Dyne and J. W. Fletcher, *Can. J. Chem.*, **38,** 851 (1960).
33. R. H. Schuler, *J. Phys. Chem.*, **61,** 1472 (1957).
34. J. R. Nash and W. H. Hamill, *J. Phys. Chem.*, **66,** 1097 (1962).
35. T. D. Nevitt and L. P. Remsberg, *J. Phys. Chem.* **64,** 969 (1960).
36. P. J. Dyne and W. M. Jenkinson, *Can. J. Chem.*, **38,** 539 (1960).
37. P. J. Dyne and W. M. Jenkinson, *Can. J. Chem.*, **39,** 2163 (1961).

38. G. R. Freeman, *J. Chem. Phys.*, **33,** 71 (1960); *Can. J. Chem.*, **38,** 1043 (1960).
39. N. Bach, *Proc. Intern. Conf. Peaceful Uses Atomic Energy,* United Nations, New York, **7,** 538 (1956).
40. G. Dobson and G. Hughes, *Proc. Chem. Soc.*, 109 (1963).
41. T. J. Hardwick, *J. Phys. Chem.*, **66,** 117, 291, 2246 (1962).
42. J. F. Hornig, G. Levey, and J. E. Willard, *J. Chem. Phys.*, **20,** 1556 (1952).
43. G. M. Harris and J. E. Willard, *J. Am. Chem. Soc.*, **76,** 4678 (1954).
44. T. A. Gover and J. E. Willard, *J. Am. Chem. Soc.*, **82,** 3816 (1960).
45. H. A. Gillis, R. R. Williams, and W. H. Hamill, *J. Am. Chem. Soc.* **83,** 17 (1961).
46. R. H. Schuler and W. H. Hamill, *J. Am. Chem. Soc.*, **74,** 6171 (1952).
47. R. C. Petry and R. H. Schuler, *J. Am. Chem. Soc.*, **75,** 3796 (1953); cf. R. H. Schuler and R. C. Petry, *ibid.*, **78,** 3954 (1956).
48. E. O. Hornig and J. E. Willard, *J. Am. Chem. Soc.*, **79,** 2429 (1957).
49. R. F. Pottie, R. Barker, and W. H. Hamill, *Radiation Res.*, **10,** 664 (1959).
50. V. H. Dibeler and R. M. Reese, *J. Res. Nat. Bur. St.*, **54,** 127 (1955).
51. J. Sturm and H. A. Schwarz, *Radiation Res.*, **17,** 531 (1962).
52. R. J. Hanrahan and J. E. Willard, *J. Am. Chem. Soc.*, **79,** 2434 (1957).
53. R. H. Luebbe and J. E. Willard, *J. Am. Chem. Soc.*, **81,** 761 (1959).
54. M. C. R. Symons and M. G. Townsend, *J. Chem. Soc.*, 263 (1959).
55. E. L. Cochran, W. H. Hamill, and R. R. Williams, *J. Am. Chem. Soc.*, **76,** 2145 (1954).
56. W. H. Hamill and R. H. Schuler, *J. Am. Chem. Soc.*, **73,** 3466 (1951).
57. W. S. Wilcox, *Radiation Res.*, **10,** 112 (1959).
58. E. B. Dismukes and W. S. Wilcox, *Radiation Res.*, **11,** 754 (1959).
59. R. H. Wiley, W. Miller, C. H. Jarboe, J. R. Harrell, and D. J. Parish, *Radiation Res.*, **13,** 479 (1960).
60. H. L. Benson and J. E. Willard, *J. Am. Chem. Soc.*, **83,** 4672 (1961).
61. T. H. Chen, K. Y. Wong, and F. J. Johnston, *J. Phys. Chem.*, **64,** 1023 (1960).
62. R. B. Bernstein, G. P. Semeluk, and C. B. Arends, *Anal. Chem.*, **25,** 139 (1953).
63. J. W. Schulte, *J. Am. Chem. Soc.*, **79,** 4643 (1957).
64. I. M. Pearson and C. S. Garner, *J. Phys. Chem.*, **64,** 501 (1960).
65. E. Collinson, F. S. Dainton, and H. Gillis, *J. Phys. Chem.*, **65,** 695 (1961).
66. S. Ciborowski, N. Colebourne, E. Collinson, and F. S. Dainton, *Trans. Faraday Soc.*, **57,** 1123 (1961).
67. A. Chapiro, *J. Phys. Chem.*, **63,** 801 (1959).
68. Zd. Spurný and I. Janovský, *Nature,* **190,** 624 (1961).
69. M. Ottolenghi and G. Stein, *Radiation Res.*, **14,** 281 (1961).
70. J. W. Schulte, J. F. Suttle, and R. Wilhelm, *J. Am. Chem. Soc.*, **75,** 2222 (1953).
71. G. V. Taplin in *Radiation Dosimetry* (ed. G. J. Hine and G. L. Brownell) Academic Press Inc., New York, 1956, Chapter 8.
72. K. Hannerz, *Research,* **9,** S1 (1956).
73. Z. Spurný, *Proc. Second Intern. Conf. Peaceful Uses Atomic Energy,* United Nations, Geneva, **23,** 419 (1958).
74. G. L. Clark and P. E. Bierstedt, *Radiation Res.*, **2,** 199, 295 (1955).
75. EL-A. I. Heiba and L. C. Anderson, *J. Am. Chem. Soc.*, **81,** 1117 (1959).
76. C. Walling, *Free Radicals in Solution,* John Wiley and Sons, New York, 1957 Tables 6.3 to 6.6.

77. EL-A. I. Heiba and L. C. Anderson, *J. Am. Chem. Soc.,* **79,** 4940 (1957).
78. I. Eliezer, H. J. G. Hayman, and G. Stein, *Proc. Second Intern. Conf. Peaceful Uses Atomic Energy,* United Nations, Geneva, **29,** 113 (1958).
79. C. E. Stoops and C. L. Furrow, *J. Org. Chem.,* **26,** 3264 (1961).
80. A. Fontijn and J. W. T. Spinks, *Can. J. Chem.,* **35,** 1384, 1397, 1410 (1957).
81. R. L. Webb, *Proc. Second Intern. Conf. Peaceful Uses Atomic Energy,* United Nations, Geneva, **29,** 331 (1958).
82. S. C. Sigoloff, *Nucleonics,* **14,** (Oct.), 54 (1956).
83. G. V. Taplin, S. W. McFarland, K. Ryan, and C. D. Kohler, *Radiation Res.,* **5,** 599 (1956).
84. L. A. Wall and R. E. Florin, *J. Appl. Polymer Sci.,* **2,** 251 (1959).
85. J. H. Golden, *J. Polymer. Sci.,* **45,** 534 (1960).
86. W. C. Francis and R. N. Haszeldine, *J. Chem. Soc.,* 2151 (1955).
87. S. U. Choi, N. N. Lichtin, and J. J. Rush, *J. Am. Chem. Soc.,* **82,** 3225 (1960).
88. J. H. Baxendale and F. W. Mellows, *J. Am. Chem. Soc.,* **83,** 4720 (1961).
89. G. Meshitsuka and M. Burton, *Radiation Res.,* **8,** 285 (1958); L. M. Theard and M. Burton, *J. Phys. Chem.,* **67,** 59 (1963).
90. G. E. Adams and J. H. Baxendale, *J. Am. Chem. Soc.,* **80,** 4215 (1958).
91. L. Friedman, F. A. Long, and M. Wolfsberg, *J. Chem. Phys.,* **27,** 613 (1957)
92. P. Wilmenius and E. Lindholm, *Arkiv Fys.,* **21,** 97 (1962).
93. E. Hayon and J. J. Weiss, *J. Chem. Soc.,* 3970 (1961).
94. J. H. Baxendale and R. D. Sedgwick, *Trans. Faraday Soc.,* **57,** 2157 (1961).
95. R. P. Porter and W. A. Noyes, *J. Am. Chem. Soc.,* **81,** 2307 (1959).
96. N. N. Lichtin, L. A. Rosenberg, and M. Immamura, *J. Am. Chem. Soc.,* **84,** 3587 (1962).
97. J. M. Ramaradhya and G. R. Freeman, *Can. J. Chem.,* **39,** 1836 (1961).
98. E. Hayon and J. J. Weiss, *J. Chem. Soc.,* 3962 (1961).
99. J. G. Burr, *J. Am. Chem. Soc.,* **79,** 751 (1957); *J. Phys. Chem.,* **61,** 1477 (1957).
100. B. Smaller and M. S. Matheson, *J. Chem. Phys.,* **28,** 1169 (1958).
101. I. A. Taub and L. M. Dorfman, *J. Am. Chem. Soc.,* **84,** 4053 (1962).
102. A. S. Newton, *J. Phys. Chem.,* **61,** 1485 (1957).
103. N. A. Bach, *Radiation Res. Suppl. 1,* 190 (1959).
104. A. S. Newton, *J. Phys. Chem.,* **61,** 1490 (1957).
105. A. S. Newton, *J. Chem. Phys.,* **26,** 1764 (1957).
106. R. H. Johnsen, *J. Phys. Chem.,* **63,** 2041 (1959).
107. G. E. Adams, J. H. Baxendale, and R. D. Sedgwick, *J. Phys. Chem.,* **63,** 854 (1959).
108. J. G. Burr, *J. Phys. Chem.,* **61,** 1481 (1957).
109. P. Ausloos and E. W. R. Steacie, *Can. J. Chem.,* **33,** 1530 (1955).
110. P. Ausloos and C. N. Trumbore, *J. Am. Chem. Soc.,* **81,** 3866 (1959).
111. R. W. Hummel, *Trans. Faraday Soc.,* **56,** 234 (1960).
112. R. F. Pottie and F. P. Lossing, *Can. J. Chem.,* **39,** 1900 (1961).
113. P. Ausloos and J. F. Paulson, *J. Am. Chem. Soc.,* **80,** 5117 (1958).
114. R. Barker, *Trans. Faraday Soc.,* **59,** 375 (1963)
115. T. J. Hardwick, *J. Phys. Chem.,* **66,** 117 (1962).
116. R. Barker, *Nature,* **192,** 62 (1961).
117. L. J. Stief and P. Ausloos, *J. Phys. Chem.,* **65,** 1560 (1961).

118. R. O. Lindblom, R. M. Lemmon, and M. Calvin, *J. Am. Chem. Soc.,* **83,** 2484 (1961).
119. R. M. Lemmon and R. O. Lindblom, *Proc. Second Intern. Conf. Peaceful Uses Atomic Energy,* United Nations, Geneva, **22,** 409 (1958).
120. I. Serlin, *Science,* **126,** 261 (1957).
121. R. L. Collin, *J. Am. Chem. Soc.,* **79,** 6086 (1957); P Shanley and R. L. Collin, *Radiation Res.,* **16,** 674 (1962).
122. W. Gordy, *Radiation Res. Suppl. 1,* 491 (1959).

CHAPTER 10

Aromatic Compounds

Aromatic compounds are generally more stable towards radiation than the corresponding aliphatic compounds. Benzene, for example, is markedly more stable than cyclohexane. The stability is associated with the presence in the aromatic ring system of electrons in π orbitals, which reduces the probability that excited and ionized aromatic molecules will dissociate and favors alternative modes of energy dissipation which do not result in decomposition of the molecule. In the mass spectrometer, for instance, aromatic ions show little tendency to break down into smaller fragments by fission of an aromatic ring. Such dissociation is even less likely under normal radiolysis conditions, where ions can lose their extra energy rapidly by collisional processes. It should be emphasized that the stability of aromatic compounds is not the result of immunity to radical attack; free radicals react with these compounds quite readily. The stabilizing influence of an aromatic ring system extends to alkyl groups and substituted alkyl groups in the same molecule and even, under favorable circumstances, to aliphatic compounds which are merely mixed with the aromatic compound.

Benzene

Comparison of the yields of radiolysis products from benzene (Table 10.1) and from cyclohexane (Table 9.3) shows that benzene gives appreciably smaller product yields, particularly when it is irradiated as a

TABLE 10.1 *Radiolysis of Benzene*

Product	G(product)		
	Vapor (α-irradiation; ref. 1)	Vapor (electron irradiation; ref. 2)	Liquid (electron irradiation; refs. 2, 3)
H_2	0.30	0.011 (H_2 + CH_4)	0.036
CH_4	0.01		0
C_2H_2	0.42	0.11	0.020
C_2H_4	0.02	0.05	0
C_2H_6	0.006	0	0
Polymer (*G* value is molecules of benzene converted to polymer per 100 ev absorbed)	4.8		0.75*

* Ref. 4.

liquid. The major product from benzene is a viscous yellow liquid, containing compounds of higher molecular weight, which is listed in Table 10.1 under the collective term "polymer." Gordon, Van Dyken, and Doumani (5) have shown that this contains a C_{12} fraction (biphenyl, phenylcyclohexadiene, phenylcyclohexene, and nonaromatic bicyclic compounds), a C_{18} fraction (hydrogenated terphenyls), and higher molecular weight material. The average molecular weight of the mixture increases with increasing absorbed dose.

The radiolysis mechanism for benzene has not been established with certainty but reactions which have been envisaged (4, 5) include

$$C_6H_6 \rightsquigarrow C_6H_6^+ + e^- \rightarrow C_6H_6^* \quad (10.1)$$

$$C_6H_6 \rightsquigarrow C_6H_6^* \quad (10.2)$$

$$C_6H_6^* + C_6H_6 \rightarrow 2C_6H_6 \quad (10.3)$$

$$C_6H_6^* \rightarrow \cdot C_6H_5 + H\cdot \tag{10.4}$$

or

$$\rightarrow C_2H_2 + ? \tag{10.5}$$

$$H\cdot + C_6H_6 \rightarrow \cdot C_6H_7 \tag{10.6}$$

$$2H\cdot \rightarrow H_2 \tag{10.7}$$

$$\cdot C_6H_5 \text{ and } \cdot C_6H_7 \xrightarrow{+C_6H_6} \text{polymer} \tag{10.8}$$

$$C_6H_6^* + C_6H_6 \rightarrow \text{polymer} \tag{10.9}$$

Polymer may be formed by radical reactions or by reactions involving excited molecules. Hydrogen atoms react by addition rather than by hydrogen abstraction and this accounts in part for the low yield of hydrogen.[1] The low over-all yield of product is explained by quenching of an appreciable fraction of the excited benzene molecules (Eq. 10.3); the greater radiation-stability of benzene in the liquid state is probably due to more efficient quenching of excited molecules in the liquid as compared to the vapor. Collisional deactivation (quenching) of excited benzene molecules is also found with the photolysis of benzene, where very low quantum yields are observed.

Benzene has been irradiated in the presence of iodine, which acts as a radical scavenger (6, 7). Aromatic compounds undergo a more complex series of reactions in the presence of iodine than do aliphatic materials and iodine-scavenging experiments must be interpreted with caution (7). Nevertheless, the results suggest that a significant number of radicals are formed in irradiated benzene and that these could account for a large part of the polymeric material formed; G(radical) is about 0.4 or 0.7. Meshitsuka and Burton (8) have also found a significant yield of hydrogen iodide, though in this instance it is not certain that the iodide arises by scavenging of hydrogen atoms. Iodine apparently has little effect upon the over-all yield of hydrogen (9), suggesting that hydrogen is formed almost entirely by "molecular" processes rather than by reactions involving hydrogen atoms. If this is so the molecular processes must involve two separate benzene molecules since Gordon and Burton (3) found an appreciable proportion of HD in the hydrogen formed by irradiating mixtures of benzene and deuterobenzene (C_6D_6). Hydrogen might, for example, be formed by

[1] It is characteristic of aromatic and unsaturated compounds that the yield of hydrogen is less than the yield of polymeric product. This contrasts with the behavior of saturated aliphatic hydrocarbons, for which hydrogen is the major radiolysis product.

$$C_6H_6^* + C_6H_6^* \rightarrow H_2 + C_{12}H_{10} \qquad \text{(biphenyl)} \qquad (10.10)$$

or

$$\rightarrow H_2 + \text{radicals} \qquad (10.11)$$

These reactions have also been postulated by Burns (10, 11) to account for the variation in hydrogen yield with changing LET (Table 10.2). The LET effect arises because of competition between reaction 10.3, which is first order, and reactions 10.10 and 10.11, which are second order, both with respect to excited benzene molecules. The change in acetylene yield can be explained in the same way, with reaction 10.3 competing with

$$C_6H_6^* + C_6H_6^* \rightarrow nC_2H_2 + \text{radicals or stable products} \qquad (10.12)$$

In both instances, reaction between two excited molecules will be favored when their concentration in the track is increased by using radiation with a higher LET.

The increase in $G(-C_6H_6)$ with increasing LET is in marked contrast with the small change in $G(-H_2O)$ when water is irradiated with different types of radiation (Table 8.2). The difference arises because the reactive species which compete in first and second order reactions to generate the LET effect are excited molecules in the case of benzene and free radicals in the case of water. Interaction of two excited benzene molecules leads to dissociation where an isolated excited molecule might not dissociate, but interaction of two water radicals does not necessarily alter the over-all number of water molecules dissociated.

TABLE 10.2 *Effect of LET on the Radiolysis of Benzene* (ref. 11)

Product	G(product)			
	γ-rays (35°C)	1 Mev electrons (25°C)	Pile radiation (25°C)	$B^{10}(n,\alpha)Li^7$ recoil nuclei (25°C)
H_2	0.039	0.040	0.14	0.57
C_2H_2	0.019	0.020	0.070	0.26
$-C_6H_6$	0.94	0.85	1.3	2.1

Alkyl Benzenes

Radiolysis of the alkyl benzenes is similar to the radiolysis of benzene and product yields are low (Table 10.3). Fission of bonds in the side-chain alkyl groups increases as these groups become larger, and it appears that carbon-carbon bonds β to the ring (i.e., $C_6H_6C—C$) are split more frequently than other carbon-carbon bonds (12, 13). However, a large part of the energy absorbed by the side chain must be transferred to the ring and dissipated, since product yields are substantially lower than would be expected if there was no interaction between the side chain and the aromatic ring system. The methane yield increases as the number of terminal methyl groups in the alkyl side chain is increased, but does not change as much with increasing methyl substitution in the benzene ring (with mesitylene, for example).

Sworski and Burton (15) have demonstrated an LET effect when the alkyl benzenes are irradiated with fast electrons and with the mixed radiation present in a nuclear reactor. In all cases the total gas yield was slightly greater (10 to 30%) with the higher LET reactor radiation, though the methane yields fell. The increase in total gaseous product was shown to be due to a marked increase in the yield of C_2 products and a small increase in the yield of hydrogen with the higher LET radiation.

TABLE 10.3 *Radiolysis of Liquid Alkyl Benzenes*

(Fast electron irradiation)

Alkyl benzene	G(total gas)	$G(H_2)$	$G(CH_4)$	G(polymer)*	Ref.
Cyclohexane	6	5.7	0.05	4.5	†
Benzene	0.056	0.036	0	0.75	**
Toluene, $C_6H_5CH_3$	0.14	0.13	0.0077	0.92	2
				1.28	12
Mesitylene, $C_6H_3(CH_3)_3$	0.26	0.24	0.02		12
Ethyl benzene, $C_6H_5CH_2CH_3$	0.21	0.18	0.03		12
Isopropyl benzene, $C_6H_5CH(CH_3)_2$	0.25	0.17	0.07		13
	0.30	0.18	0.09	1.7	14
t-Butyl benzene, $C_6H_5C(CH_3)_3$	0.19	0.11	0.07		13

* Molecules of parent compound converted to higher molecular weight products per 100 ev of energy absorbed.

† Approximate values; cf. Table 9.3.

** See Table 10.1.

Benzyl Alcohol

Benzyl alcohol gives higher yields of products when irradiated in the presence of oxygen than do the simple aliphatic alcohols under similar circumstances. Thus Proskurnin and Barelko (16) found hydrogen peroxide and organic peroxides to be formed in equal amounts with G(peroxide) about 50. The apparently anomalous radiation-sensitivity of benzyl alcohol is explained by the occurrence of a chain reaction when oxygen is present:

$$\mathrm{PhCH_2OH} \rightsquigarrow \mathrm{Ph\dot{C}HOH} + \mathrm{H\cdot} \quad (10.13)$$

$$\mathrm{Ph\dot{C}HOH} + \mathrm{O_2} \rightarrow \mathrm{PhCH(O_2\cdot)OH} \quad (10.14)$$

$$\mathrm{PhCH(O_2\cdot)OH} + \mathrm{PhCH_2OH} \rightarrow \mathrm{Ph\dot{C}HOH} + \mathrm{PhCH(O_2H)OH} \quad (10.15)$$

$$\mathrm{PhCH(O_2H)OH} \rightarrow \mathrm{PhCHO} + \mathrm{H_2O_2} \quad (10.16)$$

($\mathrm{Ph} = \mathrm{C_6H_5}$). The aromatic ring is assumed to stabilize the molecule in the normal manner, reducing the number of radicals formed in the first stage (Eq. 10.13) so that G(radical) is smaller here than for an aliphatic alcohol. However, the phenyl group facilitates the chain-propagating hydrogen abstraction, reaction 10.15, and the chain reaction more than compensates for any reduction in product yields due to stabilization. The same effect is found to an even greater extent with the aromatic hydrocarbon styrene, $\mathrm{PhCH{=}CH_2}$, which is polymerized upon irradiation. G values for the number of styrene molecules converted to polymer may run to several hundreds, though one may speculate that G (radical) is relatively small (cf. Table 11.3).

The stabilizing influence of the phenyl group is apparent when benzyl alcohol is irradiated in the absence of oxygen, relatively low yields of product being obtained. Under conditions essentially, but not completely, free of oxygen the products formed and their yields (17) were: benzaldehyde ($G = 1.32$), benzylphenylcarbinol ($\mathrm{PhCH_2CHOHPh}$)($G = 0.68$), DL ($G = 0.22$) and *meso* ($G = 0.20$) hydrobenzoin (PhCHOHCHOHPh), and dibenzyl ($\mathrm{PhCH_2CH_2Ph}$)($G = 0.29$). Assuming that irradiation produces radicals by

$$\mathrm{PhCH_2OH} \rightsquigarrow \mathrm{Ph\dot{C}HOH} + \mathrm{H\cdot} \quad (10.13)$$

and

$$\rightsquigarrow \mathrm{PhCH_2\cdot} + \mathrm{\cdot OH} \quad (10.17)$$

it is possible to account for these products by means of typical radical reactions. Apart from benzaldehyde, the products can be formed entirely by radical combination reactions, illustrating the tendency of aromatic free radicals to combine rather than disproportionate. Since a certain amount of oxygen may have been present in this experiment, benzaldehyde will probably have been formed, at least in part, by the reaction sequence 10.14 to 10.16.

When oxygen-saturated aqueous solutions of benzyl alcohol are irradiated the products formed and their yields (16), hydrogen peroxide ($G = 3$), benzaldehyde ($G = 1.6$), and phenols ($G = 1.2$), are similar to those for the aliphatic alcohols, making allowance for the additional possibility of attack on the aromatic ring. There is no evidence of a chain reaction in aqueous solution nor of any stabilization by the aromatic grouping. The absence of stabilization is not unexpected since energy is absorbed almost exclusively by water and the solute suffers radical attack rather than direct radiation decomposition.

Protection

Aromatic compounds can sometimes share their relative stability towards radiation with other compounds to which they are added. When the radiation-induced decomposition of a compound is reduced on adding a relatively small amount of a second substance the process is termed "protection," the added material serving to protect the original compound from the effects of the radiation. It should be noted however that protective agents act as such only when they are present during irradiation, and not when they are added afterwards.

Two basic types of protection can be distinguished and might be called "physical" and "chemical" respectively. The first involves transfer of energy from an energy-rich species, which may be either an ion or an excited molecule, to the protecting agent or some other energy sink. The process involves therefore either charge transfer or the transfer or dissipation of excitation energy and is essentially a physical operation. The effect is to remove energy from a molecule which would otherwise dissociate or react, and thereby diminish the extent to which the material decomposes. The second type of protection is chemical in its action and occurs at a later stage in the sequence of radiation-induced events. It often involves radical scavenging by the additive, which therefore inhibits the normal radical reactions. Chemical protection is particularly applicable to the protection of substances irradiated as dilute solutions, for example, aqueous solutions of sensitive biological materials; physical protection is more applicable to bulk materials. In a dilute solution for instance the solute might be protected by adding a "chemical" protective agent and the solvent by a "physical" protective agent; the physical agent would of course also protect the solute by reducing the number of radicals formed in the system. When the additive, whether a physical or a chemical agent, is itself destroyed the action is often referred to as "sacrificial protection."

An example of physical protection is the reduction in the radiation-induced polymerization of acetylene in the presence of benzene vapor (page 231). In this instance the protective action is believed to be due to an efficient charge transfer between acetylene ions and benzene,

$$C_2H_2^+ + C_6H_6 \rightarrow C_2H_2 + C_6H_6^+ \tag{10.18}$$

The radiolysis of several other aliphatic compounds has been shown to be inhibited by benzene, probably the best known example being cyclohexane, which is discussed in the next section. Burton and Lipsky (18) have classified processes which result in physical protection into four groups: charge transfer, energy transfer (sponge type protection), quenching, and negative-ion formation. Charge transfer and energy transfer have been discussed briefly in Chapter 5; they are most efficient when the protecting additive has a slightly lower lying ionized or excited state than the activated species. Quenching involves conversion of an excited molecule to the ground state, or to a more stable (triplet) excited state, under the influence of the additive. In the latter case the triplet excited molecule may react and form products different to those produced in the absence of the protective agent. Electron capture by the additive, resulting in negative-ion formation, can result in protection by interfering with the normal ion-neutralization process; neutralization of a positive ion by a negative ion generally liberates less energy than neutralization by an electron. Physical protection can occur intermolecularly or intramolecularly, i.e., in mixtures of solvent and protecting additive or in pure compounds where the protecting group is built into the molecule; the alkyl benzenes are examples of intramolecular protection, since the phenyl group reduces decomposition in the side chain alkyl group.

Chemical protection is useful when the substance to be preserved is present at a relatively low concentration and must be protected against radicals formed in the solvent rather than against direct radiation decomposition. An obvious application is the protection of human beings against the effects of ionizing radiation. Compounds which offer effective protection in this sense are often those which react readily with free radicals, though chemical protection can be a more complex phenomenon than simple radical scavenging. Dale and Russell (19) found that cysteine and glutathione protect the enzyme catalase from radiation-inactivation in aqueous solution; both compounds contain thiol (—SH) groups, which are particularly susceptible to free radical attack, and react with the hydrogen atoms and hydroxyl radicals formed by dissociation of the water (page 292). It should be mentioned that glutathione also protects catalase in the dry state; 2% of glutathione almost doubles the radiation resistance of the dry enzyme (20). However, here the protection is physical rather than chemical. Chemical protection can also result if the additive reacts with the compound so as to mask any chemical groups which are particularly sensitive to radiation. For example, thiol groups are very radiation-sensitive but can be protected in the compounds cysteine (I) and glutathione by reacting the amino acids with carbonyl compounds (e.g., glyoxal, pyruvic acid, diacetyl, etc.) (21). The carbonyl compound forms a complex with the thiol group which is less sensitive to radiation than the free thiol;

$$RCHO + \begin{array}{c} HS{-}CH_2 \\ | \\ H_2N{-}CH \\ | \\ COOH \\ \text{(I)} \end{array} \rightarrow RCH\!\begin{array}{l} \diagup S{-}CH_2 \\ \qquad\quad | \\ \diagdown NH{-}CH \\ \qquad\quad | \\ \qquad\; COOH \end{array} + H_2O \qquad (10.19)$$

Disulphides, e.g., cystamine $(H_2NCH_2CH_2S{-})_2$, can be used to protect thiol groups in proteins in living systems (22; cf. 23);

$$\text{Protein—SH} + \text{R—S—S—R} \rightarrow \text{Protein—S—S—R} + \text{RSH} \qquad (10.20)$$

The protein disulfide is more resistant to radiation than the original protein. However, disulfides can protect the system in other ways besides the formation of complexes; for instance, by scavenging free radicals or by lowering the oxygen pressure in the cells. Eventually the —SR group is removed, and the protein is regenerated, by the normal metabolic processes.

Radiation protection, with particular reference to biological materials, is discussed by Kalkwarf (24) who also gives an extensive list of references.

Cyclohexane-Benzene Mixtures

This system has become a classic example of radiation protection since Schoepfle and Fellows (25) first observed that a mixture of cyclohexane and benzene irradiated with cathode rays gave less gaseous product than would be expected from the irradiation of the two components separately. Subsequent work has amply confirmed this observation and it is clear that upon irradiation there is some form of interaction between the two components, or the intermediates derived from them. A plot of the hydrogen yield against the electron fraction of benzene[2] for such mixtures for example has the form shown in Fig. 10.1 (26). If there were no interaction the plot would be a straight line joining the $G(H_2)$ values for pure cyclohexane and pure benzene, as shown by the broken line. The emphasis in these studies has generally been upon the changing yield of hydrogen, though Freeman (27) and Stone and Dyne (28) have shown that when benzene is present the yields of cyclohexene, bicyclohexyl, and cyclohexylhexene fall off in a similar manner to the hydrogen yield.

A number of explanations have been advanced to account for the protective effect of benzene, generally with reference to its effect on the hydrogen yield. Schoepfle and Fellows suggested that benzene acts as a scavenger for active hydrogen liberated from the cyclohexane. Scavenging of hydrogen atoms,

$$H\cdot + C_6H_6 \rightarrow \cdot C_6H_7 \tag{10.6}$$

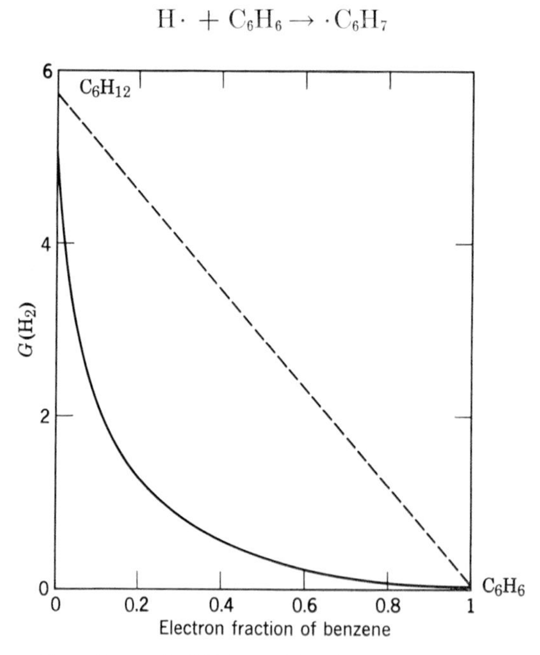

FIGURE 10.1 *Variation of $G(H_2)$ with the composition of cyclohexane-benzene mixtures (fast electron irradiation).*

[2] The electron fraction of the first component of a mixture is given by the expression $w_1(Z/A)_1/(\overline{Z/A})_{\text{mix}}$, where the symbols have the meanings assigned to them in Chapter 4 (cf. Eq. 4.23, page 93).

will reduce the yield of hydrogen by preventing the hydrogen abstraction reaction,

$$H\cdot + c\text{-}C_6H_{12} \rightarrow H_2 + \cdot C_6H_{11} \qquad (10.21)$$

More recently Burr (29) has claimed that the effect of benzene on the hydrogen yield at low (less than 10%) benzene concentrations is quantitatively consistent with such hydrogen-atom scavenging. However, earlier experiments by Burton and Patrick were interpreted, and have generally been accepted, as evidence that radical scavenging is only a minor protective mechanism in the cyclohexane-benzene system. These authors irradiated mixtures of deuterobenzene, C_6D_6, with cyclohexane (30) and with propionaldehyde (31). From the HD yield for the deuterobenzene-propionaldehyde mixture they determined the ratio of the rates of the reactions

$$H\cdot + C_6D_6 \rightarrow HD + C_6D_5\cdot \qquad (10.22)$$

and

$$H\cdot + C_6D_6 \rightarrow \text{polymer, or other product} \qquad (10.23)$$

finding k_{23}/k_{22} to be not greater than 7.3. Reaction 10.23 is the hydrogen atom scavenging reaction in deuterobenzene-cyclohexane mixtures, and from the yield of HD for such mixtures and the ratio k_{23}/k_{22} the extent to which hydrogen atoms were scavenged in the mixture could be estimated. The results showed that hydrogen atom scavenging in the cyclohexane-deuterobenzene (or benzene) mixtures would not reduce $G(H_2)$ by more than 0.6 under the most favorable circumstances (20 to 30% benzene). This is significantly less than the observed reduction in $G(H_2)$. Burton and Patrick (30) concluded that the main protecting process is energy transfer from excited cyclohexane molecules to benzene

$$c\text{-}C_6H_{12}^* + C_6H_6 \rightarrow c\text{-}C_6H_{12} + C_6H_6^* \qquad (10.24)$$

and this suggestion has received wide support (cf. 32, 33, 34). The energy transferred is subsequently dissipated, causing relatively little loss of benzene by dissociation or reaction.

Energy transfer in the manner illustrated by equation 10.24 is conditional on the accepting molecule having a lower-energy excited state than the excited states of the donor. Benzene does in fact have lower-energy excited states than the saturated hydrocarbons, though other types of compound may have lower states than benzene. Thus in mixtures of deuterobenzene and propionaldehyde, the deuterobenzene actually promotes dissociation of the aldehyde to ethane and carbon monoxide by an energy transfer process (31):

$$C_6D_6^* + C_2H_5CHO \rightarrow C_6D_6 + C_2H_5CHO^* \qquad (10.25)$$

$$C_2H_5CHO^* \rightarrow C_2H_6 + CO \qquad (10.26)$$

A low (triplet) excited state of benzene is believed responsible, the energy transferred being insufficient to dissociate the aldehyde into radicals. Energy transfer *from* excited benzene has also been demonstrated in the photolysis of solutions of alkyl iodides in benzene (35, 36).

Other evidence which supports the energy-transfer mechanism includes the fact that the yield of radicals, estimated by iodine scavenging, changes with benzene concentration in much the same way as the hydrogen yield. That is, there is a more rapid decrease in radical yield as the benzene concentration is increased than would be anticipated if there were no interaction (37), suggesting that fewer radicals are actually formed in the presence of benzene. Furthermore, there is some evidence of increased decomposition of the benzene in cyclohexane-benzene mixtures. Thus, Burton and Patrick (30) find, relatively, a higher yield of D_2 from cyclohexane-deuterobenzene mixture and Manion and Burton (26) a higher yield of acetylene from cyclohexane-benzene mixture than from pure benzene. Dyne has also produced experimental evidence in support of the energy-transfer mechanism. The relative proportions of unimolecular ("molecular") and bimolecular ("radical") hydrogen production from mixtures of c-C_6H_{12} and c-C_6D_{12} can be determined from the isotopic composition of the hydrogen evolved. Dyne and Jenkinson (34, 38) found that when either iodine or benzene was added to the cyclohexane-deuterocyclohexane mixture both the unimolecular and the bimolecular yield of hydrogen were reduced in approximately the same proportion as the total yield of hydrogen, and they argue from this that both uni- and bi-molecular hydrogen have the same precursor, an excited state of cyclohexane, and that both iodine and benzene protect cyclohexane by quenching this precursor, and not by acting as radical scavengers.

An alternative explanation of the protective effect of benzene in mixtures of cyclohexane and benzene is that charge transfer rather than energy transfer takes place, i.e.,

$$\text{c-}C_6H_{12}^+ + C_6H_6 \rightarrow \text{c-}C_6H_{12} + C_6H_6^+ \qquad (10.27)$$

This is feasible since cyclohexane has a higher ionization potential (9.9 v) than benzene (9.2 v), and it is not inconsistent with the evidence advanced in favor of energy transfer. Charge transfer was postulated by Freeman (39, 40) to account for the extremely rapid deactivation by benzene of the energy-rich form of cyclohexane. A second alternative has been proposed by Lamborn and Swallow (41), who conclude that benzene, by virtue of the aromatic π-electron system, absorbs energy from fast electrons (including the secondary electrons produced by γ-radiation) more readily than cyclohexane does, and that the protective effect is therefore one of selective energy absorption rather than energy transfer. However, it is questionable whether this process can account for the rapid fall in hydrogen yield with very low concentrations of added benzene.

Pertinent to this discussion are some recent experiments by Hardwick (42), who observed a lowering of hydrogen yield, similar to that represented in Fig. 10.1 though without the very rapid fall in yield at low concentrations of the second (protecting) component, when various binary mixtures of aliphatic compounds were irradiated. The mixtures examined included *n*-hexane with either neohexane, 2,3-dimethylbutane, isopropyl alcohol, or diisopropyl ether and, as with cyclohexane and benzene, the second component afforded some degree of protection to the *n*-hexane. It was also shown that not all the *n*-hexane molecules which would normally yield hydrogen, either by a molecular or a radical process, could be prevented from doing so by the second component, whatever its nature or amount. With *n*-hexane only 70% of the active molecules could be prevented from dissociating, and Hardwick considered these to be different from the remaining 30%. The two groups were considered to be ionized and excited molecules and it was argued that though rather more excited than ionized molecules would be formed initially, a greater proportion of the ions would be likely to lead to dissociation. Thus the larger group of active molecules were considered to be ions, and the remaining 30% excited molecules. The protecting mechanism therefore becomes one of charge transfer, represented by

$$C_6H_{14}^+ + A \rightarrow C_6H_{14} + A^+ \qquad (10.28)$$

The additives do in fact have lower ionization potentials than *n*-hexane. A significant feature of these experiments is the absence from the mixtures of compounds which would scavenge hydrogen atoms, so that protective mechanisms based on radical scavenging can be ignored.

The evidence described in this section, together with a rather greater amount that has not been included, does not lead to an unequivocal explanation of the protective effect of benzene. Nevertheless, it does indicate quite strongly that energy transfer or charge transfer is the predominant mechanism when the electron fraction of benzene is above about 0.05. At lower concentrations, radical scavenging by benzene may be the more important process, though the evidence on this point is conflicting (cf. 27, 28), and the extent of scavenging is debatable.

Other compounds which benzene protects to some degree against radiation decomposition include ethanol vapor (43), acetone (44), and methyl acetate (44); there are undoubtedly many more.

Organic Scintillators

Related to the phenomena of radiation protection, in the sense that it also involves energy transfer, is the radiation-induced fluorescence of solutions of certain organic compounds. This is the fluorescence detected in scintillation counters which employ liquid organic media as phosphors.

Kallman and Furst (45) showed that the weak light output from a number of organic solvents upon irradiation with high-energy radiation could be substantially increased by dissolving small amounts of fluorescent materials in the solvent. Direct energy absorption by the solute was insufficient to account for the higher light output from the solutions and energy transfer from the excited solvent (S*) to the solute (T), followed by fluorescence by the excited solute, was proposed:

$$S \rightsquigarrow S^* \tag{10.29}$$

$$S^* + T \rightarrow S + T^* \tag{10.30}$$

$$T^* \rightarrow T + h\nu \tag{10.31}$$

Typical of the solvents examined are benzene, toluene, and xylene while typical fluorescent solutes are polynuclear and polyphenyl aromatic compounds (e.g., naphthalene, anthracene, biphenyl, and terphenyl) and their derivatives. Subsequent work has shown that probably the most efficient combination of solvent and solute is a solution of *p*-terphenyl (II) in xylene, though even here only a small part of the energy absorbed

(II)

is re-emitted as fluorescence. Experiment has confirmed that even in dilute solutions, where energy is absorbed almost entirely by the solvent, the fluorescence is characteristic of the solute. It has also been shown (46, 47) that high-energy radiation and ultraviolet light produce similar effects in these solutions. Since ions are not formed by the ultraviolet light, this supports the postulate that energy transfer from solvent to solute involves excited states rather than ions.

It might be anticipated that fluorescent solutes would protect the solvent against radiation decomposition. However, Burton and Patrick (48) have shown that this is not so for solutions of *p*-terphenyl in benzene. The absence of protection may be due to the fact that only a very small part of the absorbed energy is actually emitted as fluorescence, or because fluorescence is induced by excited states of the solvent which do not normally dissociate or react.

Solid organic materials can exhibit similar fluorescent behavior to organic solutions. For example the light emission from naphthalene illuminated with ultraviolet light can be increased by the addition of small amounts of anthracene; at the same time the emission spectrum of naphthalene is replaced by that of anthracene. Solid organic phosphors are widely used in scintillation counters (cf. 49, 50). Generally they are in the form either of a single crystal of a pure compound (e.g., anthracene, stilbene, *p*-terphenyl) or of a solid solution in an organic polymer (e.g., *p*-terphenyl in polystyrene).

Biphenyl

Polyphenyls (biphenyl, terphenyl, quaterphenyl, etc.) and polynuclear aromatic hydrocarbons (naphthalene, anthracene, phenanthrene, etc.) are among the most radiation-resistant compounds known. On irradiation they give small amounts of a gaseous product (mainly hydrogen) and a polymeric mixture containing materials with higher molecular weights than the original compound. Table 10.4 lists the products obtained by irradiating biphenyl (III); the products and yields from the higher polyphenyls are probably similar. Some methane is formed from the higher polyphenyls, though hydrogen remains the major gaseous product; the composition of the gas depends both on the temperature during irradiation and on the total dose absorbed.

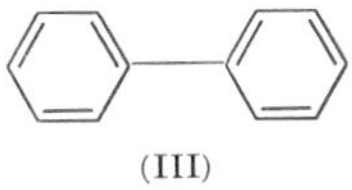

(III)

Burr and Scarborough (53) have studied the radiolysis of several deuterated biphenyls and conclude that the principal steps in the radiolysis mechanism are

$$C_{12}H_{10} \rightsquigarrow \cdot C_{12}H_9 + H\cdot \qquad (10.32)$$

$$\cdot C_{12}H_9 + C_{12}H_{10} \rightarrow \text{polymer} \qquad (10.33)$$

$$H\cdot + C_{12}H_{10} \rightarrow \cdot C_{12}H_{11} \rightarrow \text{polymer} \qquad (10.34)$$

Hydrogen is believed to arise via nonradical reactions which include a unimolecular dissociation,

$$C_{12}H_{10} \rightsquigarrow C_{12}H_{10}^* \rightarrow C_{12}H_8 + H_2 \tag{10.35}$$

and a bimolecular process (cf. 11), e.g.,

$$\left.\begin{array}{c} C_{12}H_{10}^* + C_{12}H_{10} \\ \text{or} \\ C_{12}H_{10}^* + C_{12}H_{10}^* \end{array}\right\} \rightarrow C_{24}H_{18} + H_2 \tag{10.36}$$

which contribute about equally to the hydrogen yield. There is little evidence for splitting of the central carbon-carbon bond to form phenyl radicals; products derived from phenyl radicals are not found and the polyphenyls produced tend to have even rather than odd numbers of phenyl groups. This is in line with the mass spectrum of biphenyl

TABLE 10.4 *Radiolysis of Biphenyl*

(Ref. 51; γ-irradiation, 74 or 82°C, 3 to 7 $\times$ 10^7 rads)

Product	G(product) $\times$ 10^4	
H_2	67	
CH_4	0	
C_2H_2	3.2	
C_2H_6	0	
Diacetylene	0.37	
Benzene	1.1–2.3	
Toluene	0–0.29	
Dihydrobiphenyl	>2.8	
Tetrahydrobiphenyl	>0.57	
Hexahydrobiphenyl	>0.049	
Terphenyl	0.02	relative yields* (74°C)
Quaterphenyl	1	
Quinquephenyl	0.002	
Hexaphenyl	0.02	

* G(polymer), i.e., molecules of biphenyl converted to polymer per 100 ev of energy absorbed, is 0.34 at 250°C for fast electron irradiation (ref. 52).

(51, 54), where the predominant ion is the parent ion, $C_{12}H_{10}^+$, and phenyl ions are not detected.

Organic Moderators and Coolants

Organic compounds can be used in nuclear reactors both as coolants and as moderators (52, 55, 56, 57, 58). The compounds generally preferred are the radiation-resistant polyphenyl and polynuclear aromatic hydrocarbons. As coolants they have advantages over water and liquid metals; they do not corrode metals and they have a low vapor pressure, so that expensive corrosion-resistant construction materials and high-pressure systems can be avoided. Furthermore, little radioactivity is induced in the hydrocarbon if it is pure, and it will not react dangerously with uranium if a fuel element should fail at high temperature. However, disadvantages include a certain amount of radiation decomposition, low heat conductivity, and inflammability. The radiation resistance of the polyphenyls decreases in the region of 400 to 490°C and it is desirable not to exceed these temperatures. They are also less stable in the presence of oxygen, though this is not a serious defect for the present purpose. Although organic materials are usually considered in the role of coolants they may also be used to moderate (i.e., slow down) fast neutrons in a reactor. When used as a moderator a greater volume of the organic material is exposed to very intense radiation than when the material is used as a coolant, and consequently radiation-induced decomposition is of even more concern.

Naphthalene is the least expensive of the polynuclear aromatic hydrocarbons that might be used as moderators or coolants and it has good radiation stability. However, a less desirable characteristic is the formation of solid, coke-like, pyrolysis products. The polymers formed by pyrolysis or irradiation of the polyphenyls are resinous and remain in solution, so that the polyphenyls are still usable liquids when they contain a high proportion of high molecular weight products (e.g., 30 to 40% of polymer, corresponding to a dose of the order of 10^{10} rads). Ultimately, the polyphenyls too are converted to cokes, though normally part of the coolant stream would be diverted and the polymeric material removed by distillation to limit the build-up of polymer. An incidental advantage in using the polyphenyls as coolants is that to some extent the polymer produced reduces the rate of radiolysis of the material. Similarly, mixtures of the polyphenyls are often more resistant to radiation than the individual components. Polyphenyls which are available commercially at moderate cost include biphenyl and terphenyl, the latter as a mixture of the *ortho, meta,* and *para* isomers. Since the molecular weight of the polyphenyls is increased upon irradiation it is probably advantageous to start with the lower members (biphenyl and terphenyl) and to add these whenever it is necessary to make up the volume of the coolant.

Radiation-resistant lubricants are needed in a variety of situations and, like the moderators and coolants, must have high radiation stability. For this purpose the polyphenyls are not satisfactory since they lack the necessary lubricating properties and a related series of compounds, the polyphenyl ethers (IV and V), have been developed (59).

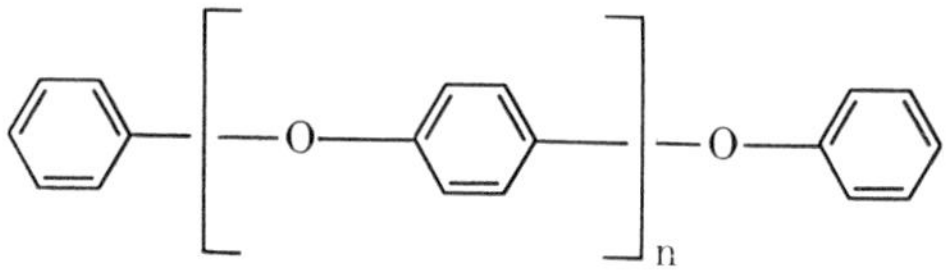

(IV) *para* polyphenyl ethers

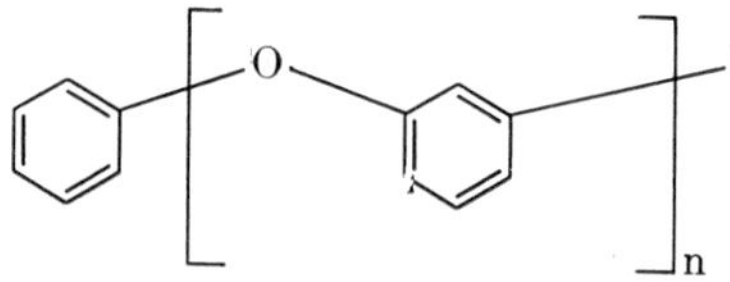

(V) *meta* polyphenyl ethers

REFERENCES

The general references given at the end of Chapter 9 (Aliphatic Compounds) also cover the radiation chemistry of aromatic compounds.

1. V. P. Henri, C. R. Maxwell, W. C. White, and D. C. Peterson, *J. Phys. Chem.*, **56,** 153 (1952).
2. J. P. Manion and M. Burton, *J. Phys. Chem.*, **56,** 560 (1952).
3. S. Gordon and M. Burton, *Discuss. Faraday Soc.*, **12,** 88 (1952).
4. W. N. Patrick and M. Burton, *J. Am. Chem. Soc.*, **76,** 2626 (1954).
5. S. Gordon, A. R. Van Dyken, and T. F. Doumani, *J. Phys. Chem.*, **62,** 20 (1958).
6. E. N. Weber, P. F. Forsyth, and R. H. Schuler, *Radiation Res.*, **3,** 68 (1955).
7. A. T. Fellows and R. H. Schuler, *J. Phys. Chem.*, **65,** 1451 (1961).
8. G. Meshitsuka and M. Burton, *Radiation Res.*, **10,** 499 (1959).
9. R. H. Schuler, *J. Phys. Chem.*, **60,** 381 (1956).
10. W. G. Burns, *Trans. Faraday Soc.*, **58,** 961 (1962).
11. W. G. Burns and C. R. V. Reed, *Trans. Faraday Soc.*, **59,** 101 (1963).
12. R. R. Hentz and M. Burton, *J. Am. Chem. Soc.*, **73,** 532 (1951).
13. T. J. Sworski, R. R. Hentz and M. Burton, *J. Am. Chem. Soc.*, **73,** 1998 (1951).
14. R. R. Hentz, *J. Phys. Chem.*, **66,** 1622 (1962).
15. T. J. Sworski and M. Burton, *J. Am. Chem. Soc.*, **73,** 3790 (1951).
16. M. A. Proskurnin and E. V. Barelko, reported by N. Bach, *Proc. Intern. Conf. Peaceful Uses Atomic Energy,* United Nations, New York, **7,** 538 (1956).
17. G. A. Swan, P. S. Timmons, and D. Wright, *Proc. Second Intern. Conf. Peaceful Uses Atomic Energy,* United Nations, Geneva, **29,** 115 (1958).
18. M. Burton and S. Lipsky, *J. Phys. Chem.*, **61,** 1461 (1957).

19. W. M. Dale and C. Russell, *Biochem. J.*, **62,** 50 (1956).
20. A. Norman and W. Ginoza, *Radiation Res.*, **9,** 77 (1958).
21. F. E. Littman, E. M. Carr and J. K. Clauss, *Science*, **125,** 737 (1957).
22. L. Eldjarn, A. Pihl, and B. Shapiro, *Proc. Intern. Conf. Peaceful Uses Atomic Energy*, United Nations, New York, **11,** 335 (1956).
23. W. Gordy and I. Miyagawa, *Radiation Res.*, **12,** 211 (1960).
24. D. R. Kalkwarf, *Nucleonics*, **18,** (May), 76 (1960).
25. C. S. Schoepfle and C. H. Fellows, *Ind. Eng. Chem.*, **23,** 1396 (1931).
26. J. P. Manion and M. Burton, *J. Phys. Chem.*, **56,** 560 (1952).
27. G. R. Freeman, *J. Chem. Phys.*, **33,** 71 (1960).
28. J. A. Stone and P. J. Dyne, *Radiation Res.*, **17,** 353 (1962).
29. J. G. Burr, *Nucleonics*, **19,** (Oct.), 49 (1961).
30. M. Burton and W. N. Patrick, *J. Phys. Chem.*, **58,** 421 (1954).
31. W. N. Patrick and M. Burton, *J. Phys. Chem.*, **58,** 424 (1954).
32. M. Burton, J. Chang, S. Lipsky, and M. P. Reddy, *Radiation Res.*, **8,** 203 (1958).
33. G. R. Freeman, *J. Chem. Phys.*, **33,** 71 (1960).
34. P. J. Dyne and W. M. Jenkinson, *Can. J. Chem.*, **39,** 2163 (1961).
35. W. West and B. Paul, *Trans. Faraday Soc.*, **28,** 688 (1932).
36. W. West and W. E. Miller, *J. Chem. Phys.*, **8,** 849 (1940).
37. E. N. Weber, P. F. Forsyth, and R. H. Schuler, *Radiation Res.*, **3,** 68 (1955).
38. P. J. Dyne and W. M. Jenkinson, *Can. J. Chem.*, **38,** 539 (1960); P. J. Dyne, *J. Phys. Chem.*, **66,** 767 (1962).
39. G. R. Freeman, *J. Chem. Phys.*, **33,** 957 (1960).
40. J. M. Ramaradhya and G. R. Freeman, *Can. J. Chem.*, **39,** 1769 (1961).
41. J. Lamborn and A. J. Swallow, *J. Phys. Chem.*, **65,** 920 (1961).
42. T. J. Hardwick, *J. Phys. Chem.*, **66,** 2132 (1962).
43. J. M. Ramaradhya and G. R. Freeman, *Can. J. Chem.*, **39,** 1843 (1961).
44. P. J. Ausloos, *J. Am. Chem. Soc.*, **83,** 1056 (1961).
45. H. Kallmann and M. Furst, *Phys. Rev.*, **79,** 857 (1950).
46. M. Furst and H. Kallmann, *Phys. Rev.*, **94,** 503 (1954).
47. S. Lipsky and M. Burton, *J. Chem. Phys.*, **31,** 1221 (1959).
48. M. Burton and W. N. Patrick, *J. Chem. Phys.*, **22,** 1150 (1954).
49. J. B. Birks, *Scintillation Counters*, McGraw-Hill, New York, 1953.
50. M. Ageno in *Actions Chimiques et Biologiques des Radiations*, (ed. M. Haissinsky) Masson et Cie, Paris, Vol. 2, 1956.
51. K. L. Hall and F. A. Elder, *J. Chem. Phys.*, **31,** 1420 (1959).
52. W. G. Burns, W. Wild, and T. F. Williams, *Proc. Second Intern. Conf. Peaceful Uses Atomic Energy*, United Nations, Geneva, **29,** 266 (1958).
53. J. G. Burr and J. M. Scarborough, *J. Phys. Chem.*, **64,** 1367 (1960)
54. J. G. Burr, J. M. Scarborough, and R. H. Schudde, *J. Phys. Chem.*, **64,** 1359 (1960).
55. R. O. Bolt and J. G. Carroll, *Proc. Intern. Conf. Peaceful Uses Atomic Energy*, United Nations, New York, **7,** 546 (1956).
56. E. L. Colichman and R. H. J. Gercke, *Nucleonics*, **14,** (July), 50 (1956).
57. E. L. Colichman and R. F. Fish, *Nucleonics*, **15,** (Feb.), 72 (1957).
58. C. A. Trilling, D. W. Bareis, J. G. Burr, and R. H. J. Gercke, *Proc. Second Intern. Conf. Peaceful Uses Atomic Energy*, United Nations, Geneva, **29,** 292 (1958).
59. W. L. R. Rice, D. A. Kirk, and W. B. Cheney, *Nucleonics*, **18,** (Feb.), 67 (1960).

CHAPTER 11

Radiation Induced Polymerization and the Irradiation of Polymers

The production of polymeric materials represents a very large chemical industry, so that matters pertaining to the formation of polymers and to the modification of their properties are of considerable interest. Ionizing radiation can be used to initiate polymerization in unsaturated organic compounds and to alter the properties (beneficially or otherwise) of polymeric materials. Thus radiation-induced polymerization and the irradiation of polymers has received a great deal of detailed study. It is beyond the scope of this book to deal with this subject at all thoroughly and we have confined our treatment to a brief survey of the chemical reactions involved.

The history of radiation-initiated polymerization goes back to 1874 when Thenard (1) described the formation of an inert solid when acetylene is exposed to a discharge.

In 1925, Mund and Koch (2) and Lind and Bardwell (3) polymerized acetylene using α-particles while Coolidge accomplished the same thing using electrons (4).

Somewhat later, 1938, the volume changes accompanying the polymerization of styrene and vinyl acetate were made the basis for one form of radiation dosimetry (5).

The decade following the war saw an intensification of studies on radiation polymerization and of the action of radiation on polymers by, among others, Dainton (6), Magat (7), Chapiro (8), Charlesby (9), and Ballantine (10), to name only a few.

Polymerization of Organic Monomers

Polymerization of unsaturated organic compounds (monomers) can be initiated by a variety of free-radical or ionic reagents. Radical reagents have received a great deal of attention and radical-initiation is used in the production of most commercially important polymers. Radical reagents include organic peroxides and azo compounds, which break down into free radicals upon heating, and 'redox' catalysts; for example, a mixture of ferrous ion and hydrogen peroxide (Fenton's reagent), which produce radicals by a charge-transfer mechanism. Ionic polymerization has been studied to a lesser extent and fewer examples are known. The ionic reagents producing polymerization may be strong acids, Friedel-Crafts catalysts (e.g., $AlCl_3$), or strong bases (e.g., Na,

TABLE 11.1 *A Comparison of the Radiolysis of Saturated and Unsaturated Hydrocarbons*

Compound (n carbon atoms)	G(product)			Ref.
	H_2	Low-intermediate molecular weight products (C_1 to C_{2n-1})	High molecular weight products ("polymer")* (C_{2n} and over)	
Ethane	6.8	1.2	1.6	Table 7.3
Ethylene	1.3	2.2	approx. 13	"
Acetylene	0	0	72	"
Hexane	5.0	3.2	2.0	Table 9.2
1-Hexene	0.8	0.2	7	11
Cyclohexane	5.7	3.6	2.2	Table 9.3
Cyclohexene	1.2	1.3	8	12

* G(polymer) = molecules of parent compound converted to polymer per 100 ev energy absorbed.

$NaNH_2$); they are not as universal in their action as free-radical reagents. Both types of initiation, radical and ionic, can be brought about by ionizing radiation.

The main differences between the radiolysis of saturated and unsaturated organic compounds can be seen from Table 11.1, where the radiolysis products from similar saturated and unsaturated compounds are compared. The products have been classified as hydrogen, low and intermediate molecular weight products (with fewer carbon atoms than twice the number present in the original compound), and high molecular weight products (with twice as many, or more, carbon atoms as the original compound). It is clear that the yield of hydrogen is smaller from the unsaturated compounds while the yield of high molecular weight products (which will be referred to rather loosely as 'polymer') is greater. The yield of low and intermediate molecular weight products, which are formed as a consequence of carbon-carbon bond fission, is generally greatest with the saturated compounds. These results are largely explicable on the assumption that unsaturated compounds are efficient radical scavengers, so that any radicals formed immediately react with the substrate. Hydrogen, for example, will be formed to a smaller extent from an unsaturated compound because hydrogen atoms formed upon irradiation will tend to add at the double bond,

$$H\cdot + \;\rangle C{=}C\langle \;\rightarrow\; \rangle CH{-}\dot{C}\langle \qquad (11.1)$$

rather than abstract hydrogen, as they would with a saturated compound,

$$H\cdot + RH \rightarrow H_2 + R\cdot \qquad (11.2)$$

However, radical scavenging will not affect products formed by molecular processes such as ion-dissociation, ion-molecule reaction, or the dissociation of excited molecules into molecular products, and the hydrogen formed from the unsaturated compounds shown in Table 11.1 may well result from reactions of this sort. Radicals formed by reaction 11.1, or similar addition reactions, will often dimerize or add to another molecule of the organic monomer, leading to the dimeric and polymeric products observed. The lower yields in the low-intermediate range of products from the unsaturated compounds suggests that carbon-carbon bond scission may make a smaller contribution to the radiolysis of unsaturated compounds than it does to the radiolysis of saturated compounds.

Product yields shown for the unsaturated compounds in Table 11.1 are reasonably typical of the yields from most other unsaturated aliphatic compounds, with the notable exception of those compounds which are able to give long-chain polymers. These compounds form a more restricted group but they are, of course, of great importance, being the basic units from which many important polymers are built up. Ethylene can be converted by irradiation to a long-chain polymer, polyethylene or Polythene, though under more drastic conditions of temperature and pressure than those corresponding to the yields in Table 11.1.

Polymerization can be initiated in gaseous and liquid materials, in solution and, in a few cases, in a solid.

If a solution of the unsaturated compound is used, care must be taken that the solvent cannot react with the organic radicals concerned in the chain reaction. Carbon tetrachloride, for example, might react to give an addition product as described earlier; this would compete with the polymerization chain reaction and might prevent it altogether. Water would be a preferable solvent because the organic radicals are not likely to be reactive enough to split the water molecule, i.e., the reactions,

$$R\cdot + H_2O \rightarrow RH + \cdot OH \quad \text{or} \quad ROH + H\cdot \tag{11.3}$$

are unlikely. The polymerization of water-soluble monomers, such as acrylamide, in aqueous solution is in fact well established; in this instance the polymer, polyacrylamide, is also water soluble.

A few typical polymers are listed in Table 11.2. It is worth noting here that generally the monomer units are joined in a head-to-tail arrangement rather than a head-to-head tail-to-tail arrangement, that is to say the unlike ends of the molecule are generally joined together. All the polymers shown can be represented by a chain of repeating units, —A—A—A—A—A—, running in many cases to lengths of thousands of units.

At ordinary temperatures irradiation of most conventional vinyl monomers, either in bulk or solution, leads to polymerization kinetics typical of free-radical reactions. The over-all reaction rate, R, is given by

$$R = \frac{k_p}{k_t^{1/2}} R_i^{1/2}[M]$$

where k_p and k_t are the rate constants for chain propagation and termination respectively, R_i is the rate of formation of free radicals, and [M] is the monomer concentration. Deviations from this equation occur if the polymer precipitates from the reaction medium (13). Typical G(radical) values for a number of monomers are listed in Table 11.3; the values are derived from kinetic and scavenger studies.

TABLE 11.2 *Polymers*

Monomer	Structure	Polymer	Repeating unit
Ethylene	$CH_2{=}CH_2$	Polyethylene, Polythene	$—CH_2—CH_2—$
Vinyl chloride	$CH_2{=}CHCl$	PVC, Vinylite-Q	$—CH_2—CHCl—$
Styrene	$CH_2{=}CHPh$	Polystyrene, Styron	$—CH_2—CH(Ph)—$
Acrylamide	$CH_2{=}CH—CONH_2$	Polyacrylamide	$—CH_2—CH(CONH_2)—$
Methyl methacrylate	$CH_2{=}C(CH_3)—COOCH_3$	Polymethyl methacrylate, Lucite, Perspex	$—CH_2—C(COOCH_3)(CH_3)—$

TABLE 11.3 *G(Radical) for Irradiated Monomers* (ref. 13)

Monomer	Method	*G*(radical)
Ethylene	Kinetics	4.0
Isobutene	DPPH	3.9
	$FeCl_3$	3.0
Styrene	Kinetics	0.69
	DPPH	0.66
Vinyl acetate	Kinetics	12.0
	DPPH	9.6
Acrylonitrile	Kinetics	5.6
	DPPH	5.0
Methyl acrylate	Kinetics	(15.0)
	DPPH	6.3
Methyl methacrylate	Kinetics	11.5
	DPPH	6.1

Ionic Polymerization

Though free radicals are postulated most often as the intermediates which initiate polymerization there are a few examples where ions are the initiators. The best known of these is the polymerization of isobutene, $(CH_3)_2C{=}CH_2$.

Isobutene is not polymerized by chemically produced radicals but the reaction can be initiated by Friedel-Crafts catalysts (e.g., $AlCl_3$ or $FeCl_3$ with traces of water). At the same time the radiation-induced polymerization is not affected by the radical-scavenger DPPH, which normally inhibits free radical polymerization. Collinson, Dainton, and Gillis (14) suggested that the radiation-induced polymerization is initiated by the ionic reactions

$$C_4H_8 \rightsquigarrow C_4H_8^+ + e^- \tag{11.4}$$

$$(CH_3)_2C{=}CH_2^+ + (CH_3)_2C{=}CH_2 \rightarrow (CH_3)_2\overset{+}{C}{-}CH_3 + \cdot CH_2{-}\underset{\displaystyle CH_3}{\underset{|}{C}}{=}CH_2 \tag{11.5}$$

and followed by the chain reaction

$$(CH_3)_2\overset{+}{C}{-}CH_3 + CH_2{=}\overset{\displaystyle CH_3}{\overset{|}{\underset{\displaystyle CH_3}{\underset{|}{C}}}} \rightarrow CH_3{-}\overset{\displaystyle CH_3}{\overset{|}{\underset{\displaystyle CH_3}{\underset{|}{C}}}}{-}CH_2{-}\overset{\displaystyle CH_3}{\overset{|}{\underset{\displaystyle CH_3}{\underset{|}{C^+}}}} \quad \text{etc.} \tag{11.6}$$

At room temperature some free radical polymerization may also take place, but at low temperatures, such as −80°C, the chain reaction is entirely ionic.

Solid-State Polymerization

When monomers are irradiated in the solid state, polymerization may take place in the solid; or trapped radicals may be formed and react subsequently when the specimen is dissolved or heated near its melting point (15). Solid monomers polymerized in this way include vinyl stearate, styrene, acrylonitrile, and methacrylonitrile. A particularly large amount of work has been done on acrylamide. Electron micrographs of single acrylamide crystals subjected to a small x-ray dose show that polymerization occurs in localized areas which appear to be parallel to the privileged lattice direction (13).

Irradiation of Polymers

Long-chain polymers, whether produced by irradiation or by chemical methods, can be modified by exposure to radiation. The chemical changes produced are similar to those produced in low molecular weight organic molecules, and the main interest arises from the small amount of chemical change required to produce a marked change in the physical properties of the polymer.

The main chemical changes taking place upon irradiation can be divided into two classes: crosslinking and degradation.

Crosslinking is a process whereby two separate long chain molecules become linked together into a single molecule, resulting in an increase in the average molecular weight of the polymer. In the case of Polythene, to take an example, the crosslinking bond between two adjacent molecules might be formed as follows:

$$\begin{array}{l} \text{—CH}_2\text{—CH}_2\text{—CH}_2\text{—CH}_2\text{—} \\ \text{—CH}_2\text{—CH}_2\text{—CH}_2\text{—CH}_2\text{—CH}_2\text{—CH}_2\text{—} \end{array} \rightsquigarrow \begin{array}{l} \text{—CH}_2\text{—CH}_2\text{—}\dot{\text{C}}\text{H—CH}_2\text{—} \\ \qquad\qquad\quad \text{H}\cdot \\ \text{—CH}_2\text{—CH}_2\text{—CH}_2\text{—CH}_2\text{—CH}_2\text{—CH}_2\text{—} \end{array}$$

$$\rightarrow \begin{array}{l} \text{—CH}_2\text{—CH}_2\text{—}\dot{\text{C}}\text{H—CH}_2\text{—} \\ \text{—CH}_2\text{—CH}_2\text{—CH}_2\text{—}\dot{\text{C}}\text{H—CH}_2\text{—CH}_2\text{—} \end{array} + \text{H}_2$$

$$\rightarrow \begin{array}{l} \text{—CH}_2\text{—CH}_2\text{—CH—CH}_2\text{—} \\ \qquad\qquad\qquad | \\ \text{—CH}_2\text{—CH}_2\text{—CH}_2\text{—CH—CH}_2\text{—CH}_2\text{—} \end{array} + \text{H}_2 \quad (11.7)$$

If the irradiation is continued long enough the material eventually becomes one gigantic molecule, which can only be broken up again by heating to temperatures sufficient to cause fission of the chemical bonds.

The physical changes consequent upon crosslinking include greater viscosity, lower solubility in solvents, and higher melting point. Thus unirradiated Polythene softens in the range 70–90°C and melts to a viscous liquid at about 115–125°C; after a dose of about 2×10^6 rads the polymer can be taken up to about 250°C without losing its shape, though above its usual melting point it is flexible and rubbery.

A polymer becomes, effectively, one large molecule when an average of one crosslink per polymer molecule has been formed. If each polymer molecule is composed of several thousand monomer units this is equivalent to less than 0.1% chemical change, and changes well below this are sufficient to cause changes in the viscosity of the polymer (or its solutions).

Crosslinking also occurs when smaller molecules such as the polyphenyls are irradiated. The increase in viscosity in this instance limits the dose to which the polyphenyl can be exposed when used as a moderator or coolant in an atomic reactor.

Other materials that have been crosslinked include rubber tires, which have been vulcanized by this process in the absence of sulfur or other additives, and silicones.

Degradation

The alternative to crosslinking, degradation, is the opposite process in the sense that it involves a reduction in the average molecular weight. It is in fact the breaking of the polymer chain without any subsequent rejoining of the broken ends, i.e.,

$$\text{—A—A—A—A—A—A—A—A—A—} \rightarrow \text{—A—A—A—A—A} + \text{A—A—A—A—} \quad (11.8)$$

Polymers which degrade include Teflon (perfluoropolyethylene), Lucite (polymethyl methacrylate), and polyisobutene. Teflon is particularly sensitive to radiation when irradiated in the presence of oxygen and eventually loses all mechanical strength and crumbles to a powder. Lucite can withstand quite large doses at ordinary temperatures, though it will eventually crack and start to break up, but upon heating gases are evolved and the material swells to a foamy mass; the gas is similar in composition to that formed by irradiation of simple esters. The radicals formed in irradiated Lucite probably disproportionate rather than combine, e.g.,

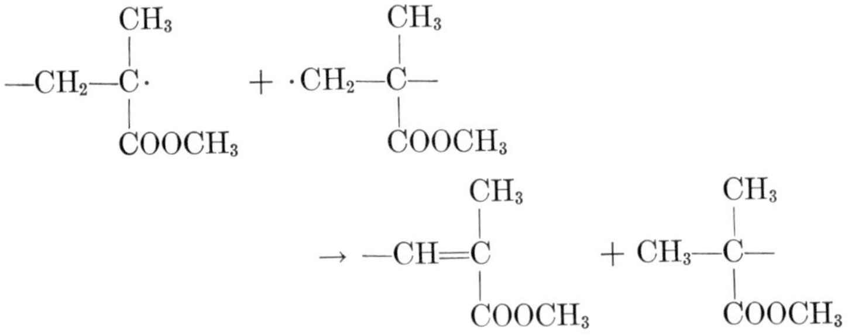

$$\text{—}CH_2\text{—}\underset{\underset{COOCH_3}{|}}{\overset{\overset{CH_3}{|}}{C}}\cdot + \cdot CH_2\text{—}\underset{\underset{COOCH_3}{|}}{\overset{\overset{CH_3}{|}}{C}}\text{—} \rightarrow \text{—}CH{=}\underset{\underset{COOCH_3}{|}}{\overset{\overset{CH_3}{|}}{C}} + CH_3\text{—}\underset{\underset{COOCH_3}{|}}{\overset{\overset{CH_3}{|}}{C}}\text{—} \quad (11.9)$$

A rough guide to the polymers that crosslink and those which degrade is as follows. Polymers containing units of the form

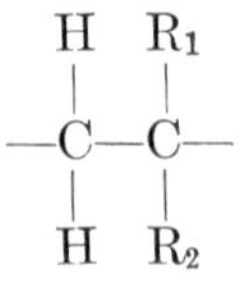

$$\text{—}\underset{\underset{H}{|}}{\overset{\overset{H}{|}}{C}}\text{—}\underset{\underset{R_2}{|}}{\overset{\overset{R_1}{|}}{C}}\text{—}$$

degrade, whereas polymers containing the units

$$\begin{array}{c} \text{H}\quad\text{H} \\ |\quad\;| \\ \text{—C—C—} \\ |\quad\;| \\ \text{H}\quad\text{H} \end{array} \qquad \text{or} \qquad \begin{array}{c} \text{H}\quad\text{R} \\ |\quad\;| \\ \text{—C—C—} \\ |\quad\;| \\ \text{H}\quad\text{H} \end{array}$$

crosslink (16). This is understandable if the bulky R_1 and R_2 groups can prevent the chains coming close enough to form a crosslink; where there is at least one α-hydrogen to the $—CH_2—$ group, crosslinks can be formed.

As in the case of smaller molecules, the benzene ring offers a considerable degree of radiation protection to molecules of which it forms a part. Polystyrene, for example, absorbs 2000 ev per crosslink formed whereas for most crosslinking polymers only about 20 to 30 ev is absorbed per crosslink. Thus at least 99% of the energy absorbed in polystyrene is diverted and produces no permanent chemical change. Furthermore, if styrene is added to other monomers prior to polymerization the final polymer will consist of chains containing both styrene (S) and other (A) units, e.g.,

$$\text{—A—A—S—A—A—A—S—S—A—A—A—S—A—}$$

The styrene units partly protect the polymer from radiation damage and, by varying the proportions of the two monomers, it can be shown that a benzene ring appears to offer protection over a distance of approximately 4 carbon atoms along the chain (17). Protection can also be observed if the additive is present as a separate molecule. A few percent of added aniline or substituted thiourea reduce the degradation of polymethyl methacrylate by a factor of about four, presumably by energy transfer to the additive and its subsequent breakdown (18).

Irradiation of a polymer in the presence of oxygen will probably produce peroxides, which may subsequently lead to degradation of the polymer chain. The chemical reactions involved are likely to be similar to those for smaller organic molecules irradiated in the presence of oxygen. For example, when Polythene is exposed to oxygen, either during or after irradiation, carbonyl compounds (which can be detected by their infrared absorption) and water are produced and may be formed by reactions such as

$$\text{—CH}_2\text{—CH}_2\text{—CH}_2\text{—CH}_2\text{—} \rightsquigarrow \text{—CH}_2\text{—CH}_2\text{—}\dot{\text{C}}\text{H—CH}_2\text{—} \quad \text{(I)}$$

$$\xrightarrow{+O_2} \text{—CH}_2\text{—CH}_2\text{—}\underset{}{\overset{\overset{\bullet}{O_2}\,|}{\text{C}}}\text{H—CH}_2\text{—} \qquad (11.10)$$

$$\begin{array}{c} \dot{O}_2 \\ | \\ -CH_2-CH_2-CH-CH_2- \rightarrow \end{array}$$
$$-CH_2-CH_2-CO-CH_2- + \cdot OH \quad (11.11)$$

and

$$-CH_2-CH_2-CH_2-CH_2- + \cdot OH \rightarrow$$
$$H_2O + -CH_2-\dot{C}H-CH_2-CH_2- \quad (11.12)$$

If Polythene is irradiated and stored under vacuum the intermediate radicals (I) are fairly stable and may be detected in the solid by e.p.r. techniques for periods of several hundred hours after irradiation.

The e.p.r. spectrum of a polymer (polymethyl methacrylate) subjected to ionizing radiation was first reported by Schneider, Day, and Stein (19). Subsequent studies have indicated that polymethyl methacrylate, polyethyl methacrylate, and polymethacrylic acid give, on irradiation, very similar spectra, and that these appear to be formed by the superposition of a 5-line and a 4-line spectrum. Ingram (20) has suggested that irradiation leads to chain rupture and the formation of two radicals, e.g., for polymethyl methacrylate,

$$-CH_2-\underset{COOCH_3}{\overset{CH_3}{\underset{|}{\overset{|}{C}}}}-CH_2-\underset{COOCH_3}{\overset{CH_3}{\underset{|}{\overset{|}{C}}}}- \rightsquigarrow$$
$$-CH_2-\underset{COOCH_3}{\overset{CH_3}{\underset{|}{\overset{|}{C}}}}\cdot + \cdot CH_2-\underset{COOCH_3}{\overset{CH_3}{\underset{|}{\overset{|}{C}}}}- \quad (11.13)$$

These radicals will tend to split off monomer units and the second radical will be converted to a more stable structure by the addition of a monomer molecule (21),

$$\underset{COOCH_3}{\overset{CH_3}{\underset{|}{\overset{|}{C}}}}=CH_2 + \cdot CH_2-\underset{COOCH_3}{\overset{CH_3}{\underset{|}{\overset{|}{C}}}}- \rightarrow \cdot\underset{COOCH_3}{\overset{CH_3}{\underset{|}{\overset{|}{C}}}}-CH_2-CH_2-\underset{COOCH_3}{\overset{CH_3}{\underset{|}{\overset{|}{C}}}}- \quad (11.14)$$

It would appear that e.p.r. spectra may throw considerable light on the free radical processes occurring in polymers upon irradiation.

Graft Polymers

Irradiation of a polymer may produce free radical sites along the chain. If now a suitable monomer is brought into contact with the irradiated polymer the radical sites can initiate polymerization of the monomer, giving chains of polymerized monomer at intervals along the original polymer chain, e.g.,

```
           B
           B             B
           B             B
-A-A-A-A-A-A-A-A-A-A-A-A-A-
   B           B
   B           B
   B
```

where AA is the original polymer chain and BB the chains produced from the added monomer. This process of graft-polymerization is useful since it enables polymers with new properties to be built up.

There are several ways of producing the graft polymer. The simplest is merely to immerse the polymer in the monomer so that it will absorb as much as possible, and then irradiate the swollen polymer. This has the disadvantage that the amount of monomer that can be absorbed by the polymer is limited, and also that the monomer may form chains that are not attached to the original polymer chain. If the radical sites are relatively stable the polymer can be irradiated and then immersed in the monomer. By using radiations which have a limited penetrating power (e.g., x-rays of low energy) the radical sites can be limited to the surface of the polymer, giving a graft polymer in which the second polymer forms a layer on the surface of the original material. Yet another approach that can be used in some cases is to irradiate the first polymer in the presence of air, so that peroxides are formed, immerse it in the monomer, and heat the mixture so that the peroxides are decomposed and form radical sites onto which the monomer grafts.

REFERENCES

A number of reviews and books have been published which deal with radiation-induced polymerization and the irradiation of polymers, including the following:

F. S. Dainton, *Chain Reactions,* Methuen, London, 1956.

F. A. Bovey, *The Effects of Ionizing Radiation on Natural and Synthetic High Polymers.* Interscience, New York, 1958.

Actions Chimiques et Biologiques des Radiations, (ed. M. Haissinsky), Masson et Cie, Paris, Vol. 3, 1958. Parts II and III.

J. J. Harwood, H. H. Hausner, J. G. Morse, and W. G. Rauch, *Effects of Radiations on Materials,* Reinhold, New York, 1958. Chapter 10.

H. Mohler, *Chemische reaktionen ionisierenden Strahlen,* Verlag H. R. Sauerländer, Frankfort am Main, 1958. Chapter 5.

A. Charlesby, *Atomic Radiation and Polymers,* Pergamon Press, New York, 1960.

A. J. Swallow, *Radiation Chemistry of Organic Compounds,* Pergamon Press, Oxford, 1960. Chapters 4 and 6.

A. Chapiro, *Radiation Chemistry of Polymeric Systems,* Interscience, New York, 1962.

1. P. and A. Thenard *Compt. Rend.,* **78,** 219 (1874).
2. W. Mund and W. Koch, *Bull. Soc. Chim. Belges,* **34,** 125, 241 (1925).
3. S. C. Lind and D. C. Bardwell, *Science,* **62,** 422 (1925).
4. W. D. Coolidge, *Science,* **62,** 441 (1925).
5. F. L. Hopwood and J. T. Phillips, *Proc. Phys. Soc. (London),* **50,** 438 (1938); *Nature,* **143,** 640 (1939).
6. F. S. Dainton, *Nature,* **160,** 268 (1947).
7. I. Landler and M. Magat, *Bull. Soc. Chim. Belges,* **57,** 381 (1948).
8. A. Chapiro, *Compt. Rend.,* **28,** 1490 (1949).
9. A. Charlesby, *Proc. Roy. Soc. (London), Ser. A* **215,** 187 (1952).
10. D. S. Ballantine and B. Manowitz, *BNL* 229 (T-35), 1953.
11. M. S. Kharasch, P. C. Chang, and C. D. Wagner, *J. Org. Chem.,* **23,** 779 (1958).
12. G. R. Freeman, *Can. J. Chem.,* **38,** 1043 (1960).
13. A. Chapiro, *Nucleonics,* **19,** (Oct.), 65 (1961).
14. E. Collinson, F. S. Dainton, and H. A. Gillis, *J. Phys. Chem.,* **63,** 909 (1959).
15. A. Charlesby, *Atomic Radiation and Polymers,* Pergamon Press, New York, 1960, p. 382.
16. J. J. Harwood, H. H. Hausner, J. G. Morse, and W. G. Rauch, *Effects of Radiation on Materials,* Reinhold, New York, 1958, p. 273.
17. P. Alexander and A. Charlesby, *Proc. Roy. Soc. (London), Ser. A* **230,** 136 (1955).
18. P. Alexander, A. Charlesby, and M. Ross, *Proc. Roy. Soc. (London), Ser. A* **223,** 392 (1954).
19. E. E. Schneider, M. J. Day, and G. Stein, *Nature,* **168,** 645 (1951).
20. D. J. E. Ingram, M. C. R. Symons, and M. G. Townsend, *Trans. Faraday Soc.,* **54,** 409 (1958).
21. A. M. Bass and H. P. Broida, *Formation and Trapping of Free Radicals,* Academic Press, New York, 1960, p. 376.

CHAPTER 12

Effects of Radiation on Solids

The advance of nuclear technology has prompted the study of the behavior of solid materials when exposed to nuclear radiations. For example, for a material to be useful within a nuclear reactor it must be able to withstand high intensities of nuclear radiations for long periods of time, and materials which suffer little damage upon irradiation are sought. In other fields the beneficial effects of radiation on solids are examined and effects which, if not beneficial in the usual sense of the word, may lead to increased knowledge of the solid state.

From the historical point of view, one of the earliest examples of the action of radiation on solids was the production of pleochroic haloes in mica by the radiation from inclusions of radioactive substances such as uranium or thorium (1, p. 269). A related effect is the production of metamict minerals in which the regular crystal structure of a mineral such as gadolinite has been disordered by nuclear radiations. Such minerals, on heating, often release the stored up energy as heat or light(2, p. 6).

Early studies of the action of nuclear radiations on solids showed, among other effects, that colorless glass became colored by exposure to radiation, the coloration being discharged by the action of heat or light, that the rays from radium exert a destructive action on paper, linen and silk, that rubber becomes hard and stopcock grease is destroyed, that nitrogen iodide will explode when exposed to a sufficient intensity of α-rays, and that silver halides are decomposed. Quite obviously, a variety of effects may be observed, depending on the nature of the radiation and the solid. Much of the information is concerned with physical rather than chemical effects (3), and no attempt is made here at an exhaustive treatment. The aim is rather to touch on a field closely related to radiation chemistry for the sake of completeness.

All types of ionizing radiation are able to produce ionized and excited atoms in the solid, and in addition, heavy particles (protons, deuterons, α-particles, etc.) can cause an appreciable number of atoms to be displaced from their normal position. γ-rays, x-rays, and electrons produce mainly excitation and ionization but, if the radiation is sufficiently energetic (greater than 0.5 Mev for an atom of atomic weight between 50 and 100), may also cause a small amount of atomic displacement (4). For γ-rays of sufficient energy one speaks of the displacement cross section $\sigma_c{}^{\gamma}{}_{,d}$ where the Compton process is effective. For example, for γ-rays of 1.22-Mev energy, $\sigma_c{}^{\gamma}{}_{,d}$ for $Z = 22$ is 0.114 barns, for $Z = 50$ it is 0.0161 barns (2, p. 28). The extent to which displacements occur in copper with several different types of radiation is shown in Table 12.1.

TABLE 12.1 *Displacements Produced by Various Radiations* (ref. 4)

Radiation	Energy (Mev)	Flux cm^{-2} sec^{-1}	Time	Number of displacements per atom in copper
Neutrons	2	10^{13}	1 month	10^{-1}
Deuterons	10	6×10^{12}	10 hour	10^{-2}
Electrons	2	6×10^{14}	10 hour	10^{-3}
γ-rays	1.3	10^{11}	1 month	10^{-8}

Another useful concept is that of the "thermal spike," in which changes in the solid are attributed to brief, intense heating of minute volumes. For example, a copper atom of say 300 ev energy (resulting from Mev deuteron bombardment) has a range of about 30 Å in copper. Dissipation of the atom's energy in a sphere of 30 Å radius would raise the material to the melting point (1083°C) in 5×10^{-12} second. The temperature would fall about equally rapidly. Elaborations of the simple concept include electron spikes, displacement spikes, plasticity spikes, and fission fragment spikes. In contrast to the evidence for some of the spike theory elaborations, evidence for fission fragment spikes is relatively good (2, p. 44).

The nature of the changes produced in a solid depends upon the type of material irradiated. In the treatment which follows materials are divided into metals, ionic crystals, glasses, and organic compounds.

Metals

Metals consist of a regular array of positive ions in a sea of electrons. Thus the ionization produced by radiation in a metal is without effect since the positive hole left by ionization is rapidly refilled by an electron from the common pool of electrons (the conduction band). On the other hand, atoms displaced by heavy particle irradiation may not be able to return to their original position if they are displaced more than a few atoms distance, and the result will be a vacancy at the original position and an (interstitial) atom in a position not occupied by one in the original lattice. Physically, this may result in hardening of the metal and increased electrical resistance (for example, 10^{17} 12-Mev deuterons/cm^2 increase the resistance of pure copper by a factor of about two) since a very regular, or perfect, lattice is needed for the lowest electrical resistance.

Semiconductors (e.g., germanium) are similar to metals but have a much smaller number of common electrons. The electrical resistance of semiconducting metals is very much more sensitive to radiation than that of typical metals because the radiation-induced defects may markedly alter the number of electrons available for conduction. Irradiation of one type of germanium with 10^{15} 9.6-Mev deuterons/cm^2, for example, increased the resistance by a factor of about 10^5 to 10^6. It has been suggested that the change in resistance of semiconductors on irradiation may provide a very useful means of dosimetry.

Appreciable changes in volume and density also accompany radiation-induced changes in metals. In copper, for example, a dose of 10^{17} 10-Mev deuterons/cm^2 produces a fractional increase in length of 3.8×10^{-4}.

Radiation damage in uranium, and in fuel elements generally, has been exhaustively studied and is complicated by the production and retention of fission fragments, some of them gaseous, within the solid. Dimensional changes are an order of magnitude greater than with most other, nonfissionable, metals. For single uranium crystals, a lengthening takes place in the (010) direction and a contraction in the (100) direction (5, p. 29). Considerations of radiation damage are of great importance in the design of fuel elements and the excessively high amounts of damage occurring in uranium have led to the consideration of alternative materials such as uranium oxide, which apparently has a much greater resistance to radiation damage.

Ionic Crystals

When alkali halide crystals are irradiated, absorption bands in the visible and ultraviolet regions are developed. The color in the visible region varies with the nature of the crystal; for example, lithium chloride gives a yellow color and caesium and potassium chlorides blue colors. The absorption bands responsible for these colors are called *F bands* and the defects in the crystal that give rise to them *F centers*. Other absorption bands are also produced as shown, for potassium chloride, below:

Name	Wavelength	Region
V bands	2200 Å 3550	ultraviolet
F band	5500	yellow-green
R bands	6700 7200	red
F′ band	7400	red-infrared
M band	8200	infrared

Yet other absorption bands are produced when the crystal contains small amounts of impurities, calcium chloride, for example, giving a series of *Z* bands and hydrides a series of *U* bands.

The colors can be bleached by heating or by irradiation with light and are believed to be formed as follows. The crystal is made up of a regular three-dimensional array of positive and negative ions as shown in (I). However, holes (vacancies) may exist in the structure where either

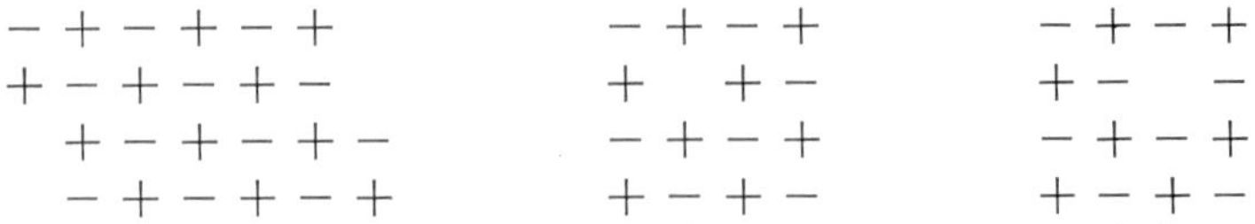

```
− + − + − +            − + − +            − + − +
+ − + − + −            +   + −            + −   −
  + − + − + −          − + − +            − + − +
  − + − + − +          + − + −            + − + −
      (I)                (II)               (III)
                    negative-ion        positive-ion
                       vacancy             vacancy
```

a negative ion (II) or a positive ion (III) is missing (similar holes are believed to be formed by irradiation). Irradiation causes electrons to be ejected from some of the atoms in the crystal lattice and, while most of these electrons will return to their parent atom or a similar atom which has lost an electron, some will be trapped and held in a negative-ion vacancy (IV). This constitutes an F center. The electron can be detected

$$\begin{array}{cccc} - & + & - & + \\ + & e & + & - \\ - & + & - & + \\ + & - & + & - \end{array}$$

(IV)
F center

by e.p.r. measurements, which show that it interacts quite strongly with the surrounding six (in three dimensions) positive ions. The electron can be made to move to some other negative-ion vacancy, in the direction of the anode, by applying an electric potential to the crystal. The opposite process to that giving an F center gives a V_1 center, which is associated with a positive-ion vacancy. This is best illustrated by reference to a particular crystal, and a positive-ion vacancy and a V_1 center in potassium chloride are illustrated in (V) and (VI) respectively. The

$$\begin{array}{ccc} K^+ & Cl^- & K^+ \\ Cl^- & & Cl^- \\ K^+ & Cl^- & K^+ \end{array}$$

(V)
positive-ion vacancy

$$\begin{array}{ccc} K^+ & Cl^- & K^+ \\ Cl^- & & Cl\cdot \\ K^+ & Cl^- & K^+ \end{array}$$

(VI)
V_1 center

formation of a V_1 center follows the loss of an electron from one of the negative chlorine ions surrounding a positive-ion vacancy, giving a chlorine atom. The positive-ion vacancy-chlorine atom system is stable and electrically neutral; in practice the chlorine atom is in equilibrium with the five chloride ions surrounding the positive-ion vacancy, and the five electrons associated with these ions are shared between the six nuclei.

If the irradiated crystal is heated to a few hundred degrees Centigrade the F and V_1 centers created by ionizing radiation can be removed, the electrons being released from their traps (F centers) to combine with the electron-deficient V_1 centers.

Color centers (F and V_1) can also be formed by electrolysis of an alkali halide crystal below its melting point, and F and V_1 centers separately by heating the crystal in the presence of the appropriate alkali metal vapor or halogen. Potassium vapor and chlorine, for example, produce

F and V_1 centers respectively in potassium chloride crystals. Under these conditions the potassium (or chlorine) is deposited on the surface of the crystal and new crystal layers are built up as chloride ions diffuse to this surface. In doing so the chloride ions leave negative-ion vacancies in the crystal and these, or similar vacancies, in the interior of the crystal trap the electrons released by the potassium atoms in forming ions, giving F centers.

Centers other than F and V_1 can arise from the displacement of atoms and ions from their normal position in the crystal, in much the same way as the dislocation of atoms in metals. Impurity ions in the lattice may also form other types of absorption center. In irradiated potassium chloride, displaced chlorine atoms can combine with chloride ions to give the radical-ion Cl_2^-,

$$Cl\cdot + Cl^- \rightarrow Cl_2^- \quad (12.1)$$

which has been detected and identified by its absorption at 3650 Å.

Chemical changes can be observed when the irradiated crystals are dissolved in water. Potassium chloride, for example, gives a slightly alkaline oxidizing solution, presumably through reaction of the trapped electrons and holes (chlorine atoms) with the water, e.g.,

$$e^- + H_2O \rightarrow e_{aq}^- \quad (12.2)$$

$$Cl\cdot \text{ (crystal)} \rightarrow Cl\cdot \text{ (solution)} \quad (12.3)$$

followed by

$$2\, e_{aq}^- \rightarrow H_2 + 2OH^- \quad (12.4)$$

$$2Cl\cdot \rightarrow Cl_2 \qquad \text{etc.} \quad (12.5)$$

Radiation also affects physical properties of the crystals, such as ionic conductivity, density, hardness, etc. (2, Chapter 8). Thus potassium chloride exposed to 6×10^6 r of cobalt-60 γ-radiation shows a decrease in ionic conductivity (σ) of an order of magnitude. By contrast, exposure to 3×10^{18} fast neutrons/cm^2 increases the ionic conductivity by two orders of magnitude. In the case of the γ-irradiated material, σ can be brought near to its pre-irradiation value by annealing at 240°C. X-rays produce a decrease in density in the alkali halides (the fractional decrease at saturation is about 7×10^{-5}), indicating strongly that lattice defects are produced. Changes in the x-ray diffraction pattern corresponding to the lattice expansion are also observed. Similar effects have been found with heavy particle irradiation. Proton and electron bombardment of potassium chloride crystals produce a marked increase in hardness, while lithium fluoride crystals show an increase in yield stress after exposure to neutrons.

Glass

The coloring of glass exposed to radiation probably resembles the coloring of ionic crystals, though the greater complexity of glass means that there are more possibilities for forming color centers. Thus the radiation-induced absorption in glass generally consists of overlapping absorption bands rather than discrete bands as are formed in ionic crystals.

Silver-activated phosphate glass has been mentioned earlier (p. 118) as a means of dosimetry. In this instance, silver ions are believed to be reduced to metallic silver, the silver atoms being responsible for the orange fluorescence observed when the irradiated glass is exposed to ultraviolet light. The process is analogous to the reduction of silver ions in a photographic emulsion on exposure to light.

Manganese in glass causes a purple color to develop on irradiation, which is most likely due to oxidation of manganous to manganic ions,

$$Mn^{2+} + h\nu \rightarrow Mn^{3+} + e^- \qquad (12.6)$$

The electron is trapped in some other part of the system, possibly by a ferric ion,

$$Fe^{3+} + e^- \rightarrow Fe^{2+} \qquad (12.7)$$

A similar reaction may be responsible for the protection against radiation-induced coloration that 1 to 2% of cerium oxide (CeO_2) affords glass, the ceric ions acting as efficient electron traps,

$$Ce^{4+} + e^- \rightarrow Ce^{3+} \qquad (12.8)$$

Irradiated glass contains unpaired electron centers which give rise to e.p.r. spectra, and attempts have been made to correlate these with the optical absorption bands. Fast particle bombardment of silica glass produces two prominent ultraviolet absorption bands, the *C* and *E* bands. At the same time a narrow system of e.p.r. lines and a broad e.p.r. system are produced, which have been correlated with the *C* and *E* bands respectively. Furthermore, the *C* band has been identified as an electron localized at an oxygen ion vacancy and the *E* band interpreted as a hole trapped at an interstitial oxygen ion (2, p. 264). Electron paramagnetic resonance in crystals has recently been summarized by Shulman (6).

Graphite

Graphite has been of great interest technologically, starting with the early speculations of E. P. Wigner on possible radiation damage. Of particular engineering concern are such changes as a doubling in mechanical strength, a fifty-fold reduction in thermal conductivity, a linear expansion of 3%, and an accumulation of stored energy in excess of 500 calories per gram, all of which have been observed with an exposure of about 2×10^{21} neutrons/cm^2 at 30°C. The stored energy is released on heating, the temperature-release curve showing a marked peaking. A knowledge of this and related phenomena is obviously of first importance in graphite moderated reactor technology.

Chemical Decomposition

Covalent bonds present in solids may be broken upon irradiation and bring about chemical changes. This has already been mentioned in the case of organic polymers, and other organic solids as well as nitrates, chlorates, perchlorates, etc., decompose in this way.

Nitrates decompose giving oxygen and nitrite, and it is possible to demonstrate that the final products are formed in the crystal by magnetic-susceptibility measurements, which have the value expected if the oxygen formed is present as molecular oxygen, and by optical spectroscopy, which shows absorption at 3450 Å that can be attributed to nitrite ions (4). If the irradiated nitrate is dissolved in water, both of the products can be measured and the ratio of nitrite to oxygen is found to be 2 : 1, as expected for,

$$NO_3^- \rightarrow NO_2^- + \tfrac{1}{2}O_2 \tag{12.9}$$

$G(\text{-}NO_3^-)$ values from 0.01 to 3 are found for different nitrates (7). Absorption centers similar to F centers are also formed, but the situation is more complicated than in the case of the alkali halides because the centers may react with the products, NO_2^- and O_2. Thermal annealing causes some recombination of the radiation-produced fragments (8).

Potassium chlorate decomposes under the influence of reactor radiations (G is about 2) but potassium sulfate, lithium sulfate, potassium chromate, and calcium carbonate crystals are only colored in a reactor, without apparent decomposition (9, p. 383). Patrick and McCallum (10) have studied the radiation decomposition of a number of alkali chlorates and have found perchlorate, chlorite, hypochlorite, chloride, and oxygen as products. The G values for these species depend on the cation present, and are profoundly influenced by thermal annealing or ultraviolet irradiation of the solid following exposure to γ-rays. The mechanism of the changes produced in the solid by heat treatment appears to be complicated. When silver oxalate is pre-irradiated with γ-radiation the kinetics of its thermal decomposition at 128°C follows a cube root law rather than the exponential law found for unirradiated material (11).

A number of explosive salts can be detonated by ionizing radiations; for example, barium azide using x-rays or electrons, sodium azide by electrons, and nitrogen azide by fission fragments and polonium α-particles (10, p. 383). Bowden and Singh (12) concluded from a study of the explosive decomposition of a number of azides on exposure to an electron beam that explosion results from the production of a "hot spot" of the order of 10^{-4} cm in diameter.

Radiation effects in organic solids are generally similar to those for the same compound in the liquid state when allowance is made for the restricted mobility of the active species in the solid. However, this is not invariably true. Choline chloride, for example, is about a hundred times as sensitive to γ-radiation in the solid state as in solution (cf. p. 358), apparently because the molecular alignment in the crystalline material is conducive to a chain decomposition.

Reactions in Solids at Low Temperatures

In the last few years many studies have been made of the effect of radiations on solids at low temperatures. Such studies have the advantage that at low temperatures the intermediates produced by the radiation will not ordinarily react with the substrate and they may therefore be examined by such techniques as optical and emission spectroscopy, electron paramagnetic resonance, etc. The theoretical possibility of high energy reactions between radicals has added to the interest in the subject (13, 14, 15).

Hydrogen atoms and deuterium atoms are readily produced in frozen, acid or alkaline, H_2O and D_2O by irradiation with γ-radiation or tritium-β radiation (16, 17). $G(H)_\gamma$ for a 0.125 mole fraction perchloric acid solution is close to 2, but the yield in 16% hydrofluoric acid solution is much lower, and the yield in alkaline solutions containing lithium, sodium, or potassium hydroxide is lower still. Hayon (18) has discussed the results in terms of solvated electrons. The radiation chemistry of both liquid and frozen aqueous solutions of nitrous oxide and ferrous ion has been described by Dainton and Jones (19) for the temperature range $-196°$ to 77°C. It was found that whenever a transition from a crystalline or a fluid state to a glassy state occurred, $G(N_2)$ increased abruptly, though $G(H_2)$ and $G(O_2)$ were largely unaffected. It was suggested that electrons generated in the primary act migrate distances of about 50 Å in the glass, and invariably react with any solute molecule (N_2O or Fe^{2+}) they encounter during this migration. Polymer chains with repeating units such as $(-SO_3-)_n$, which are probably responsible for the glassy structure, may also furnish preferred paths for electron migration.

Collinson, Conlay, and Dainton (20) claim to have found strong evidence for energy transfer in certain systems where there is considerable overlap between the absorption spectrum of the solute and that of the solvent. In a solution of ferric chloride in diphenyl ether just above the melting point, or in the supercooled liquid, $G(\text{-FeCl}_3)$ was low and independent of solute concentration and absorbed dose. In the solid phase, however, $G(\text{-FeCl}_3)$ became much larger and increased with decrease in temperature and decrease in solute concentration. In solvents with absorption bands which do not overlap those of the solute, ferric chloride, $G(\text{-FeCl}_3)$ is the same in the solid and in the liquid at temperatures near the melting point. An ordered structure of the donor (solvent) molecules is apparently necessary for this type of energy transfer (21).

The thermal behavior of trapped radicals seems to indicate that phase changes are of considerable importance. Gurman et al. (22) have reported that the e.p.r. spectrum of the radicals in frozen aqueous hydrogen peroxide irradiated at −196°C decays rapidly between −125 and −120°C, but irradiation of the sample above −115°C leads again to the production of radicals, which are stable up to −53°C. Thermograms of nonirradiated specimens showed an exothermic phase change at −116°C and an endothermic change at −53°C (23).

Numerous e.p.r. studies have been made of the thermal stability of radicals produced by the irradiation of organic solids at low temperatures. Thus the radicals in irradiated cyclohexane disappear between −113 and −98°C, and those from cyclohexyl iodide, cyclohexyl bromide, and cyclohexyl chloride between −158 to −143°C, −88 to −68°C, and −103 to −53°C respectively. Activation energies for the radical disappearance, which follow second order kinetics, are about 20–25 kcal per mole (24, 25, 26). Electron paramagnetic resonance spectra of a sample of *n*-hexadecene-1 irradiated at −196°C and then warmed with temperature increments of 20° showed a rapid fall in the number of trapped radicals during heating. Most of the radicals had disappeared by the time the temperature reached −77°C. It was suggested that the disappearance of a proportion of the radicals each time the temperature was raised in the region between −196° and −77°C was due to the progressive release of a mobile species, probably electrons, from traps of various energies, since massive molecular motions were thought unlikely at these temperatures (27).

A few studies of conventional reactions carried out at low temperatures have appeared. The radiolysis of equimolar mixtures of hydrogen bromide and ethylene at liquid nitrogen and liquid oxygen temperatures, for example, leads to the production of virtually pure ethyl bromide (28, 29). Similar results were obtained just above the freezing point (−165°C) of the mixture. The reaction is a chain reaction with G of the order of 10^5 and it would appear that radiation produces reactive entities (radicals) in the frozen and liquid mixtures which subsequently initiate the reaction chain. The chain reaction must occur during melting of the frozen samples, and in support of this it was found that the reaction could be initiated in an unirradiated mixture by condensing it onto irradiated frozen material at liquid nitrogen temperature, and then melting the combined samples. When, for example, equal amounts of unirradiated and irradiated mixture were used, the amount of product formed in the combined sample, on melting, was 60% greater than that formed in the irradiated mixture alone. Electron paramagnetic resonance studies at liquid nitrogen temperature (−196°C) indicate that hydrogen atoms are present in irradiated hydrogen bromide and large amounts of ethyl radicals, with a small amount of hydrogen atoms, in irradiated ethylene. An irradiated mixture of hydrogen bromide and ethylene shows no evidence of ethyl radicals and only a weak spectrum similar to that obtained by irradiating ethyl bromide, indicating a large measure of reaction of the primary radiation-produced radicals even at −196°C.

The importance of phase transitions in low temperature reactions has been emphasized by Semenov (30).

The foregoing section indicates that the study of low temperature radiolysis reactions is still in its infancy. However, it would seem to be worth pursuing further since the resulting radical reactions might be expected to be of considerable theoretical and perhaps even practical interest. It is of particular interest in view of the importance of the direct experimental observation and measurement of the primary products and transient intermediates for our understanding of radiolytic processes (31).

Catalysts

In several cases radiation has been shown to affect the activity of solid catalysts (cf. 32), and it is very likely that this field of study will grow rapidly within the next few years.

Typical of the systems examined are hydrogen-deuterium exchange over silica, alumina, and other oxides; *ortho-para* hydrogen conversion over the oxides of iron, molybdenum, and other metals; oxidation of sulfur dioxide over vanadium pentoxide, etc. (4).

The effects observed range from zero to as much as a thousandfold change in activity and have been attributed to a variety of causes, such as an effect on catalyst poisons, the formation of holes, trapped electrons, or displaced atoms, and a change in adsorptive capacity. In relation to the latter, it is of interest that Charman and Dell (33) reported that nickel oxide and magnesium oxide pre-irradiated with doses up to 6×10^{19} fast neutrons/cm^2 showed a strong enhancement of oxygen adsorption and also an increase in hydrogen adsorption. They suggested that the irradiation effects may be explained in terms of the creation of excess metal and excess oxygen centers (cf. 34).

REFERENCES

1. G. Hevesy and F. A. Paneth, *Radioactivity,* Oxford University Press, 1938.
2. D. S. Billington and J. H. Crawford, *Radiation Damage in Solids,* Princeton University Press, 1961.
3. *Radiation Effects in Inorganic Solids,* Faraday Soc. Discussion No. 31, 1961.
4. E. H. Taylor, *J. Chem. Educ.,* **36,** 396 (1959).
5. J. J. Harwood, H. H. Hausner, J. G. Morse, and W. G. Rauch, *Effects of Radiations on Materials,* Reinhold, New York, 1958.
6. R. G. Shulman, *Ann. Rev. Phys. Chem.,* **13,** 326 (1962).
7. E. R. Johnson and J. Forten, Faraday Soc. Discussion No. 31, 1961, p. 238.
8. A. G. Maddock and S. R. Mohanty, Faraday Soc. Discussion No. 31, 1961, p. 193.
9. M. Haissinsky, *La Chimie Nucléaire,* Masson et Cie., Paris, 1957.
10. P. F. Patrick and K. J. McCallum, *Nature,* **194,** 766 (1962).
11. R. M. Haynes and D. A. Young, Faraday Soc. Discussion No. 31, 1961, p. 229.
12. F. P. Bowden and K. Singh, *Proc. Roy. Soc. (London), Ser. A* **227,** 22 (1954).
13. M. S. Matheson, *Nucleonics,* **19,** (Oct.), 57 (1961).
14. A. M. Bass and H. P. Broida, *Formation and Trapping of Free Radicals,* Academic Press, New York, 1960.
15. G. J. Minkoff, *Frozen Free Radicals,* Interscience, New York, 1960.
16. J. Kroh, B. C. Green, and J. W. T. Spinks, *Can. J. Chem.,* **40,** 413 (1962).
17. R. Livingston and A. J. Weinberger, *J. Chem. Phys.,* **33,** 499 (1960).
18. E. Hayon, *Nature,* **194,** 737 (1962).
19. F. S. Dainton and F. T. Jones, *Radiation Res.,* **17,** 388 (1962).
20. E. Collinson, J. J. Conlay, and F. S. Dainton, *Nature,* **194,** 1074 (1962).
21. P. J. Dyne, D. R. Smith, and J. A. Stone, *Ann. Rev. Phys. Chem.,* **14,** (1963).
22. G. B. Sergeev, V. S. Gurman, V. I. Papissova, and E. I. Yakovenko, *Fifth Intern. Free Radical Symp. Uppsala,* 1961.
23. V. S. Gurman, E. I. Yakovenko, and V. I. Papissova, *Zh. Fiz. Khim.,* **34,** 1126 (1960).
24. R. Bensasson, K. Liebler, R. Marx, and H. Szwarc, *Bull. Ampére. 9ᵉ année, fasc. special 1960,* 303.
25. K. Leibler and H. Szwarc, *J. Chim. Phys.,* 1109 (1960).
26. K. Leibler, *J. Chim. Phys.,* 1111 (1960).

27. P. B. Ayscough, A. P. McCann, C. Thomson, and D. C. Walker, *Trans. Faraday Soc.,* **57,** 1487 (1961).
28. D. A. Armstrong and J. W. T. Spinks, *Can. J. Chem.,* **37,** 1002 (1959).
29. F. W. Mitchell, B. C. Green, and J. W. T. Spinks, *Can. J. Chem.,* **38,** 689 (1960).
30. N. Semenov, *Plenary lecture at IUPAC Conf. Montreal 1961; Pure and Applied Chem. XVIII International Congress, Montreal, 1961,* Butterworth, London, 1962.
31. M. S. Matheson, *Ann. Rev. Phys. Chem.,* **13,** 77 (1962).
32. E. H. Taylor, *Nucleonics,* **20,** (Jan.), 53 (1962).
33. H. B. Charman and R. M. Dell, *Trans. Faraday Soc.,* **59,** 470 (1963).
34. W. H. Cropper, *Science,* **137,** 955 (1962).

CHAPTER 13

Industrial Uses of Radiation

The controlled release of nuclear energy and the accompanying release of nuclear radiations has focused a good deal of attention on the possible uses of such radiations in chemical industry. The preceding chapters have indicated that radiation may be used to bring about many different types of chemical change and therefore it should, in principle, be possible to establish a radiation-chemical industry. Whether such an industry will in fact develop is largely a matter of economics. Prominent among the questions of economics are those of volume of product and of the possibility of exploiting any advantages inherent in the use of radiation.

An estimate of the volume, or tonnage, that might be expected of a radiation-chemical industry can be made as follows. Remembering that G is the number of molecules of product formed per 100 ev absorbed, it can easily be shown that the number of pounds of product produced per kilowatt-hour of radiation energy absorbed is $G \times M \times 8.3 \times 10^{-4}$, where M is the molecular weight of the product. In the near future, we might expect nuclear energy production to be in the neighborhood of 10 million kilowatts. If we suppose that 15% of this energy is available for industrial processes other than power production, either as fission product energy or for other methods of chemical utilization (e.g., in special chemical reactors), the potential output of chemicals from a radiation-chemical industry is $11 \times 10^6 GM$ pounds, or $5.5 \times 10^3 GM$ tons, per year. Putting M equal to 100, this gives $5.5 \times 10^5 G$ tons per year. If G is 1, the calculated output is only half a million tons per year, which is not very attractive. However, if G is 100, or better still 10^5, we get a possible production rising into the tens of millions of tons and one could hope to base several world industries on it, provided the energy is not too expensive and the process possesses some attractive competitive features.

An alternative approach is to consider the utilization of fission products. It has been suggested that by 1965 the British nuclear power program will generate 6000 megawatts and produce 3×10^9 curies of fission products per year (1). Assuming that the fission products emit radiation similar to cobalt-60 γ-rays and knowing that 1000 curies of cobalt-60 can give $0.13G$ mole of product per day, the fission products from the British program could convert $160GM$ tons of material per year. Again one reaches the conclusion that for G values of 100 or higher, or for very high molecular weight materials, a possibility exists for an industry or industries. Thus one requires a chain reaction, to give a high G, or alternatively a process in which a small percentage chemical change brings about the desired change in the product. A good many reactions of these two types, leading to desirable products, are known so that the first criterion is met. The estimated radiation costs found in the literature vary all the way from a fraction of a cent to several cents per pound so that the second criterion is certainly met in a number of cases. The radiation cost per pound is easily calculated knowing the G value and the cost of the absorbed radiation (2) and the relationship between absorbed dose, radiation yield, molecular weight, and radiation cost is shown graphically in the nomogram in Fig. 13.1. Scales A, B, and C allow one to read off the kilowatt-hours absorbed per pound; scales D and E then allow one to calculate the radiation cost. As an example, the lines drawn in Fig. 13.1 are for the formation of benzene hexachloride, for which the molecular weight is 291 and the G value 85,000. It is seen from scale C that this reaction requires an absorbed dose of 4.9×10^{-5} kilowatt-hour per pound of benzene hexachloride formed. Moving from scale C to scales D and E and assuming the cost of radiation to be $8.00 per kilowatt-hour absorbed, we find the cost of chlorinating benzene to be 0.025¢ per pound or 50¢ per ton of product.

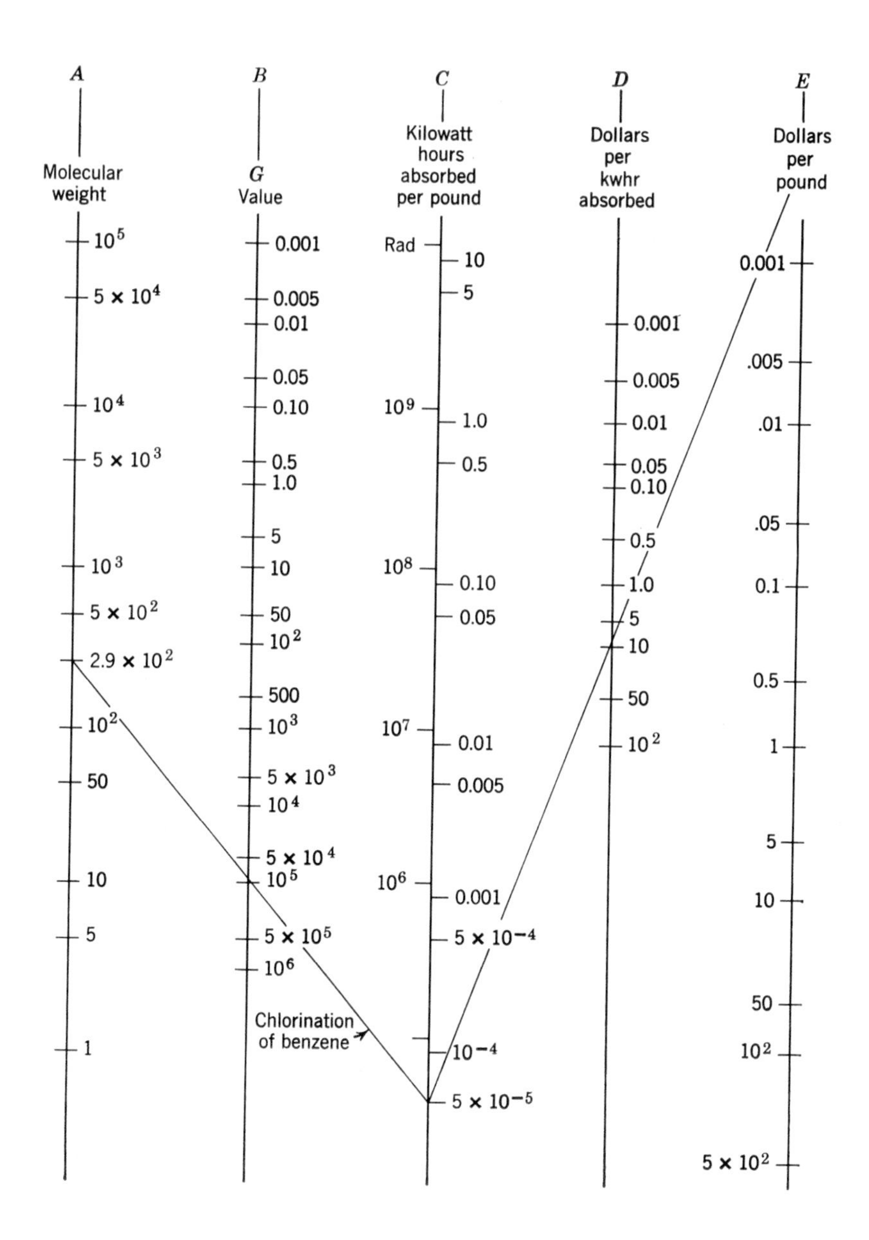

FIGURE 13.1 *Radiation cost in relation to G value and molecular weight (ref. 2). Courtesy United States Atomic Energy Commission, Washington, D.C.*

Radiation chemical processes possess several attractive features as compared to conventional processes.

(i) They may lead to the synthesis of materials which cannot easily be prepared otherwise, e.g., graft polymers such as nylon grafted to styrene.
(ii) They may modify a material in a desirable manner, e.g., polyethylene cross linked by irradiation.
(iii) They may result in a purer product, e.g., where radiation replaces a catalyst, contamination resulting from incomplete removal of the catalyst is not a problem.
(iv) The quality of a product produced using a solid catalyst often depends on the catalyst activity, which may vary with the method of forming the catalyst or because of catalyst poisoning. This variation is absent when a constant radiation intensity is used to trigger the reaction.
(v) Radiation-induced reactions can be carried out at relatively low temperatures, and this may lead to new products or the absence of competing side reactions.
(vi) The possible elimination of some stages of a synthesis.
(vii) Compared to reactions initiated by ultraviolet light, ionizing radiation offers the advantage of greater penetrating power so that more uniform reaction takes place in larger volumes of reactants, avoiding the build-up of product on the walls of the reaction vessel. The use of metal rather than glass vessels is also possible.
(viii) The penetrating power of ionizing radiation also makes it possible to irradiate materials in pressure vessels without the provision of special equipment.

As an example of (iii), ethyl bromide can be synthesized with 99.5% purity by irradiating a mixture of ethylene and hydrogen bromide at room temperature; the G value is about 10^5 (3). An example of (vii) is the formation of Gammexane (gamma benzene hexachloride) by a radiation-induced chain reaction with G about 10^5 (4); the over-all reaction being,

$$C_6H_6 + 3Cl_2 \rightarrow C_6H_6Cl_6 \tag{13.1}$$

Radiation should have several advantages in comparison with the usual photochemical method using glass reaction vessels. The reaction liberates a considerable amount of heat and there is also a rapid fall in light intensity as light passes through the mixture, leading to large local temperature variations. These are largely obviated using γ-rays. Furthermore, using metal tubes, transparent to γ-rays but not to light, greater safety and ease of cooling are realized (5).

The actual industrial interest in radiation chemistry is hard to estimate at the moment since no industry wishes to show its hand to its competitors. This situation is particularly acute in a new and potentially very profitable field — it is not often possible to get in on the ground floor of a new industry, but the rapid developments in the atomic energy field do appear to offer some such opportunities at the present time. Some estimate of the interest in this field is given by the information concerning patents in Table 13.1 (6).

Looking to the future, one can only hazard the guess that in 1963 the possibilities of founding an industry based on radiation chemistry are better than the possibility of basing one on equilibrium constants in 1913, when Haber used equilibria as the basis for the ammonia synthesis. North America, with ample supplies of uranium and a great deal of atomic "know-how," has much to gain scientifically, industrially, and nationally by being in the lead in the development of a radiation chemical industry. It would seem to be a good investment to encourage one or two suitable industrial groups to put a good deal of effort into it.

TABLE 13.1 *Patents Concerning Radiation* (ref. 6)

Process	Patents		
	U.K.	U.S.	Total
Organic reactions	16	12	28
Inorganic reactions	3	1	4
Sterilization	1	7	8
Polymer			
Polymerization	24	3	27
Cross linking	33	16	49
Degradation	7	2	9
Graft-polymers	22	4	26
Other polymer	22	6	28

SOURCES OF RADIATION

Sources of radiation include fission products, artificial isotopes, reactors, linear accelerators, and so on. These have been mentioned briefly in Chapter 2 and will now be discussed in somewhat greater detail.

Nuclear Reactors

Most nuclear reactors contain uranium as the fissile material with graphite or water (ordinary or heavy) as the moderator (for a useful summary, see ref. 7). If the reactor core is used as a source of radiation, neutron irradiation will take place simultaneously with γ-irradiation and neutron activation will induce radioactivity sufficient, in many cases, to make the material irradiated unusable. The only materials to be considered for irradiation in a reactor core therefore would be either those containing elements with very low neutron cross sections or those forming radioisotopes with relatively short half-lives; for example, materials containing only the elements carbon, hydrogen, oxygen, and nitrogen.

A good deal of radiation research on polymers and polymerization has been carried out using the slow neutron reactors at Harwell, Brookhaven, and Oak Ridge, but the use of a reactor for the radiation treatment of materials on an industrial scale seems to be subject to a good many difficulties. If irradiation is a secondary use of a power reactor, the engineering problems arising from introducing the material into the reactor and subsequently removing it are considerable, and the amount of useful space which can be devoted to irradiations is rather small. Charlesby (8) calculates that with the BEPO graphite moderated reactor about 0.2% of the energy released might be used for radiation purposes. An alternative proposal is to put the material to be irradiated in the reactor shield, where it would merely absorb radiation which would otherwise be lost. This would seem to be an attractive proposal, but to have any chance of success it would probably be necessary to include the process in the original reactor design and this would not allow any great flexibility in operating parameters. At all events detailed consideration of such a proposal has not yet been seen in the literature.

While the use of the prompt γ-radiation from fission reactions would not seem to be generally feasible at the present time other, more attractive, possibilities have been suggested involving the use of materials emerging from the reactor core as sources of γ-radiation. These might be gaseous fission products (9, 10), fission products from homogeneous reactors, spent reactor fuel elements, or coolants such as liquid sodium which become radioactive in the reactor core (cf. 7). Figure 13.2 illustrates diagrammatically a proposal to use a liquid sodium cooled reactor as a source of heat, power, and radiation.

Spent Fuel Rods

Spent fuel rods have been considered for radiation purposes and would seem to have considerable potential value, particularly when used within a reasonable distance of the reactor so as to avoid transportation problems. It has been calculated for example that a reactor operating at

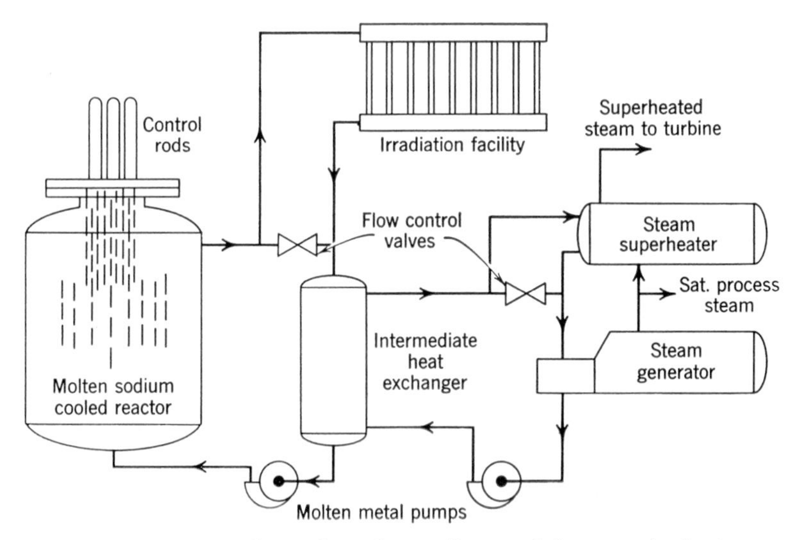

FIGURE 13.2 *Proposed use of a molten sodium cooled reactor for heat, power, and irradiation service. Courtesy United States Atomic Energy Commission, Washington, D.C. (Ref. 7, p. 105).*

960 megawatts would provide 6000 kilowatt hours of useful radiation per day (11).

A large irradiation unit containing over a million curies of fuel rod activity has been described by a United Kingdom group (12). The spent fuel elements are stored under 12 feet of water and materials to be irradiated are placed in watertight containers of aluminum (Fig. 13.3).

Fission Products

Fission products, separated from spent fuel elements, are now available in kilocurie amounts. One of the most attractive is caesium-137 which emits 0.66-Mev γ-rays and has a half-life of 33 years. The γ-radiation from 1 megacurie of caesium-137 corresponds to 3.91 kilowatts of radiation power. Strontium-90, in the form of $SrTiO_3$, has been advocated as a source of β-radiation.

Radioactive Cobalt

One of the most popular radiation sources is cobalt-60, which is made by neutron irradiation of ordinary cobalt in a nuclear reactor. Each cobalt-60 disintegration gives rise to two γ-rays of energy 1.17 and 1.33

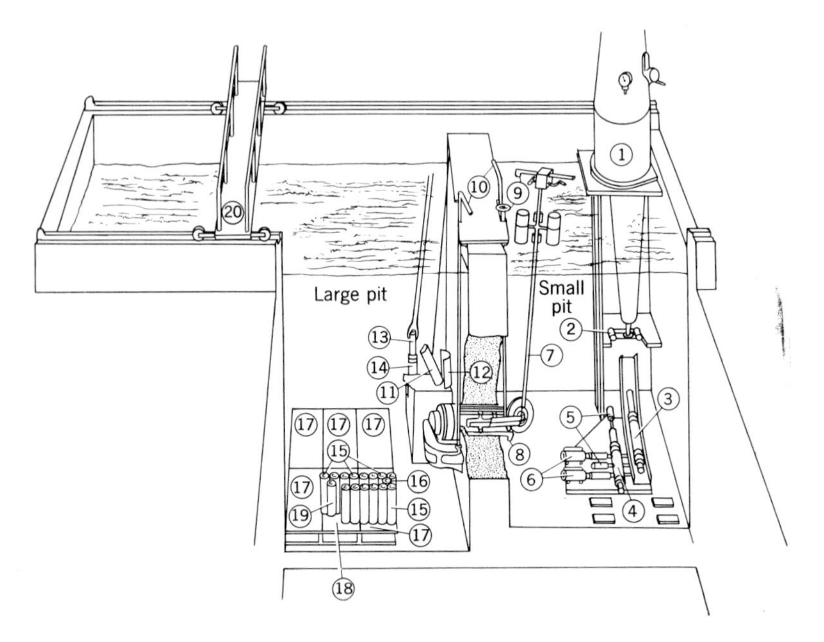

FIGURE 13.3 *Fuel rod radiation unit. Courtesy International Atomic Energy Agency, Vienna (Ref. 12, p. 181).*

1 Transport coffin
2 Pneumatic guillotine
3 Fuel rod on chute
4 Fuel rod on cutting jig
5 Pneumatic rams for locating fuel rod in jig
6 Pneumatic guillotine
7 Floating tongs placing fuel rod on transfer trolley
8 Transfer port
9 Handwheel for operation of transfer trolley
10 Operating handles for transfer port doors
11 Fuel rod in tilting channel
12 Fixed channel
13 Tongs placing fuel rod in box
14 Caps for fuel rod boxes
15 Fuel rod boxes on irradiation bases
16 Sample
17 Plain base
18 Base with driven turntables
19 Sample on Turntable
20 Mobile bridge

Mev respectively, as well as β-radiation which is mainly absorbed by the source and its container. A kilocurie source provides a total γ-ray power of 14.8 watts.

Kilocurie cobalt-60 sources are available commercially for laboratory purposes (cf. Fig. 2.7; 13) and give radiation doses of the order of 10^6 r per hour.

Numerous large-scale cobalt-60 installations have been described and are usually of the cave type, where shielding is provided by concrete or water. In a 10,000 curie Japanese facility, for example, protection is provided by a concrete cave (14). A concrete cave and a water pond for storing the radioactive cobalt are used in the case of a 150,000 curie unit (Fig. 13.4) described by a United Kingdom group (12). This installation can treat 200 cubic feet of material per day with a dose of 2.5 megarad. It is reported (15) that the United States Army radiation laboratory will contain a cobalt-60 irradiation cell designed for 3 megacuries, though the initial loading is expected to be 1.38 megacuries. Food packages to be irradiated will be carried into the cell by a continuous, overhead conveyor. The source will be lowered to the bottom of a 24-foot storage pool to allow entrance to the cell for service work.

RADIATION STERILIZATION

The ability of high-energy radiation to destroy microorganisms without appreciable temperature rise in the substrate offers an attractive means of sterilizing foods, drugs, and miscellaneous complex biological systems.

Since 1896, one year after Roentgen's discovery of x-rays, the bactericidal effects of radiation have been under study. Early patents covering both sterilization and deinfestation were granted and have long since expired. Early experimenters were troubled by two major problems, lack of an economic source of radiation, and insufficient information about the biological and biochemical effects of radiation. While these two problems have not been entirely solved, much progress has been made toward their eventual solution.

One of the most favorable markets for waste fission products appears to be the field of food sterilization. While this is not a direct application of radiation chemistry, the development of the large radiation sources that would be required for food sterilization is of first importance to a radiation chemical industry and furthermore such facilities might initially be built with a multipurpose use. Brief mention of food irradiation, the control of infestation and sprouting, and the sterilization of drugs and pharmaceuticals is therefore appropriate. The doses required for these purposes are roughly as follows: to destroy the eggs of insects, 2000–5000 rads; to inhibit the sprouting of tubers, 5000–10,000 rads; to bring about the reproductive sterilization of adult insects in bulk stored grain, about 20,000 rads; and to bring about the radiosterilization of foods, about 2–5 Mrads.

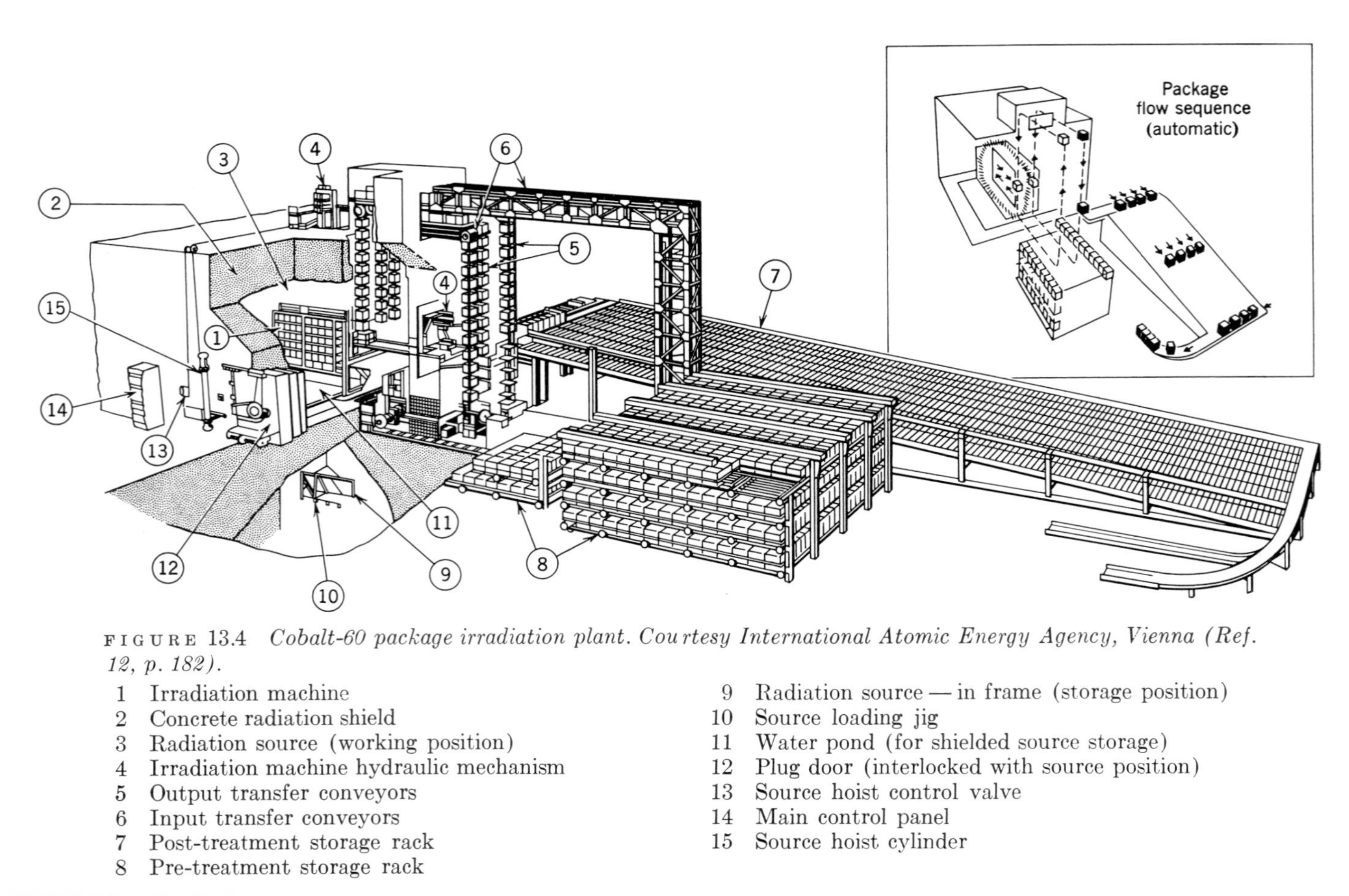

FIGURE 13.4 *Cobalt-60 package irradiation plant. Courtesy International Atomic Energy Agency, Vienna (Ref. 12, p. 182).*

1 Irradiation machine
2 Concrete radiation shield
3 Radiation source (working position)
4 Irradiation machine hydraulic mechanism
5 Output transfer conveyors
6 Input transfer conveyors
7 Post-treatment storage rack
8 Pre-treatment storage rack
9 Radiation source — in frame (storage position)
10 Source loading jig
11 Water pond (for shielded source storage)
12 Plug door (interlocked with source position)
13 Source hoist control valve
14 Main control panel
15 Source hoist cylinder

Food Irradiation

Radiation-sterilization of food is not without its problems. Foods contain a few key components which, although present in micromole per gram concentrations, regulate the flavor and nutritional value. Experimental evidence indicates that some of these key components are very radiation-labile, and radiation-sterilization often brings about deleterious transformations in flavor, odor, and aesthetic quality. Proctor and Goldblith (16) have discussed the problems of radiation-sterilization. They concluded that it is possible to destroy all types of microorganism with radiation and were able to demonstrate that the species of organism is the prime factor in determining the magnitude of the sterilizing dose. They also point out that spoilage of certain foods occurs partly through enzymatic action so that it is also necessary to inactivate these enzymes. In the case of thermal sterilization the heat applied is sufficient to do this. However radiation-sterilization does not produce heating and some other means of inactivating the enzyme would have to be provided. High frequency electronic heating, to heat evenly the whole mass of the food, is suggested as a possibility. Here the exterior surface would not be overheated and only the minimum quantity of heat necessary for enzyme inactivation would be applied to the interior of the food.

Several means have been suggested for obviating the undesirable side reactions which lead to changes in color, texture, and flavor in irradiated food. These include irradiation of the food in the frozen state or in an inert atmosphere, or the addition of free-radical acceptors.

Although large doses are necessary to completely sterilize a food, much smaller doses have the useful property of extending the storage life of the food. Costwise, this application presents a more favorable picture than does the use of radiation as a sterilization agent and, even more important, a low radiation dose brings about almost no changes in the quality of most foods. Irradiation does appear a distinctly promising alternative to refrigeration for extending the storage life of food. Aebersold (17), for example, has stated that radiation doses in the range 100,000–800,000 rads are sufficient to depress and delay microbial multiplication in fish, and hence to effect radiopasteurization; about ten times this dose is required to kill all the organisms found in food. It was suggested that one ton of pasteurized product per hour would be produced by a cobalt-60 irradiation unit containing 300,000 curies of the isotope.

Control of Insects

Reproduction of the confused flour beetle, the insect most commonly found in flour, is halted by a dose of about 25,000 rads. Flour irradiation facilities have been proposed, based on spent fuel elements as radiation sources (7, p. 355). Irradiation of grain using a 15,000 curie cobalt-60 source, at a cost of approximately 1¢ per bushel, has also been proposed (7, p. 357).

Sprout Inhibition

Tests in several countries have indicated that a dose of about 10,000 rads effectively inhibits sprouting in potatoes (18; 19; 7, p. 291) while sprouting in onions is effectively controlled by a dose of 7000–10,000 rads (7, p. 296).

Rice (12, 20) has described a mobile irradiator containing 8500 curies of cobalt-60 designed to treat potatoes and similar crops (Fig. 13.5). The unit gives a dose of 8000 rads to 6000 pounds of material per hour and it is thought that the cost might be brought down to about 0.2¢ per pound.

Sterilization of Drugs and Pharmaceuticals

Radiation sterilization of drugs and pharmaceuticals has already been carried out on a limited commercial scale. In comparison with food sterilization this field presents an ideal case. One is usually dealing with a concentrated, reasonably well-defined single substance and since pharmaceuticals are usually not regularly consumed, no notice need be taken of chemical changes which may produce small amounts of cumulative poisons. The economic position is also favorable since pharmaceuticals are generally products of high unit cost, and if irradiation sterilization should cost a trifle more its advantages with respect to product standards could easily outweigh the difference.

Very little work has been published in this field but the following types of material have been successfully sterilized by irradiation:

(i) General products — vitamins, patent medicines, and household supplies. Experiment has shown that vitamins, when present as concentrates, do not lose much potency upon irradiation.
(ii) Chemotherapeutic agents — drugs such as aureomycin, penicillin, streptomycin, and many others have been irradiated without loss in potency.
(iii) Medical and surgical specialities — such items as sutures, dressings, bone-bank bone, and surgical catgut may be radiation-sterilized (21).

Sterilization of Medical Supplies

This is an extremely promising field for the application of radiation, which has already been employed to sterilize such bulky items as cotton

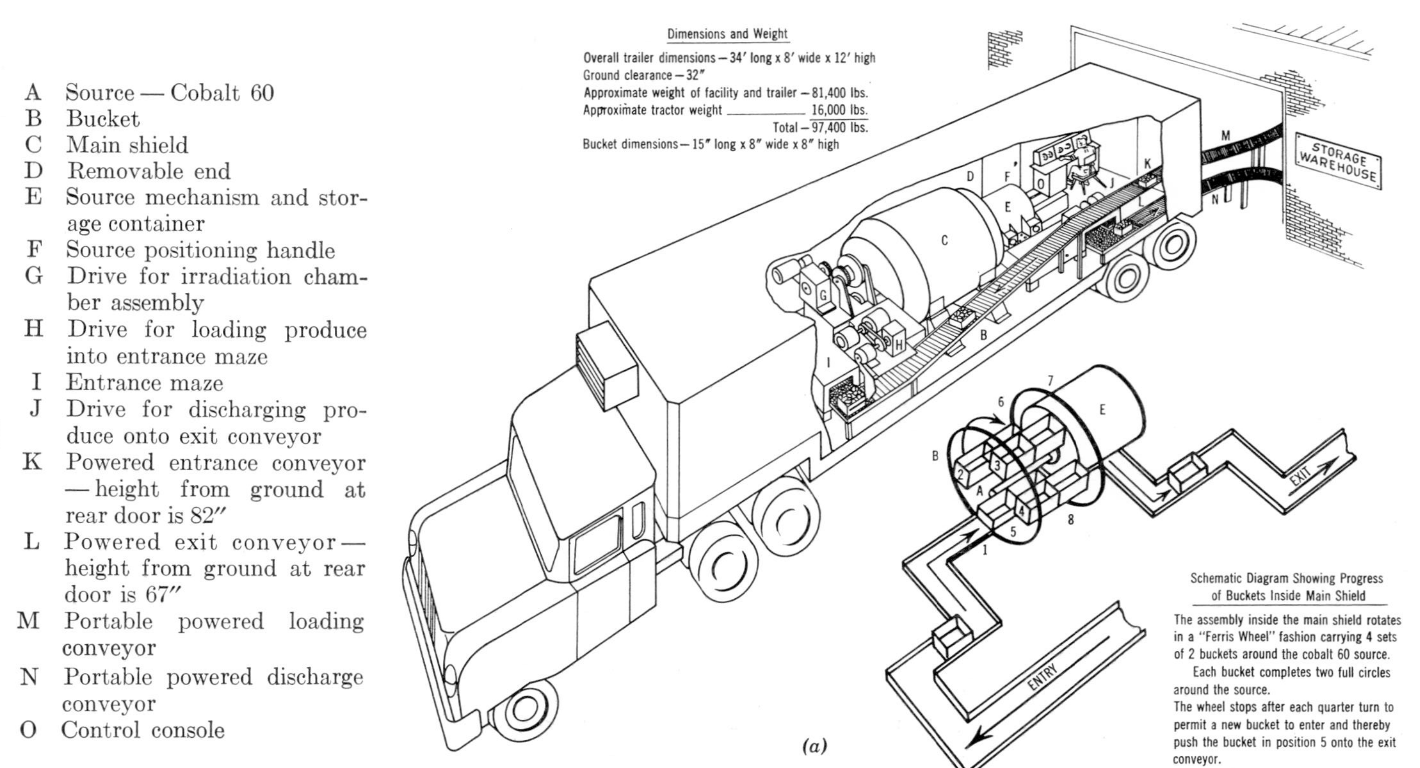

A Source — Cobalt 60
B Bucket
C Main shield
D Removable end
E Source mechanism and storage container
F Source positioning handle
G Drive for irradiation chamber assembly
H Drive for loading produce into entrance maze
I Entrance maze
J Drive for discharging produce onto exit conveyor
K Powered entrance conveyor — height from ground at rear door is 82″
L Powered exit conveyor — height from ground at rear door is 67″
M Portable powered loading conveyor
N Portable powered discharge conveyor
O Control console

FIGURE 13.5 *Mobile cobalt-60 source for irradiating potatoes and similar crops (ref. 12, 20). Courtesy Atomic Energy of Canada Limited, Ottawa.*

gauze, adhesive bandages, and surgical dressings. Sterilization of medical supplies by penetrating radiation such as γ-rays presents many advantages including:

(i) The radiation is extremely penetrating.
(ii) Complete sterilization is possible even in the most tightly packaged containers.
(iii) There are no limitations to the types of packaging which can be used.
(iv) A wider range of colored packaging materials may be used, enabling manufacturers to use color more effectively to promote sales appeal.
(v) There is no damage to heat-sensitive materials.
(vi) Continuous processing is possible.

CHEMICAL SYNTHESIS

As mentioned earlier, the actual interest of industry in radiation chemistry is difficult to estimate, and details of industrial chemical processes are lacking. Information concerning a number of reactions of potential interest has been published, however, and will be briefly commented on.

Synthesis of Gammexane (Gamma Benzene Hexachloride)

$$C_6H_6 + 3Cl_2 \rightarrow C_6H_6Cl_6 \tag{13.1}$$

Gamma benzene hexachloride, which is one of the six stereoisomers formed by the addition of chlorine to benzene, is widely used as an insecticide, usually admixed with a large excess of the other isomers. The usual method of manufacture is by photochlorination using glass vessels. Pilot plant experiments have shown, however, that it can also be prepared with ionizing radiation to initiate the chlorination (4); G(benzene hexachloride) is about 10^5. By using cobalt-60 γ-rays the proportion of γ-isomer in the product is about 12%, which is very similar to the proportion produced photochemically. The reaction is highly exothermic and requires efficient heat exchange. Here γ-rays have the advantage that a metal reaction vessel can be used in place of a glass one, at once improving the mechanical safety and the over-all rate of heat transfer. γ-radiation also has the advantage of providing a relatively uniform radiation intensity in the reactor in contrast with the high local intensities using light. The experimental arrangement used for pilot plant studies by Harmer and his colleagues (4) is shown in Fig. 13.6. The cost of the radiation-produced γ-isomer has been estimated as 1.51 and 1.60 dollars per kilogram using gross fission products and caesium-137 respectively as the source of radiation (22, cf. also 23), which is in line with

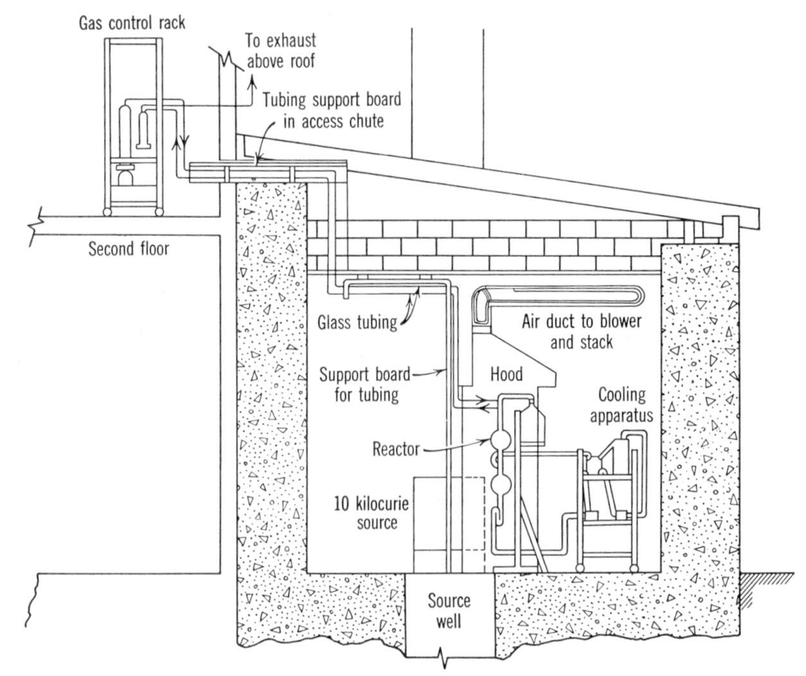

FIGURE 13.6 *Pilot plant arrangement to study the γ-ray initiated chlorination of benzene. Courtesy American Institute of Chemical Engineers, New York (Ref. 4, p. 255).*

the cost of commercial γ-benzene hexachloride produced photochemically (quoted as 1.90–3.00 per kilogram).

The radiation-induced chlorination of toluene is known to be intensity dependent and it is likely that the chlorination of benzene is also. In this event, the arrangement of the radiation sources and the resultant radiation intensity distribution would be important factors in the overall economics. For example, it would be better to have a number of radiation sources arranged in such a way as to give a low intensity through a large volume rather than to give a high intensity in a small volume (cf. p. 178). Another, and perhaps not so immediately obvious factor, is the rate of flow and the rate of recirculation of the material through the reaction zone. For a chain reaction of the $I^{1/2}$ type, increasing the rate of flow of the material through the reaction zone will be expected, in general, to increase the effective G value. However, if the material is recirculated, a limiting G value will be reached, the optimum recirculation time being related to the mean lifetime of the free radicals involved in the chain reaction (cf. p. 180).

Sulfochlorination of Hydrocarbons

Liquid cyclohexane reacts with sulfur dioxide and chlorine under γ-irradiation to give high yields of cyclohexanesulfonyl chloride and, to a smaller extent, chlorocyclohexane and cyclohexanedisulfonyl chloride (24). The reaction rate is proportional to the square root of the radiation intensity up to a dose rate of 40 rads per minute, but becomes independent of the dose rate at dose rates above 400 rads per minute; the G value is over 10^6. The radiation sources employed consisted of spent fuel elements, providing a γ-ray intensity of up to 2.5 Mrads per hour. A basic plant design (Fig. 13.7) was developed for continuous sulfochlorination, and it was concluded that the reaction might become attractive economically as cheap radiation sources became available.

Radiation-initiated sulfochlorination of hydrocarbons seems to occur generally. Thus the sulfochlorination of heptane has been reported (25), with G values up to 10^6, and similar high yields have been reported for the sulfochlorination of dodecane.

Nitrogen Fixation

Harteck and Dondes (26; 12, p. 234) have shown that nitrogen can be oxidized in a reactor core and that fission energy can thus be converted directly to chemical energy. The yield of nitrogen oxides is increased

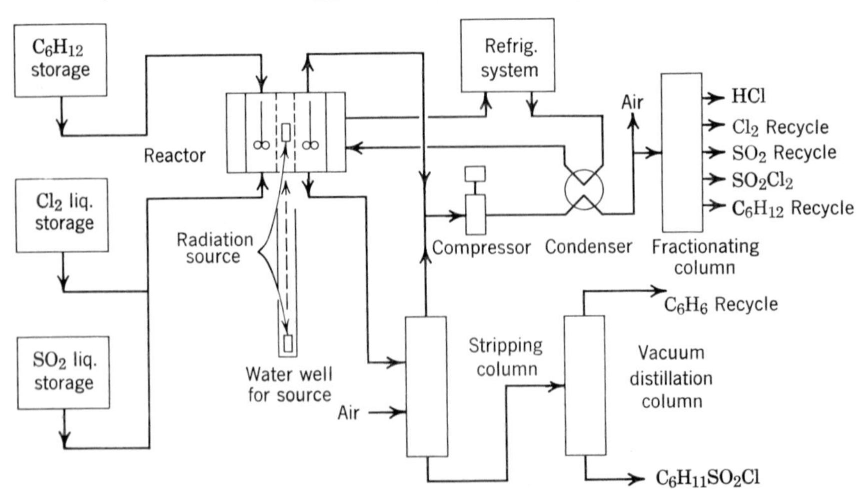

FIGURE 13.7 *Flow diagram for the commercial sulfochlorination of cyclohexane. Courtesy Argonne National Laboratory, Lemont, Illinois (Ref. 24, p. 73).*

when the irradiation takes place in the presence of enriched U_3O_8 powder and the authors found a maximum yield of NO_2 from a 4:1 nitrogen-oxygen mixture at a pressure of 10 atmospheres and a temperature of 200°C. Under these optimum conditions the G value for NO_2 production was about 4 and for N_2O production about 2. It was calculated that the burnup of 1 mole of U^{235} would "fix" 70 to 80 tons of nitrogen as NO_2. A somewhat later survey carried out for the United States Atomic Energy Commission suggested that decontamination costs might be a limiting factor but that further experimental work would be worthwhile (2, p. 139).

Summarizing, it would appear that thus far there is no radiation-initiated chemical synthesis in the production stage although three or four have reached the stage of process investigation.[1] Radiation-chemical processes which have been considered as commercial possibilities are listed in Table 13.2 (2, p. 144).

IRRADIATION OF MONOMERS AND POLYMERS

Radiation initiates the polymerization of monomers, graft and block copolymerization, and also causes crosslinking and degradation in polymers. These reactions have been reviewed in Chapter 11 but will be considered briefly here from the industrial standpoint.

Polymerization of Monomers

Many monomers have been polymerized by radiation, including such compounds as vinyl chloride, methyl methacrylate, and styrene. However the properties of the polymers produced resemble those of the conventional products, and there is no particular cost advantage. Thus the probability of commercial development seems low and will probably wait the appearance of a radiation product possessing superior characteristics (2).

Crosslinking of Polymers

One of the earliest discoveries in the field of radiation chemistry to attract the attention of industry was the disclosure that thermoplastic polymers such as polyethylene become crosslinked upon irradiation. The vulcanized products exhibit new properties such as better resistance to

[1] An industrial process for the production of ethyl bromide has recently been reported(27).

TABLE 13.2 *Summary of Radiation Processes for Chemical Synthesis* (Ref. 2)

Reaction	Status	Interest by Industry	G value	Prospects
Benzene + $Cl_2 \rightarrow$ benzene hexachloride	Process development	Considerable	85,000	Present market trend unfavorable
Sulfochlorination of hydrocarbons	Laboratory	Unknown	10^5–10^6	Good if market develops, but small volume at present
Fluorinated hydrocarbons	Laboratory	None	1–3; 55 in one case	Poor; need higher G value
Radiation-induced oxidation of hydrocarbons	Laboratory	Unknown	Not stated	Possibly good; more data needed
Oxidation of benzene to phenol	Laboratory	Unknown	50 at 220°C and 50 atm. + H_2O	Hopeful; deserves closer study at radiation costs of 10¢ per kilowatt-hour
Oxidation of ethylene to acetaldehyde	Laboratory	Unknown	60 at 8 atm. + H_2O	Not favorable; low-cost product; need to raise G value
Sulfoxidation of hydrocarbons	Laboratory	Unknown	4000–6500	Uncertain; more data needed on role of impurities or additives
Preparation of chlorinated hydrocarbons by radiolysis of simpler chlorinated hydrocarbons	Laboratory	Unknown	2–10	Unknown; polymerization possibly of interest
Condensation of olefins with bromotrichloromethane	Laboratory	Unknown	2000–20,000	Small-volume market
Direct methanation of coal	Laboratory	Active	Not given	Appear unfavorable

Reduction of particle size of coal	Laboratory	Active	Not given	Potentially important if cheap radiation and high efficiency of utilization of radiation result
Direct amination of aromatic hydrocarbons	Laboratory	Unknown	Not given	Possibly of interest using high frequency discharge
Irradiation of yeast to improve egosterol yield	Production (USSR)	Unknown	Fivefold increase in egosterol yield	Uncertain in United States
Irradiation of silicones to form lubricants	Laboratory	Patent assigned	Not given	Probably requires reasonably high G values for small-volume product
Methanol to ethylene glycol	Laboratory	Patents applied for	3 to 4 (reactor)	Present market over-supplied; G value should be higher, but worth close evaluation and technical research
Nitric acid by nuclear reactor	Laboratory	None	4–5 (reactor)	Possibly hopeful; decontamination not yet solved
Ammonia by nuclear reactor	Laboratory	None	0.69 (reactor)	Unfavorable unless G value increased
Hydrazine	Laboratory	Unknown	2.5 by dc discharge, high frequency better method, but G value unavailable	Present market small but could increase considerably if price reduced to half of current price; radiation route worth further attention
Oxidation of sulfur dioxide	Laboratory	None	Not given	Not promising; too small an effect

heat and chemical action and improved mechanical strength (28). Commercial crosslinked products include nonmelting electrical insulating tape, extruded wire insulation, and special electronic parts. Radiation appears to be advantageous for crosslinking plastic film and possibly small diameter wire insulation (2, p. 152).

Radiovulcanization of rubber has also been accomplished, but for the moment the cost seems unfavorable compared with conventional methods.

Graft and Block Copolymerization

When polymers are irradiated, radicals are formed which can react with monomers to produce graft or block copolymers. These products often possess unusual properties having commercial possibilities. Suggested applications are production of flexible polymers with high melting points, production of oil-resistant rubbers, and the improvement of materials such as cotton.

Favorable features of radiation-induced graft and block copolymerization include low dose requirements, close control of dose and dose rate, reaction in depth if necessary, and the possibility of continuous processing if desired. Cost estimates look favorable (1) and there is undoubtedly a great deal of research activity in this field. Unfortunately, details of any well established industrial process have yet to be published.

Radiation-induced grafting of certain vinyl monomers to cellulose materials has been described by Chapiro (28). The substrates are materials such as rayon, paper, wood pulp, cotton cloth, yarn, and jute; the monomers grafted on to these include styrene, methyl methacrylate, and other acrylic monomers. Cellulose grafting opens up new possibilities for dyed textiles since cellulose materials are easily dyed and may then be grafted with a material such as polystyrene to give a lasting color. Furthermore, by grafting a hydrophobic material such as polystyrene to a hydrophilic material such as cotton cloth, the latter may be made water repellent.

Mechanical properties such as tensile strength and elasticity may also be manipulated by grafting (29).

REFERENCES

1. R. Roberts, *J. Roy. Inst. Chem.*, **82,** 643, 839 (1958).
2. *Radiation—A Tool for Industry,* ALI 52, 1959.
3. D. A. Armstrong and J. W. T. Spinks, *Can. J. Chem.*, **37,** 1210 (1959).
4. D. E. Harmer, L. C. Anderson, and J. J. Martin, *Nuclear Engineering, Part I, Chem. Eng. Progr., Symp. Ser.,* **50,** no. 11 (1954) (AECU 2981).

5. H. Mohler, *Chemische reaktionen ionisierenden Strahlen,* Verlag H. R. Sauerlander, Aarau and Frankfort am Main, 1958, p. 241.
6. S. H. Pinner and W. T. H. Davison, *Nuclear Instruments and Methods,* **2,** no. 1, 227 (1961).
7. L. E. Brownell, *Radiation Uses in Industry and Science,* U. S. Atomic Energy Commission, 1961.
8. A. Charlesby, *Atomic Radiation and Polymers,* Pergamon Press, New York, 1960, p. 61.
9. B. Manowitz, *Nuclear Engineering, Part II, Chem. Eng. Progr., Symp. Ser.,* **50,** no. 12 (1954).
10. R. C. Loftness, *Proc. 1955 Conf. on Nuclear Eng.,* University of California, Los Angeles, 1955.
11. W. Wild and J. Wright, *Symposum on Utilization of Radiation from Fission Products,* A.E.R.E. (Gt. Britain) Report No. C/R 1231, 1953, p. 3.
12. *Large Radiation Sources in Industry,* International Atomic Energy Agency, Vienna, 1960. Vol. 1, p. 180.
13. *Gamma Irradiation in Canada,* Atomic Energy of Canada Limited, Report no. PP-19-60, p. 44.
14. *Seventh Hot Laboratories and Equipment Conference,* Cleveland, Ohio, 1959, p. 350.
15. "New Army Radiation Lab.", *Chem. Eng. News,* no. 28, 28 (1962).
16. B. E. Proctor and S. A. Goldblith, *Proc. Intern. Conf. Peaceful Uses Atomic Energy,* United Nations, New York, **15,** 245 (1956).
17. P. C. Aebersold, speech to National Fisheries Institute, New Orleans, April, 1962.
18. A. H. Sparrow and E. Christensen, *Nucleonics,* **12,** (Aug.), 16 (1954).
19. G. Tripp, *Intern. J. Appl. Radiation Isotopes,* **6,** 174 (1959).
20. *Gamma Irradiation in Canada,* Atomic Energy of Canada Limited, Report no. AECL 1329, 1961, p. 67.
21. C. Artandi and W. Van Winkle, *Nucleonics,* **17,** (Mar.), 86 (1959).
22. L. C. Anderson, B. G. Bray and J. J. Martin, *Proc. Intern. Conf. Peaceful Uses Atomic Energy,* United Nations, New York, **15,** 235 (1956).
23. D. E. Harmer, *Engineering Research Institute, University of Michigan, Progress Report No. 7,* 1954 (AECU 3077).
24. A. Schneider, ANL 5863 (1958).
25. A. Henglein and H. Url, *Z. Physik. Chem. (Leipzig),* **9,** 285, 516 (1956).
26. P. Harteck and S. Dondes, *Nucleonics,* **14,** (July), 22 (1956).
27. *Nucleonics,* **21,** (Jan.), 74 (1963).
28. A. Chapiro, *Nucleonics,* **19,** (Oct.), 65 (1961).
29. W. H. Rapson, *Can. Nuclear Tech.,* no. 3, 20 (1962).

APPENDIX 1

Tables of Data

Physical Constants

Avogadro's number	$N_0 = 6.025 \times 10^{23}$ molecules per gram-mole
Electron, charge	$e = 4.803 \times 10^{-10}$ e.s.u.
Electron, rest mass	$m_0 = 9.108 \times 10^{-28}$ g
Electron, energy equivalent of rest mass	$m_0c^2 = 0.5110$ Mev
Planck's constant	$h = 6.625 \times 10^{-27}$ erg sec
Proton, rest mass	$m_p = 1.672 \times 10^{-24}$ g
Proton, energy equivalent of rest mass	$m_pc^2 = 938.2$ Mev
Velocity of light	$c = 2.998 \times 10^{10}$ cm/sec

Numerical Constants

$\pi = 3.1416$	$\log_{10} e = 0.4343$
$e = 2.7183$	$\log_e 10 = 2.303$
	$\log_e 2 = 0.6931$

Units and Conversion Factors

Ångström	Å	$= 10^{-8}$ cm
Barn		$= 10^{-24}$ cm^2
Calorie		$= 4.185 \times 10^7$ erg
Curie	c	$= 3.700 \times 10^{10}$ disintegrations/sec
Electron volt	ev	$= 1.602 \times 10^{-12}$ erg
		$= 1.602 \times 10^{-19}$ watt sec
		$= 3.828 \times 10^{-20}$ calorie
1 Electron volt/molecule		= 23.06 kilocalories/gram-mole
Erg		$= 6.242 \times 10^{11}$ ev
		$= 2.389 \times 10^{-8}$ calorie
1 Kilocalorie/gram-mole		= 0.04336 ev/molecule
Micron	μ	$= 10^{-4}$ cm
Rad		= 100 erg/g
		$= 6.242 \times 10^{13}$ ev/g
		$= 6.242\rho \times 10^{13}$ ev/cm^3 where ρ is the density of the material in g/cm^3
		$= 2.389 \times 10^{-6}$ calorie/g
		$= 2.78 \times 10^{-9}$ watt hour/g
Roentgen (hard x-rays or γ-rays)		
Roentgen, absorbed in air		$= 0.87_7$ rad
Roentgen, absorbed in water		$= 0.97_5$ rad
Watt		$= 6.242 \times 10^{18}$ ev/sec
		$= 10^7$ erg/sec

The Electromagnetic Spectrum

(quantum energy $\times$ wavelength; $h\nu \times \lambda = 12.40$ kev Å)

Description	Wavelength (Å)	Photon energy (ev)
Cosmic rays	$\sim 10^{-5}$	Bev range
γ-rays	0.01–0.1	about 1Mev to 0.1Mev
X-rays	less than 100	above 100
Ultraviolet	100–4000	120–3.1
Visible: violet	4000	3.1
Visible: red	7000	1.77
Infrared	7000–10^6	1.77–10^{-2}
Microwave region	10^8–10^9	10^{-4}–10^{-5}
Radio waves	greater than 10^9	less than 10^{-5}

APPENDIX 2

Symbols and Abbreviations Used

(These are in order of first appearance. The units shown are those commonly used, though ev should be understood to include kev and Mev.)

Chapter 1

Å	Ångström unit ($= 10^{-8}$ cm).
M/N	Ion pair, or ionic, yield. This is the ratio of the number of molecules undergoing change (M) to the number of ion pairs formed (N).
$\rightsquigarrow$	Used to distinguish reactions brought about by the absorption of ionizing radiation.
e^-	Negative electron.
W	The average energy lost in forming an ion pair in a gas (ev or ergs).
I (i)	Ionization potential (v); the energy (ev) necessary to remove an electron from an atom or molecule.
G	The G value is used as a measure of radiation–chemical yields and is the number of molecules changed per 100 ev of energy absorbed.

Chapter 2

c (i)	Curie. The curie is the unit of radioactivity and is defined as the quantity of any radioactive nuclide in which the number of disintegrations per second is 3.700×10^{10}. The millicurie (mc) is equal to one thousandth of the curie.
ev	Electron-volt.
kev	Kilo electron-volt (10^3 ev).
Mev	Mega electron-volt (10^6 ev).
R_0 (i)	Mean range of heavy charged particles (e.g., α-particles) in matter (cm; mg/cm^2).
LET	Linear energy transfer (kev/μ). This is defined as the linear-rate of loss of energy (locally absorbed) by an ionizing particle traversing a material medium.
μ (i)	Micron ($= 10^{-4}$ cm).
E_β	Maximum energy of β-particles from a radioactive nuclide (ev).
$\overline{E}_\beta$	Average energy of β-particles from a radioactive nuclide (ev).
E_γ	Energy of γ-ray photon (ev).
E_s	Binding energy of an atomic electron (ev).
R_0 (ii)	Maximum range of β-particles in matter (cm; mg/cm^2).
E	Energy (kinetic) of a particle or photon (ev).
h	Planck's constant (erg sec).
c (ii)	Velocity of light (cm/sec).
λ (i)	Wavelength of radiation (Å; cm).
N_i	Number of incident photons.
N (i)	Number of photons transmitted without change of energy or direction.
μ (ii)	Total linear (photon) absorption coefficient (cm^{-1}).
x	Thickness of absorber (cm).
C_0 (i)	Initial activity of a radioactive source (curies).
C_t	Activity of a radioactive source after a period (t) of decay (curies).

I_0	Initial radiation intensity (from a radioactive source) (erg/cm^2 sec).
I_t	Radiation intensity from a radioactive source after a period (t) of radioactive decay (erg/cm^2 sec).
λ (ii)	Radioactive decay constant (time^{-1}, e.g., sec^{-1}).
Z	Atomic number (i.e., the charge on the atomic nucleus).
m_0	Rest mass of an electron (g or ev).
HVL	Half-value layer. This is the thickness of an absorber required to reduce the intensity of an x-ray beam to half its original value (mm).

Chapter 3

z	The charge on a charged particle.
m	The mass of a particle.
N (ii)	Number of atoms per cm^3.
e	Charge on an electron (e.s.u.).
v	Particle velocity (cm/sec).
β (i)	The ratio of the velocity of a particle to the velocity of light, i.e., v/c.
I (ii)	Mean excitation potential (erg).
ρ	Density of absorbing material (g/cm^3).
${}_mS$	Mass stopping power (erg cm^2/g).
R_p	Extrapolated, or practical, range of monoenergetic electrons in matter (cm; mg/cm^2).
R_0 (iii)	Maximum range of monoenergetic electrons in matter (cm; mg/cm^2).
R_e	Extrapolated range of heavy charged particles in matter (cm; mg/cm^2).
A	Atomic weight.
I_i	Intensity of incident radiation (erg/cm^2 sec).
I (iii)	Radiation intensity (generally the intensity of radiation transmitted through an absorber) (erg/cm^2 sec).
μ/ρ	Total mass absorption coefficient (cm^2/g).

$_a\mu$	Total atomic absorption coefficient (cm^2/atom or cm^2/molecule); this is also known as the atomic cross section.
$_e\mu$	Total electronic absorption coefficient (cm^2/electron); also known as the electronic cross section.
N_0	Avogadro's number.
E_0	Energy of incident photon (ev).
E_e	Energy of electron (ev).
$_e\sigma$	Compton electronic absorption coefficient (cm^2/electron).
$_e\sigma_s$	Compton electronic scatter coefficient (cm^2/electron).
$_e\sigma_a$	Compton electronic energy absorption coefficient (cm^2/electron).
E_p	Energy of positron (ev).
τ	Total linear photoelectric absorption coefficient (cm^{-1}).
σ	Total linear Compton absorption coefficient (cm^{-1}).
κ	Total linear pair-production absorption coefficient (cm^{-1}).
B	Build-up factor.
w_i	Weight fraction of the ith component of a mixture, i.e., the weight of this component divided by the weight of the mixture.
μ_s	Total linear scatter coefficient (cm^{-1}).
μ_a	Total linear energy absorption coefficient (cm^{-1}).
I_s	Transmitted radiation intensity if energy transfer to secondary electrons is ignored (erg/cm^2 sec).
I_a	Transmitted radiation intensity if scattering is ignored (erg/cm^2 sec).
E_i	Energy incident on absorber (erg/cm^2).
E_a	Radiation energy absorbed, i.e., transferred to secondary electrons (erg/cm^2 or erg/g).
N_E	Number of photons or particles with energy E.

(The symbols used for the various absorption coefficients are collected in Table 3.3, page 65.)

Chapter 4

r	Roentgen.
D	Absorbed dose (rad).
D_A	Absorbed does in air (rad).
D_M	Absorbed dose in material M (rad).
R_A	Exposure in air (roentgens).
μ_a/ρ	Total mass energy absorption coefficient (cm^2/g).
$\overline{Z/A}$	Mean value of the ratio of atomic number to atomic weight for a medium containing more than one element.
E_M	Energy absorbed by a medium M (erg/g) ($= E_a$).
J_G	Ionization produced in a gas-filled cavity (e.s.u./g).
s_m	Mass stopping power ratio for two materials; the materials are specified by a superscript and a subscript as in $(s_m)_{\text{air}}^{\text{medium}}$.
N (iii)	Particle flux (particles/cm^2 sec).
Q	Charge produced in an ionization chamber (e.s.u./cm^3 at NTP).
$\overline{E}$	Average energy transferred to ionizing particles by a radioactive nuclide per disintegration (ev).
C_0 (ii)	Concentration of radioactive material present at the start of an internal irradiation (mc/g).
T_M	Absorbed dose rate in material M (rad/unit time).
N (iv)	Normal concentration; a normal solution contains one gram equivalent of the solute in one liter of solution.
M	Molar concentration; a molar solution contains one gram molecular weight (mole) of the solute in one liter of solution.
$O.D.$	Optical density.
ϵ	Molar extinction coefficient (liter/mole cm).
d	Thickness of sample used when measuring optical density (cm).
mμ	Millimicron ($= 10^{-7}$ cm).
mr	Milliroentgen ($= 10^{-3}$ r).
Mrad	10^6 rads.

Chapter 5

*	An asterisk, as in A*, is used to signify that a species is in an excited state. Double asterisks (A**) are used to distinguish the excited species formed by recombination of a positive ion and an electron, where this is necessary; under these circumstances a single asterisk marks the primary excited species, formed directly upon irradiation.
$h\nu$	Ultraviolet light (Planck's constant multiplied by the frequency of the radiation, which gives the energy of the photons).
R· and S·	These are used as general symbols for free radicals. In later chapters R· is often an organic free radical.
V	The accelerating potential in a mass spectrometer (v).
V_i	The ionizing potential in a mass spectrometer (v).
H	Magnetic field (gauss).
M and N	These are used as general symbols for molecular reaction products where the reaction might give either molecular products or free radicals.

Chapter 6

D	Bond dissociation energy (ev; kcal/mole).
M	Represents the molecule necessary in a number of gas reactions to remove part of the energy liberated by the reaction (the so-called "third body"); it will be one of the molecules present in the system under consideration.
[X]	Concentration of a substance X.
g	Spectroscopic splitting factor.
β (ii)	Bohr magneton (erg/gauss).
I (iv)	Nuclear spin.
a	Nuclear magnetic field (gauss).

APPENDIX 3

Radiation Chemistry Problems

These simple worked examples are intended to illustrate the use of the equations given in the earlier chapters.

Problem 1

It is necessary to reduce the radiation level several feet from a small cobalt-60 source from 10 r/min to 10 mr/hr. What is the minimum thickness of lead shielding (to the nearest cm) required to do this? Assume a half-thickness value of 1.06 cm for Co^{60} γ-rays in lead.

The linear absorption coefficient (μ) can be calculated from the half-thickness value since

$$\mu = 0.693/\text{half-thickness value}$$

Thus, for Co^{60} γ-rays in lead,

$$\begin{aligned}\mu &= 0.693/1.06 \\ &= 0.654 \text{ cm}^{-1}\end{aligned}$$

This value can be substituted in

$$I = I_0 e^{-\mu x} \qquad (2.4; 3.13)$$

to determine the thickness of lead needed to reduce the radiation intensity (or exposure dose rate) at a point to any given value. In the present example I_0 is 600 r/hr and I is to be 0.01 r/hr, thus,

$$0.01 = 600\, e^{-\mu x}$$

$$\log_{10}(0.01/600) = -\log_{10}e \times 0.654x$$

$$\bar{5}.2218 = -0.4343 \times 0.654x$$

$$-4.7782 = -0.284x$$

$$x = 16.8 \text{ cm}$$

i.e., *17 cm to the nearest cm*

Problem 2

The exposure dose rate at a point near a cobalt-60 source was 235 r/min on October 15, 1962. Calculate the exposure dose rate at the same point on August 15, 1963 and on February 15, 1964. Take 5.27 years as the half-life of cobalt-60.

$$5.27 \text{ years} = 63.24 \text{ months}$$

The decay constant for a radioactive nuclide is given by

$$\lambda = 0.693/\text{half-life}$$

and therefore, for Co^{60},

$$\lambda = 0.693/63.24$$

$$= 0.01096 \text{ month}^{-1}$$

The intensity of the radiation emitted by a radioactive source, and the dose rate near it, fall at the same rate as the activity of the source falls due to radioactive decay, and

$$I_t = I_0 e^{-\lambda t} \tag{2.7}$$

$$\log_{10}(I_t/I_0) = -\lambda t \log_{10}e$$

In this example t has the values 10 months and 16 months and λ is 0.01096 month^{-1}. The ratios of I_t/I_0 calculated by substituting these figures in the preceding equation are 0.896 and 0.839 for 10 months and 16 months respectively, and the exposure dose rates at the point of interest after these periods of radioactive decay are therefore 235 $\times$ 0.896 and 235 $\times$ 0.839 r/min, i.e., *211 r/min* and *197 r/min* respectively.

Problem 3

From the range-energy data for protons given below calculate the range in air of 6-Mev and 12-Mev tritium nuclei ($_1H^3$) and 6-Mev and 12-Mev α-particles.

Proton energy (Mev):	1	1.5	2	3	4	5	6	7	8	9
Range in air (cm):	2.3	4.3	7.2	14.1	23.1	33.9	46.7	61.2	77.3	95.3

This problem makes use of the equations:

$$\text{Range of particle A} = \frac{m_A Z_B^2}{m_B Z_A^2} \times \text{Range of particle B} \qquad (3.9a)$$

when

$$\text{Energy of particle A} = \frac{m_A}{m_B} \times \text{Energy of particle B} \qquad (3.9b)$$

For tritium nuclei, $m = 3$ and $Z = 1$, while for protons $m = 1$ and $Z = 1$. Thus the range of a tritium nucleus is equal to three times the range of a proton with one third the energy, i.e.,

range of a *6-Mev tritium nucleus* in air = 3 × range 2-Mev proton
= *21.6 cm*

range of a *12-Mev tritium nucleus* = 3 × range 4-Mev proton
= *69.3 cm*

For α-particles, $m = 4$ and $Z = 2$, and the range of an α-particle is equal to that of a proton with one quarter the energy. However, in the case of α-particles a constant, found by experiment to be 0.20 cm in air, must be added to the calculated range (see page 45) and

range *6-Mev α-particle* in air = range 1.5-Mev proton + 0.20 cm
= *4.5 cm*

range of a *12-Mev α-particle* = range 3-Mev proton + 0.20 cm
= *14.3 cm*

Problem 4

The exposure dose rate 1.2 inches from a cobalt-60 source is 300 r/min. How thick must concrete shielding walls be to reduce the radiation level (i) at the operating face, 4 feet from the source, to less than 1 mr/hr and (ii) in an adjoining laboratory, 20 feet from the source, to less than 10 mr/week. Give the result to the nearest 3 inches and take the half-thickness value for Co^{60} γ-rays in concrete as 2.0 inches.

In this problem the combined effect of distance and shielding must be estimated.

(i) *To estimate the shielding required between source and operating face.*

The reduced dose rate at the operating face due to distance alone is found by applying the inverse square relationship; i.e., since the dose rate 1.2 inches from the source is 300 r/min, the dose rate 48 inches from the source will be $300(1.2/48)^2 = 0.1875$ r/min or 11.25 r/hr. The concrete shielding is therefore required to reduce the dose rate at the operating face from 11.25 r/hr to 0.001 r/hr. The thickness of concrete necessary is found by substituting these values for I_0 and I respectively in the expression

$$I = I_0 e^{-\mu x} \qquad (2.4;\ 3.13)$$

taking the linear absorption coefficient (μ) as $0.693/2.0 = 0.3465$ inch^{-1}; the procedure is that used in Problem 1.[1] The thickness required is 26.9 inches or, to the nearest three inches, *2 feet 3 inches.*

(ii) *To estimate the shielding required between source and laboratory.*

In this case distance reduces the dose rate at the laboratory to $300(1.2/240)^2 = 0.0075$ r/min or 75.6 r/week. Proceeding as in part (i), the thickness of concrete needed to reduce the dose rate from 75.6 r/week to 0.01 r/week is found to be 25.8 inches or, to the nearest three inches, *2 feet.* However, in shielding calculations it is usual to err on the side of safety and this result would normally be given to the next higher three inches, i.e., as *2 feet 3 inches;* this is implied by the question, which asks for the shielding necessary to reduce the dose rate to *less* than 10 mr/week.

Problem 5

If the mass energy absorption coefficient for cobalt-60 γ-rays in water is 0.0296 cm^2/g, what are the values of the corresponding linear, atomic, and electronic energy absorption coefficients?

The linear energy absorption coefficient (μ_a) is simply the mass coefficient multiplied by the density, which is one in the case of water so that

$$(\mu_a)_{H_2O} = (\mu_a/\rho)_{H_2O} = 0.0296\ cm^{-1}$$

[1] The calculation is simplified if the expression shown (Eqs. 2.4, 3.13) is put in log form and rearranged slightly, when

$$x = \frac{2 \cdot 303}{\mu} \log_{10}(I_0/I)$$

The atomic, energy absorption coefficient ($_a\mu_a$) is given by

$$_a\mu_a = \frac{A}{N_0}(\mu_a/\rho) \qquad (3.32)$$

Thus, for water,

$$(_a\mu_a)_{H_2O} = \frac{18}{6.025 \times 10^{23}} \times 0.0296$$
$$= \mathit{8.84 \times 10^{-25}\ cm^2/molecule} \text{ or } \mathit{0.884\ barn/molecule}$$

The electronic energy absorption coefficient ($_e\mu_a$) is given by

$$_e\mu_a = (_a\mu_a)/Z \qquad (3.31)$$

For a compound, Z is the sum of the atomic numbers of the constituent elements, that is, 10 for water. Thus

$$(_e\mu_a)_{H_2O} = \mathit{8.84 \times 10^{-26}\ cm^2/electron} \text{ or } \mathit{0.0884\ barn/electron}$$

Problem 6

Calculate the mass absorption coefficient for 1-Mev γ-rays for sodium iodide and for calcium metaphosphate, $Ca(PO_3)_2$, from data for the elements present. The atomic absorption coefficients (barns/atom) for the elements are oxygen, 1.69; sodium, 2.32; phosphorus, 3.17; calcium, 4.22; iodine, 12.03 (for 1-Mev photons).

SODIUM IODIDE. The atomic absorption coefficient for a compound is equal to the sum of the atomic absorption coefficients for the constituent atoms, that is, for sodium iodide

$$(_a\mu)_{NaI} = (_a\mu)_{Na} + (_a\mu)_I$$
$$= 2.32 + 12.03$$
$$= 14.35 \text{ barns/molecule}$$

While the mass absorption coefficient can be obtained from the atomic coefficient using the relationship,

$$\mu/\rho = \frac{N_0}{A}(_a\mu) \qquad (3.32)$$

where A is the molecular weight of the compound. For sodium iodide,

$$(\mu/\rho)_{NaI} = 14.35 \times 10^{-24} \times \frac{6.025 \times 10^{23}}{150}$$
$$= \mathit{0.0576\ cm^2/g}$$

CALCIUM METAPHOSPHATE. The atomic and mass absorption coefficients are calculated as shown for sodium iodide; thus,

$$
\begin{aligned}
({}_a\mu)_{\text{Ca phosphate}} &= ({}_a\mu)_{\text{Ca}} + 2({}_a\mu)_{\text{P}} + 6({}_a\mu)_{\text{O}} \\
&= 4.22 + 6.34 + 10.14 \\
&= 20.70 \text{ barns/molecule}
\end{aligned}
$$

$$
\begin{aligned}
(\mu/\rho)_{\text{Ca phosphate}} &= 20.70 \times 10^{-24} \times \frac{6.025 \times 10^{23}}{198} \\
&= \mathit{0.0630\ cm^2/g}
\end{aligned}
$$

Problem 7

Small samples of pure methanol and pure acetic acid are irradiated with cobalt-60 γ-rays at a position at which the exposure dose (measured by means of an ionization chamber) is 360 r/min. How much energy (in rads) will the samples absorb if they are irradiated for 10 hours?

METHANOL. Organic compounds, apart from those containing appreciable amounts of heavy elements, interact with cobalt-60 γ-radiation by the Compton process almost exclusively. Under these circumstances the absorbed dose is related to the exposure dose by

$$
D_M = 0.87_7 R_A \times \frac{(Z/A)_M}{(Z/A)_A} \tag{4.8}
$$

where the subscripts A and M signify air and organic material respectively.

In the present example R_A is the exposure dose delivered during 10 hours, i.e., $360 \times 600 = 2.16 \times 10^5$ r, and $(\overline{Z/A})_A$ is 0.499 (Table 4.4). $(\overline{Z/A})_{\text{methanol}}$ is equal to the sum of the atomic numbers of the atoms present in methanol divided by the molecular weight; i.e., $18/32 = 0.562$. Therefore the absorbed dose in the methanol is

$$
\begin{aligned}
D_{\text{methanol}} &= 0.87_7 \times 2.16 \times 10^5 \times (0.562/0.499) \\
&= \mathit{2.1_3 \times 10^5\ rads}
\end{aligned}
$$

ACETIC ACID. For acetic acid $(\overline{Z/A})_{\text{acetic acid}} = 32/60 = 0.533$ and

$$
\begin{aligned}
D_{\text{acetic acid}} &= 0.87_7 \times 2.16 \times 10^5 \times (0.533/0.499) \\
&= \mathit{2.0_2 \times 10^5\ rads}
\end{aligned}
$$

Problem 8

The apparent exposure dose rate inside an aluminum block, measured with an air-filled cavity ionization chamber, is 79 r/min. The ionization chamber has walls of bakelite. What is the absorbed dose rate at this point in the aluminum if the chamber walls are (i) very thin (ii) thick, compared with the range of the secondary electrons produced?

For cobalt-60 γ-rays; $(\mu_a/\rho)_{\text{Al}} = 0.0258\ \text{cm}^2/\text{g}$, $(\mu_a/\rho)_{\text{Bakelite}} = 0.0284\ \text{cm}^2/\text{g}$, $(s_m)_{\text{air}}^{\text{Al}} = 0.89$, and $(s_m)_{\text{air}}^{\text{Bakelite}} = 1.07$.

THIN-WALLED IONIZATION CHAMBER. For a thin-walled, air-filled, cavity ionization chamber the absorbed dose in the surrounding medium is related to the ionization produced in the cavity (Q) by

$$D_M = 0.87_7 Q (s_m)_{\text{air}}^{\text{medium}} \tag{4.18}$$

Substituting numerical values for Q and $(s_m)_{\text{air}}^{\text{Al}}$, the absorbed dose rate at the point of interest in the aluminum will be

$$\begin{aligned} D_{\text{Al}} &= 0.87_7 \times 79 \times 0.89 \\ &= \mathit{61.7\ rads/min} \end{aligned}$$

THICK-WALLED IONIZATION CHAMBER. If the ionization chamber used has a relatively thick Bakelite wall the absorbed dose rate in the aluminum will be given by

$$\begin{aligned} D_{\text{Al}} &= 0.87_7 Q\ (s_m)_{\text{air}}^{\text{Bakelite}} \frac{(\mu_a/\rho)_{\text{Al}}}{(\mu_a/\rho)_{\text{Bakelite}}} \qquad (4.19) \\ &= 0.87_7 \times 79 \times 1.07 \times (0.0258/0.0284) \\ &= \mathit{67.4\ rads/min} \end{aligned}$$

Problem 9

A mixture composed of equal parts by weight of methanol and acetic acid is irradiated with cobalt-60 γ-rays. What part of the total energy absorbed is absorbed by the methanol?

Only Compton absorption need be considered here, and the fraction of the total energy absorbed that is absorbed by the methanol is

$$\frac{D_{\text{methanol}}}{D_{\text{mixture}}} = w_m \times \frac{(\overline{Z/A})_{\text{methanol}}}{(\overline{Z/A})_{\text{mixture}}} \tag{4.23}$$

where w_m is the fraction by weight of methanol.

Values of $(\overline{Z/A})$ for methanol and acetic acid are 0.562 and 0.533 respectively (Problem 7) while $(\overline{Z/A})$ for the mixture of methanol and acetic acid is the mean of these values, since each component contributes equally by weight, i.e., is 0.5475. Substituting these values in the equation above,

$$\frac{D_{\text{methanol}}}{D_{\text{mixture}}} = \frac{1}{2} \times \frac{0.562}{0.5475} = 0.513$$

i.e., *51.3%* of the energy absorbed is absorbed by the methanol.

It should be pointed out that this calculation assumes that the energy absorbed by a particular component is governed entirely by the extent to which it interacts with the primary radiation; secondary electrons are assumed to deposit their energy with the components in the same proportions as these interact with the primary radiation. The assumption appears to be reasonably valid for mixtures containing saturated, chemically similar, compounds, but in other cases its validity is uncertain.

Problem 10

Five hundred microcuries of tritium oxide is mixed with 250 mg of ethanol (the weight of the T_2O is negligible). Assuming that all the radiation emitted is absorbed by the ethanol, how much energy (rads) will be absorbed in (i) 1 day, (ii) 1 week, (iii) 1 month (30 days)?

The average energy of the β-particles emitted by tritium is 5.5 kev.

The absorbed dose rate for an internal irradiation is given by

$$T_M = 0.593 \times C \times \bar{E} \text{ rad/sec} \tag{4.31}$$

where C is the concentration of the radioisotope in millicuries per gram and $\bar{E}$ (Mev) is the mean energy released to ionizing particles per disintegration. In this problem $C = 0.5/0.25 = 2$ mc/g, $\bar{E}$ is 5.5×10^{-3} Mev, and the absorbed dose rate is

$$\begin{aligned} T_M &= 0.593 \times 2 \times 5.5 \times 10^{-3} \\ &= 6.52 \times 10^{-3} \text{ rads/sec} \end{aligned}$$

Thus the absorbed dose in 1 day (8.64×10^4 sec) is *564 rads*

in 7 days (6.05×10^5 sec) is *3950 rads*

in 30 days (2.60×10^6 sec) is *16,900 rads*

Since the half-life of tritium is long (12.26 years), compared with the duration of the experiment, it is not necessary to correct here for radioactive decay.

Problem 11

A solution containing phosphorus-32 was counted on Monday and found to contain 1.50 millicurie of P^{32}. On Wednesday, 48 hours later, the solution was added to a solution of ferrous sulfate in sulfuric acid such that the mixed solution was $0.001M$ with respect to $FeSO_4$ and $0.8N$ with respect to H_2SO_4; the final volume of the mixture was 10 ml. The mixture was left in a dark cupboard at room temperature.

On Friday, 48 hours after mixing, the optical density of the mixed solution was measured at 304 mμ (24°C) and found to be 0.324, and a blank solution similar in composition to the mixture had an optical density of 0.003; both were measured using a 1 cm quartz cell. Calculate G(ferric) for phosphorus-32 β-rays.

How great would the absorbed dose be if the mixture were left until all the radioactive phosphorus had decayed?

The molar extinction coefficient for ferric ion at 304 mμ, 24°C, is 2175 and the density of $0.8N$ sulfuric acid at 24°C is 1.024 g/cm³. Phosphorus-32 has a half-life of 14.22 days and the average energy of the β-rays emitted by it is 0.70 Mev.

In this example allowance will be made for the decay of the radioactive material between counting and making up the experimental solution and also during the irradiation itself.

The activity present at the start of the irradiation, two days after counting, is calculated using the equation for radioactive decay,

$$C_t = C_0 e^{-\lambda t} \tag{2.5}$$

and putting $C_0 = 1.50$ mc, $t = 2$ days, and $\lambda = 0.693/14.22 = 0.04873$ day^{-1}; thus $C_t = 1.361$ mc.

The absorbed dose received during irradiation is given by

$$D_M = \frac{5.121 \times 10^4 \times \bar{E} \times C_0}{\lambda} (1 - e^{-\lambda t}) \quad \text{rads} \tag{4.36}$$

here C_0 is the activity present at the start of the irradiation in units of millicuries per gram of solution. The absorbed dose is found by substituting $\bar{E} = 0.70$ Mev, $C_0 = 1.361/10.24 = 0.1329$ mc/g, $t = 2$ days, and $\lambda = 0.04873$ day^{-1}; when

$$\begin{aligned} D_M &= \frac{5.121 \times 10^4 \times 0.70 \times 0.1329}{0.04873} (1 - e^{-0.09746}) \\ &= 9.776 \times 10^4 (1 - 0.9071) \\ &= 9079 \text{ rads} \end{aligned}$$

(The absorbed dose can also be calculated by assuming that the mean dose rate during the irradiation is the dose rate at the midpoint of the experiment; three days after counting the radioactivity in the present instance. The dose rate at this time can be calculated as in Problem 10 after calculating the activity present at the midpoint. In this example the activity present three days after counting is 1.296 mc, and this leads to a value of 9073 rads for the absorbed dose, in very good agreement with the value calculated using the integrated expression. However, when the duration of the experiment is longer, relative to the half-life of the isotope being used, the agreement will be poorer and the integrated equation should be used.)

For the ferrous sulfate solution the absorbed dose is given by

$$D_M = \frac{0.965 \times 10^9\ (O.D_i - O.D_b)}{\epsilon d\rho\ G(\text{Fe}^{3+})} \quad \text{rads} \qquad (4.44)$$

Since the absorbed dose is known, G(ferric) can be found by substitution;

$$G(\text{Fe}^{3+}) = \frac{0.965 \times 10^9 (0.324 - 0.003)}{9079 \times 2175 \times 1 \times 1.024}$$

and

$$G(Fe^{3+}) = 15.3 \ (\textit{for phosphorus-32}\ \beta\textit{-rays})$$

If the sample were left until all the phosphorus had decayed, the total absorbed dose would be

$$D_M = \frac{5.121 \times 10^4 \times \bar{E} \times C_0}{\lambda} \qquad (4.37)$$

$$= \frac{5.121 \times 10^4 \times 0.70 \times 0.1329}{0.04873}$$

$$= 9.78 \times 10^4 \ \textit{rads}$$

Problem 12

A sample of Fricke dosimeter solution was irradiated for 20 minutes with cobalt-60 γ-rays and then the optical densities of the irradiated and a nonirradiated solution measured; they were found to be 0.254 and 0.002 respectively (304 mμ, 24°C). A solution of ceric sulfate in 0.8N sulfuric acid was irradiated in the same position for 100 mins, causing the optical density at 320 mμ (the ceric absorption peak) to change from 0.695 to 0.234. Assuming that the same silica cells were used for all the optical density measurements, calculate G(-ceric ion).

Assume G(ferric) for cobalt-60 γ-rays to be 15.5 and the extinction coefficients for ferric ion at 304 mμ (24°C) and ceric ion at 320 mμ to be 2175 and 5580 liters/mole cm respectively.

The absorbed dose in both ferrous and ceric solutions is given by

$$D_M = \frac{0.965 \times 10^9\ (O.D_{i} - O.D_b)}{\epsilon d\rho\ G(\text{Fe}^{3+} \text{ or } \text{Ce}^{3+})} \tag{4.44}$$

Thus, for the ferrous solution,

$$D_{\text{Fe}} = \frac{0.965 \times 10^9\ (0.254 - 0.002)}{2175 \times d \times \rho \times 15.5} \qquad \text{rads/20 min}$$

and for the ceric solution,

$$D_{\text{Ce}} = \frac{0.965 \times 10^9\ (0.695 - 0.234)}{5580 \times d \times \rho \times G(\text{Ce}^{3+})} \qquad \text{rads/100 min}$$

The absorbed dose will be the same for both solutions if they are irradiated for the same length of time since they are both predominantly 0.8N sulfuric acid, i.e., $5D_{\text{Fe}} = D_{\text{Ce}}$. Since d and ρ are the same for the two solutions G(cerous), which is equal to G(-ceric), can be determined, thus,

$$G(-Ce^{4+}) = G(Ce^{3+}) = 2.21 \ (\textit{for cobalt-60}\ \gamma\textit{-rays})$$

Problem 13

A 5 ml sample of pure chloroform was irradiated with cobalt-60 γ-radiation for 10 minutes. Acid products were extracted by stirring with water and were titrated with dilute alkali; 15 micro equivalents (15×10^{-6} mole monobasic acid) of acid were found. The dose rate was determined with the Fricke dosimeter; 60 minutes irradiation causing the optical density of the solution to change from 0.003 to 0.341 (304 mμ; 24°C) when measured in a 1 cm cell. Calculate the G value for the production of monobasic acid from chloroform.

The density and $\overline{Z/A}$ of the Fricke dosimeter solution are 1.024 and 0.553 respectively; G(ferric) for cobalt-60 γ-radiation is 15.5. For ferric ion the molar extinction coefficient at 304 mμ (24°C) is 2175. The density and $\overline{Z/A}$ of chloroform are 1.50 and 0.486 respectively.

The dose absorbed by the Fricke dosimeter solution is given by

$$D_D = 2.80 \times 10^4\ (O.D_{i} - O.D_b) \qquad \text{rads} \tag{4.46}$$

when $\epsilon = 2175$, $\rho = 1.024$, $d = 1$, and $G(Fe^{3+}) = 15.5$ Thus, in the example above,

$$D_D = 2.80 \times 10^4 \times (0.341 - 0.003) \qquad \text{rads/60 min}$$
$$= 1577 \text{ rads/10 min}$$

Energy absorption in both the dosimeter solution and in chloroform is predominantly by the Compton process with cobalt-60 γ-rays and the absorbed dose in the two media are related by

$$D_{CHCl_3} = D_{\text{dosimeter}} \times \frac{(\overline{Z/A})_{CHCl_3}}{(\overline{Z/A})_{\text{dosimeter}}} \tag{4.24}$$
$$= 1577 \times (0.486/0.553)$$
$$= 1387 \text{ rads/10 min}$$

The number of molecules of acid formed $= 15 \times 10^{-6} \times 6.025 \times 10^{23}$ molecules/5 ml

or

$$= \frac{15 \times 6.025 \times 10^{17}}{5 \times 1.50} \qquad \text{molecules/g}$$
$$= 1.205 \times 10^{18} \text{ molecules/g}$$

while

$$G(\text{acid}) = \frac{\text{molecules of acid formed}}{100 \text{ ev absorbed}}$$
$$= \frac{\text{molecules of acid formed/g}}{\text{absorbed dose (rad)}} \times 1.602 \times 10^{-12}$$
$$= \frac{1.205 \times 10^{18} \times 1.602 \times 10^{-12}}{1387}$$
$$= \mathit{1390}$$

An alternative, though similar, method of calculating the G value is as follows. It is based on energy units of ev/ml rather than rads. The dose absorbed by the dosimeter solution is then

$$(D_v)_D = 1.75 \times 10^{18} (O.D_i - O.D_b)\rho \qquad \text{ev/ml} \tag{4.47}$$
$$= 1.75 \times 10^{18} \times 0.338 \times 1.024 \qquad \text{ev/ml in 60 min}$$
$$= 5.047 \times 10^{17} \text{ ev/5 ml in 10 min}$$

This is converted to the dose absorbed by 5 ml of chloroform in a 10-minute irradiation by

$$(D_v)_{\text{CHCl}_3} = (D_v)_{\text{dosimeter}} \times \frac{(\overline{Z/A})_{\text{CHCl}_3}}{(\overline{Z/A})_{\text{dosimeter}}} \times \frac{\rho_{\text{CHCl}_3}}{\rho_{\text{dosimeter}}} \tag{4.26}$$

$$= 5.047 \times 10^{17} \times \frac{0.486}{0.553} \times \frac{1.5}{1.024}$$

$$= 6.497 \times 10^{17} \text{ ev/5 ml}$$

The number of molecules of acid formed is, as above,

$$= 15 \times 10^{-6} \times 6.025 \times 10^{23} \text{ molecules/5 ml}$$

$$= 9.038 \times 10^{18} \text{ molecules/5 ml}$$

and

$$G(\text{acid}) = \frac{\text{molecules of acid formed/5 ml}}{\text{100 ev absorbed/5 ml}}$$

$$= \frac{9.038 \times 10^{18}}{6.497 \times 10^{15}}$$

$$= \mathit{1390}$$

AUTHOR INDEX

SUBJECT INDEX